ADVANCES IN
MATERIALS

ORGANISING COMMITTEE

Mr. L. Holliday, M.A., B.Sc., F.R.I.C., C.Eng., M.I. Chem.E.
Mr. B. F. Street, B.Sc., C. Eng., A.M.I. Chem.E.
Dr. P. E. Evans, M.A., Ph.D.
Mr. J. M. Hutcheon, B.Sc., A.R.I.C.
Mr. M. Shaw, B.Sc., D.L.C., A.R.I.C., C.Eng., A.M.I. Chem.E.

Honorary Editor of these Proceedings
Mr. P. A. Rottenburg, M.A., C.Eng., A.M.I.Chem.E.

ADVANCES IN MATERIALS

Proceedings of a Symposium organised by the

North Western Branch of the

The Institution of Chemical Engineers

held at

Manchester, 6-9 April, 1964

Published for

THE INSTITUTION OF CHEMICAL ENGINEERS

by

PERGAMON PRESS

OXFORD · LONDON · EDINBURGH · NEW YORK

TORONTO · PARIS · FRANKFURT

Pergamon Press Ltd., Headington Hill Hall, Oxford
4 & 5 Fitzroy Square, London W.1

Pergamon Press (Scotland) Ltd., 2 & 3 Teviot Place, Edinburgh 1

Pergamon Press Inc., 44-01 21st St., Long Island City, New York 11101

Pergamon of Canada Ltd., 6 Adelaide Street East, Toronto, Ontario

Pergamon Press, S.A.R.L., 24 rue des Ecoles, Paris 5e

Friedr. Vieweg & Sohn Verlag, Postfach 185, 33 Braunschweig, West Germany

The Institution of Chemical Engineers, 16 Belgrave Square, London S.W.1

First edition 1966

Library of Congress Catalog Card No. 65-26566

PRINTED IN GREAT BRITAIN BY C. F. HODGSON & SON, LTD.
(2374/66)

CONTENTS

PREFACE

THE symposium on "Advances in Materials" was held in the Renold Building, Manchester College of Science and Technology, Altrincham Street, Manchester 1. The organisers and hosts were the North Western Branch of The Institution of Chemical Engineers.

The object of the symposium was to survey the latest developments in materials science and technology. The limitations imposed by materials on the progress of modern technology were examined, together with developments to meet the increasingly exacting requirements of industry. The meeting considered the subject on a broad front and was not restricted to chemical engineering.

FIRST SESSION

CHALLENGES TO MATERIALS SCIENCE IN THE CHEMICAL INDUSTRY: INDUSTRIAL NEEDS AND AN INFLUENCE ON DESIGN

By C. EDELEANU, M.A., Ph.D.*

SYNOPSIS

During recent years very much effort has been devoted to studies of materials largely as a result of defence requirements. Progress has been extremely fast in certain fields, and perhaps the largest current problem is the assimilation of new information.

In a new project there are three district stages at which questions of materials arise. The earliest stage is that represented by laboratory work. At this stage various process possibilities may be discounted as liable to present insurmountable materials difficulties. Frequently these decisions are made almost subconsciously and tend to reduce both the challenge to the materials specialist and the scope of the project.

The next stage is the preparation of the flowsheet when the physical shape of the plant is visualized. During this stage materials " problems " can be avoided but it is equally easy to miss opportunities which progress in materials have made possible.

The final and most common stage at which materials are considered is the detail or functional stage of design. By this time practically all the major decisions have already been made, but clear thinking on materials is still important. Attention to detail will make all the difference between a plant which works satisfactorily and one which gives a great deal of trouble during start-up. Frequently this is the only stage at which materials are considered seriously because it is the only one during which the result of not doing so is obvious.

Introduction

Not all of us who are interested in materials are motivated by the same things, but the final expression of our work is a piece of hardware. Expressing ourselves through the designers involves establishing understanding and this presents some of the most challenging problems which have to be solved if anything is to happen. Important as the designer may be to us there are others who are more directly involved in creating the ever-pressing technical challenge in the field of materials. The purpose of this paper is to examine just how problems arise and how we can resolve them so that our work is eventually used rather than to dwell on actual present problems. Naturally many people in the materials field are not greatly concerned with practical issues and, to some, the study of materials and their properties is an end itself. No one must underestimate the contribution made by such people, but when they feel let down by the practical people who are slow to " appreciate " and use their work they might like to know some of the difficulties involved. If they then still feel strongly perhaps they might even consider giving a helping hand to the rest of us, but not necessarily at the expense of their own task. The presentation of their work in a suitable " language " would help a great deal.

Final Selection of a Material

The critical step in the selection of a material is an engineering decision and it is important to realize what is involved in it. Basically this is a marriage between the technicalities and economics, and both words are used in the broadest possible sense. The economic decision does, of course, take account of capital costs but this is only one of the many factors such as process and maintenance costs, probable market fluctuation, transport, storage and other such costs.

Not so obvious, time is of the utmost importance not only because of the cost of idle capital which is very high if construction is slow but because, in a competitive world, being ready just at the right time may make all the difference between winning or losing a market. Being late, after having sold the product of a yet unfinished plant, can be a disaster. These are among the things which have to be considered by anyone expecting to have his recommendations taken seriously.

The problem is one of communication and it is worth considering some of the difficulties which are found in practice. Two types of people are involved in the exercise: the engineers and the materials specialist are the technical parties while the buyer and salesman are concerned with the commercial aspects of the negotiations. Roughly the technical people decide *what* is to be bought whilst the commercial people decide *how* it is bought. Difficulties arise when either the buyer or the salesman does not know what is being bought, and unfortunately this is not unknown. Perhaps the task is made even more difficult when the materials expert has no idea of the commercial implications of his recommendations and has no appreciation of the engineer's problems. Equally frustrating is the situation when the engineer is so engrossed in his own problems that he does not stop to think just what are his problems, and asks for answers to meaningless questions. In practice, difficulties arise just as frequently because of the shortcomings of the technical people as those of their commercial colleagues. The matter is even further complicated when for either good or bad reasons secrecy on either commercial or technical matters is involved.

It is perhaps worth illustrating the problem with a few examples. New materials and some which are not at all new are sold under trade names and there are no national specifications, standards, *etc.* The technical information is available in trade publications and, as often as not, gives " typical " properties, and is very uninformative about actual minimum properties. Recommendations on design stress or on similarly useful matters are not given and even greater coyness is displayed on costs, availability or anything

* Imperial Chemical Industries Ltd., Billingham.

else that may help anyone to decide whether it is even worth shortlisting the material. All this is done presumably for good commercial reasons and the relevant information can eventually be extracted, normally after spending time first with a commercial man who cannot help with the technical side but agrees to send along his technical people who are then floored by any questions of price, delivery, *etc.* Commercial contact is then made again in the form of a firm enquiry and as sure as fate the preliminary information on cost, delivery, *etc.*, is utterly wrong, and if it is not, it turns out that say Grade B strongly recommended by the technical man as slightly superior and worth having every time is twice the price of Grade A, or it is an experimental grade which is on a year's delivery. Naturally there are alternatives to this but it is no wonder that a project engineer faced with numerous routine materials decisions, possibly hundreds, and with a year to complete detailed design, clear a site and erect a plant will not be delighted to consider what he thinks, and rightly so under the circumstances, are crackpot ideas. The meals that have to be consumed in order to arrive at an understanding are in themselves a reason to avoid novelty. In most projects there are only one, two, or at the most three really important novel decisions to make, but even so the work which has to be done in connection with the remainder does tend to make life difficult.

The most valuable contribution a materials man working for a supplier can make is to be sure that the trade literature means something and fulfils a purpose. This exercise will teach him a few lessons and he must not forget that it is no use him recommending, which is the polite word for selling, a material on the basis of its physical or chemical properties if he ignores the price (which includes delivery, fabrication, *etc.*) and which is also a property. Furthermore, when he selects topics for development or research work and looks at the various properties of materials he must look realistically at the one universally important property which is cost to the buyer. This property is at least as complicated as any others the material has and it is sometimes governed by what at first appear completely illogical laws. The relationship with production costs is sometimes statistically non-existent, and whilst sometimes there are good commercial reasons for this there are situations in which a good product which may cost the same or even less to manufacture than a bad one does not require extra manufacturing capital or cause any other inconvenience is priced out. It may not be the recognized function of a materials man to concern himself with prices but it is the thesis of this paper that he should, and it is suggested that he will find at least as much challenge in investigating the interesting laws governing accountants and bodies such as the Iron and Steel Board as the physical laws of nature.

Price as stated above means price of the final item, and this in turn involves a knowledge of methods of construction and their costs. It is no use for instance specifying a PTFE lining and stating the price of PTFE without also considering whether and how such a construction can be made and the final cost.

Stages in a Project at which Material Decisions are Taken

Thinking in terms of a chemical project it is possible to divide the decisions made on materials into three stages. Initially there is a stage during which an idea is conceived and laboratory work on the chemistry of the various reactions is done. During this stage a great many materials decisions can be made, either consciously or subconsciously. Indeed even before laboratory work is sanctioned the matter of materials may influence the project. To give an example, a chemist may say that he can visualize a process involving a pressure

system operating at say 900°C which would be highly economic. It could well be that he would get no further since the consequential container problem might label the whole idea as unrealistic. This is a case which actually arose at Billingham a few years ago but fortunately the project was not killed even though it was fully appreciated that the conventional power industry was having difficulties in going even to 650°C. Chances had to be taken, but in a matter of some three years the first pressure steam reforming plant for light distillate was on line, and now some two years later there are at least 33 such plants on line or in various states of completion.

Assuming that an idea is not killed from the start, and laboratory work proceeds, various decisions on materials are made again sometimes almost subconsciously during the research. For instance, everyone knows that hydrochloric acid is a difficult acid and no matter what other merits it has it could well be excluded in an investigation simply on this basis. It may also be that artificial limits on pressure, temperature or other such factors may be imposed just in order to avoid potential materials problems. Naturally this may be justified and certainly it will reduce the eventual demands on materials, but it is also likely to reduce the chances of a really spectacular new project. The nitric acid process universally used now is a good example, also from Billingham, of a process which would not have seen the light of day when it did had it not occurred to someone at the time that there was what then was a novel material—stainless steel —and that it was not merely a laboratory curiosity and that it could be considered seriously for a major engineering construction. The realization, of course, not only caused progress in chemical engineering, but brought forward the development of the stainless steel industry which in turn transformed chemical engineering.

The second stage in the project comes when the laboratory work has been finished and it has been established that something can be done. During this stage it is necessary to decide exactly *what* shall be done and finish up with a flowsheet. This stage is very similar for a really new or for an only slightly modified process, and again a variety of decisions are made which, consciously or subconsciously, involve assumptions about materials. For instance, important factors are the size of plant, the operating pressures, temperatures, compositions of various streams, *etc.*, and the limits are imposed by what are commonly called engineering factors. A typical such limit may be the size of the pressure vessel, but is this really a true engineering limitation? The basic physics of a pressure vessel are not affected appreciably by size, and if there are limits to the size of pressure vessels these are imposed by metallurgical factors such as the metallurgy of thick plates, on being able to weld and inspect the vessel, and other factors which are in the materials field. Naturally there are also practical matters such as the transport of the vessel to a particular site which may impose limits, but the metallurgist can overcome sometimes even these by allowing site welding. By the time this second stage is reached generally time is becoming short, and unless the necessary homework was done during the first stage, conventional materials and modes of construction are the order of the day. Savings, even if considerable, which might be possible by adopting completely novel methods have become less attractive especially since it has already been established that the exercise as a whole is economically rewarding and there is already a " bird in the hand ".

Finally, when it has been established what shall be done, design starts which involves decisions on *how* it is to be done. By now things are moving at all possible speed, capital has been committed and every single day may cost £1000 or more depending on the size of the project. The project has splintered into various design tasks and many designers are involved. It is perhaps regrettable, but by far the greatest number of decisions on materials have to be taken during this stage. Even if the major decisions have been taken, there are numerous minor ones and these involve, amongst other things, the laying down of detailed specifications, establishment of standards, instruction on welding, inspection, and the unforeseen difficulties which crop up during detail design. The odd joint, gland, inspection point or delay in delivery of a preferred material are typical details which all cause hold-ups, and equally important, if not considered adequately, endless start-up troubles. At this stage, like at all others, decisions must be correct, but one thing is never permitted now and that is to take time to make them. These two requirements may appear contradictory but in practice they frequently are not and the way out may be to do something which appears quite stupid economically or clumsy from a design point of view but which is bound to work. When it has worked unfortunately it then becomes established and the mistakes, because this is what these compromises are, are then repeated when new plants are built.

To sum up, the really big challenge arises at the conception of a novel idea for a process. There is then freedom of action and time. Unfortunately decisions at that stage are often made subconsciously and even at the next stage, the flowsheet stage, when worthwhile things can still be done, it is not always appreciated just where materials stand. The final stage is a race against time, the decisions are still important because they make all the difference between a plant with or without start-up difficulties. That engineering is applied material science amongst other things is appreciated at this stage especially when things go wrong, but it is too late to do anything really big.

Present Challenging Problems

This is a most difficult topic and each person is bound to be influenced by his immediate experience. As I see it, the most interesting feature at present is the hotting up of the competition between metallic and non-metallic materials, and this is becoming quite real. It is not confined to the exotic novel ceramics, cermets, *etc.*, which allow one to do things undreamt of only a few years ago. A simple thing like the tile lining of a vessel was a very adequate way of dealing with a reasonably innocuous acid, but now it is possible to build a prestressed tile-lined vessel and consider for instance holding hyrdochloric acid in it, or building a pressure vessel in this way. The first French reactors showed how quite large pressure vessels can be built in concrete whilst the Dracone and the various smaller rubber-cum-plastic transport vessels are finding many uses.

In this competition metals have a great advantage in being well known to the engineer and easy to use since there are many codes, national specifications, standards, *etc.*, and a well-organized and established engineering industry to back them up. Strangely these are also their handicaps because many of the standards and established engineering practices are out of date and greatly restrictive. For instance, B.S. 1500 lays down that pressure vessels must be designed to a quarter of the U.T.S.—a standard laid down countless years ago which admittedly is being revised, but only after it has been shown by many years experience in Germany that much higher stresses are safe in practice. There are countless other examples—to quote one other it is traditional to use forged steel for critical items, but why? The economics of the steam reforming process already mentioned were greatly affected by using centrispun tubes of high alloy steel at roughly a third the cost of the extruded tubes, and on a six-week delivery instead of one year. As it happens they have also proved technically better, but in order to obtain these advantages one has to fight tradition. Those who feel safe that they have a good quality product unlikely to be replaceable by others may be fortunate, but are more likely to be mistaken, and they have to consider exactly what the customer buys and not assume that this is the same thing as the manufacturing description. A manufacturer may think he is selling forgings but in fact the customer buys vessels, tubes, *etc.*, and provided they are technically sound he does not care if they are knitted. An example is provided by the railways which would not be in trouble now if from the start they had realized they were in the transport business and not in the railway business.

Many of the people in the traditional metal industry would do well to spend more effort on the deadly boring subject of codes, standards, *etc.* If they feel that, as highly trained people, it would be a waste of time to do so, they have to remember that ultimately the man at the drawing board can only make use of developments when these have been incorporated in such codes or at least in trade publications. Papers in the various metallurgical journals are *no use at all* for this particular purpose and there are obvious disadvantages in sending the second fifteen to B.S. committees.

Technically it is hardly worth saying that most of the challenge comes from the desire to go even to higher temperatures, the wish to build even larger cold items, the use of higher pressures, and from the numerous compatibility problems (*i.e.* corrosion, product purity, catalyst performance, *etc.*). There are numerous challenges in every field, but a practical hint may amuse some. Pumps, fans and other such items sometimes suffer rapid deterioration in service. They are then buttered up with various hard metals, *etc.*, and are still in trouble, and then someone bodges them up with an epoxy resin or some similar compound, and that often is the end of the problem. It is these small things which are often so very important.

B

DESIGN FOR DIFFICULT ENVIRONMENTS

By D. R. LOVELL, D.L.C., M.Inst.F., A.M.I.Chem.E.,* and A. E. S. WHITE, A.R.C.S., B.Sc.*

SYNOPSIS

Difficult environments are defined for the purposes of this paper as those in which mechanical stress, chemical attack, and thermal shock occur at high temperatures (above about 1200°C).

Existing or new designs may be combined with existing or new materials to form four possible methods of combating these conditions. Examples of each method are discussed with reference to problems of kiln-roof design; tube-furnace design; liquid-metal temperature measurement; reactive-metal containers: high-temperature gas-turbine blades and rocket nozzles.

Two cases are mentioned where design and materials have advanced independently with the result that progress has been very limited.

It is emphasised that the design must suit the properties of the material and that when new materials are developed the application of theoretical principles of, for example, thermodynamics and solid-state physics, can be of great value in guiding the practical investigations and in predicting new compounds and properties.

Introduction

In the design of chemical-engineering plant it is necessary to select materials of construction that will withstand the operating conditions and to produce the component in an appropriate shape to suit both the available methods of manufacture for the chosen material and the application.

Where the difficult environments considered in this paper occur, consisting of chemical attack, erosion, mechanical stress, and thermal shock at temperatures above about 1200°C, the material selected is frequently a ceramic and design problems are increased by the special properties of this type of material and the variability in properties from piece to piece.

Sometimes it is possible to avoid the difficulties by modifying the design and using ordinary materials, but as environments become more difficult new materials have to be developed, and these often require a different design because of limitations imposed by the material.

There are four possible routes to the solution of a problem. In order of complexity, cost, time required, and effort involved these are:

(1) The use of an existing design using an existing material.

(2) The production of a new design using an existing material.

(3) The use of an existing design using a new material.

(4) The production of a new design using a new material.

For the designer to be able to consider all these routes it is essential that the problem is clearly understood and stated in the broadest terms. For example, by stating a problem as " Design a plant to melt titanium " rather than restricting it to " Provide a crucible to contain molten titanium " it is possible to avoid a difficult materials problem.

The first route is worth some study because a knowledge of the present " state of the art ", especially under operating conditions approaching the limits which the materials will withstand, provides a basis on which to develop new designs.

The second route—new design, existing material—has been illustrated in the example on melting titanium and other examples will be mentioned later. This route is the most

* Morganite Research and Development Ltd., Battersea Church Road, London, S.W.11.

challenging and, if successful, the most satisfying to a designer, since it requires all his ingenuity and inspiration to devise a solution which in effect avoids the difficulties.

The third route—existing design, new material—is encountered in three forms:

(1) The development which occurs in a family of materials. The heat-resisting alloys are an example where improvements in materials allow furnace components of the same design to withstand more difficult environments— higher temperature and larger stresses in corrosive atmospheres—and successive alloys of a series are suitable for progressively more severe conditions.

(2) When a material of the same family with the necessary properties is not available, a change of material can sometimes be made without affecting the design. In the construction of muffle tubes for furnaces it is often possible to use a similar design, although a ceramic is substituted for a metal casting.

(3) Where neither of these approaches provides a satisfactory material an attempt has to be made to produce a " tailor-made ", entirely new material to meet the application. This is a challenge to the materials scientist and it becomes increasingly necessary as environments become more difficult. To carry out such a development successfully, the thermodynamics and solid-state properties of the system must be considered and this makes possible the prediction of properties and of possible new compounds.

The fourth route—new design, new material—has to be used if the available form of the new material prevents the existing design being used, e.g. the new material is available only as a casting when the previous design was formed from wrought materials, or if the properties of the material impose some restriction on the shape or size of the article, as frequently occurs with ceramics. In this case especially, the designer must consider both the material and the application, and the interrelation between them.[1]

Sometimes the designer and the materials scientist find themselves out of step so that materials are available that the designer can find very little use for, or the materials scientist is unable to provide a material meeting the designer's needs and the designer cannot devise an economic way of avoiding the problem.

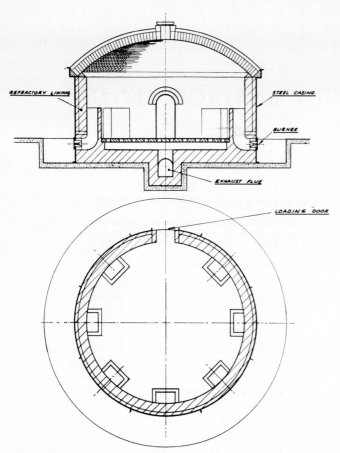

Fig. 1.—*General arrangement of round downdraught kiln*

Examples of each of the above routes to a solution have occurred in our experience and a description of some of the more interesting ones will illustrate the close interrelationship between design and materials which is essential when dealing with difficult environments.

Existing Design Using Existing Materials

The use of hot-face insulating bricks has become widespread in the last 10 to 15 years because of their two great advantages, low-heat storage capacity and low thermal conductivity, compared with ordinary firebrick. Table I provides comparative figures. Because of the low density and high porosity

of hot-face insulating bricks their mechanical strength is low. These same properties, however, mean that they can be cut easily to shape and rubbed to make mating joints which require only a very thin layer of cement.

TABLE I.—*Comparison of Some Properties of Firebrick and Hot-face Insulation Brick*

	Firebrick	H.F.I. brick
Refractoriness:		
Seger cone	32 (1710°C)	32 (1710°C)
Porosity (%)	23	72
Bulk density (lb/ft³)	125	47·5
Thermal conductivity at mean temperature of 800°C (Btu/h ft² degF in.)	10	3
Cold crushing strength (lb/in²)	2500–5500	140

We have had in use for many years a series of round down-draught kilns working up to 1450°C on a five-day cycle and some of these have been constructed or reconstructed using hot-face insulating bricks. The general arrangement of this type of kiln is shown in Fig. 1 and the roof illustrates the effect of the properties of the material on design.

This roof weighs only one-third as much as it would if constructed in firebrick and is best built by laying the bricks in circular courses, each brick being rubbed down from a standard rectangular shape to match the curvature required and the dome being developed by a rotating jig (Fig. 2). It is necessary to cut bricks occasionally to prevent radial joints in a number of courses coming into line, because this would provide a path for a crack to develop. Fig. 3 shows a well-constructed roof and Fig. 4 a poorly-constructed one in which staggering of the radial joints has not been carried out and the rotating jig has moved during the construction. It should be noted that the use of cement between the bricks is theoretically unnecessary as the bricks are tapered and should support each other. Although cement is in fact used to enable the rings to be built, the movement of the roof during firing produces a number of radial and circumferential cracks between courses which separate the dome into a series of mutually supporting panels. Because the expansion cracks open and close as the roof rises and falls on heating and cooling, it is not desirable to cover it with powder insulation since this percolates into the cracks and prevents them closing. However, a diatomaceous-brick insulation or a slightly flexible asbestos–sodium silicate paste layer can be used.

One disadvantage of hot-face insulation bricks has recently been overcome by mechanically keying a thin layer of dense castable refractory to the hot face. This provides an erosion

Fig. 2.—*Method of constructing domed roof*

and abrasion-resistant surface without sacrificing much thermal efficiency. A thin firebrick lining to achieve the same purpose would be difficult to bond into the brickwork. In some cases a washcoating can be used.

Later in this paper we refer to metal–ceramic thermocouple sheaths for temperature measurement in liquid metals. The design of the furnaces in which these pieces are fired is another interesting example of the effect of the use of refractory materials on design. The problem is essentially that of heating a tube of the largest economic diameter to a temperature of 1600–1850°C over a length of about 18 in. uniformly while maintaining an atmosphere which may be slightly oxidising, inert or reducing, inside it. The heating and cooling rates are not critical but the selected temperature must be controlled to within 5°C (i.e. $\frac{1}{4}\%$ of the operating temperature). The cost of kilning the product must be kept reasonably low.

The problem is about as easy, in general terms, as it is possible to imagine—merely to heat repeatedly the central portion of a tube to a given temperature—but because the temperature is close to the melting-point of the ceramic material, and the atmosphere must be closely controlled, necessitating an impermeable tube, it is in fact difficult to achieve an economical solution.

Nine major issues must be considered: these are detailed below (see also Fig. 5).

Material

The most readily available material capable of withstanding 1850°C and providing an impermeable tube about 48 in. long (to give an 18-in. uniform hot zone) is recrystallised alumina. It can be obtained in tubes with diameters up to about 4 in. O/D from stock and larger as special orders.

Heating method

The cheapest way of heating 30 in. of tube (to give 18 in. uniform) to 1850°C is to wind a molybdenum wire on the tube and use it as an electrical element in a hydrogen atmosphere to prevent oxidization.

Size

The larger the diameter of the tube the more expensive it is and the lower its resistance to thermal gradients, shock, and mechanical stresses. It is therefore most economic to use the smallest permissible diameter.

Temperature control

For the accuracy stated a total-radiation pyrometer sighted on a closed sheath touching the heating element is now used. This controls the power to the winding by on/off switching. The performance of tungsten/rhenium thermocouples is now being investigated.

Temperature gradients

Longitudinal gradients must be restricted to about 125°C/in. for alumina, and with the available length of tube being 48 in. the 15 in. at each end just accommodates such a gradient, provided the distribution is a uniform rate of fall from the end of the 18-in. hot zone.

Insulation

The insulating material must be of equal purity to the alumina tube to prevent contaminants migrating, and alumina powder is used. To reduce the quantity of expensive powder the lower-temperature outer areas are constructed in insulating brick. The whole is cased in steel to provide a gas-tight container for the hydrogen used to protect the heating element.

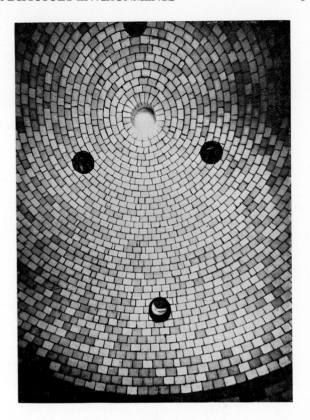

Fig. 3.—*Well-constructed domed roof*

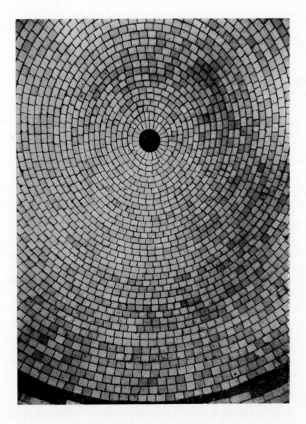

Fig. 4.—*Poorly-constructed domed roof*

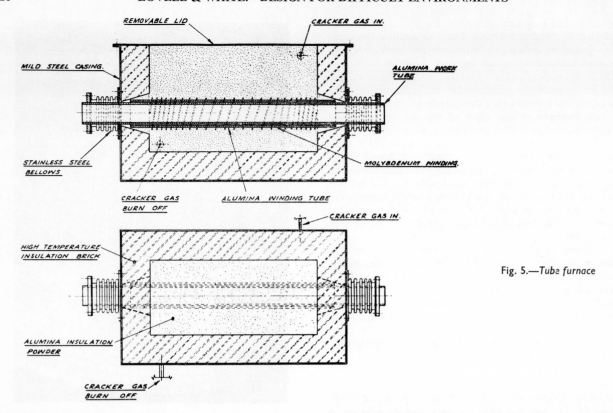

Fig. 5.—*Tube furnace*

Maintenance

One of the largest expenses of kilning in this type of furnace is the labour and material costs for maintenance. When operating for 120 hours a week on a 20- to 30-hour cycle it is usual to achieve a furnace-life between rebuilding of 4 to 12 weeks. The range reflects to some extent the variability of alumina tubes. A small error in operation or variations in power supply can shorten the life drastically. It has been found more satisfactory to use the double tube assembly shown in Fig. 5 in spite of the fact that the operating temperature of the larger tube is increased by this arrangement.

Maintenance is facilitated by the following features: the larger diameter tube does not need to be impervious and has slightly better thermal shock properties; the recrystallised alumina work tube can be salvaged in case the wound tube or winding fails, and vice versa; the work tube can be rotated a quarter turn occasionally to counteract sagging; the gap between the tubes encourages hydrogen to flow between the molybdenum element and the work tube so that any gas which permeates through the work tube will be removed from the furnace before it attacks the metal; the wound tube can be supported independently of the steel casing.

Protective atmosphere

Inside the tube the atmosphere can theoretically be any gas because the tube is impervious, but in fact after some time at high temperatures some permeability develops.

Outside the tube the atmosphere is cracked ammonia to provide the hydrogen needed to protect the molybdenum element. This is introduced at the top of the casing and burnt off from a cock at the bottom. Arranging for the gas to flow preferentially around the element and to purge out all the air conflicts with the need for the powder to support the wound tube, and is difficult because the insulating powder is of lower porosity than the bricks.

Power supply

The temperature coefficient of resistance of molybdenum is very large so that at low temperatures the voltage supplied

must be a small fraction of that required at working temperature. Sudden power changes affect tube-life and a continuously variable voltage regulator is therefore used. On/off switching for temperature control is permissible because the response of the pyrometer to changes in the temperature of the sheath is much quicker than that of the wound tube.

All these factors have to be taken into account to solve economically one of the simplest problems. Imagine then the considerations governing the design of something as involved as a turbine blade in a new refractory material.

New Design Using Existing Materials

In investigating new refractory compounds it is frequently necessary to determine melting-points, study reactions, and to make samples of known composition and purity. At very high temperatures in oxidising atmospheres, such as are necessary for oxide materials, one of the most convenient methods is to use an arc-image furnace because the specimen can be heated in any atmosphere without contamination. This is done by ensuring that the reactive zone is wholly within the pure material, by using a container which is lined with a sufficient thickness of the heated material. As the arc-image furnace produces high temperatures over a small area only, about $\frac{1}{4}$ in. diameter over 2000°C, the quantity of material needed to meet this requirement is quite small. Fig. 6 shows one design of rotating sample holder producing a tapered hollow cylinder by sintering and melting a powder, which allows any gas to be passed through the shaft of the cup and over the molten surface of the specimen. By viewing the cup from the open end, the temperature can be measured and the progress of the reaction viewed.

Another interesting example of the use of existing materials in a new design of plant is now being developed for a number of applications by at least two companies in different parts of the world. The equipment is a fluidised bed of carbon or graphite powder which is self-heated by direct passage of a current through the particles. In Canada[2] and South

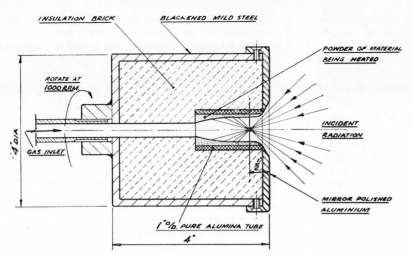

Fig. 6.—*Arc-image furnace sample holder*

Africa,[3] it is being applied as a chemical reactor for the manufacture of hydrogen cyanide, carbon disulphide, and other carbon compounds; while in Japan,[4] it is being used as a carburising furnace for metal treatment. It has another obvious application as a gas heater.

Existing Design Using New Materials

Theoretical considerations

Where new materials are to be investigated which are not just an improvement on existing materials of the same family, it is important that the development of the new materials is guided by a thorough understanding of the theoretical considerations.

To this end, methods of estimating unknown data are of great importance as materials practice often tends to run ahead of basic science, and the background data, although often available at ambient temperatures, are lacking at high temperatures. The first task of the materials scientist is therefore to observe general trends in properties to aid in prediction. Thus, in thermodynamics, various empirical factors, homologous and other series, based on molecular weights, similar structures, *etc.*, often enable unknown values to be predicted or interpolated.[5, 6]

In order to predict the approximate course of high-temperature reactions it is noted that reactions between condensed phases, giving only condensed-phase products, have little entropy change, whereas, in reactions involving gases and condensed phases the entropy change is approximately 22 cal/degC/mole of gas. Hence, if ambient temperature data are known or can be estimated the effect of temperature can be predicted.

Possible new high-temperature compounds can also often be predicted. In the case of solids, crystal chemistry[7] enables us to suggest new compounds based on atom replacements in known lattices, and, providing atomic radii, co-ordination numbers, and electrical neutrality are preserved these substitutions can often be quite unexpected. For example, the perovskite lattice structure can give compounds of the following form:

$$A^{3+}B^{3+}O_3 \qquad (e.g.\ YBO_3)$$
$$A^{2+}B^{4+}O_3 \qquad (e.g.\ CaTiO_3)$$
$$A^{1+}B^{5+}O_3 \qquad (e.g.\ KNbO_3)$$
$$A^{1+}B^{2+}F_3 \qquad (e.g.\ RbCaF_3)$$

The compound $BeSiN_2$ was also predicted from the known AlN by substitution of Be^{2+} and Si^{4+} for $2Al^{3+}$.

The most stable high-temperature interstitial compounds[8] can also be predicted by a consideration of the electron/atom ratio just as the Cu–Zn system is explained by the Hume Rothery electron/atom ratio rules.

In this case, from the elements, one observes the maximum melting-points to occur around Groups 5 and 6 at tungsten which has the maximum number of unpaired " d " electrons (five) for optimum resonance bonding and one " s " electron/atom. It is next postulated that when nitrogen and carbon enter interstitially into the transition metal, roughly one electron per interstitial is given up to the metal atoms, thus effectively increasing the number of electrons in the metal. Hence carbon or nitrogen additions to molybdenum and tungsten increase the electron/atom ratio above the optimum, but in the case of niobium and tantalum these are effectively converted to molybdenum and tungsten, but with an increased bond density, thus accounting for the increased melting-points of these compounds. However, as nitrogen is normally a gas, the entropy effect already mentioned reduces the stability of nitrides at high temperatures and the carbides, in particular tantalum carbide, are the most refractory. The mixture 4TaC.1HfC is slightly more refractory again and it has been suggested that this is due to the fact that in tantalum carbide the electron/metal atom ratio is slightly over the optimum and therefore hafnium carbide additions (hafnium having one electron/atom less than tantalum) bring the ratio to its optimum.

Entropy and chemical considerations also show that when solids vaporize, unexpected high-temperature gaseous molecules are likely, *e.g.* Al_2O_3 does not vaporize primarily as Al_2O_3 but as Al_2O, AlO and O_2: SiC vaporizes as Si_2C, SiC_2, and Si_2: Si_3N_4 vaporizes as SiN and N_2 while MoO_3 vaporizes as $(MoO_3)_n$.[9]

This is partly explained by entropy considerations, which favour the maximum volume of gas—*i.e.* $A_xB_y(C)$ vaporizes to n (AB, A_2B, AB_2, A, B) molecules rather than one A_xB_y (gas) as the free energy change is greater—and partly by the relative bond energies of simple molecules, including ring molecules, which can exist in the gas phase compared with the bond energies in infinite three-dimensional solids.

Examples

Two problems which have been tackled by developing new materials in which to make articles of existing design are: the measurement of the temperature of liquid metals, for which a number of metal–ceramic compositions have been produced, and the containment of molten reactive metals.

In the manufacture of both ferrous and non-ferrous metals the measurement of liquid metal temperature has usually been carried out intermittently by dipping a thermocouple into the liquid for a short period. This requires the material of the thermocouple sheath to have the following properties:

Refractoriness; resistance to thermal shock; resistance to attack by the slag, metal, and atmosphere; high thermal conductivity; compatibility with thermocouple materials, and mechanical strength.

Silica has been used most commonly but is limited to about 1600°C and is mechanically weak. It is known that alumina is highly resistant to attack, is reasonably strong and compatible with thermocouple materials at temperatures up to 1800°C but it has poor thermal shock resistance and thermal conductivity. It was considered that a metal/ceramic sheath in which the advantages of a ceramic were combined with those of a metal was worth investigating and suitable materials have now been developed and operate successfully.[10]

Briefly, the idea was that the thermal conductivity and maximum strain of alumina could be increased if a continuous metal phase could be introduced and, provided a reasonably continuous alumina phase still existed, the mechanical properties of the alumina would be substantially retained. This would be expected to increase the thermal-shock resistance of the alumina, while its non-wetting nature would prevent the liquid metal dissolving more than a thin surface layer of metal from the metal/ceramic.

However, the metals that can be combined with alumina are very limited. An ideal metal would have a similar thermal expansion to alumina; be very refractory (melting-point above 1600°C); be compatible with alumina during processing; be oxidation resistant; be ductile, and give a good bond with alumina. Not surprisingly, no such metal is available and a compromise has to be sought. Thus molybdenum and chromium and their alloys appear promising when combined with alumina by powder metallurgy methods, while porous alumina can be infiltrated with silver by using copper oxide as wetting agent.

Although it might be thought that the poor oxidation resistance of molybdenum limits the use of a molybdenum/alumina combination, in practice the slag appears to coat the metal and protect it from rapid oxidation.

Chromium is not ideal as it tends to contaminate platinum couples and this must be overcome by providing a thin internal alumina lining.

Molybdenum/alumina thermocouple sheaths have given good results when used in molten steel in an open-hearth furnace,[11] being capable of several dips each of 1 to $1\frac{1}{2}$ hours duration, and also in vacuum melting furnaces where they are now standard equipment for repeated dip immersions. They have also been used for measuring the roof temperature of open-hearth furnaces where conditions of thermal shock, erosion, chemical attack, and temperature are very severe.

Chromium/alumina sheaths are used for continuous immersion in molten copper alloys at about 1400°C and last several months.

Mention has been made earlier of the selection of a refactory for making a crucible to contain liquid titanium. Such metals as titanium are extremely reactive in the liquid form and attack all common crucible materials. However, it is possible by thermodynamic calculations to get some idea of the type of refractory that might be suitable.[12] Thus, the following reactions between titanium and a crucible material, MeX are possible:

$$\mathrm{Ti+MeX} = \begin{cases} \mathrm{Ti}_n\mathrm{X} \\ \mathrm{Me} \\ \mathrm{MeX}_{(1-x)} \\ \mathrm{TiMe}_{(z)} \end{cases}$$

Even if the crucible is not destroyed the titanium may be contaminated and its properties adversely affected.

A suitable material must have the following properties:

(1) A melting-point well above that of titanium, say, 1800°C or higher.

(2) The free energy change of any possible reactions must be appreciably positive.

(3) None of the possible reaction products must be gaseous at the temperature of use.

(4) The solubility of the crucible material, MeX, in titanium must be low.

Very few materials are suitable; certainly all oxides and probably all nitrides are ruled out by thermodynamic considerations and only the most stable silicides, borides, carbides, and sulphides at the lower end of their homogeneity ranges are likely to be satisfactory. In practice, it has been found that cerium sulphide, CeS, is fairly satisfactory. It is not however, used industrially. Instead, by considering the requirement in the widest terms as a plant for melting titanium rather than as a container for molten titanium, the designers have been able to avoid the materials problem and the metal is arc-melted on a water-cooled hearth which becomes lined with solidified titanium.

New Design Using New Materials

In order to take advantage of the increased thermal efficiency of a gas turbine when operating at about 1200°C a development programme with which we were associated was initiated with the objective of an experimental single-stage gas turbine.[13]

The temperature was such that this necessitated the use of new materials especially for the highly loaded blades. The blade material requirements can be summarized under the seven headings given below.

Refractoriness

Melting-point data are usually readily available from the literature or if not, can often be interpolated or deduced from series based on the periodic table, as in fact many other properties can. If necessary the arc-image furnace technique described earlier provides a good experimental method.

Mechanical strength (including creep resistance and absence of brittleness)

This is much more complex. It is micro-structure and design sensitive, and generally the two requirements of creep resistance and absence of brittleness are rather incompatible. However, in general, metallic materials are ductile but have poor hot strength; ionic materials are brittle and have fairly good hot strength, while covalent materials are brittle and have very good hot strength (due to the directed nature of their bonding).

Thermal shock resistance

This is not a basic property but rather depends on a combination of basic properties—for brittle materials mainly on thermal expansion, thermal conductivity, and maximum strain.

Oxidation resistance

This depends on the formation of an oxide film (except for oxides and noble metals) as thermodynamically oxides are always more stable than other compounds at high temperatures. If this oxide film is mechanically sound and has a low diffusion rate for the reacting species, oxidation resistance will be good. In general glassy oxide films (e.g. silica, silicates, and borates) are probably best, though beryllia, alumina, chromia and spinel films are often also good.

Thermal stability

This really depends on two different properties—tendency to dissociate, expressed by the thermodynamic free energy of formation; and volatility, depending on vapour pressure.

Cost and ease of shaping

Neither of these is a basic property and each needs to be considered individually.

Taking all these factors into account, pure (self-bonded) silicon carbide was chosen as the best all-round material for the stator blades as it is very refractory, has good high-temperature strength and creep resistance due to its covalent nature, has good thermal-shock resistance due to its low thermal expansion and good thermal conductivity, has good oxidation resistance due to its protective silica film, and is cheap (see Table II). Its drawbacks are difficulty of shaping and brittleness. The latter was a serious problem, but it was felt that as the blades were stationary, design modification could overcome this.

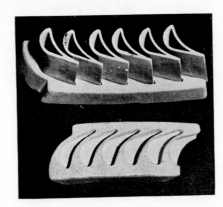

Fig. 7.—Gas-turbine refractory-blade segment—partly dismantled

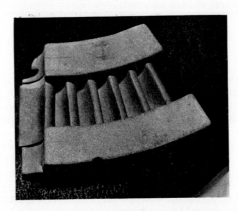

Fig. 8.—Gas-turbine refractory-blade segment assembly

TABLE II.—*Properties of Pure, Dense Silicon Carbide*

Melting-point	Dissociates at about 2400°C
Mechanical properties:	
Bend strength (20–1400°C)	$20–30 \times 10^3$ lb/in²
Modulus of elasticity	$50–60 \times 10^6$ lb/in²
Temperature for which 2 tons/in² for 300 hours promotes 0·125% tensile strain	Above 1300°C
Thermal expansion	4×10^{-6}/degC (20–1000°C)
Thermal conductivity	0·15 to 0·25 cal/cm² s degC cm 440 to 730 Btu/h ft² deg Fin.
Oxidation resistance	Good to 1650°C
Shaping	Difficult. Usually roughly shaped at green stage and final machine after firing
Cost	Raw materials—cheap; sintering—fairly expensive; machining—very expensive

It was necessary to alter the design of the stator blade to give a short, stubby blade with a thicker trailing edge in order to improve thermal-shock resistance. This unfortunately reduced the aerodynamic efficiency, but this was offset to a certain extent by the higher Carnot-cycle efficiency obtained when working at the higher temperature. The normal root-fixing method employed for metal blades was also unsuitable for brittle materials, which could not yield and redistribute stresses, so the blades were held relatively loosely at each end in refractory recesses which however prevented any twisting motion. (See Figs. 7, 8, and 9.)

For the rotor blades, brittle ceramic materials were considered impractical because of the need to hold these blades at one end only. Instead a cooled conventional blade was evolved, using liquid sodium inside a hollow metal shape. The centrifugal force assisted convection cooling to the rotor disc and in this case the difficult environment was in fact utilized to advantage.

This design of a single-stage turbine eventually ran successfully at temperatures up to 1200°C and although many problems still exist it demonstrates that the solution of a single problem is available by the combination of new designs and new materials.

Another example of new materials which had to be developed forcing a change in the design of the component, occurs in the manufacture of rocket-motor nozzles.

Here the problem is to find a material to resist very high temperature, high velocity, abrasive gases—a combination of

Fig. 9.—Gas-turbine refractory blades assembled in casing

hardness, refractoriness, and thermal-shock resistance is required. The principles already discussed and small-scale tests showed that compounds such as zirconium carbide, silicon carbide, and zirconium diboride would satisfy most of these requirements but that thermal shock resistance was either marginal or inadequate in any practical size of rocket motor.

These materials have been used by applying two methods which can loosely be considered as design modifications:

(1) The nozzle is precracked under controlled conditions to give interlocking pieces. The loss of strength does not matter as the nozzle is held in an outer retaining ring under slight compression.

(2) The material is used as a thin surface coating on a material that satisfies the thermal-shock requirements only—e.g. graphite. Providing the coating and base match together well in thermal expansion, and adhesion and compatability are good, such a design can combine the advantages of both materials.

Under-exploited material

Cases sometimes occur of a material being developed before the designers are able to make use of it. This leads to the situation where only small trial quantities are available in a few restricted sizes and grades at high cost (representing manufacture on a laboratory scale), which causes the designer to pass it over when selecting a material for an otherwise suitable application. This situation can be resolved only by close co-operation between the designer and the materials supplier so that material is made available in the required shape, size, and grade at a special price reflecting the advantages to be gained from getting an introduction to the market on an industrial scale.

A material which appears to be in this state, at least in the United Kingdom, is carbon fibre. This is available in laboratory quantities as carbon or graphite cord, cloth, wool, or felt. It has the ordinary properties of carbon or graphite which, for graphite, are unusual, for example in that the strength increases with temperature; creep is negligible and it is extremely resistant to thermal shock, but it has the disadvantage of oxidising above about 300°C. These properties when combined with the forms in which it is available should provide many applications but so far its use has been limited to insulation in induction and vacuum furnaces, in place of radiation shields, on a small scale.

Unrealisable Design

One problem that is just beginning to concern us is the method of heating a reasonably large high-temperature furnace (1800–2500°C with a 6 in. cube chamber) for use in oxidising conditions over long periods for synthesis and testing purposes. The obvious answer is to modify existing, or produce new, materials to provide either flames or heater elements operating at higher temperatures and to use them in a furnace which is essentially of existing design.

Hotter gas flames can be obtained by the use of highly-energetic combustants giving stable high-temperature molecules (e.g. combustion of C_2N_2 and O_3 to $CO+N_2$) or by electrical augmentation of more normal flames,[14,15] but both give undesirable contamination problems. A more novel solution would be the use of a plasma flame of an inert gas, but temperature control could be difficult.

Present high-temperature electric heater elements are based

on either silicides (SiC or $MoSi_2$) or oxides (ThO_2, ZrO_2). The former can be shown to be already at their theoretical temperature limits (SiC, 1650°C set by reaction of SiO_2 and SiC; $MoSi_2$, 1700°C set by softening of SiO_2)[16] while the oxides mentioned which conduct by ionic diffusion have large negative temperature coefficients of resistance rendering them rather impractical for industrial operation. It does, however, seem likely that research may discover better materials, and a high-temperature analogue of Fe_3O_4 which conducts electronically may eventually emerge. This probably demands a material with a crystal lattice in which the same element is present in two valency states on the same lattice site.[17] Considerations of crystal chemistry and high-temperature stability in air suggest compounds of chromium and uranium such as " doped " Cr_2O_3, $LaCrO_3$, UO_2, and $BaUO_3$ might meet these requirements but further research is obviously required to provide a suitable material.

Conclusions

The design of plant and components to operate in difficult environments at high temperatures demands a wide knowledge of the properties of the materials and of the action of the environment on them. Where existing materials are inadequate, alternative types of material may be substituted but the design must often then be modified, and this applies especially when metallic, ductile materials are replaced by brittle ceramics.

Where no existing material meets the requirements the development of a new material " tailor-made " to the application is increasingly occurring. This requires the study of theoretical principles which need new basic facts about the materials and reactions. Where no facts are available, methods of predicting data, reaction equilibria, new compounds, and properties are of great importance.

In many cases a new pure material is not satisfactory and the desired properties can only be obtained in a multi-phase structure which combines the best properties of the constituents.

The advances to be made in the future will require that materials scientists and designers work closely together to be effective and provided this occurs the problems posed by increasingly difficult environments are likely to be solved successfully.

Acknowledgments

The authors gratefully acknowledge the assistance of Mr. L. T. I. Bentall in the preparation of diagrams; the permission of the North-East Coast Institute of Engineers and Shipbuilders to reproduce Figs. 7, 8, and 9, and the permission of the Directors of Morganite Research and Development Limited to publish this paper.

References

1 Glenny, E. *Trans. Brit. Ceram. Soc.*, 1963, **62**, 565.

2 Johnson, H. S. *Canadian Journal of Chemical Engineering*, 1961, **39**, 145.

3 Anon. *Industrial Chemist*, 1963, **39**, 531.

4 Tanaka, Y. *Paper N. 303, Section 3, Proceedings 5th International Congress of Electroheat*, Wiesbaden, October 1963.

5 Kingery, W. D., and Wygant, J. F. *Bull. Amer. ceram. Soc.*, 1952, **31**, 344.

[6]   Kubaschewski, O., and Evans, E. L. L.   "*Metallurgical Thermochemistry* ", 3rd Edition, 1958 (Oxford: Pergamon Press Ltd.).

[7]   Wells, A. F.   " *Structural Inorganic Chemistry* ", 3rd Edition, 1962 (Oxford: The University Press).

[8]   Brewer, L.   *In* Beck, P. A. (Ed.), " *Electronic Structure and Alloy Chemistry of the Transition Elements* ", 1963 (London: John Wiley & Sons Ltd.).

[9]   Searcy, A. W.   *In* Cotton, P. A. (Ed.), " *Progress in Inorganic Chemistry* ", 1962 (London: John Wiley & Sons Ltd.).

[10]   White, A. E. S., and Blakeley, T. H.   *Chem. & Ind. (Rev.)*, 1962, p. 1740.

[11]   Sharp, J. D.   *Iron & Steel, Lond.*, 1962, **200**, 590.

[12]   Brewer, L.   " *United States Atomic Energy Commission Report, Union Carbide Research Laboratory* ", 762, June, 1950 (Washington: State Publishing Department).

[13]   Blakeley, T. H., and Darling, R. F.   *Trans. N.-E. Cst Instn Engrs Shipb.*, 1957, **73**, 321.

[14]   Richardson, D. L., and Tobey, A. C.   *Industr. Heat.*, 1963, **30**, 2162.

[15]   Karlovitz, B.   *International Science and Technology*, 1962, **1**, No. 6, p. 36.

[16]   Chown, J., Deacon, R. F., Singer, N., and White, A. E. S.   *In* Popper, P. (Ed.), " *Special Ceramics* 1962 ", 1963 (London: Academic Press Inc.).

[17]   Verwey, E. J. W.   *In* Henisch, H. K. (Ed.), " *Semi-Conducting Materials* ", 1951 (London: Butterworth & Co. (Publishers) Ltd.).

The manuscript of this paper was received on 12 *February*, 1964.

DISCUSSION OF PAPERS PRESENTED AT THE FIRST SESSION

Professor FRANK MORTON said that the meeting was the first official meeting of the Institution of Chemical Engineers in the North-West. In the past, all meetings in the North-West had been organised by that indefatigable body, the North-West Branch, and they had also organised this one; but at the same time they had invited the Institution to participate officially, and so, as President of the Institution, he was very happy to open the symposium on materials science in the North-West Branch. As usual, with a symposium of the Institution, the chair at each of the various sessions would be taken by particular experts in their own fields, and that morning the chair was to be taken by Mr. Leslie Holliday. Mr. Holliday needed very little introduction to people interested in materials science. He had been the chairman of the Institution's working party on materials science, a small group of Institution and non-Institution members, which over the past two years had been investigating how best to promote the inter-disciplinary activities necessary in order to bring the field of materials science more into the knowledge of the engineers who were likely to use developing materials. The present symposium was a result of the discussions of that group, and it was hoped from the papers presented and the discussions that would accompany the papers and the subsequent publications, to prove that something had been done to establish materials science as an inter-disciplinary activity worthy of study in advanced universities.

Discussion

Professor FRANK MORTON said that he had listened with great interest that morning to both Professor Zwikker* and Dr. Edeleanu. They had presented what he thought was the major problem, preventing advances of materials in certain fields. Professor Zwikker* dealt with a number of instances of new materials being right for the time. Dr. Edeleanu made the point of the lack of communication between the expert in materials and the man who wished to use the materials. It seemed to him that the question of information dissemination and retrieval and information usage was the first problem that had to be solved if there was to be benefit from advances in materials in all the fields in which such materials could be applied; particularly in the chemical industry was that necessary, not only, he pointed out, in materials of construction which were required for a furnace to carry out an operation at a particular temperature or a particular condition, but also, even, for the development of a catalyst which would not clog in a fluidised bed; for materials which would not corrode in flowing conditions when a metallurgist would have said that they would quite clearly not corrode in a beaker in a laboratory; but when the materials began to flow along a system, it was at such points that the information needed had to be fitted into some form of pipeline where it might be tapped off by the people who needed it.

So far publications had been almost entirely in the fields in which there had been devoted scientific work. There had not been very much feed-back from the user, and if he had a

* Paper not available for publication.

criticism of Dr. Edeleanu's paper, it would be: if the information was available and if they had found a material suitable for X, Y, or Z, why did that also not find its way into some application in which it could be generally utilised. The answer, he thought, was that despite the fact that there was a national committee for materials testing, it had not so far been concerned with chemical usage of materials; it had been essentially concerned with mechanical use of materials. The committee had produced useful information on strengths and ductilities and other properties of materials without providing the information which was needed for use in cladding, for high temperature, low temperature, or high pressures in the right circumstances. How it could be overcome he was not sure, but certainly it seemed that the scientific publications were not what was needed but the technical know-how in published form, and in order to enhance and encourage scientific work in the universities user experience was needed, published and documented. He thought that industry found that very difficult to do, because it had not the time; having solved a problem nobody was prepared to spend time writing up how it had been solved. Frequently one branch of an organisation attempted to solve the same problem which had been solved by another branch of the organisation previously, without the knowledge that it had been solved. There were ways and means by which it could be disseminated, and one was through the ABCM/BPMA system.

Those who were visiting the Department of Chemical Engineering and the Metallurgy Department the following evening would see the new approach to corrosion which the Chemical Engineering Group had taken. Corrosion was not a static problem. Too much information on the properties of materials to withstand acids and conditions of oxidation or reduction depended on their being tried out in a static system. Corrosion in the chemical engineering industry particularly was of a dynamic system, corrosion brought about by movement as well as chemical reaction. This was a new field, a field in which there was a great deal to be learnt about existing materials, but there was also a great deal to be learnt about new materials. Both in the Metallurgy and Chemical Engineering Departments there would be an opportunity to see such things. He thanked the two speakers for an interesting introduction to the symposium. He asked Dr. Edeleanu how best the information was to be published which was being accumulated on every desk in every industry without appearing in the Press.

Dr. EDELEANU said that the question was extremely important but that it was difficult to be constructive. He thought that a fair amount of information was being published but agreed that this was the minority. What was published appeared in numerous journals and was not easy to find but perhaps a greater difficulty was that few practical problems were ever solved properly and the incentive to tidy up a job once a practical solution was found was small. The incentive to write about it and impart the experience to others was even smaller. Such information was, however, available generally to those who bought a process but of course they then had to

C

pay for it. Things, however, are not perhaps quite as bad as they might appear since the available scientific information can, in fact, be used by a suitably qualified man to make reasonable decisions although in the field of corrosion there was the problem of finding people who can use the information. The analogy with information on mechanical properties is a good one since in that case there would also be a difficulty if there were no engineers who were able to calculate stresses. Dr. Edeleanu did not favour the publication of half-baked information which generally confused the issues. We all now suffer from the so-called information explosion and, whilst it is conceivable to visualise retrieval systems which might help us in the future, these would fail if the basic information were unreliable. Critical reading of material offered for publication is especially necessary when a paper relates to a practical situation since the readers of such papers can well be expected to act on them. Whilst we could have sympathy with people who may wish to have nothing but simple situations to work with, providing them with a simple answer when there is no simple answer does not in any way help. Corrosion is a complicated heterogeneous reaction and there is no reason to expect such a reaction to be simple just because it is called erosion and there is very much reason to expect it to be a more difficult situation to analyse because:

(1) we are concerned with reactions occurring at almost imperceptible rates by usual standards;

(2) the chemical composition of the medium is frequently very variable, often unknown and certainly difficult to control;

(3) a number of non-chemical factors have to be considered. For instance, detail design is important, metallurgical factors such as heat treatment, welding can affect the situation spectacularly, whilst the effect of corrosion on mechanical properties is not always dismissable by recommending a corrosion allowance.

Mr. J. P. A. WORTLEY said that he had found the papers both interesting and informative but Dr. Edeleanu had raised several points with which he could not agree. He could only speak from his own experience and that of his colleagues who were selling or " recommending " zirconium and titanium in the chemical engineering industry both in this country and abroad. His company had always ensured that sales of the new metals they produced were developed by people capable of putting forward both the technical and commercial aspects of these metals at the same time. They fully appreciated the considerable waste of time that could take place if the two aspects were divorced, and that the question of communication was well-nigh impossible under such conditions. The futility of discussing with the customer an application for titanium which would immediately be ruled out on economic grounds was understood and therefore they always introduced, at a very early stage in the discussions, the economic case for the use of the newer materials. However, it was felt to be most important that the material supplier was brought into the discussion at stage one, mentioned by Dr. Edeleanu, so that their experience could be brought to bear on the matter and their economic comments could be made as meaningful as possible.

The matter of specification and trade literature was another point. Titanium had been initially introduced for use in aircraft, where the specifications and conditions of acceptance were among the most stringent in industry. While a large proportion of the annual production of titanium was now sold for non-aircraft use, all the company's production of the newer material was made to the same exacting specifications, specifications which stated minimum and maximum properties. That was true of the trade literature, produced by his firm where maximum and minimum properties were also stated. His company fully recognised the important point raised by Professor Morton, that corrosion was a dynamic state of affairs, and it was always recommended that plant trials should be carried out in addition to those done in the laboratory; his company's literature contained many examples of tests that had been carried out under plant conditions.

He had also been interested in Dr. Edeleanu's remarks about the reduction that took place in the duration of the stages of the projects, as one approached the starting-up period. His company had encountered such a state in their attempt to introduce titanium. They had found that although in the initial stages of a project titanium had been shown technically to be acceptable, in the final stages because of lack of time and also perhaps because of lack of faith in the material, people tended to fall back on the old standbys, saying they knew it would last only about six months but that they could always buy another pump or valve to replace it when it did fail. His company felt that that was a backward-looking attitude by an industry in general, and wished to appeal to the engineer again to discuss with them the problems he had, so that their experience with the new metals could be used to advantage. It had been one of his company's objects to work very closely with commercial firms to ensure that by careful design the cost of titanium and zirconium apparatus was brought as low as possible, and now, for pumps, larger heat-exchangers and lined vessels some very favourable comparisons could be drawn with existing stainless-steel apparatus.

Several references had been made to stainless steel, which had been described as a relatively new material, its introduction on a wide scale having been only quite recent. He felt that at the present time titanium was in a somewhat similar position in that it now needed someone to see the light and introduce it for major plant construction.

Dr. EDELEANU said that the speaker was in another part of the same Company, which made it difficult to argue with him. The problem of introducing a metal such as titanium in the chemical industry on a large scale was an important one at present, but perhaps the remarks made did emphasise the difference which exists between the mentality of those at the producing end of the material and those concerned with using it. The selection of the material implies that there is a technical choice and the users' concern is to decide which of a number of alternatives is economically the preferred one. The point of comparison must be the finished installed item and four factors are normally involved: (1) initial capital cost, (2) time, (3) design and other effort necessary, and (4) maintenance. The relative importance of these depends in part on the accounting system used and, in the chemical industry, one normally used some variant of cash discount flow calculations which tend to favour using expendable items, more so than, for instance, in civil engineering. In order to balance the relative importance of the four factors, matters such as the forward order book or, in other words, the availability of excess capacity, the availability of an attractive market in the near future, etc., have to be considered. Titanium, of course, is technically an excellent material but, generally, the failure to select it is governed by these other factors at the present moment rather than its physical and chemical properties. It is a personal opinion that this particular material is not being used as widely as it might be in the chemical industry because its development has been greatly influenced by the economics of a completely different industry, the aircraft industry, which for good reasons places different relative values to the non-technical factors mentioned. One has to accept that these are normal growing pains for a new material and that things will settle eventually to the right level. The technician must remember, however, that whilst, for instance, wax-coated paper may appear technically an unsuitable vessel material for containing aqueous solutions, it is nevertheless a very reasonable selection for certain beverages including milk, when marketed in a particular manner. It is a situation of this kind which leads the user to dismiss a material to the great disappointment of those who are trying to sell it but, generally, the decisions are by no means arbitrary.

Professor R. W. CAHN said that one difficulty that seemed to exist from time to time was that when a new material had been introduced by some research laboratory it might prove very difficult for the material, however good it had been shown to be for a specific purpose, to be obtained commercially. The Plessey Company Ltd. had developed a material called vitreous carbon which was quite revolutionary as a non-corroding and highly compatible crucible material for the electronics industry. The last he had heard was that there was no intention of making it commercially in this country, and he heard that that was partly because there did not seem to be a market for it. It was the usual vicious circle. It was a material which had been enthusiastically proclaimed as having all sorts of possibilities. The only way to obtain it was by personal contacts with people making it on a laboratory scale. It might well be that it would eventually be made abroad, and one day people in the United Kingdom would want to manufacture it and would have to pay licence fees.

He did not know what mechanisms there were, when the material had withstood the tests of experimentation and proved to have many possibilities, for pressing for its manufacture by some suitable organisation.

The other point that occurred to him concerned the comment made by Professor Morton that it was difficult to find out what had already been done in industry in solving particular problems, or comparing alternative materials for a particular application. He thought that what was really needed was an " Industrial Consumers' Association " and the publication of an industrial " Which? ". One could see a number of delicate difficulties arising but he thought there was something to be said in its favour. For example, recently in the design of a new building, it had been required to find out which of a number of thermoplastic tiles would stand up best to the kind of liquids a student might be expected to spill. One of the assistants got hold of a number of tiles and stewed them in acetone, hydrochloric acid, etc., and obtained clear answers. The architect had been so impressed that he thought of informing the Consumers' Association, but he could not see that kind of information being published in " Which? ", because it was only the most murderously inclined housewife who would spill hydrochloric acid on the floor. If there were an Industrial Consumers' Association such data would very readily be published.

Mr. J. M. HUTCHEON said that Professor Cahn was optimistic if he expected an industry to be set up to manufacture a material because it might be useful! It had to be accepted that materials were sometimes developed ahead of their time.

Dr. J. K. HIGGINS said that at UKAEA, Harwell, they had been interested in vitreous carbon in connection with the Winfrith high-temperature reactor. The material had been developed largely in connection with possible nuclear applications. Oxidation studies had been made, and it was found that on a surface-to-surface basis it was comparable to ordinary Pile grade A carbon, and it looked promising for containing fission products at Winfrith. But the radiation

scientists had made prolonged experiments on the material in the pile and found that its shrinkage was about 2%, which ruled it out for nuclear applications. Since that had occurred, he thought that a lot of the backing for the material as a nuclear product was lost, and hence the possible market for it, but he believed that it had been developed by the company which had originally discovered it for crucibles and possibly for rockets.

Dr. EDELEANU sympathised with much that Professor Cahn said, but found it somewhat difficult to agree with the suggestion of an industrial " Which? ". As he saw it, we already have such an organisation in the various standards institutes, such as the B.S.I., and these did provide people with specifications, codes of practice, etc., which allowed the great bulk of design to be completed to adequate safety standards. Both Which? and the B.S.I. were organisations meant to help the somewhat ignorant buyer or designer and one could not expect such organisations to express opinions on the borders where progress has been made. In the field of materials the greatest difficulty arises with the novel, sophisticated development, and if anyone hopes to use such a material successfully without employing a man who can do some critical thinking but by merely looking data up in a book, he is destined to a disappointment, and so are his customers. Dr. Edeleanu was surprised that Professor Cahn should, at least by implication, suggest that the field of materials is more easily classified, simplified and documented than, for instance, the field of physics, chemistry or motor-car engineering. In his opinion, there was no alternative to anyone who wished to take advantage of developments in the last 20 years or so to the employment of the type of person Professor Cahn was teaching. Those who can afford to be 20 years out of date can rely entirely on British standards.

Mr. J. M. HUTCHEON said that such qualitative thinking was dangerous. It was just not true that when a material allowed one to do something that had not been done before, one was willing to pay almost anything for it. The price and the improvement had to be taken together.

Professor A. J. KENNEDY said that achievements in the development of new materials often passed unnoticed because of the failure on the part of those responsible for designing things to get out of the rut of classical design. He thought that there was no more urgent requirement than that design should be seriously regarded as a subject, and that it should be seen to be something else than an extension of classical elasticity. The situation which Dr. Edeleanu had cited was a criticism of the knowledge of designers; if the data they had were inadequate, what did they want from the producer companies? Unfortunately, designers were not prepared to be specific enough, and continued to reject new materials because they failed to conform to outworn specifications. It did, of course, take courage for a man on a project costing several million pounds, such as an aeroplane, to use a new material which might prove advantageous, without having behind him an accepted body of design method to fall back on in defence. The difficulty started as soon as one got into plastic regimes, but with, for example, temperature and corrosion problems as well, decisions became less matters of formal design, but rather guesses hedged around with safety factors. He had sympathy for those caught up in such a situation, and was on their side; the system did not make it easy to bridge the gap between, say, metallurgy and design, and this exercised a continuing limitation to technological advance.

Mr. S. A. GREGORY said that he had to congratulate Lovell and White for bringing out so clearly the interrelationship required between the designer and the materials technologist. Earlier in the session he had imagined that the meeting was an environment difficult for designers, but the paper had made it clear that the designers and the materials specialist must get together, and worked most fruitfully when they had the same objects in mind. As a student of design he was very much aware that not everyone knew the different varieties of constraint under which a designer had to work. Some believed, quite clearly, that a designer should always put in the most advanced material, whereas others believed that he should put in the cheapest material. Neither was true. He had to put in what was the most advantageous material, and what constituted " advantageous " was extremely difficult to define in general. The full range of the term " advantageous " was worth much more study by those who were looking at the principles of design. One could not always define " advantageous " in terms of quantity or principle; it was sometimes a matter of judgment, even of intuition, and people had to be very sympathetic. Quite clearly, if one was going to design to land a vehicle on another planet, one had to be absolutely sure, whereas if one was building a tiny plant in which one wanted to put any of the latest advances one could possibly imagine, then one was going to take chances. Those represented possibly the two extremes in which the designer had to work.

He asked the authors whether in fact they would be prepared to underline even further the suggestion implicit in their paper that the designer and the materials men should work closer together, and in fact that they should attempt strongly to understand one another's problems.

Mr. LOVELL said that he entirely agreed. It was absolutely essential that the designer should be at least half a materials scientist, and the materials scientist should be at least half a designer.

Mr. F. ROBERTS said that in several of the examples which Lovell and White had given in their paper they were fortunate in that they themselves had an appreciation of the design problems, because in their organisation they had themselves a very wide experience of the design and construction of kilns, furnaces, and thermocouples because it was part of their particular production technology. That was why he thought that the designers and the materials scientist were able to go closer together. He himself was worried about the future, when environmental conditions were getting more and more severe; he was worried as to whether the adequate co-operation would be obtained between the consumer and the producer, because one of the important things about developing special materials was that the cost of testing such materials in actual environmental conditions was going to be astronomical. One had only to think of the Mach 3 aircraft, or a modern high-temperature gas-cooled graphite-moderated reactor in the nuclear field, and the cost of testing the structural materials could vastly exceed the actual cost of production: thus it had to be decided who was going to bear the cost of the environmental testing: the producer or the consumer. The only way of getting the really intensive co-operation necessary was by having a complete reappraisal of how the manufacturer and the consumer could work closer together. They had to be much more open with each other than in the past.

To take specific examples, in the very early stages of a product the consumer had to give some idea to the producer of the potential market. If the material was successful he had to indicate the quantity required, so that the producer could assess the economics as to whether it was worth entering the field. The materials technologist had to give some idea as to the size of components, their geometry, wall thicknesses, and which jointing methods, sealing, and welding techniques could possibly be developed if the project were successful. Only thus could materials be designed for much more stringent conditions than the authors had so far given in their papers.

Professor R. W. CAHN said he was struck by one problem mentioned in the paper by Lovell and White, namely, the problem of obtaining suitable heating elements in the high-temperature furnace for use in oxidising atmosphere. It had been mentioned that zirconium oxide was not of use because of its strong negative temperature coefficient. Was that not a field where the materials scientist might think of setting one material against another, trying to make a compound element of an oxide of the kind described together with another material with strongly positive temperature coefficient? If one made a cermet of zirconium dioxide with particles of tantalum protected from the atmosphere by a thin surface layer either of the oxide itself or another insulating oxide, then, if the proportions of the material and the geometry of the material were appropriate for sintering, it might be possible in the temperature ranges of interest to have a material of more or less constant resistivity over a range of temperatures. That might be safer to operate in industrial circumstances than something which was apt to " run away ".

Mr. WHITE said that people had already thought along these lines. The furnace described, based on molybdenum wire heating an alumina tube, had also been used with a molybdenum wire heating a zirconia tube. With this kind of an arrangement the electrical conductivity became much more uniform with temperature because the zirconia started conducting when it got hot. This did not solve the problem of a heater element that was flatter in its characteristics. The limitation was still the geometry of that type of furnace, so one arrived at the suggestion of a combination of metal with a positive temperature coefficient and a ceramic with a negative one, but the speaker had put his finger on the key problem. He had said: " Let us combine the two and put a thin coating on the top to stop oxygen getting in." This was easier said than done, because in any case, if that could be done one might as well put the coating straight on the metal. After all, a metal with a positive temperature coefficient was not unreasonable for a furnace. It had advantages in that it tended to stabilise the temperature of the furnace. Nevertheless, one had only to look at the efforts which people had made to put protective coatings on molybdenum to see this problem had not really been solved, even for relatively low temperatures such as 1200 to 1500°C. At the moment there seemed to be very little prospect of satisfying this requirement above 2000°C.

However, if one had a rod with connections at each end, consisting of cermet down the middle and pure zirconia on the outside, it might be possible to make a sintered composition that way. The likely trouble was thermal expansion mismatch. At high temperature this would not matter because there was sufficient plasticity to accommodate it, but one had to let it come down to room temperature at some time and one would probably end up with cracks in the coating. There seemed to be just one possible approach. One might make the ceramic tube separately, and put molybdenum, tungsten or tantalum wire loosely down the middle. This type of construction had been used and there was a small firm at Cambridge manufacturing heating elements consisting of an alumina tube with a molybdenum winding inside. The trouble was that as soon as one got away from alumina, all the other refractory materials appeared to let the oxygen through too rapidly at high temperatures for them to be a practical proposition. Zirconia and thoria, which were the two obvious high-temperature alternatives, did not appear to be satisfactory on these grounds. Also their thermal shock resistance was not very good. Beryllia was a possibility, however.

Dr. J. K. HIGGINS referred to Table II of the paper by Lovell and White, where it was stated that silicon carbide was efficient up to 1650°C as far as oxidation resistance was concerned. Earlier in the paper it was stated that silicon carbide vaporised as Si_2C. He was surprised that that was stated because a few years ago, in the nuclear industry, when people were interested in silica carbide they found that in an oxidising atmosphere the carbide would form silica but the oxide layer was unstable because of the formation of silicon monoxide, which was volatile. It seemed to him that in the oxidising atmosphere of a rocket nozzle there could be formation of silicon monoxide and volatilisation of the monoxide/oxide film, and it would not be a good material to use in rocket nozzles. Did it mean that the authors had taken the problem into account and it was satisfactory from this point of view?

Mr. WHITE said that in the case of the rocket nozzle it was found that there was quite a sudden change over from silicon carbide being a good material to being a very poor one, and this occurred at temperatures within the range of 1650 to 1800°. It appeared to correspond to the temperature at which the viscosity of the silica was such that it could be blown away rapidly by the high speed gases in the rocket nozzle. As long as the silicon film stayed more or less in position, silicon carbide was good. When the temperature got higher, to 1700–1800°C., the viscosity of the silica was getting lower and it started being blown away by the gas, and silicon carbide became a poor material.

Dr. HIGGINS said that the temperatures of which he was thinking were round about 1000°C. He did not know the stability of the silicon monoxide. Did Mr. White imagine that this volatile oxide would play an important part?

Mr. WHITE said that the reaction of silicon carbide and silica to produce silicon monoxide was such that at 1000°C the pressure of silicon monoxide would be well under a millimetre, so unless one was working in a high vacuum it could be forgotten about.

Mr. G. SANDS said he thought the questioner might be confused with the familiar oxidation behaviour of silicon carbide refractories, in which the silica formed causes growth and disruption of the refractory. His own company was a major user of silicon-carbide refractories in the vertical-retort production of zinc, and from experience he would place the temperature range in which this disruption effect occurred at between 950° and 1150°C. That was a different problem from the high-temperature oxidation about which Dr. Beddow was talking.

Mr. R. N. YOUNGER said that he wished to mention a technology which was almost completely limited by the materials problem. It was the liquid end of the iron and steel industry. When members of the industry looked at Billingham and at some of the non-ferrous industries and saw materials being pumped through pipework systems, they looked with envy. However, they were considerable problems. The working temperature was rarely below 1600°C, the atmospheres were usually highly reducing, and the steel was a particularly good solvent. His company, however, was active in trying to determine how to handle materials of very high temperatures in a chemical engineering way. He asked for the opinions of Lovell and White on the use of carbon and graphite for such applications. They were already being used in the United States in pressure and continuous casting.

Mr. LOVELL said he could not see carbon on its own being used for the purpose. There might be appreciable carbon pick-up in the mild steel which would not be acceptable. Carbon used in the form of bonded material was in fact being tried in this application at the moment. Clay-graphite material which had been used for crucibles for melting non-ferrous metals for 100 years or more was now being tried for launders and blast furnaces for molten iron. There were various other ideas along the same lines for a material which contained graphite to improve the thermal conductivity and other properties. The graphite was protected from oxidation and from reaction with the molten iron by a clay or some other bond. He thought that in a suitable form carbon or graphite might very well be applied to this problem.

C*

SECOND SESSION

MATERIALS IN GAS DISCHARGES

By R. A. DUGDALE*

SYNOPSIS

Intense gas discharges, such as those employed in thermonuclear research, cause a number of significant effects to occur on material surfaces exposed to them. An experimental investigation of some of these effects has been made and the results obtained are described. The initiation of arcing on metal surfaces appears to involve bursts of vapour generated by the electrical breakdown of insulating inclusions, but an essential factor is associated with other surface contamination and may involve electron emission at fields of order 10^5 V cm^{-1}. Intense heat pulses delivered to glasses and ceramics cause surface damage by thermal shock, evaporation, and erosion; the nature of the effects appears to depend on the magnitude and duration of the heat pulse, the dynamics of moving cracks, the thermal properties and microstructure of the materials. Cracking of metal surfaces occurs on the repeated application of heat pulses of sufficient intensity. Sputtering of glasses and ceramics by argon ions from a 12 kV ion gun is sensitive to ambient temperature and angle of incidence; evaporation from thermal spikes is proposed as the important mechanism.

Introduction

Gas-discharge devices are increasing in number and variety; the applications include thermonuclear apparatus, space propulsion, lasers, and plasma torches, to name a few. In these various applications materials come into contact with dense hot plasma and many interesting and significant effects may occur. The work to be described here was stimulated by the U.K.A.E.A.'s programme of research to control thermonuclear power and embraces some of the effects relevant to this field; some of them, however, may also be of more general interest.

In gas discharges for thermonuclear research a considerable quantity of thermal energy is often put into the plasma. When the plasma comes into contact with a material surface, as it usually does at some stage during its existence, the surface may be subjected to intense transient bombardment by ions and electrons of energies in a wide range going up to tens of keV. Two conditions of special interest here may be set up; these are (i) the appearance of a potential difference of tens or hundreds of volts between plasma and surface and associated with this, an electric field at the surface of 10^4 to 10^5 or more V cm^{-1}, (ii) the delivery of heat fluxes to the surface of magnitudes up to 10^6 W cm^{-2}; both conditions may endure for times in the range 10^{-6} to 10^{-3} s. When the surface is metallic, arcing may be initiated, causing erosion of the metal and pollution of the plasma. In particular, a novel type of arc, given the name " unipolar arc " by Thonemann[1] may appear; in this arc the metal acts as both cathode and anode simultaneously, the thermal energy of the plasma providing its motivation.[2] The problem associated with these arcs is to understand the processes involved in their initiation. If the surface is insulated, arcs will not occur, but the surface may nevertheless suffer physical damage by thermal shock since insulating materials are usually brittle. Thus, due to the transport of heat in solids by a diffusion process, the transient application of energy to the surface can produce a large rise in temperature within a thin layer of material beneath the surface which, being constrained by the cool substrate, will become highly stressed in compression. Spalling may then occur, or plastic deformation may take place and in turn cause tensile stresses upon cooling after the shock to crack the surface layer. Metals will not usually be cracked by a single exposure, but, even with the most ductile, surface cracking may develop after many exposures by the processes responsible for thermal fatigue. Heat pulses delivering still more energy or occurring in a shorter time will cause melting and evaporation of both insulators and metals.

An experimental investigation of these effects is being made by the author and his colleagues and the results so far obtained are described and summarised. While some of the work has already been published in detail elsewhere, some is reported here for the first time.

In addition to the macroscopic effects mentioned above, ion bombardment will cause erosion of surfaces by sputtering. While considerable attention has been given in the past to the sputtering of metals and conducting materials, sputtering of insulating materials has been relatively neglected. Some preliminary work on this topic will also be described; besides being of interest to gas-discharge technology it would seem to have a useful application as a technique for etching ceramics.

Arc Initiation

The first experimental investigations of arc initiation caused by a toroidal gas discharge have been reported by Craston et al.[1] These workers inserted a specimen of various metals into the torus, biassing it negatively, at up to 2 kV, with respect to a neighbouring electrode by means of a charged capacitor connected between the two. When the discharge was fired both specimen and electrode were immersed in a hydrogen plasma, the first drawing ions and the second electrons from it under the influence of the bias voltage. Due to the much greater mobility of the electrons, most of the bias voltage appeared across the plasma sheath at the specimen surface; the ion current density at this surface was of order 1 A cm^{-2}. The relations between the sheath thickness d, voltage V, current density J_1, and electric field E, for a hydrogen plasma, are (in practical units) :

$$d = 2.34 \times 10^{-4} \, V^{3/4} J_i^{-1/2} \quad \cdot \quad \cdot \quad \cdot \quad (1)$$

$$E = \tfrac{4}{3} V d^{-1} \quad \cdot \quad \cdot \quad \cdot \quad (2)$$

The experimental conditions quoted gave therefore $d = 7 \times 10^{-2}$ cm and $E = 3.8 \times 10^4$ V cm^{-1}. In this way arc initiation under specific conditions, simulating those of a high temperature discharge, could be studied. These workers

* U.K.A.E.A., A.E.R.E., Harwell, Berks.

25

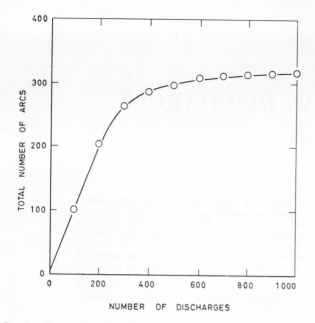

Fig. 1.—*The number of arcs initiated as a function of the number of hydrogen discharges for a stainless-steel specimen exposed in a torus while biassed negatively at 500 V*
(pulsed ion current density = 2·5 A cm⁻²)

found that in general all metals arced during each discharge in the early stage of a test, but later conditioned to a low " rate of arcing ", *i.e.* one initiation every several discharges. Arc initiation was associated with surface contamination in various forms and the process of conditioning was attributed to its removal or reduction by sputtering and arcing. It was suggested that the mechanism of arc initiation might involve a burst of vapour produced by the contaminants during the ion bombardment.

This work has since been developed and extended in several ways. Pfeil and Griffiths,[3] using a simple spark gap in which ionisation was induced by a Tesla coil, drew attention to the role of non-metallic inclusions in arc initiation. Hancox,[4] using a toroidal discharge and aluminium specimens whose surfaces were impregnated with alumina particles, measured the time delay before arc initiation. He found that it was inversely proportional to ion current density, suggesting that the mechanism of arc initiation involved the charging up of the alumina particles to a critical internal field of about 3×10^6 V cm⁻¹.

In preliminary work, using essentially the same technique as that of Craston *et al.*, Maskrey and Barnfield[5] confirmed their general observations on conditioning. A typical plot of the number of arcs initiated as a function of the number of discharges is given in Fig. 1. As this work proceeded, however, it became apparent that measurements of the arcing rate as a function of the number of discharges, for fresh specimens of various materials, were not reproducible; in addition the conditioning curve was strongly influenced by moderate vacuum baking (to 300°C) before testing.

An investigation of the effect of temperature, both before and during arc testing, was therefore begun using, as a specimen, molybdenum wire which could be heated electrically to high temperatures (1800°C) *in situ*. The electrical test conditions included a specimen voltage of up to 2 kV and ion current density up to 23 A cm⁻² (hydrogen plasma, pulse length 200 μs); these conditions gave a maximum electric field at the specimen surface of $1·8 \times 10^5$ V cm⁻¹ and associated plasma sheath thickness of $1·5 \times 10^{-2}$ cm. Arcing rate was measured as a function of temperature and under these conditions gave the results shown in Fig. 2. The eventual

breaking of the wire limited the number of thermal cycles to about six or seven, but during this time the transition from arcing to non-arcing on heating, and vice versa on cooling, remained. These transitions were attributed to the solution and re-precipitation of second phases such as oxides, nitrides, and possibly carbides of impurity elements present in the molybdenum.[6, 7] By quenching the wire from 1800°C a non-arcing condition could be achieved at low temperatures. Under less intense electrical conditions a fresh wire sooner or later became conditioned to effectively zero arcing rate over the whole temperature range. These results were interpreted to indicate that charge-up breakdown of second-phase particles (inclusions) on the surface, leading to bursts of vapour, was an essential part of the initiation process, but that a critical size of particle and, hence, a critical quantity of vapour, related to the electrical conditions, must be exceeded to start an arc. This latter point was exploited to prepare specimens arc-free under all conditions, since sub-critical breakdown was expected to evaporate off a portion of each particle; thus a technique involving slow cooling during discharges depleted the surface of the precipitating second phases. Experiments in which oxygen and nitrogen were injected into the surface by ion bombardment to chemically combine with the residual impurity elements present supported these conclusions.

Unfortunately the minimum temperature of the molybdenum wire in this simple technique was about 700°C, due to the heat input by ion bombardment. In recent experimental work a return has been made to the study of arc initiation on specimens maintained at room temperature by water cooling. While attention has been mainly concentrated on stainless steel because of practical applications, a variety of other metals have also been studied. By careful standardization of preliminary treatment, which consisted of degreasing and vacuum baking to 320°C, reproducible results, shown in Fig. 3, were obtained on specimens made from a piece of commercial 18–8–1 stainless steel (at 1 kV, 8 A cm⁻²). The main features of this curve are the initial period of 100% arcing followed by conditioning towards zero arcing rate.

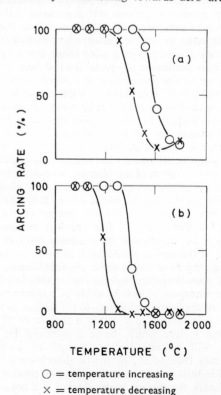

$\bigcirc$ = temperature increasing

$\times$ = temperature decreasing

Fig. 2.—*Arcing rate of molybdenum as a function of temperature at 2 kV, 23 A cm⁻², (a) on the first cycle, (b) on the fourth cycle*

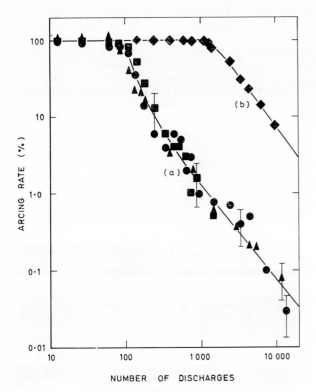

Fig. 3.—*Arcing rate of stainless steel as a function of the number of discharges at* 1 kV, 8 A cm^{-2} *(logarithmic scales), (a) degreased and baked, (b) not cleaned*

Once conditioned, exposure to the laboratory atmosphere did not cause further arcing. Although this steel was rich in inclusions of various types the conditioning was associated with the removal of other superficial contamination, since handling afterwards induced extended arcing as illustrated by curve (b) in Fig. 3; photographs demonstrating the effect are shown in Fig. 4. Fresh specimens, given the standard preliminary cleaning and baking treatment, were conditioned to a low arcing rate then deliberately contaminated with various substances. In this way it was found that both organic and inorganic contaminants contributed to arc initiation, the latter being the most difficult to remove. The most effective cleaning treatment was found to be prolonged sputtering with argon ions (2·5 kV) to the extent that several microns of the steel surface were removed. In the same experiments it was found that the presence of oxygen and nitrogen in the toroidal atmosphere had negligible effect, in agreement with the expected absence of chemical activity within the specimen surface at about room temperature; it was also found that visible tarnish films, provided no scaling occurred, did not cause arcing. Arc-free specimens, upon examination under

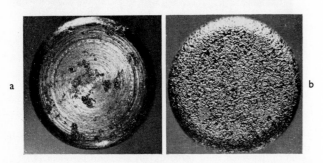

Fig. 4.—*The appearance of stainless-steel specimens after* 10 000 *exposures at* 1 kV, 8 A cm^{-2}, *(a) initially degreased and baked, (b) not cleaned* ($\frac{1}{4}$ in. dia.)

the microscope after test, showed clearly an abundance of inclusions etched into prominence by the ion bombardment. These experiments[8] show that, for stainless steel at low temperatures, inclusions on their own do not initiate arcing, but additional contamination is necessary for arcing to occur. Limited tests made with other metals appear to show that one group, consisting of iron, nickel, molybdenum and titanium, behaves like stainless steel and another group, consisting of copper, silver, and gold, do not do so, but instead condition to a final arcing rate, the magnitude of which depends on the applied electrical conditions. It is possible that this second group is sensitive to mercury vapour present in the system.

Thus it is apparent that arc initiation depends on a number of factors : inclusions, contamination, temperature, and electrical conditions, the relative importance of which varies with the metal. The phenomena seem obviously related to other fields of electric breakdown such as glow to arc transitions, gas and vacuum breakdown, and it is possible that surface processes facilitating electron emission at fields of $\sim 10^5$ V cm^{-1} (see for example the review by Llewellyn-Jones[9]), as well as those producing bursts of vapour, are essential to the mechanism of arc initiation.

Heat Pulses on Glass and Ceramic Surfaces

If energy Q per unit area is delivered to a material surface in time t, a rise in surface temperature ΔT takes place, given by:

$$\Delta T = aQ \, (\pi k c \rho t)^{-\frac{1}{2}} \qquad . \qquad . \qquad (3)$$

where k is the thermal conductivity, c the specific heat and ρ the density of the material; a is a constant of magnitude 1 to 2 depending on the heat-pulse waveform ($a = 1·08$ for an exponential waveform). During the heat pulse the temperature rise is confined to a depth d below the surface, given by :

$$d \sim 2(kt/c\rho)^{\frac{1}{2}} \qquad . \qquad . \qquad . \qquad (4)$$

This depth lies in the range 10^{-4} to 10^{-2} cm for glasses and ceramics subjected to heat pulses of duration 10^{-6} to 10^{-3} s, the range of interest to thermonuclear research. The restraint imposed by the unheated substrate may cause compressive stresses σ to develop in the hot surface layer of magnitudes up to :

$$\sigma = \frac{E\alpha\Delta T}{1-\nu} \qquad . \qquad . \qquad . \qquad (5)$$

where E is Young's modulus, α is the coefficient of expansion and ν is Poisson's ratio. Thus thermal-shock damage in the surface layer may occur. For example, an alumina surface heated to 1000°C in this way would reach a stress of 5×10^5 lb in^{-2}. Taking averaged values for the thermal constants and $a = 1·5$, equation (1) shows that this condition is achieved in alumina for an energy input $Q \simeq 800 \, t^{\frac{1}{2}}$ J cm^{-2}. Due mainly to their lower thermal conductivities, similar heating is produced on glasses and porcelains at about one-third the energy input. For a given temperature rise, the stresses set up will also be smaller due largely to the lower values of Young's modulus.

It is a simple matter to generate heat pulses of the desired magnitude to study experimentally their effect on these materials. A pulsed confined arc produced by the discharge of a capacitor between electrodes enclosed in a tube of suitably chosen dimensions achieves this purpose readily. Small specimens are placed in the tube for exposure to the discharge. Calibration for surface temperatures is achieved mainly by noting the conditions for surface melting of small metal plugs inserted into the surface of specimens.

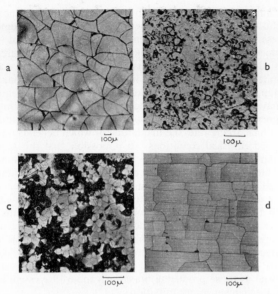

Fig. 5.—*The appearance of various surfaces after one thermal shock in a 400 μs gas discharge: (a) soda glass (3000°C), (b) electrical porcelain (1800°C), (c) polycrystalline alumina (Lucalox, 1400°C), (d) sapphire {1100} (2200°C). The peak surface temperatures quoted are estimated*

Some examples of thermally-shocked surfaces produced by a 400 μs discharge (of exponential waveform) are shown in Fig. 5. These pictures were chosen for illustration because they show several features typical of this type of thermal shock. Glasses tend to form a network of loosely-held flakes, the size and depth of which is a function of the magnitude and duration of the heat pulse and of the coefficient of expansion. The cracking here appears to occur on cooling due to a surface layer of tensile stresses which arise after viscous flow while hot. Electrical porcelain also cracks on cooling but in addition shows signs of flaking in compression due possibly to internal weakness associated with the porosity; inhomogeneity due to the microstructure, as revealed in the photograph, may also influence the damage. Polycrystalline alumina spalls in compression, many of the grains becoming detached from the substrate and then melted as indicated by the dark areas in the photograph. The remaining grains deform, notably by twinning under the compressive stresses, so that cracking in tension occurs on cooling; the cracks appear mainly to follow grain boundaries. Deformation by twinning is clearly evident on single sapphire crystals; crystals of known orientation suggest the main process to be rhombohedral twinning. Thresholds for cracking are given in Table I.

TABLE I.—*Thresholds for Surface Cracking Produced by a 400 μs Heat Pulse*

Material	Peak surface temperature (°C)
Soda glass	580 ± 130
Borosilicate glass	870 ± 60
Elec. porcelain	1610 ± 90
Fused silica	2700 ± 200
Polycrystalline alumina	1030 ± 80

Another factor which influences the pattern of surface cracking is believed to be associated with the kinetics of moving cracks since the paths followed by the cracks in glasses often enter regions of compressive stress and are not such as to minimize the residual elastic energy of the material near the surface. By measuring the surface area produced and estimating the elastic energy released, the apparent

surface energy for fast-moving cracks in glasses can be obtained ; it comes out to be several thousand erg cm^{-2}, *i.e.* much larger than the measured surface energy quoted in the literature (~300 erg cm^{-2}), and is roughly in agreement with results obtained by Shand[10] for moving cracks.

Larger heat pulses not only cause thermal-shock damage, but also cause the surface to melt and evaporate. Since the boiling-points of the materials investigated lie in the range

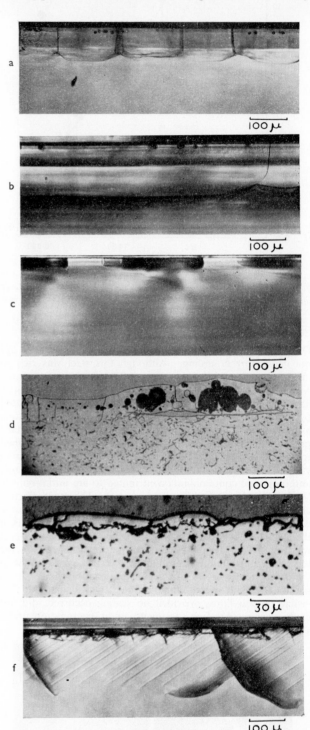

a, b, c, and f = transmitted light, polarised for card f

Fig. 6.—*Sections through materials exposed to a single gas discharge of 400 μs duration : (a) soda glass (3900°C), (b) borosilicate glass (4700°C), (c) fused silica (4700°C), (d) electrical porcelain (4700°C), (e) polycrystalline alumina (1850°C), (f) sapphire {1100} showing {1120} section (2200°C). The peak surface temperatures quoted are estimated*

2000°K to 4000°K and since thermal conductivities are low for all materials when melted, surface boiling is caused by heat pulses of only about a factor or two greater than those causing thermal shock. This has been confirmed experimentally by measuring the impulse generated within the tube during a discharge. Since the vapour pressure tends to increase exponentially with surface temperature, high transient pressures can easily occur in gas-discharge tubes. Tubes may readily burst under these pressures, especially since the surface damage tends to reduce the strength of the material. At lower levels the repeated application of heat pulses causes erosion due to evaporation and spalling and can change the composition of the surface material. Although the presence of a glassy phase in a ceramic tends to increase evaporation, it also tends to reduce spalling by yielding viscously to the compressive stresses and a net reduction in erosion can be obtained.

A series of sections of various materials exposed to a single heat pulse, illustrating the effects described, is shown in Fig. 6. Further details of this work have been given elsewhere.[11,12,13]

Heat Pulses on Metal Surfaces

A single heat pulse, of sufficient intensity, will usually produce only plastic deformation of a metal surface, but repeated application may eventually crack the surface. An experimental investigation of this form of thermal fatigue, produced by ion bombardment from a plasma, is complicated by the phenomenon of arc initiation described above. An alternative approach using electron bombardment to generate the heat pulse was therefore adopted. The apparatus used employed an electron gun of the converging-beam type and is shown schematically in Fig. 7. A capacitor was repetitively discharged through the gun to produce heat pulses on an area of about 0·3 cm^2 of the specimen surface at a rate of 35 min^{-1}. Due to the emission characteristics of the gun, the time dependence of the beam power P during the pulse is:

$$P/P_0 = (1+t/4\tau)^{-5} \quad \cdot \quad \cdot \quad \cdot \quad (6)$$

where τ is a time constant depending on the operating conditions and given by:

$$\tau = \tfrac{1}{2}K^{-1}V_0^{-\frac{1}{2}}C \quad \cdot \quad \cdot \quad \cdot \quad (7)$$

where K is the perveance, V_0 the initial voltage, and C the capacity. Typical operating conditions were: C from 0·03

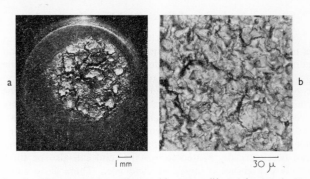

Fig. 8.—*Thermal-fatigue surfaces:* (a) *copper,* (b) *stainless steel. The surfaces were originally metallographically polished*

to 0·1 μF and V_0 from 11 to 16 kV which, with a perveance of 0·8 μA V$^{-3/2}$, gave τ from 150 to 500 μs. The waveform of the pulse is near exponential for the larger part of the energy delivered and the temperature rise of the specimen surface may be estimated approximately from equation (3) with $a = 1$.

Examples of the effects produced with this apparatus are shown in Fig. 8. The copper surface received $\sim 10^4$ pulses at 50 J cm^{-2} ($\tau = 500$ μs) giving an estimated temperature rise of ~ 400°C per pulse; the stainless steel surface received $\sim 2 \times 10^4$ pulses at 13 J cm^{-2} ($\tau = 150$ μs) giving $\Delta T \sim 800$°C. Both surfaces were originally highly polished.

While these results are of a preliminary nature they indicate, as may be estimated from the operating conditions, that considerable surface damage is caused to metals at inputs of $Qt^{-\frac{1}{2}}$ in the range 1000 to 2000 J cm^{-2} s$^{-\frac{1}{2}}$ in a life of 10^4 cycles.

The electron-bombardment technique is also being applied to insulators to investigate crack formation in thermal shock, but the operating voltage must be such that the secondary electron-emission coefficient is equal to or greater than unity ($V \leqslant 3$ kV for glasses).

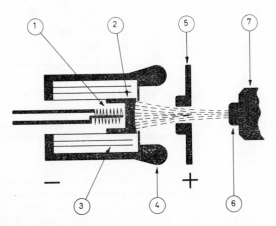

Fig. 7.—*Schematic diagram (to scale) of electron-gun assembly for the investigation of thermal fatigue of materials :* (1) *heater,* (2) *oxide-coated cathode,* (3) *radiation shields,* (4) *shaped focussing electrode,* (5) *anode,* (6) *specimen,* (7) *water-cooled mount. The dimensions can be judged by the size of the specimen which was 0·5 in. diameter*

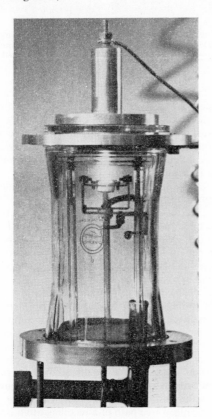

Fig. 9.—*Sputtering apparatus with heated stage*

Sputtering of Glasses and Ceramics

An investigation of the sputtering of glasses and ceramics is in progress with the apparatus shown in Fig. 9. The ion gun consists of a hollow anode-discharge tube in which the gas pressure is adjusted to obtain the desired operating conditions. The ion beam is brought out of a hole in the cathode and through a third floating electrode in close proximity to the cathode which serves to maintain the gas-discharge condition. Specimens are placed on the alumina stage at any convenient distance from the cathode; the stage can be electrically heated to $\sim$900°C and can also be tilted to allow a choice of angle of incidence. There is no significant charging of specimen or stage due to neutralisation by the plasma associated with the beam. The atmosphere employed is usually argon, which requires a pressure of about 50 μm to operate the gun at 12 kV, 0·1 mA.

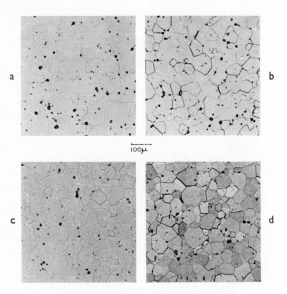

Fig. 10.—*The surface of sputtered polycrystalline alumina (Lucalox, argon, 12 kV): (a) 300°C, normal incidence, (b) 600°C, normal incidence, (c) 200°C, angle of incidence, 60° to normal, (d) 600°C, 60° to normal*

The surface of polycrystalline alumina (Lucalox) after equal sputtering exposure at 12 kV under four different conditions is shown in Fig. 10. It is clear that the detail etched into the surface increased with ambient temperature and angle of incidence. Further tests in which the operating voltage was varied in the range 4 to 12 kV showed that the detail also increased with voltage.

A series of measurements of eroded depths made on fused silica by optical techniques led to the results plotted in Fig. 11. It is seen that the sputtering yield at 12 kV increases with ambient temperature and angle of incidence. (In absolute magnitude the yield at normal incidence is of the order of one atom per incident ion.) Recent work with sapphire single crystals shows the same trends, although eroded depths for the same exposures are smaller.

The significant feature of these results is the marked influence of ambient temperature on sputtering characteristics. While the sputtering mechanism will include simple collision processes which eject atoms by momentum transfer, it would seem that an additional process becomes important with increasing temperature. This second process is probably one of evaporation from thermal spikes at the material surface caused by the dissipation of the energy of the incoming argon ions. From the radiation-damage theory (see, e.g. Seitz and Koehler[14] the mean free path of a recoiling atom is estimated to be of the order of 10^{-6} cm. If all the incoming energy

is absorbed in a volume of this dimension a temperature rise of the order of 1000°C will be sustained for a time of $\sim 10^{-12}$ s. Due to the statistical nature of the process there will be some smaller but hotter spikes and it may be estimated from vapour-pressure data that the order of one atom per spike may be evaporated from the more favourable events. An increase in ambient temperature would obviously increase the number of atoms evaporated in a given sputtering exposure. Experimental evidence for the contribution of such a mechanism to the sputtering of gold has been given by Thomson and Nelson.[15]

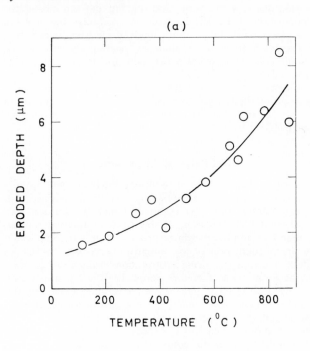

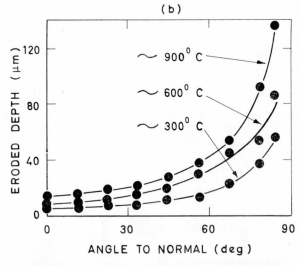

Fig. 11.—*Eroded depth due to spattering of fused silica by argon at 12 kV: (a) as a function of temperature, (b) as a function of angle of incidence*

Thus, under the sputtering conditions here employed, an evaporation process is probably an important mechanism at elevated ambient temperature and glancing angle. The etching of glass and ceramic surfaces under these conditions should therefore depend on the free energy and thermal properties of the material and the detailed structure etched into polycrystalline alumina at 600°C and angle 60°, shown in Fig. 10D, is qualitatively explained in this way.

Acknowledgments

The author is grateful to his colleagues, S. D. Ford, J. T. Maskrey, and R. C. McVickers, for their contributions to the work described, to other members of the Metallurgy Division, A.E.R.E., Harwell, for their assistance in various ways and particularly to R. S. Nelson and M. W. Thomson for discussions on sputtering.

References

1 Craston, J. L., Hancox, R., Robson, A. E., Kaufman, S., Miles, H. T., Ware, A. A., and Wesson, J. A. "*Second U.N. International Conference, Geneva*", 1958 (Geneva: United Nations), p. 34.

2 Robson, A. E., and Thonemann, P. C. *Proc. roy. Soc.*, 1959, **73**, 508.

3 Pfeil, P. C. L., and Griffiths, L. B. *Nature, Lond.*, 1959, **183**, 1481; *Journal of Nuclear Materials*, 1959, **3**, 244.

4 Hancox, R. *Brit. J. appl. Phys.*, 1960, **11**, 468.

5 Maskrey, J. T., and Barnfield, R. W. "*A.E.R.E.-R.*3161", 1959 (Harwell : U.K.A.E.A.).

6 Dugdale, R. A., Maskrey, J. T., and McVickers, R. C. *Journal of Nuclear Materials*, 1962, **6**, 35.

7 Maskrey, J. T., and Dugdale, R. A. *Journal of Nuclear Materials*, 1962, **7**, 197.

8 Maskrey, J. T., and Dugdale, R. A. *Journal of Nuclear Materials*, 1963, **10**, 233.

9 Llewellyn-Jones, F. *Elect. Rev., Lond.*, 1962, **171**, 125.

10 Shand, E. B. *J. Amer. ceram. Soc.*, 1961, **44**, 21.

11 Dugdale, R. A., Maskrey, J. T., and McVickers, R. C. *Trans. Brit. Ceram. Soc.*, 1961, **60**, 427.

12 Dugdale, R. A., McVickers, R.C., and Ford, S. D. *Brit. J. appl. Phys.*, 1962, **13**, 508.

13 Dugdale, R. A., and McVickers, F. C. *Journal of Nuclear Materials*, to be published.

14 Seitz, F., and Koehler, J. S. *Solid State Physics*, 1956, **2**, 305.

15 Thompson, M. W., and Nelson, R. S. *Phil. Mag.*, 1962, 7, 2015.

The manuscript of this paper was received on 19 *December,* 1963.

MATERIALS FOR NUCLEAR THERMIONIC CONVERTERS

By J. ADAM, B.Sc., Ph.D., A.Inst.P.*

SYNOPSIS

Successful development of nuclear thermionic converters hinges heavily on the development of materials capable of withstanding rather difficult working conditions for long periods of time.

Description is given of fabrication, testing, and properties of fuel for a thermionic converter which operated in reactor with surface temperature of 2000°C. Post-irradiation examination revealed that evaporation had taken place at the surface of the fuel and that the chemical composition of the evaporated material differed from that of the original fuel. Fuels canned in refractory metals are considered.

Caesium vapour which is needed in the converter for space charge neutralization introduces many compatibility problems. The most serious of these is the problem of a ceramic to metal seal. Experiments show that low grade alumina frequently used in seals is heavily attacked by caesium and some of the most commonly used brazes fail in caesium atmosphere. Seals adequate for comparatively short term experiments are now available but the development of caesium resistant seals suitable for operation at temperatures in excess of 1000°C is necessary for future practical thermionic converters.

Introduction

Although a practical and economic solution of the problem of direct conversion of heat into electricity is not yet evident there is a growing confidence that the problems involved are not beyond the limits of present-day technology. The direct conversion methods fall into three major categories, *viz.*:

(*a*) thermoelectric,

(*b*) thermionic,

(*c*) magneto-hydrodynamic.

There are also other less extensively studied methods based on ferro-magnetic and ferro-electric properties of materials. Conversion of chemical energy into electrical in fuel cells is a somewhat different problem but it is also classified as a direct conversion method.

The main scope for devices based on thermo-electric and thermionic conversion methods is without doubt in specialised fields such as auxiliary power sources in space craft or as power sources located in inaccessible places on earth. The magneto-hydrodynamic machines on the other hand appear promising as large power generators for commercial purposes.

All direct conversion generators are suitable for operation with a variety of heat sources and fossil fuels, solar energy, radio-active heat sources, and fission heat have been used or were considered for use in various experimental devices. This paper is concerned however only with thermionic converters operating on fissile fuel. The work described was undertaken as a basic study of a nuclear thermionic conversion system mainly for the purpose of defining important research and development areas which must be explored before a design of a converter reactor is undertaken. Success in reactor experiments showed that the system has development potential not only for special purposes as mentioned above but also in nuclear power production. With the heat rejection temperature of a thermionic converter close to 700°C it should be possible to charge a gas-cooled power reactor with converter type fuel elements and thus utilize the temperature difference between the fuel and the can for power production. However, the economic future of nuclear thermionic converters hinges heavily on the development of materials capable of withstanding rather difficult working conditions for long periods of time.

* U.K.A.E.A., Atomic Energy Research Establishment, Harwell. Didcot, Berks.

Thermionic Converters

The concept of a thermionic converter and nuclear thermionic converters has been explained in several publications.[1-3] Basically, a thermionic converter consists of two electrodes, one of which, the cathode, operates at a temperature sufficiently high to give large emission of electrons, and the other, the anode, collects the emitted electrons and must operate at temperatures at which the back emission is negligible. If the flow of electrons could be maintained in such a diode, electric current would flow in an external circuit connecting the two electrodes and useful power would be produced. In general, a simple diode as described above would not function because of a space charge build-up in the region surrounding the cathode which arrests the flow of electrons. It is possible however to neutralize the space charge by introducing positive ions into the inter-electrode space. The energy required to produce the ions must be supplied by the heat source, *i.e.* the cathode, or by an external source, and it seems that the thermal ionisation at the hot cathode is by far the simplest way of introducing ions into the diode. Caesium has one of the lowest known ionisation potentials of 3·88 V and is therefore a natural choice as space charge neutralizer; furthermore, it is generally believed that caesium vapour is deposited on the anode and helps to keep its work function low when it becomes contaminated by material evaporated from the cathode. This additional role of caesium is very important because the voltage generated by a thermionic converter is a function of the difference in the cathode and anode work functions and contamination of the anode by a layer of high work function material could stop the operation of the converter.

Fig. 1 shows a schematic diagram of a thermionic converter used for in-pile experiments at A.E.R.E., Harwell.[3] Four diodes of this type were irradiated during 1962 and 1963. The first two of these contained an internal shunt resistance and therefore produced no useful power in an external circuit, while the second pair contained an insulating seal and consequently a variable external load could be used and valve characteristics were obtained for a variety of operating conditions. With the cathode temperature in excess of 2000°C currents of the order of 100 A were obtained from an area of 10 cm². In all these experiments the reactor power level was used for controlling the cathode temperature and for this reason the time available for experiments had to be limited to

D

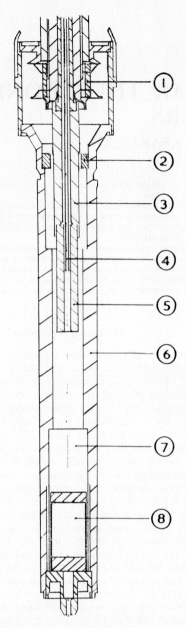

1 = ceramic to metal seal   5 = cathode

2 = spacer ring   6 = anode

3 = tantalum support   7 = catch pot

4 = cathode thermocouple   8 = caesium reservoir

Fig. I.—*In-pile thermionic converter*

two days per pair of diodes. The longest run was of 60 h duration, and in all cases the performance remained steady.

Thermionic Converter Cathodes

Canned and unclad fuels were considered in the design stage of the diode experiments. It was difficult, in the absence of adequate experimental data, to assess the relative merits of the two systems and it was decided therefore to use unclad ceramic cathodes, mainly to avoid high temperature compatibility problems between fuel and can and to see how successful or otherwise the unclad cathodes can be. There are several requirements which an acceptable cathode material must satisfy, *viz.*:

(1) Its electron work function must have a value which is sufficiently high to yield a reasonable output voltage but low enough to secure adequate electron emission at the operating surface temperature.

(2) Its electrical conductivity must be high to minimise Joule losses in the cathode.

(3) Its melting point must be comfortably above the operating surface temperature and a high thermal conductivity is required if melting at the centre is to be avoided.

(4) Its evaporation rate must be low.

(5) Its chemical compatibility with its mechanical support and with caesium vapour must be satisfactory.

(6) Its mechanical stability and dimensional stability under irradiation must be excellent.

Uranium carbide of composition UC is an obvious choice for the cathode material from the list of nuclear fuels which have been adequately investigated. Reports from Los Alamos indicated however that pure UC sinters showed a tendency toward cracking during thermal cycling and that this weakness could be eliminated by alloying uranium carbide with zirconium carbide. Thermal cycling experiments performed on carbides produced by sintering at A.E.R.E. showed that these behaved like the American material and consequently a UC-ZrC alloy of composition 67% UC-33% ZrC has been selected as a fuel for the first series of diode experiments.

The cathode consisted of two parts sintered together, *viz.*: a 3 cm long cylinder 1 cm diameter of UC-ZrC with a high degree of enrichment in ^{235}U joined to a cylinder 2·7 cm long of the same diameter and chemical composition but containing natural uranium. This last section was brazed with zirconium to a tantalum support and acted as a barrier preventing undue axial heat losses.

Several fabrication routes have been considered[4] for the production of cathodes, and preliminary tests indicated that hot pressing and two-stage sintering offered the best possibilities of fabricating satisfactory bodies. The two-stage sintering technique appeared more flexible and the main development effort was deployed in the investigation of fabrication parameters. In the first stage elemental powders (U, Zr, C) were compacted, and reacted for 2 h at 1400°C. The sinters obtained were then crushed and vibro-energy milled in argon and the resultant powder was hydrostatically compressed and outgassed at 1400°C and finally heat treated at 2130°C in vacuum. Densities of the final product depended on the milling time and final sintering temperature and by varying these parameters bodies of densities between 80%–96% of theoretical were produced. After grinding to size an autoradiograph was obtained from the bar on a piece of photographic film wrapped around it and it showed that the boundary between the enriched and non-enriched portions was sharp.

X-ray and metallographic examination showed the material to be single-phase but after heat treatment at 2500°C examination by electron microscope of replicas taken from polished and etched samples revealed small precipitates of a second phase (Fig. 2B). The appearance of these precipitates may possibly be caused by a change in chemical composition due to preferential evaporation of uranium at high temperatures.

Direct cathode temperature measurements in the reactor were impossible because of materials compatibility problems. At temperatures in excess of 2000°C tantalum reacts with UC-ZrC and consequently high-temperature thermocouples which are generally sheathed in tantalum could not be inserted into the hottest portion of the cathode. For this reason a calibration scale had to be established relating the cathode surface temperature to readings of a thermocouple positioned at the boundary between the sections of the cathode containing the enriched and natural uranium. The calibration curve was obtained by placing a UC-ZrC rod containing a thermocouple in an eddy current heater and measuring its surface temperature with an optical pyrometer. The temperature distribution within the rod is not the same when nuclear and eddy current heating methods are used, but calculations taking into account the thermal neutron flux depression and the skin effect yield suitable corrections.[5]

After irradiation the diodes were transferred to hot cells for examination.[4]

A—After irradiation at 2000°C. Magnification × 7500

B—After heat treatment at 2500°C. Magnification × 3000

Fig. 2.—*Precipitates formed in UC-ZrC*

The macroscopic examination of the cathode indicated a slight decrease in diameter of the hottest section of the rod and a dark deposit was observed on the anode opposite this section. It was possible to identify the deposit on the anode by X-ray diffraction as a mixture of UC-ZrC and UO_2-ZrO_2. Lattice parameters of both these mixed compounds are sensitive to the U/Zr ratio and measurements showed that the uranium content of the deposit was greater than that of the original cathode material. Furthermore lattice parameter measurements of UC-ZrC on the cathode surface indicated that the uranium content was somewhat lower than before

irradiation. Although quantitative analysis of these measurements is not possible because unit cell sizes of uranium carbides depend also on stoichiometry of the compounds, qualitatively it appears that uranium carbide is evaporated preferentially from UC-ZrC. The evaporation rate was estimated as 2×10^{-7} g cm^{-2} s^{-1} at 2270°K.

A polishing technique which was satisfactory for unirradiated UC-ZrC left a slightly chipped surface on the irradiated material. Apart from the surface roughening there was no other marked difference in appearance under microscopic examination between irradiated and unirradiated UC-ZrC. Examination in an electron microscope of a shadowed replica taken from the etched surface of irradiated material revealed presence of unidentified grain boundary precipitates very similar in appearance to those found in unirradiated UC-ZrC which had been heat treated for 3 h at 2500°C (Fig. 2).

It has been appreciated that the evolution of fission gas from the cathode will have a decisive effect on the performance and life of nuclear thermionic converters. In a successful gas sampling operation carried out on one of the irradiated diodes only 20% of the estimated amount of krypton and xenon produced has been collected. This suggests that a very large proportion of fission gases is retained in the fuel and consequently swelling of the cathode is likely to occur at high burn-up.

Although it is clear that the performance and life of thermionic converters with unclad cathodes will be limited by the evaporation of fissile material on to the anode and probable swelling by fission product gases the limits of operating temperatures and burn-up are not yet assessed.

The work functions of refractory metals are too high for operation at reasonable temperatures in a low-pressure caesium neutralized converter but it is possible to obtain high currents from refractory metal cathodes when caesium pressure is sufficiently high to modify the work function. A refractory metal cathode of a nuclear thermionic converter can be constructed by filling a metal can with a fissile material. Very high dimensional stability will be required from cathodes of this type because the cathode to anode spacing must be small (0·005–0·025 cm) if power losses in the caesium plasma are to be kept to a minimum. It would appear that with a very small cathode to anode spacing and good stability of materials efficiencies of about 15% can be obtained with cathode surface temperatures of the order of 1500°C.

A nuclear fuel clad in a refractory metal can would thus be suitable for thermionic converter cathodes. The evaporation problems are virtually eliminated and some fuel swelling could be tolerated if an adequate free space was provided inside the can. Some new problems arise however and these are being tackled at present in various laboratories.

The choice of fuel and can materials is influenced by work function, compatibility and nuclear considerations. Uranium dioxide fuel is compatible with refractory metals but its thermal conductivity is low and consequently the fuel would operate with a molten centre when its surface temperature exceeds 1500°C. A cermet fuel would not suffer from this disadvantage and properties of tungsten-UO_2 cermets are currently investigated. Work is also in progress on compatibility studies of UC-ZrC alloys with refractory metals. Results obtained indicate that this fuel is compatible with tungsten at temperatures below 2200°C. However, UC-ZrC reacts with tantalum above 2000°C, with niobium above 1800°C, and with molybdenum above 1650°C. All temperatures quoted relate to tests of not more than three hours duration and UC-ZrC used in this work was slightly substoichiometric in carbon.

While tungsten cans are favoured on the grounds of work function, compatibility, and negligible evaporation, the difficulty with which they are fabricated and their high neutron

A—Silica after 100 h at 600°C in caesium

B—85% pure alumina after 100 h at 450°C in caesium

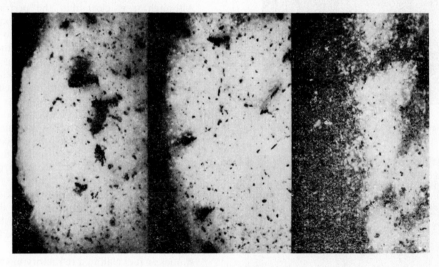

1 = control   2 = 100 h at 450°C in Cs   3 = 100 h at 600°C in Cs

C—90% pure alumina before and after exposure to caesium

Fig. 3.—*Caesium attack on silica and alumina*

absorption cross-section for thermal neutrons indicate that other refractory metals would be preferable. Niobium and molybdenum are particularly attractive; their use, however, depends on the development of adherent diffusion barriers between the fuel and can. Tungsten coatings produced by a spraying and halide decomposition processes are currently evaluated.

Structural Materials

Structural materials used in the construction of in-pile thermionic converters must of course satisfy normal nuclear engineering criteria and must show good resistance to attack by caesium liquid and vapour at operating temperatures. A large number of tests carried out in various laboratories[6-8] indicate that stainless steel, zirconium, and zircalloy are compatible with caesium and therefore the converter body can be made from standard nuclear engineering materials. The ceramic to metal seal presents problems because certain ceramics and brazes used commercially in the seal construction show comparatively poor resistance to caesium attack.

Alumina is one of the more important materials on which tests have been carried out and it is generally agreed that only high-purity sinters are resistant to caesium attack. Low-grade aluminas with a high silica content disintegrate when exposed to caesium liquid or vapour at temperatures approaching 450°C. The attack is on the silica phase and consequently the silica must be eliminated from aluminas intended for use in caesium. Fig. 3 shows the effects of caesium corrosion on silica, low-purity alumina and on 90% pure alumina.[7]

Although sealing of silica-free alumina to metals is difficult vacuum-tight and caesium-resistant seals have been produced. Failures of pure alumina to metal seals are generally associated with brazing materials and experiments indicate[8] that the commonly used brazes containing copper, silver or gold are attacked by caesium. Pure copper is resistant to caesium attack and suffers only surface discolouration at temperatures below 600°C but alloys of copper with silver or gold become porous after contact with caesium at temperatures of 450°C. The process of attack is not clearly understood; it appears that gold and silver are leached out from the alloys.

Outline of Future Developments

The estimates of efficiencies obtained from the first series of converter experiments were highly approximate and for this reason all future experiments are planned in new rigs containing calorimeters. Further single-element diodes with uncanned and canned fuels will be tested and an irradiation is planned of a converter in which four elements are placed in series within a single envelope.

Future work on materials includes high-temperature irradiations of cathode materials to high burn-ups, caesium compatibility tests at 450°C and 550°C for 10 months in a reactor and development of ceramic to metal seals suitable for operation in caesium at temperatures approaching 1000°C or higher.

References

[1] Kaye, J., and Welsh, J. A. " Direct Conversion of Heat into Electricity ", 1960 (New York: John Wiley & Sons Inc.).

[2] Grover, G. M. Nucleonics, 1959, 17, No. 7, p. 54.

[3] Dunn, P. D., Rice, G., Sanders, L. G., Watt, D. A., Adam, J., Hill, R. J., Purchas, J. G., Wheatley, C. C. H., and McWilliams, J. A. Nature, Lond., 1962, 195, No. 4836, p. 65.

[4] Adam, J., Harrison, J. W., Riviere, J. C., and Thorpe, T. Paper presented at the Symposium on Carbides in Nuclear Energy, Harwell, 1963.

[5] Hill, R. J. "AERE Report R.4075 ", 1963 (Harwell: UKAEA).

[6] Wagner, P., and Coriell, S. R. Rev. sci. Instrum., 1959, 30, No. 10, p. 937.

[7] Keddy, E. S. " LAMS Report 2948 ", 1963 (Los Alamos Scientific Laboratory).

[8] Smith, R. G., Hargreaves, F., Mayo, G. T. J., and Thomas, A. G. Journal of Nuclear Materials, 1963, 10, No. 3, p. 191.

The manuscript of this paper was received on 1 January, 1964.

SOME ADVANCES IN SEMICONDUCTORS

By D. W. F. JAMES

SYNOPSIS

A brief review will be given of semiconductor properties and the parameters of importance in device operation. Recent techniques, such as epitaxy and the planar technique, used in the production of devices will be described together with one or two of the newer devices. Some of the newer materials now exciting interest will also be described and discussed.

Introduction

The object of this paper is to review some of the advances made in recent years in the field of semiconductor materials and their utilisation. In an inter-disciplinary conference of this nature and with a subject so vast as semiconductors it would be inappropriate to attempt to deal with the subject for the benefit of the semiconductor expert. It is therefore intended that the paper will deal briefly with the semiconductor parameters which are of importance for device fabrication and with a few of the recent advances with new materials and fabrication techniques which have enabled improved performance to be obtained with devices made from the older used materials. The intention is to provide a general picture of progress for the benefit of the non-specialist.

Semiconductor Parameters

Semiconductors represent a fairly large class of materials having resistivities in the approximate range of 10^{-2} to 10^6 ohm cm and exhibiting a negative temperature coefficient of resistance over some range of temperature. They are characterized by an energy gap between a band of allowed energies which are normally fully occupied by electrons (valency band) and a band of allowed energies which are normally empty (conduction band). The presence of a small number of electrons in the higher band gives rise to conductivity, there being many empty energy levels into which they can be excited. The concentration of electrons in the conduction band of an intrinsic semiconductor is accompanied by an equal concentration of vacant energy levels or holes in the valency band; these also contribute to conductivity. The " hole " behaves as a positively charged current carrier having an effective mass which is similar to the effective mass an electron has in the solid state. In an extrinsic semiconductor further conductivity is produced by the presence of donor or acceptor impurity atoms which either give rise to extra electrons in the conduction band (n-type) or holes in the valency band (p-type) (Fig. 1). Junctions between p and n-type regions are rectifying and exhibit capacitance effects. Transistors may have n–p–n or p–n–p structures and may be used in many ways such as in amplifying or switching applications. More complex device structures may also be made. For many device applications semiconductors are normally required having final resistivities of the order of 1 ohm cm. For a material to be of practical value one must therefore be able to dope it with impurities which can occupy lattice sites or interstitial sites in the material and be readily ionised.

In an intrinsic semiconductor the concentration of charge carriers in the conduction band is given by the expression:

$$n = \text{constant} \times \exp\left[-Eg/(2kT)\right]$$

where Eg is the energy gap, T the absolute temperature and k is Boltzman's constant. It follows from this expression that n, and consequently the conductivity, of a semiconductor will be strongly influenced by temperature if the energy gap is too small. In many possible applications of semiconductor devices it would be desirable to produce devices which operate reliably at elevated temperatures. Such devices would need to be fabricated from high energy gap materials. At the present time commercial devices are made almost exclusively from germanium and silicon with energy gaps of 0·66 eV and 1·1 eV respectively. Such devices are limited to operation in ambient temperatures of about 70°C–200°C or less. While the above statement is undoubtedly true it is important to realize that many devices and device applications exist or can be envisaged in which low energy gap materials are used. Many of these applications involve refrigeration of the device or material to liquid nitrogen temperatures or below in order to overcome the disadvantage of the low energy gap but to take advantage of other properties, particularly high mobility of charge carriers which is dealt with below, varactor diodes made from indium antimonide serve as an example.

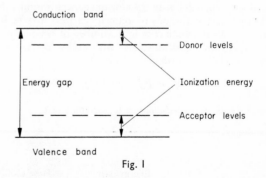

Fig. I

Of considerable importance to device operation is the mobility (μ) of charge carriers which has just been mentioned. Mobility is the average velocity acquired by charge carriers under the influence of a unit electric field and is related to the diffusion constant of charge carriers (D), by the Einstein equation:

$$\frac{\mu}{D} = \frac{e}{kT} \quad \text{where } e \text{ is the electronic charge.}$$

The small signal analysis for transistors at low frequencies shows that the cut-off frequency of such a device may be defined as:

$$\omega_c = \frac{2D}{W^2}$$

where W is the effective base width of the device, and ω is the angular frequency. The importance of mobility is therefore apparent. A more detailed examination shows* that the maximum frequency at which a transistor can be made to oscillate is given by the expression:

$$f_{\max} = \frac{\mu_h \mu_e}{\epsilon^a}$$

where a is $\frac{1}{2}$ or $\frac{2}{3}$ according to the nature of the junctions between n- and p-type regions in the device. μ_h and μ_e are the hole and electron mobilities and ϵ the dielectric constant of the material.

The ratio $\mu_h \mu_e / \epsilon^a$ may be taken as a figure of merit for materials for high frequency use.

The mobility, which is characteristic for a material, arises from interaction of charge carriers with the lattice of the material. This interaction is generally of two forms:

(i) Scattering by lattice vibrations.

(ii) Scattering by impurity centres or crystal defects (dislocations).

Both these processes may be considered as contributing separately to the total scattering of the charge carriers. We may therefore define our carrier mobility as being made up of two parts due to the two scattering processes:

$$\frac{1}{\mu} = \frac{1}{\mu_i} + \frac{1}{\mu_{ii}}$$

For materials of high purity and crystal perfection the first process will dominate and lead to a decrease of mobility with an increase of temperature. For crystals having many imperfections and/or impurity centres the second process becomes important and leads to lower mobilities.

It is important to realise that in a semiconductor of one type charge carriers of the opposite type will also exist—there will be a small concentration of holes say in n-type material. These are referred to as minority carriers and in the normal way will exist as an equilibrium concentration. Non-equilibrium concentrations of minority carriers may be introduced into a semiconductor in a number of ways and such non-equilibrium concentrations will decay or recombine approximately in accordance with the law

$$P' = P_0' \exp(-t/\tau)$$

* F. J. Hyde, *Semiconductors*—a forthcoming text.

where

P' is the non-equilibrium concentration.

P_0' is the value of P' at time $t = 0$.

τ is a decay constant termed the lifetime of the minority carriers.

Recombination of minority carriers is possible in the bulk of a semiconductor or at its surfaces. The rate of recombination is often much higher at the surfaces than in the volume of the material and a total lifetime will normally result from both processes in accordance with the expression:

$$\frac{1}{\tau} = \frac{1}{\tau_v} + \frac{1}{\tau_s}$$

where τ_v and τ_s are the lifetimes due to volume and surface effects respectively.

In multi-junction devices minority carriers and minority carrier lifetime are of great importance. Charge carriers crossing from a region of one conductivity type to another may become minority carriers in so doing. Consequently their behaviour in the region into which they have entered will be dependent on the value of lifetime in that region. To take what is perhaps the simplest example the minority carrier lifetime will govern the ability of charge carriers to cross the base region of a transistor. In low lifetime material this region will need to be very thin and in consequence fabrication problems arise.

Established and Potential Device Materials

We have already noted that the great majority of semiconductor devices are produced from germanium and silicon. The principal properties of these two elements as device materials are listed in Table 1, together with the same properties for a number of other materials of interest. We note that while germanium is somewhat inferior to silicon for applications at high temperatures it possesses a considerable advantage from the point of view of high frequency use. From the point of view of operation at elevated temperatures we might look to silicon carbide, gallium arsenide, gallium phosphide and aluminium antimonide as potentially useful materials. From the point of view of high frequency use only indium antimonide and indium arsenide provide a great improvement over germanium. It should be noted that both gallium arsenide and gallium antimonide exhibit useful properties from the point of view of high frequency work although the energy gap of gallium antimonide is somewhat low.

Returning to the higher energy gap materials we notice that aluminium antimonide, gallium phosphide and silicon carbide do not hold out much hope for high frequency work. These three materials also carry with them a number of other problems which make one question their usefulness. For example, the equilibrium vapour pressure of phosphorus over

TABLE I.

Material	Energy gap (eV)	Hole mobility (μ_h cm²/V s)	Electron mobility (μ_e cm²/V s)	Dielectric constant (ϵ)	$\frac{\mu_e \times \mu_h}{\epsilon^{\frac{1}{2}}}$ (cm²/V s)² × 10⁻⁶
Ge	0·66	1900	3 900	15·8	1·9
Si	1·1	480	1 350	11·7	0·19
AlSb	1·52	300	300	10·1	0·03
GaP	2·25	75	110	8·4	0·0028
GaAs	1·43	420	8 500	11·1	1·1
GaSb	0·70	1400	4 000	14·0	1·5
InP	1·27	150	4 600	10·9	0·21
InAs	0·33	460	33 000	11·7	4·4
InSb	0·17	750	78 000	15·9	15
SiC	2·8	2	32	10	0·00002

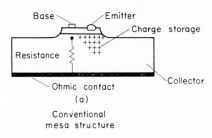

Fig. 2

Conventional
mesa structure

molten gallium phosphide requires one to work with pressures of many atmospheres of phosphorus. Surface oxidation is a major problem in aluminium antimonide. Polycrystalline material and relatively impure single crystals are quickly reduced to powder by atmospheric attack. The material is also very difficult to prepare in the pure form. In spite of the frequency limitations silicon carbide is attracting a certain amount of attention as a potentially useful material because of its high chemical stability and high energy gap. We shall therefore consider silicon carbide, gallium arsenide and indium antimonide a little more fully.

In recent years a great deal of effort has been put not only into the problem of improved materials, but into the problem of more effective utilisation of established materials, i.e., silicon and germanium. The problems of crystalline perfection and purity and of improved device fabrication techniques have both received a great deal of attention. The development of the techniques of zone refining—particularly floating zone refining for silicon resulted in materials of great purity having high values of minority carrier lifetime. These improvements are now generally well known. It is in the field of direct crystal growth from the vapour phase and in the field of miniaturisation that the greatest advances have been made.

Epitaxial Deposition of Silicon and Germanium

Considerable advantages may be obtained from fabricating semiconductor devices in thin layers of silicon and germanium deposited epitaxially on an orientated substrate. As an example let us consider a mesa transistor which has the form shown in Fig. 2. N-type impurity is diffused into a p-type slice of material producing a junction. A p-type region is then alloyed in to form the emitter of the device as indicated in the diagram. In a conventional structure made as described the starting material needs to be of high resistivity in order to ensure a high collector-base breakdown voltage. As the starting material will be in the form of a relatively thick slice this represents a considerable series resistance in the finished device. This in turn increases the saturation emitter–collector voltage of the device. By use of epitaxial techniques a structure such as that shown in Fig. 3 may be produced. In this case the starting material, upon which an

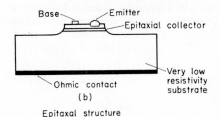

Epitaxal structure

After Sigler and Watelski *Solid State Journal* 1963

Fig. 3

epitaxial layer of high resistivity is deposited, can be of very low resistivity and serves only as a mechanical support and as an electrical contact to the collector of the device which is the epitaxial layer itself. Thus the undesirable series resistance of the device is removed and a high collector–base breakdown voltage is maintained.

The great interest in epitaxial techniques which has developed in the field of semiconductor technology dates back only to mid-1960 although there had been a few publications on this type of work prior to that time.[1] The bulk of the work carried out on silicon and germanium has involved the decomposition or reduction of a volatile compound of these elements, although an interest has developed in evaporation and sputtering techniques.

Transport of silicon and germanium via the iodide onto a heated silicon or germanium substrate has been studied by numbers of workers.[2,3] Reactions of the following type occur:

(i) $Si + 2I_2 \rightarrow SiI_4$

(ii) $SiI_4 + Si \rightarrow 2SiI_2$

(iii) $2SiI_2 \rightarrow Si + SiI_4$

By carrying out these reactions in a furnace with two separately controlled temperature zones the semiconductor may be transported from a source material onto a substrate. This particular process was investigated by Wajda, Kippenham and White[4] who showed that epitaxial growth was severely affected by the nature of the substrate surface. It was found extremely difficult to produce good oxide-free surfaces. When an oxide layer existed on the silicon surface prismatic growth of silicon would occur through any pin holes present and then spread over the surface. Attempts to carry out a reverse reaction, removing some of the substrate surface by chemical attack prior to deposition, were not successful. Erosion of the substrate occured through the pin holes leaving the oxide untouched. The process was further investigated by Wajda and Glang.[5] The thermodynamics of the process were examined. This examination showed that an equilibrium condition would exist in which no molecular iodine would be present regardless of pressure and temperature. They obtained a considerable degree of control over the growth rate of the epitaxial layer and obtained controlled impurity addition in the range 5×10^{16} atoms/cm³ to 2×10^{20} atoms/cm³ for both n- and p-type impurities. Multilayer structures were also successfully prepared.

The iodide transport process has since been used by many workers for silicon, germanium and other materials. The process has been used in evacuated closed tubes as described and in open tube systems with the addition of an inert carrier gas. Work on the open tube system for germanium has recently been reported from the laboratories of the I.B.M. organization.[6-8]

Epitaxial deposition of silicon may readily be obtained from the decomposition of silane (SiH_4) and from the reduction of silicon tetrachloride ($SiCl_4$) or trichlorosilane ($SiHCl_3$). All three processes have been widely studied and found capable of producing high quality layers on silicon substrates. Silane has the advantage that it can be decomposed at a much lower temperature than either $SiCl_4$ or $SiHCl_3$, a fact which might be of great importance when depositing doped multilayers. Higher temperatures encourage the diffusion of impurities from layer to layer or from the original substrate into the first layer.[9,10] The extreme versatility of the vapour deposition process has been clearly demonstrated by Allegretti, Shombert, Schaarschmidt and Waldman[11] who produced large multilayer structures of doped silicon and constructed a complete relaxation oscillator circuit in a block of silicon.

In recent times attention has been paid to the problem of surface defects which often appear on epitaxial silicon. Open and closed triangular defects made up of shallow grooves are seen and small pyramidal outgrowths are sometimes observed. Booker and Stickler[12] have studied the triangular defects very thoroughly and have explained them in terms of stacking faults occuring at the substrate–epitaxial layer interface. The pyramidal outgrowths have been shown to be due to silicon carbide.[13] The reaction kinetics of such processes have been studied by a number of people. For example Charing and Joyce[14,15] have investigated the reduction of trichlorosilane and the decomposition of silane.

A technique which has developed alongside that of epitaxial crystal growth has been the so-called planar technique for device fabrication. Both alone and in conjunction with epitaxial developments it has led to considerable advances in material utilisation and device production. The technique is particularly suited to silicon. A slice of material is first given a passive surface, usually by high temperature oxidation in steam or wet oxygen. A photoresistive resin is then applied to the surface and a desired pattern is developed in the resin by the usual photographic techniques now commonly employed in producing printed circuits. Following this, holes are etched in the oxide layer, the resin removed and impurities diffused into the semiconductor through the holes in the oxide thereby producing well-defined junctions in the material. This step may be followed by reoxidation and etching with diffusion of further impurities to build up complete transistor structure. The process may in fact be extended to allow different types of devices to be built into the same piece of silicon and an approach is now being widely used to produce integrated solid circuits (Fig. 4 and Fig. 5). The technique has recently been used by Schnable, Hillegas and Thornton to obtain preferential silicon epitaxy through oxide masking.[16] Silicon was oxide masked and the required pattern produced in the oxide layer. The exposed silicon was etched in dilute chloride atmospheres at elevated temperatures (1250°C) and this was followed by preferential epitaxial deposition without removing the substrate from the apparatus. The authors of this paper have prepared a number of diodes this way and propose to use the technique to produce a completely epitaxial transistor with oxide passivation of all surfaces. Related work has been reported by Steinmaier and Bloem[17] who have succeeded in producing alternate layers of silicon and silicon dioxide by introducing water vapour or carbon dioxide into a gas stream of hydrogen and silicon tetrachloride.

In considering the problem of producing simple planar junctions Barson, Armstrong and Mutter[18] have found that reoxidation of diffused regions for subsequent masking leads to degradation of the initial diffused junction. The effect is clearly associated with oxidation as heating in non-oxidising atmospheres does not produce the effect which is shown by a change in the breakdown voltage of the junction in question. They have shown also that degraded junctions might be improved or completely restored by heating in a dry atmosphere at 1100°C and that for a given oxidizing ambient, higher temperature oxidations damage the junctions less than lower temperature ones. A diffusion reoxidation cycle was proposed which produced a yield of about 95% high quality junctions.

New Materials

Indium Antimonide

Indium antimonide has been the subject of an extensive review by Hulme and Mullen.[19] Preparation, properties and device applications were considered. There is little that can be added to their survey. The energy gap and mobilities for

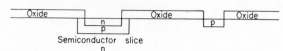

Fig. 4.—*A transistor and diode in the same slice of semiconductor*

the material have already been quoted. The low energy gap means that the material has a high absorption coefficient associated with band to band transitions for wavelengths below 5–7 microns. This makes the material useful as an infrared detector and filter. Many infrared detecting devices have in fact been made. Three main effects may be used in such devices. The photoconductive effect occurs when radiation falls on the material producing hole–electron pairs thereby modulating the conductivity. The photovoltaic effect occurs when radiation falls on the surface of a p–n-junction device. Carriers created by the incident radiation are collected by the electric field of the p–n junction. The photoelectromagnetic detector requires a d.c. magnetic field on an electrically uniform sample of indium antimonide. Radiation falling on the material produces a diffusion of charge carriers from the illuminated surface. This flow is acted upon by the magnetic field and an e.m.f. is produced.

The material is made directly from the elements which are available with nominal purities of better than 99·99% and may be processed by simple zone melting. Zinc and cadmium are acceptor impurities in indium antimonide and are difficult to remove unless a special stage is introduced into the processing which takes advantage of the fact that these elements are volatile from InSb just above the melting point. The volatilisation stage is then followed by zone refining under conditions designed to minimise the tendency for loss of antimony vapour. The technique has been described by Hulme.[20] Single crystals may be prepared by the Czochralski pulling technique and by horizontal zone melting in silica boats. Zone melting techniques produce better quality crystals both in terms of carrier concentration and mobility. Evaporated films of indium antimonide have been prepared but of much lower quality than crystals grown from the melt.

Due to the energy gap p–n junctions will not show much rectification unless cooled to well below room temperatures. Provided refrigeration is acceptable useful devices may be used.   Lee and Kaminsky[21] have described small area diodes suitable for variable capacitance parametric amplifiers. Similar indium antimonide diodes are now being produced in small quantities for this purpose. Other experimental devices have been made using this material including an experimental transistor.[22]

Gallium Arsenide

We have already indicated that gallium arsenide is one of the most attractive of the more recently studied semiconductors. It should prove much better than silicon for high frequency work and has a higher energy gap than either silicon or germanium. Consequently the material has been extensively studied over the last three or four years. In Britain a great deal of the stimulus for this work has come from the Services Electronic Research Laboratory.

Gallium arsenide may be made by direct combination of the elements. To maintain the material in the molten state a vapour pressure of about 1 atm of arsenic is required. To

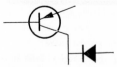

Fig. 5.—*The same structure as Fig. 4 in conventional forms*

maintain this pressure a minimum containing vessel temperature of 600°C is required with an excess of arsenic, the region containing the molten material being at 1240°C. The arsenic pressure required imposes severe problems if one wishes to obtain single crystals of gallium arsenide by modifications of the Czochralski pulling technique or the zone refining technique. In spite of this successful techniques have been worked out which enable gallium arsenide to be grown from the melt.[23,24] For example, floating zone refinement of gallium arsenide may be achieved by supporting the polycrystalline material within a sealed quartz tube and zone melting with a 4 Mc/s radio frequency heater. Above and below the heater coil auxiliary wire wound or graphite heaters are placed to obtain the required arsenic vapour pressure within the tube.[25,26] Good quality crystals may be made this way having dislocation densities of $10^3 cm^{-2}$ or less. The material may also be processed by horizontal crystal growth in graphite silicon or carbon coated silicon boats, although it is difficult to obtain single crystals this way. The introduction of vitreous carbon[27] as a crucible material has led to considerable advancement in the horizontal method of crystal growth. Silicon contamination can be reduced to below the level of detection by mass spectrometry (0·05 ppm).[28] Single crystals may also be obtained in vitreous graphite boats.[29] Prior to the very recent introduction of vitreous graphite many techniques were tried to improve the conventional methods of crystal growth from the melt. For example, sand blasted silica boats were found to be better than etched boats. Oxygen was added to containing vessels to suppress reaction between the GaAs and silica and aluminium nitride crucibles were used.

In more recent times attention has been paid to the problem of obtaining crystal growth from the vapour phase. Gallium arsenide has been grown epitaxially on germanium by means of iodide transport.[30] Iodide transport has also been used to produce blade-like crystals 10 cm × 0·5 cm × 0·01 cm. These crystals were found to contain trace quantities of iodine but had quite good electrical characteristics. They were successfully doped with zinc and diodes were made from them.[31]

Very recently cathodic sputtering has been used to obtain epitaxial deposition of gallium arsenide on germanium and on cleaved calcium fluoride surfaces.[32] Epitaxial deposition has also been achieved by means of a flash evaporation technique in which a fine powder of gallium arsenide is delivered continuously onto a heater whose temperature is high enough to produce volatilisation of the least volatile component. A stoichiometric vapour is produced which condenses onto a heated substrate. With this technique epitaxy has been obtained on germanium; calcium fluoride and gallium arsenide itself.[33] Many studies have been made on the diffusion of impurities into gallium arsenide from the point of view of device fabrication but these need not be considered further here.[34-37]

Silicon Carbide

Silicon carbide is perhaps the most difficult of all the semiconductor materials from the point of view of preparation and crystal growth. The well-established melt techniques cannot be used and consequently a great deal of the work carried out on the material has centred on producing crystalline forms directly from the vapour phase. As yet no really satisfactory controlled crystal growth has been achieved. Crystal growth by vapour transport in a temperature gradient at 2500° to 2600°C was achieved by Lely.[38] Doping of the crystals was obtained by adding nitrogen, phosphorus or boron to the furnace atmosphere. Various modifications to this method have been introduced[39] including epitaxial deposition onto seeds obtained from the commercial silicon carbide process

which produces accidental clumps of imperfect single crystals. Various workers have produced small crystals of silicon carbide by gaseous reactions between silicon tetrachloride and toluene and by the decomposition of organo-chlorosilanes.[40]

Small crystals of α and β silicon carbide have been produced together with silicon carbide whiskers. At Bangor we have been attempting to produce epitaxial deposition of silicon carbide onto silicon and hexagonal silicon carbide by reduction of methyl-trichlorosilane and trimethyl-chlorosilane. Small isolated areas of epitaxial deposition have been observed and microcrystalline layers and whiskers, many of them kinked, have also been produced. But no useful large size crystals have been produced. Recently we have observed that low concentrations of chloride in hydrogen will etch silicon carbide. Gaseous etching of silicon carbide in chlorine-containing atmospheres has also recently been reported by Smith.[41] In spite of the enormous difficulties quite good quality junctions have been produced in silicon carbide. Experimental rectifiers capable of operation up to 500°C have been produced[42] and the problems associated with an experimental high temperature transistor have also been examined[43] it being estimated that the device would have a maximum operating frequency of 2 Mc/s.

One very significant advance in silicon carbide technology has been made during the past year by A. I. Mlavsky and co-workers. A travelling solvent method has been used for crystal growth. A temperature gradient is maintained across a thin layer of solvent sandwiched between a seed and a source of silicon carbide. Providing certain solubility conditions are met the solvent layer can be made to travel as a molten zone and crystal growth results. In their latest work, using chromium–2% silicon alloy as solvent, a crystal $\frac{3}{8}$ in. long by $\frac{1}{4}$ in. square has been produced. X-ray analysis showed the entire piece to be monocrystalline. A successful *p–n* junction diode has been made.[44-46]

Conclusion

Some of the problems associated with semiconductor materials and some of the advances have been briefly reviewed. In an area so vast as semiconductor technology this has of necessity been a somewhat superficial examination but it is hoped it will serve to provide some slight outline of what is still a rapidly expanding field.

References

1 Sangster, R. C., Maverick, E. F. and Croutch, M. L. *J. Electrochem. Soc.*, **104**, 317 (1957).

2 Marinace, J. C. *I.B.M. Journal Res. Dev.*, **4**, 248 (1960).

3 Glang, R. and Kippenham, B. W. *I.B.M. Journal Res. Dev.*, **4**, 299 (1960).

4 Wajda, E. S., Kippenham, B. W. and White, W. H. *I.B.M. Journal Res. Dev.*, **4**, 288 (1960).

5 Wajda, E. S. and Glang, R. "Metallurgy of elemental and compound semiconductors". *Metallurgical Society Conferences*, Vol. 12, pp. 229.

6 Reisman, A. and Alyanakyan, S. A. Electrochem. Soc. New York meeting, October 1963.

7 Reisman, A., Berkenblit, M. and Alyanakyan, S. A. Electrochem. Soc. New York meeting, October 1963.

8 Jona, F., Lever, R. F. and Wandt, H. R. Electrochem. Soc. New York meeting, October 1963.

9 Joyce, B. A. Private communication.

10 Runyan, W. R. Electrochem. Soc. New York meeting, October 1963.

11 Allegretti, J. E., Shombert, D. J., Schaarschmidt, E. and Waldman, J. Metallurgy of elemental and compound semiconductors: *Metallurgical Society Conferences*, Vol. 12, p. 255.

[12] Booker, G. R. and Stickler, R.   *J. App. Phys.*, **33**, 3281 (1962).

[13] Miller, D., Wateski, S. and Moore, C.   *J. App. Phys.*, **34**, 2813 (1963).

[14] Charing, J. M. and Joyce, B. A.   *J. Electrochem. Soc.*, **109**, 957 (1962).

[15] Joyce, B. A.   Private communication.

[16] Schnable, G. L., Hillegas, W. J. and Thornton, C. G.   Electrochem. Soc. New York meeting, October 1963.

[17] Steinmaier, W. and Bloem, J.   Electrochem. Soc. New York meeting, October 1963.

[18] Barson, F., Armstrong, W. J. and Mutter, W. E.   Electrochem. Soc. New York meeting, October 1963.

[19] Hulme, K. F. and Mullen, J. B.   *Solid State Electronics*, **5**, 211 (1962).

[20] Hulme, K. F.   *J. Electron. Control*, **6**, 397 (1959).

[21] Lee, C. A. and Kaminsky, G.   *J. Appl. Phys.*, **30**, 2021 (1959); *ibid.*, **31**, 1717 (1960).

[22] Henneke, H. L.   *Solid State Electronics*, **3**, 159 (1961).

[23] Rosi, F. D. and Herkart, P. G.   " Properties of elemental and compound semiconductors ".   *Metallurgical Society Conferences*, Vol. 5, p. 25.

[24] Gremmelmaier, R.   *Z. Naturforsch*, **11a**, 511 (1956).

[25] Whelan, J. M. and Wheatley, G. H.   *J. Phys. Chem. Solids*, **6**, 169 (1958).

[26] Rosi, F. D. and Herkart, P. G., loc cit.

[27] Lewis, J. C., Redfern, B. and Cowlard, F. C.   *Solid State Electronics*, **6**, 251 (1963).

[28] Harding, W. R. and Hilsum.   C.V.D. Electronic Materials Res. Conference, Bangor: September 1962.

[29] Knight, J. R.   Quoted by J. C. Lewis *et al*, loc cit.

[30] Holanyak, N., Jillson, D. C. and Bevaqua, S. F.   " Metallurgy of semiconductor materials ", *Metallurgical Society Conferences*, Vol. 15, p. 49.

[31] McAller, J., Barkmeyer, H. R. and Pollack, P. I.   *J. Elect. Chem. Soc.*, **108**, 1168 (1961).

[32] Flood, J. J., Molnar, B. and Francombe, M. H.   Electrochem. Soc. New York meeting, October 1963.

[33] Richards, J. L., Hart, P. B. and Gallone, L. M.   Electrochem. Soc. New York meeting, October 1963.

[34] Fane, R. W. and Goss, A. J.   *Solid State Electronics*, **6**, 383 (1963).

[35] Cunnell, F. A. and Gooch, C. H.   *J. Phys. Chem. Solids*, **15**, 127 (1960).

[36] Goldstein, B.   *Phys. Revs.*, **121**, 1305 (1961).

[37] Vieland, L. J.   *J. Phys. Chem. Solids*, **21**, 318 (1961).

[38] Lely, J. A.   *Bev. deut. keram. Ges.*, **32**, 229 (1955).

[39] Hergenrotter, K. M., Mayer, S. E. and Mlavsky, A. I.   *Silicon Carbide*. Ed. O'Connor and Smiltens (Pergamon Press, 1960), p. 60.

[40] *Silicon Carbide*.   Ed. O'Connor and Smiltens, 1960.

[41] Smith, C.   Electrochem. Soc. New York meeting, October 1963.

[42] Goldberg, C. and Ostroski, J. W.   *Silicon Carbide*, 1960, p. 453.

[43] Chang, H., LeMay, C. Z. and Wallace, L. F.   *Silicon Carbide*, 1960, p. 496.

[44] Pfann, W. G.   *Trans. A.I.M.E.*, **203**, 961 (1955).

[45] Griffiths, L. B., Mlavsky, A. I. and Weinsrein, M.   *J. Electrochem. Soc.*, **110**, 593 (1963).

[46] Wright, M. A. and Mlavsky, A. I.   Electrochem. Soc. New York meeting, October 1963.

PROGRESS IN MATERIALS, DESIGNS, AND FABRICATION TECHNIQUES IN THE POWER GENERATION INDUSTRY

By D. W. C. BAKER, B.Sc., A.I.M.*

SYNOPSIS

The economic and operational factors which regulate progress in the utilization of new materials, designs and fabrication techniques in the power generation industry are reviewed.

The development of conventional boiler-turbine units of increasing size and level of steam conditions is outlined and the attendant improvements in materials and fabrication techniques described. Reference is made to the influence of design codes on the selection of materials for boilers and to anomalies which may arise from differences in design criteria. Attention is drawn to material requirements for components subjected to particularly arduous conditions, including: sight glasses for boiler drum water level indicators, superheater tubes exposed to flue gas corrosion, high temperature steam valves, turbine blades subjected to water droplet erosion and alternator coil binding rings. Advances in the materials and construction of ancillary plant such as condensers, feed heaters and cooling towers are described. Brief mention is made of the introduction of new materials for the construction of station building superstructures.

In the field of nuclear power the use of concrete for pressure vessel construction and the special quality requirements of stainless steel for AGR fuel element cans are topics selected for discussion.

Materials and design developments are also evident in transmission and the matters considered include de-icing of overhead line conductors, semiconducting glazes for ceramic insulators and the prospects of utilizing superconducting materials.

Introduction

In examining recent and potential developments in the utilization of new materials, designs and fabrication techniques in the power generation industry it is relevant, first, to consider the economic and operational factors which regulate progress.

The cost of electricity generation is determined by three main factors: the capital cost of the plant, the cost of fuel and the cost of operation. The approximate capital costs of modern coal-fired, nuclear and gas turbine plant, respectively, are given in Table I together with corresponding fuel costs per unit generated.

TABLE I.—*Capital and Fuel Costs for Coal-fired, Nuclear and Gas Turbine Generating Plant* (1963)

Type of plant	Capital cost £/kW	Fuel cost d./kWh
Coal-fired	38	0·4
Nuclear	112	0·15
Gas turbine	25	1·0 (approx.)

The relative contribution of these factors to the total cost of the electricity generated clearly depends upon the extent to which the plant is utilized. Nevertheless, in general, an increase in capital cost incurred by using more expensive materials or designs will be justified if the resultant reduction in fuel costs or improvement in thermal efficiency are of sufficient magnitude. It is the prospect of very low fuel costs that has stimulated nuclear generation despite the higher capital charges and inferior steam cycle conditions (at present) compared with those of conventional plant. Equally, there are circumstances where relatively low thermal efficiency or high fuel costs may be tolerated if capital costs and plant utilization are low. Thus, either old and relatively inefficient coal-

* Research and Development Department, Central Electricity Generating Board, London, S.E.1.

fired plant or low cost gas turbine plant burning expensive fuel may be used economically to satisfy intermittent peak load requirements which are a feature of the United Kingdom system. Essentially, the benefits to be gained from adopting more advanced thermodynamic cycles or methods of generation are dependent upon achieving low fuel costs while the disadvantages stem from the need for more costly materials, designs, fabrication techniques and inspection procedures.

Certain other features of central station generating plant are also relevant in the context of design and material developments. First, the main plant items, such as boilers and turbines, are designed and constructed for operating lives in excess of 10^5 h, that is, total real lives of 25–30 years without significant replacement of metal parts. Secondly, the rapid rate of increase in demand for electricity, coupled with the relatively long period between conception and commissioning is such that design philosophy has inevitably run ahead of present-day operational experience. For example, the 500 MW units now under construction were designed in considerable detail before a 200 MW unit had been operated successfully over a period of several years. Thirdly, in addition to the statutory obligation on the C.E.G.B. to maintain supplies at all times there is a heavy premium on the reliability of plant particularly during the early part of its life when, compared with pre-existing plant, it offers relatively high efficiency and any outage necessitates the operation of less efficient equipment. The economic penalties become increasingly severe as the total demand rises and the unplanned outage of a single modern unit may incur additional fuel costs of over £10 000 per day, during a high load period.

The complex interaction of all these factors means that a compromise must be effected between the conflicting demands of:

(a) Reliability, based on sound operational experience, established design and the use of proven materials in explored environments.

45

(b) The urgent need for the construction of further generating capacity.

(c) The economic benefits offered by reductions in capital costs or improvements in thermal efficiency stemming from advances in design and materials.

It must also be recognized that the use of new materials and realization of novel designs is often dependent upon developments in fabrication techniques, particularly welding.

Developments in Conventional Turbine–Boiler Plant

The installed capacity of the C.E.G.B. generating plant by the end of 1964 will be about 38 000 MW (sent out) of which approximately 5% will be nuclear, and it is estimated that this will continue to rise at about 8% per annum to reach 50 000 MW by 1968.[1] A large proportion of the power stations are equipped with 30 or 60 MW units, but since the war the size of generating units has increased progressively from 100, 120 and 200 MW to the 275 MW single shaft and 550 MW cross-compound machines commissioned in 1963. There are under construction for operation in 1965 two supercritical pressure units, each of 375 MW capacity and using steam at 593°C (1100°F) and 3500 lb/in² with single reheat to 565°C (1050°F). The first 500 MW single shaft unit with steam conditions of 565°C (1050°F) and 2350 lb/in² with single reheat to 565°C will be commissioned in 1965 and more than thirty of these will be in operation by 1968. The rapid increase in unit size and improvements in the temperature and pressure of the steam delivered to the turbine in this period are summarized in Table II.

The prediction of further developments is clearly speculative but the size of boilers would not appear to be a major restriction.[2] With regard to the increase in the size of turbo-generators an important limitation in this country is the weight of a generator which can be transported by road; even with special authorization this is limited to 240 tons. Much of the increase in capacity which has been achieved in the past is due to the development of improved cooling arrangements for the alternator rotor and stator to permit greater output from a given physical size. Hydrogen cooling of the rotor and water cooling of the stator bars are standard features of all generators ordered of 300 MW or greater capacity. At present it would appear that generators of up to 600 MW capacity could be constructed at works and transported to site. Modest increases with some degree of site assembly, are conceivable but this limitation may determine the maximum size of single-line machines.

Boiler Components
Drums

The current level of superheater outlet pressures of about 2400 lb/in² corresponds to a design pressure for the boiler drum of 2700 lb/in². This, incidentally, represents the maximum practical value for a sub-critical boiler using natural circulation; thus both natural and assisted circulation boilers designed to work at this pressure are included in current constructions. Increased unit size has been accompanied by progressive changes from solid forged drums (limited in size by the capacity available to steelmakers and forgemasters to deal with large pieces) to drums assembled by welding together two or more solid forgings and to welded drums fabricated from rolled plates previously manipulated into the required shapes. The forged drums of the 200 MW units at High Marnham commissioned in 1962[3] were 4 ft 6 in. internal diameter, 5⅝ in. thick and 53 ft 0 in. long over the parallel portion. The shop-welded drum of a typical 500 MW unit to be commissioned in 1965 is 96 ft long with an internal diameter of 5 ft 0 in. and a wall thickness of 5 7/16 in. and it weighs 180 tons.[3] At the same time the materials have been changed from plain low carbon steel with a minimum tensile strength of 28 ton/in² to carbon–manganese and low alloy steels having ultimate tensile strengths in the ranges 32 to 38 and 36 to 42 ton/in² respectively. Even with these higher strength materials such as Ducol W30* [Composition: 0·17%C–1·5%Mn (max.)–0·7%Cr (max.)–0·28%Mo (max.)–0·1%V (max.)] British design codes based on an allowable stress criterion of

$$\frac{\text{ultimate tensile strength}}{3 \cdot 5}$$

have still necessitated wall thicknesses for these very large drums nearing 5½ in. This, understandably, has presented difficulties in fabrication, welding, heat treatment and non-destructive examination of the vessels. The acceptance of the tentative I.S.O. Boiler Design Code has recently offered the prospect of full advantage being taken of materials having relatively high proof or yield stress values at the relevant design temperature [*circa* 363°C (685°F)]. On this basis the allowable stress for Ducol W30, based on $S_T/1 \cdot 6$ (where S_T = the 0·2% proof stress at maximum operating temperature), can be raised by over 15% compared with the value obtained from the previous design criteria of U.T.S./3·5. It is a chastening thought for the materials scientist that such a dramatic improvement in allowable stress or reduction in section thickness can be achieved simply by exchanging one arbitrary criterion for another.

Manual metal-arc welding using coated electrodes has been largely superseded by other gas-shielded arc and automatic submerged-arc techniques. It is also becoming common practice to weld longitudinal seams in the vertical position by electro-slag methods. Use of the latter process for welding circumferential seams is currently under development by the boiler-makers.

* Proprietary designation of a steel manufactured by Colvilles Ltd.

TABLE II.—*Developments in Unit Size and Steam Conditions*

Unit rating (MW)	Turbine stop valve steam conditions		Reheat steam temperature °C (°F)	Year commissioned
	Temperature °C (°F)	Pressure lb/in²		
60	483 (900)	900	—	1950
100	565 (1050)	1500	—	1955
100	524 (975)	1500	510 (950)	1956
120	538 (1000)	1500	538 (1000)	1957
200	565 (1050)	2350	538 (1000)	1959
275	565 (1050)	2300	565 (1050)	1962
550ᵃ	565 (1050)	2300	565 (1050)	1963
350	565 (1050)	2300	565 (1050)	1964
375	593 (1100)	3500	565 (1050)	1965
500	565 (1050)	2300	565 (1050)	1965

ᵃ Cross compound machines.

The improved productivity offered by these modern welding processes may be deduced from the following data on average rates of weld metal deposition:

Manual metal arc— 4 lb/h

Submerged-arc   —20 lb/h

Electro-slag   —50 lb/h

Manual metal arc welding is the established method of making boiler drum stub tube welds, but automatic bare wire CO_2 and submerged-arc processes are being used to an increasing extent.

While dealing with boiler drums it is appropriate to mention a problem encountered with an associated piece of equipment, namely, materials for the sight glasses of drum water level gauges. It is a requirement of the Factories Act that ". . . at least one water gauge of transparent material . . . to show the water level in the boiler . . ." must be fitted. Originally the sight glass comprised a single plate running the whole length of the gauge but the increase in pressure in recent years has necessitated the introduction of the " bull's-eye " type where the single plate is replaced by a succession of separate glass discs about 1 in. in diameter, perhaps 7–8 in number, mounted in a strong frame. The difficulty arises because the glass suffers rapid obscuration due to etching by water under the conditions prevailing in the drum. A disc of mica is clamped over each glass to mitigate this effect. Unfortunately, while this prolongs the life of the glasses it reduces their initial clarity and they ultimately deteriorate because the mica tends to craze, delaminate and " bow " away from the surface of the glass. A research investigation has been undertaken by the North Eastern Regional Research and Development Laboratory of the C.E.G.B. to evaluate the resistance of a number of possible transparent materials to attack by boiler water under these conditions including, alumino-silicate and alumino-boro-silicate glasses, pure silica glass, fused alumina and artificial sapphire. The possibility of coating mica to improve its performance with substances such as silicones has also been investigated.

To date no wholly satisfactory material or treatment has been discovered. White sapphire appears, on the basis of short-term tests, to be the most resistant to chemical attack, but it is relatively fragile and presents mechanical problems of mounting in the frame of the gauge.

Furnace Wall and Roof Tubes

Changes in furnace design brought about by increases in unit size, in addition to the overall increase in furnace volume, include the division of the combustion space into separate twin furnaces, which may feed either a common drum or separate interconnected drums, and the introduction of dividing walls. The principal reason for these changes is the need to preserve the correct surface area to volume ratio. An appropriate area of radiant heat absorbing surface must be provided to take full advantage of the heat available in this form and to cool the combustion products before they enter the convective passes. There are also considerations of economy in minimising the overall size of furnaces and consequently boiler house superstructures.

There is a strong incentive for boilermakers to exploit prefabrication techniques which allow an increasing proportion of the construction to be carried out in their works where greater control can be exercised over welding, heat treatment and inspection and where special techniques unsuited to power station site application may be available. This trend is manifest in the recent introduction of " membrane " or " integral fin-tube " boiler walls. These comprise panels of boiler tubes which are assembled by shop welding, transported

Fig. 1.—Section showing continuous membrane wall

to site, erected in position and welded together to form the sides of the furnace chamber. Typically, each panel consists of an assembly of parallel tubes perhaps 60 ft in length, joined together by steel fins into an element about 10 ft wide. A section of such a panel is illustrated in Fig. 1. The furnace setting obtained is much tighter than with previous designs and this reduces air leakage into the furnace and eases the problem of efficient control of combustion.

Automatic CO_2 welding processes appear to be particularly suited to the task of making the longitudinal welds between the fins and the tubes thereby contributing to improved productivity and lower costs. The same process is also used to improve the cost and effectiveness of welding of mild steel fins on to the creep-resistant ($1\%Cr-\frac{1}{2}\%Mo$) tubes used to form the walls of superheater sections of the boiler.

This trend has been extended still further in one of the boilers for the supercritical units where the furnace wall tubes are arranged horizontally and are supported by ties joining special corner pillars. Sections of these corner pillars each comprising assemblies of 36 vertical tubes in $1\%Cr-\frac{1}{2}\%Mo$ steel are prefabricated using special jigs at the boilermakers' works as shown in Fig. 2.

Traditionally, seamless tubing has been used for furnace applications but the use of electric resistance welded tube is increasing and, more recently, high frequency welded tubing has been tendered. These types of tubing clearly present advantages, but particular care must be exercised to ensure that inspection procedures are sufficiently discriminating to detect defects which may impair the long life demanded of these components.

A particularly severe and yet sporadic problem encountered with boiler tubes is " on-load " corrosion.[4] This term is used to describe a form of corrosion in which the normally protective action of the magnetite oxide film formed on the water-side surface of boiler tubes breaks down and catastrophic local corrosion occurs with the production of massive non-protective magnetite, sometimes accompanied by hydrogen embrittlement of the tube material. The circumstances which give rise to this phenomenon are extremely complex and ill-understood, but common sites for the attack are discontinuities in the surface which can disturb flow and provide crevices for the " hideout " and concentration of salt impurities in the boiler water. Such a discontinuity is often afforded by a flash butt weld in the vertical furnace tubes where the weld intrusion into the bore has not been completely removed. Frequently in the past the broaching or

Fig. 2.—Assembly of furnace corner pillar sections in 1% Cr–$\frac{1}{2}\%$ Mo steel for supercritical boiler (Courtesy: International Combustion Ltd.)

reaming techniques used to remove the intrusion left a flash of metal which was as dangerous as the original discontinuity or more so. Internal machining is difficult to accomplish successfully when one considers the lengths of the tubes involved and the mismatch which may arise between the ends of tubes within normal tolerances. Failures are particularly marked in the highly rated parts of the boiler and attention is being given to the elimination of welds from these areas or to the use of joining or finishing techniques which eliminate discontinuities. At the same time the possibility of modifying the composition of the tube material to improve its resistance to this form of attack is being investigated. It is known that " hydrogen embrittlement " of the sort encountered may be prevented by addition of a carbide stabilizer such as chromium to the steel, but embrittlement is probably only a consequence and symptom of corrosion and there is no evidence at present that alloying will alleviate the basic problem.

Mention has already been made of the I.S.O. Boiler Design Code and its possible influence on the design of drums. In that case a saving in material and a higher utilization of its properties resulted and there was no evidence that this economy could be associated with anything adverse. In the case of boiler tubes, however, a rather curious situation may arise. For many years the section sizes of boiler tubes in mild steel have been determined using the tensile strength design criterion U.T.S./3·5 and no cognisance has been taken of yield or proof stress values. There is a long history to show that tubes designed on this basis have adequate strength and offer the required life. The I.S.O. Code, however, requires that the design be based on the lowest value of allowable stress given by the alternative design criteria, in the relevant temperature range:

$$\frac{\text{U.T.S.}}{2\cdot7} \text{ or } \frac{0\cdot2\% \text{ proof or yield stress}}{1\cdot6}$$

It so happens that for these steels the latter criterion is predominant and gives a lower value of allowable stress than the present criterion of U.T.S./3·5. With the guaranteed values of proof stress for the steels currently used, the rigorous adoption of the Code could mean that the tube wall thicknesses would need to be increased. Not only would this appear to be unjustified on the basis of operational experience, but it may even be detrimental in increasing the thermal resistance of the walls of the furnace chamber and enhancing the development of hot spots which may be a prime factor in the development of " on-load " corrosion. It is also worth emphasizing the views that have already been stated by Glen et al.[5] regarding the difficulties in measuring and assessing the practical significance of these proof and yield stress parameters. Briefly these are that differences in test procedure may give very different results for the values of the yield or proof stresses depending on the strain rate used and the " strain ageing " response of the steel and for this reason an internationally agreed standard test procedure is required. Furthermore, the same authors report tests which show that carbon steels of the same nominal composition and tensile strength at atmospheric temperature may have different stress–strain characteristics depending upon the steelmaking de-oxidation practice, the addition of niobium and their sensitivity to strain ageing.

Superheater and Reheater Tubing

The increases in steam pressure and temperature have altered the relative proportions of heat exchanger surface required for evaporative and superheating (including reheating) purposes respectively. Typically, the proportion of heat required for superheating has increased from 24% for a 60 MW unit to 47% for a modern unit delivering steam at 2350 lb/in² and 565°C with reheat to 540°C. The materials commonly used for superheater and reheater tubes are summarized below together with the limitations on maximum metal temperatures which are normally adopted for design purposes.

Tube material	Type of steel	Maximum working metal temperature
1% Cr–$\frac{1}{2}\%$ Mo	} Ferritic	565°C (1050°F)
$2\frac{1}{4}\%$ Cr–1% Mo		580°C (1076°F)
18% Cr–12% Ni– 1% Nb		
18% Cr–12% Ni–$2\frac{1}{2}\%$ Mo	} Austenitic	648°C (1200°F)
18% Cr–12% Ni– 1% Ti		

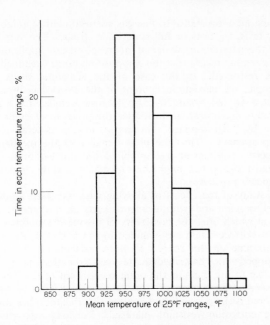

Fig. 3.—*Histogram showing time–temperature history of superheater over a period of 2550 hours. Nominal design steam temperature 940°F (504°C)*

These are metal temperatures and the corresponding steam temperatures will vary depending upon the location of the superheating surface but for design the metal is generally assumed to be 35°–50°C hotter than the steam. Unfortunately, there is a good deal of evidence to indicate that metal temperatures may often rise to values in excess of those intended by the designer. Few detailed temperature measurements have been reported but the histogram of Fig. 3 illustrates how great the discrepancies may be. The arrangement of the various stages of the superheater in a typical modern sub-critical boiler is illustrated schematically in Fig. 4. The platen superheater stage which has been introduced in the throat of the furnace is designed to absorb a high proportion of heat radiantly and also to cool the gas entering the convective passes. The position of the platen stage in the circuit is such that it is carrying relatively low temperature steam and this prevents undue increase in the metal temperature as a result of immersion in the very hot gas leaving the furnace chamber. This type of superheater consists of close pitch tube loops welded together to form a flat panel or " platen ". The platens are suspended from the top of the furnace, in line with the gas flow, and pitched at distances of at least 2 ft to prevent ash deposits bridging the gap and restricting the gas passes.

A radiant superheater lining part of the furnace chamber is also evident in Fig. 4 and it is noteworthy that the area of boiler

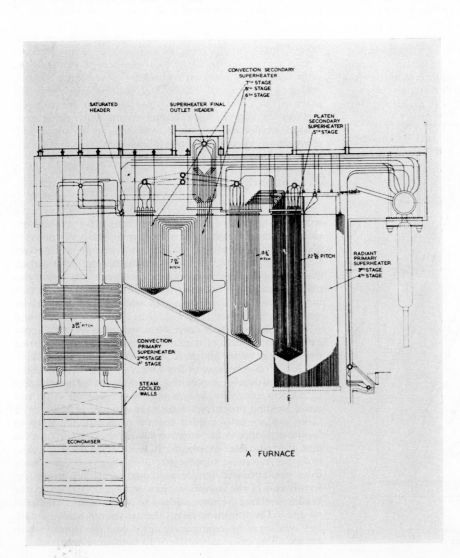

Fig. 4.—*Diagram showing location of super-heater surfaces in a modern boiler (Courtesy: The Superheater Co. Ltd.)*

E

wall tubing which has to carry up behind it is rendered less effective.[3] An alternative solution is to introduce an appropriate area of heat exchanger surface in the form of curtain walls. Essentially these are very widely spaced platen elements and they are supported rather differently and may extend across the whole throat of the furnace.

In the modern pulverized coal- or oil-fired boiler the super-heater and reheater tubes present one of the most severe material problems. This arises, not so much because they have to sustain the full steam pressure at high temperatures for very long periods of time, but because they are often subject to corrosive attack by the constituents of the flue gases. Indeed, many materials are available which offer greater creep strength and the ability to operate at higher temperatures than the austenitic steels currently employed, as can be seen from Fig. 5; but materials of significantly better corrosion resistance under these conditions have yet to be devised. This complex problem has been reviewed elsewhere[6] and the results of material evaluation trials carried out in C.E.G.B. boilers under various combustion conditions have been reported in a series of papers to the Institute of Fuel.[7,8,9] For these reasons no attempt is made here to discuss the problem in detail, but only to indicate that the corrosion in pulverized fuel fired boilers is attributable to aggressive ash deposits derived from certain coals. The alkali metal chloride and sulphur containing constituents of the fuel are known to be important factors. The outlet steam temperatures of oil-fired boilers are currently restricted to 540°C (1005°F) because of the possibility of corrosive attack of the superheater tubes by sodium and vanadium compounds present as impurities in the fuel ash.

High temperature flue gas corrosion of superheater tubing presents one of the most serious barriers to further advance-ment of steam conditions. To date, the problem of material selection has been approached by taking the materials currently available for creep-resistant applications and evaluating their comparative resistance to flue gas corrosion either in labora-tory tests, rig tests or full-scale boiler trials. The very fact that the materials are designed for creep-resistant applications, however, has meant that the composition range examined has been restricted. In the case of the austenitic steels, for example, the chromium content of the alloys has been re-stricted to less than 20–25% because significantly higher amounts are known to introduce the problem of embrittle-ment by "sigma-phase" formation and, in general, lower creep strength. Thus the predominance of the mechanical property requirement has inhibited the full exploration of compositions which might be expected to exhibit improved corrosion resistance.

A study of the effects of alloying with increased amounts of chromium and with elements such as aluminium and silicon which offer the possibility of favourable modification of the surface oxide are included in the C.E.G.B. Research Programme on this topic. If more resistant alloys can be developed which have inadequate creep strength it may still be possible to use them as the outer component of a bimetallic tube. Another facet of this approach which is being explored is the possibility of coating superheater tubes with a more corrosion resistant material. Previous attempts to protect tubes by coating with materials such as MgO, Al_2O_3 and chromium metal have met with little success, often, one suspects, because the coating lacked not corrosion resistance but adequate bonding to the tube material. Recent develop-ments in vitreous enamelling and refractory glasses with controlled physical properties, particularly expansion charac-teristics, offer hope that satisfactory coatings and techniques of application will be devised. It is often claimed, with some reason, that coatings must be self-healing otherwise small discontinuities will result in local perforation in much the same time as an uncoated component would fail. Systems having a measure of self-healing can be envisaged: for example, an outer alumina coating changing progressively through an alumina-alloy cermet to an alloy either con-taining aluminium or locally enriched at its surface by aluminizing or similar diffusion treatment.

Headers and H.P. Steam Piping

Headers are characterized by being of relatively heavy section and, in their function as terminations for smaller bore thinner tubing, necessarily feature a multiplicity of stub tube connections. Water wall headers which operate at relatively low temperatures (<350°C) can be made from plain carbon steel but the increase in pressure is encouraging the use of this class of material at higher tensile levels at which greater care has to be exercised in welding. The steam superheater header materials used are 1%Cr–½%Mo, 2¼%Cr–1%Mo and ½%Cr–½%Mo–¼%V in order of increasing severity of appli-cation. In the case of the latter material, welding is carried out with electrodes and filler wires giving a weld deposit of 2¼%Cr–1%Mo because of the danger of poor creep ductility in welds made with a matching composition. The thickness of headers in current designs may be as great as 4½ in. and again welding procedures must take account of this. Stub tubes are normally welded on the header in the shop to facilitate joining to the water or steam tubes on site. In the case of ferritic steel superheater headers which act as termina-tions for austenitic superheater tubes these stubs are made from pre-fabricated ferritic–austenitic transition pieces, the ferritic end of the transition piece being shop-welded to the header, enabling the austenitic end to be joined to like material on site. The transition pieces themselves are made by flash butt welding or by joining using nickel base weld metals which are metallurgically compatible with both components.

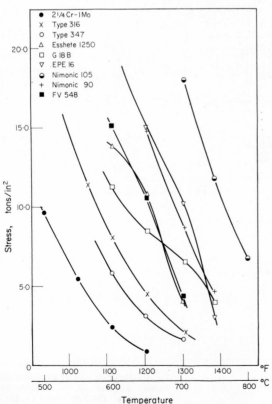

Fig. 5.—*Stress to rupture in 100 000 hours (estimated) for various high temperature materials*

could be made relatively easily, methods other than the established brazing techniques will have to be developed if tempering and softening of the steel are to be avoided. Electron beam and, in the future, laser welding offer possible methods of joining while confining the deterioration in properties to a very narrow heat affected zone which need be exposed only in an area remote from the most severe attack. Another approach would be to develop steels of high resistance to tempering to permit a short exposure at brazing temperatures (say 650°C) without significant deterioration.

There are other materials and design developments in the higher temperature parts of the turbine but perhaps the most interesting is the problem of selection of materials for i.p. rotors. The inlet temperature of the steam to the i.p. cylinder of reheat machines is often as high as that to the h.p. cylinder but the lower pressure means that the volume of steam and hence rotor diameter and blade lengths are greater. The centrifugal stresses are therefore higher and at the inlet end the rotor may present a more severe creep problem than the h.p. rotor. At the same time the still greater size of the outlet end demands high strength at lower temperature. Thus for this single forging it is necessary to select materials which offer high creep strength to meet the conditions at one end and sufficient hardenability to permit the development of high strength at the bore of the rotor at the other end. The delicacy of this balance is discussed in a recent paper by Bates and Ridal.[14]

Generators

Again the increase in size of units has led to more stringent requirements for rotor forgings and improved steel making practices, including vacuum de-gassing during casting for the removal of hydrogen and repeated upset forging are being adopted. The strength of suitable steels (in this country 3%Cr–Mo and Ni–Cr–Mo steels) does not appear to be a serious limitation to increases in size. On the contrary, a barrier to further increases in rotor diameter is rather the availability of materials for coil binding rings. These rings are designed to secure the ends of the copper windings in place as shown in Fig. 7. The material for these rings must sustain the very high centrifugal forces arising from both the copper winding and its own mass. At the same time it is very desirable that it should be of non-magnetic material to minimize flux leakage. It will also be appreciated that the utmost integrity is required of these components. In the present method of manufacture the high level of strength required is developed by the cold expansion of a forged ring of a suitable austenitic steel (such as 18%Mn–4%Cr steel) which will not suffer significant transformation to martensite as a result of deformation. Proof stress (0.2%) and U.T.S. values of 57 ton/in² and 67 ton/in² respectively in section thickness of up to 3 in. can be realised at present with a reasonable measure of ductility, but any further increase in diameter will demand properties significantly better than these. Attempts are being made to devise improved precipitation hardening austenitic steels with proof stress values of up to 70 ton/in², but the development to which attention is drawn here is the possibility of making the rings from high strength tape. A technique, evolved by Imperial Metal Industries (Kynoch) consists of laying down on a suitable mandrel successive layers of helically wound tape until the required wall thickness is obtained, each layer being displaced from the former to avoid coincidence of the butt joints and the whole being bonded together by an epoxy resin or other suitable adhesive. There remain many problems to be overcome before the simple shapes which are practicable can be utilized. Not the least of these is the method of attachment of the ring to the rotor; at present rings are shrunk on to the rotor body but this would

appear to be ruled out by the temperature limitations of the adhesives used and alternative methods of attachment must be devised.

Fig. 7a.—A coil binding ring.

Fig. 7b.—End of alternator rotor showing the arrangement of the windings and the end of the rotor body on to which the coil binding ring is shrunk (Courtesy: Associated Electrical Industries Ltd.)

E*

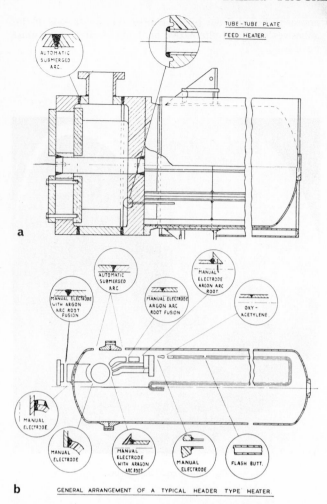

TUBE-TUBE PLATE
FEED HEATER.

a

b

GENERAL ARRANGEMENT OF A TYPICAL HEADER TYPE HEATER

Fig. 8.—*Diagrams illustrating alternative methods of feedheater construction: (a) Tube-tube plate; (b) Header type. (Courtesy: English Electric Co. Ltd.)*

Ancillary Plant

Feed Water Heaters

An established method of construction for feedheaters uses a tubeplate termination for the heat exchanger tubes. To meet the current levels of feedwater pressure and the size of units, however, very thick tube plates are needed (10 in. thick ×6 ft diameter) and while a number of techniques have been developed for making the tube plate to tube welds,[15] including that shown in Fig. 8(a), the difficulties of ensuring a watertight assembly may be expected to increase with continued advances in pressure and size. Furthermore, it becomes progressively more difficult to ensure the integrity of the tube plate itself and as a result alternative methods of construction have been considered which appear to offer greater scope for development. One approach, which is shown schematically in Fig. 8(b), involves a succession of header tubes and bifurcated junctions progressively sub-dividing down to the final heater tube size. This example illustrates how advantage can be taken of the different welding techniques now available and the importance of achieving sound joints.

Condensers

The established form of condenser construction involves the prefabrication of mild steel shell sections, which are transported to site, assembled and joined, either by bolting, welding or a combination of both, to the exhaust casing. The shell is

normally fitted with cast-iron water boxes, but increases in size have stimulated interest in lighter and more corrosion resistant material, such as fibreglass either for the complete component or for parts such as access doors. The protection of ferrous metals in a condenser, however, does not present serious problems and cathodic protection with the electrode materials now available, such as platinized titanium, provides an effective and often more economic solution than the use of expensive materials of construction.[19]

The multiplicity of exhaust flows in the low pressure cylinders and the increase in their size present problems in accommodating and supporting the massive condensers required for the larger units. One approach by the English Electric Company for a six-flow 500 MW unit has been to replace the reinforced concrete l.p. turbine foundation block by a steel structure integrating the l.p. case and condenser shell and bridging the gap between the remaining turbine foundation and the generator block. A model of this " bridge condenser " showing the form of construction and the condenser tube nests is illustrated in Fig. 9. It is noteworthy that the welding techniques employed in the construction included electro-slag welding of the vertical seams in the $1\frac{1}{2}$ in. thick side plates and submerged-arc welding of the horizontal corner welds of the main side beams.

The difficulties associated with the location of large condensers beneath the turbine bed and the wide span to be supported have also encouraged the development of integral turbine case-condenser shells in which the condensing surfaces are located alongside the l.p. cylinders. These again involve substantial welded fabrications.

The established tube materials include 70/30 brass, Admiralty brass, aluminium brass, 90/10 copper–nickel and 70/30 copper–nickel alloys containing varying amounts of iron and manganese. In the U.S.A. aluminium alloy and, more particularly, stainless steel condenser tubes are in service either in specific locations in the condenser tube nest or throughout. Interest in stainless steel in this country is quickening and trials are in progress at at least one station where the cooling water contains quantities of silt. Relevant work is also in progress at the Sea Water Corrosion Laboratory of the South Eastern Region of the C.E.G.B. at Brighton. Future developments will continue to include interest in methods of construction which offer reduced possibility of leakage and the prospect of elimination of the double tube plate construction used at present.

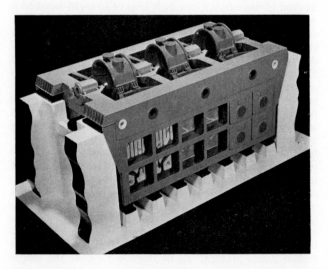

Fig. 9.—*Model showing principle of construction of the " Bridge " condenser for a 6-flow LP exhaust 500 MW machine (Courtesy: English Electric Co. Ltd.)*

Dry Cooling Towers

The principle and design of the dry cooling tower, which offers freedom from dependence on supplies of natural cooling water, and its associated jet condenser and the construction of the first plant at Rugeley Power Station have been described previously.[16]

From the materials standpoint the aluminium heat exchanger elements are of greatest interest. Aluminium offers low specific weight, good thermal conduction and amenability to the fabrication processes involved in the construction of the elements. Initially there were misgivings regarding its corrosion resistance and various surface treatments were studied to improve this property and to determine whether water conditioning was required to prevent contamination of the water entering the boiler circuit. In the event complex adjustment of the pH on either side of the tower has not been required and the dissolution of aluminium is not significant.

Building Structures

The importance of minimizing capital costs has already been mentioned and to this end every effort is made to reduce the cost of station buildings while maintaining or enhancing their appearance. Big reductions in building volume and cost have been achieved in the past decade largely as a result of reduction in plant volume per unit capacity but a significant contribution has been made also by the availability of new materials.

These trends to reduce costs and improve appearance are exemplified by the changes in cladding and roofing adopted for buildings. In the postwar era many station buildings were clad with brickwork which served no structural purpose, being connected to the structural framework only by ties, but which could be given an acceptable architectural treatment. Brickwork cladding is now largely supplanted by aluminium alloy, resin bonded laminate, plastic or fibreglass sheetings that require no protective painting, offer reasonable resistance to fire and are comparatively light. They can be rolled or moulded in a wide range of sections and can be given a permanent colour treatment during manufacture. These sheet materials can be attached directly to rough brickwork, to the structural steel members or used as curtain walling in steel or aluminium frames. Hollow precast reinforced concrete beams are commonly used for constructing roofs but again economics and reduction in weight have been effected by the use of troughed aluminium or steel sheet overlaid with suitable thermal insulation and asphalt or roofing felt.

Nuclear Power Generation

Space precludes an extended discussion of the advances in materials which have been a feature of the utilization of nuclear power, but the diversity of these developments is illustrated by the adoption of concrete for the pressure vessels of later stations and the special quality requirements of stainless steel for A.G.R. fuel element cans.

The C.E.G.B. are actively interested in pressure vessels manufactured in pre-stressed concrete and have placed contracts for stations at Oldbury and Wylfa incorporating these constructions. The desire for greater economy and safety have stimulated development of alternatives to steel for pressure vessel construction and the advantages offered by concrete include:

(a) The ability to combine the function of the pressure vessel with that of the biological shield.

(b) Greater flexibility in design which permits the heat exchangers to be located along with the reactor core in the same concrete structure and eliminates the ducting required to interconnect steel vessels and, therefore, a potential source of failure.

(c) A concrete pressure vessel will not fail in a catastrophic manner and if properly designed it should show progressive signs of failure in the unlikely event of the ultimate loading being approached.

(d) The specialized skills required on site for the construction of steel vessels by welding are obviated and the labour normally used for civil engineering works may be employed.

At present the C.E.G.B. have imposed a design criterion that a concrete vessel should be capable of withstanding $3 \times$ nominal design pressure before ultimate failure occurs, i.e. a state of continued deformation and rupture without further increase in pressure. This margin of safety is a reflection of the novelty of this application and the absence of an appropriate and agreed code of design practice.[17] As a branch of structural engineering concrete pressure vessel design is clearly in its formative stage and with advances in knowledge of the materials involved, more sophisticated design may be expected. At present too little is known of the creep behaviour, other time dependent changes, thermal stress effects and moisture migration in large masses of concrete. Essentially in this type of construction the reactor coolant gas is contained by an inner gas-tight mild steel lining which in turn is supported by the concrete vessel. The temperature of the coolant gas may be up to 400°C and this must be contained without damage to the concrete. To this end the inner lining is provided with thermal insulation in the form of layers of stainless steel foil supported on pins with spacers between them to control the interlaminar gap. The concrete vessel is also liberally provided with water cooling pipes as a further assurance. The surface of the concrete should not exceed 60°C and the bulk of the sub-surface material is maintained below 55°C. The differing physical characteristics of steel and concrete obviously present problems of compatibility and the lining must be capable of withstanding local and possibly repeated straining.

Pre-stressing cables also present a creep relaxation problem and the initial level of prestrain is adjusted in each to prevent all of them having to be re-tightened during service. A difficulty encountered in adjusting the level of tension is the frictional resistance between the cables and the ducts where these follow a curved path.

The stainless steel fuel element cans designed to contain the UO_2 fuel in an A.G.R. type reactor present special problems. While the wall thickness must be minimized to prevent undue capture of neutrons the cans must be of the highest integrity and be able to accept a certain amount of deformation in service, for example by fission gas swelling, without suffering perforation. The wall thickness is limited to about 0·010 in. and this means that the inclusion and detrimental impurity content of the material must be kept at an absolute minimum if adequate ductility is to be achieved. It has been shown that this can be realized by using the purest starting materials available and double vacuum melting: the first melt is made using vacuum induction techniques and the material produced is used for subsequent vacuum-arc remelting.

Overhead Line Equipment

The possibility of ice formation on overhead line conductors and insulators requires that both these components and the transmission towers must be designed to meet these occasional extra load and wind forces. Furthermore, the intermittent loss of large pieces of ice during a thaw has been known to cause the conductors to oscillate and clash with their neighbours. The possibility of making use of the evolution of heat from magnetic hysteresis loss to prevent icing has obvious attractions. In order to evolve this heat only under icing conditions and minimize losses under normal conditions, materials with Curie temperatures of about 0–5°C are required which can be used as tape wrapped around the conductor. Certain magnetic ferrites appear promising for this purpose. There is also a possibility that additional heat evolution may be achieved by adding a further coating of aluminium which can act as the secondary of a transformer with the ferrite as the primary.

In humid and dirty atmospheres the surface of an overhead line insulator may suffer contamination which gives rise to a non-uniform distribution of voltage over its surface. This may result in surface discharges and radio noise or to complete flashover. One method of stabilizing the voltage distribution over the surface and preventing these occurences is to incorporate a semi-conductor in the glaze imparted to the insulator during manufacture. Unfortunately the semi-conducting glazes used are liable to deterioration by electro-lytic corrosion. Work at the Central Electricity Research Laboratories[18] has done much to elucidate the mechanism of corrosion and to formulate improved compositions but a completely satisfactory semiconducting glaze has yet to be devised. A glaze with a positive temperature coefficient of resistivity would be advantageous if it could be arranged for the leakage losses to heat the surface a few degrees above the ambient temperature, thereby hastening the evaporation of moisture and stifling electrolytic corrosion.

Superconducting Materials

The prospect of utilizing niobium-base superconducting materials for transmission application has excited considerable interest in recent years, the more so because it is a potential alternative to overhead transmission lines and the amenity problems which they raise. At present, however, the prospects are not encouraging because of the difficulties of refrigeration. Current densities upwards of 10^5 A/cm^2 appear feasible for d.c. transmission with existing niobium-base materials but the heat evolved as a result of energy losses, although apparently small, requires the expenditure of about 1500 times as much refrigerating power to remove it at the low temperature of operation (4°K). An even more severe problem is presented by the thermal leak at the ends of the cable. The reliability required of the vacuum and refrigeration plant would also have to be remarkably high. The present cost of superconducting materials is probably about £350 000/ ton and while this could be expected to fall with increased usage there would not appear to be much prospect for a reduction in refrigeration costs. The most promising hope is that materials which exhibit superconducting properties at significantly higher temperatures will be devised. The present superconducting materials, however, appear to have application in the construction of large magnets such as are required to provide the field for a magnetohydrodynamic generator. Here the relatively compact construction eases the refrigeration and insulation problems enormously.

Concluding Remarks

It has not been possible within the compass of this review to deal with all the many material developments or to dwell in any detail on any particular topic. Indeed, apart from a passing mention, no consideration has been given to the materials problems posed by the environments of certain novel methods of power generation such as magnetohydro-dynamic generation and fuel cells. Nevertheless, it is hoped that a glimpse has been given of the requirements of the power generation industry that will stimulate the exchange of ideas between it and other branches of technology.

Acknowledgments

The author would like to thank the Central Electricity Generating Board for permission to publish this paper. He would also like to acknowledge the assistance given both by his colleagues and by staff of a number of boiler and turbine plant manufacturers.

References

1   Central Electricity Generating Board. Annual Report and Accounts 1962–3 (London: H.M.S.O., 1963).

2   Brown, F. H. S. "*The Duty and Development of Modern Power Station Plant*", 27th Parsons Memorial Lecture, 12 December 1962 (L3/63) (Inst. Mech. Eng.).

3   Davis, R. F. "*The Development of the Large Assisted-Circulation Boiler in England*". Presented, Manchester, 14 February 1963 (Reprint P 20/63) (Inst. Mech. Eng. 1963).

4   Potter, E. C. and Mann, G. M. W. "*Mechanism of magnetite growth on low carbon steel in steam and aqueous solutions up to 550°C*". Second International Congress on Metallic Corrosion (New York: 1963).

5   Glen, J., Lessells, J. and Barr, R. R. "*High temperature yield and proof stress of some carbon steels*". Paper 33, Joint International Conference on Creep, 30 September– 4 October 1963 (Inst. Mech. Eng.).

6   Johnson, H. R. and Littler, D. J., Eds. "The mechanism of corrosion by fuel impurities", *Proceedings of the International Conference held at Marchwood Engineering Laboratories*, C.E.G.B., 20–24 May 1963 (London: Butter-worths, 1963).

7   Edwards, A. M., Jackson, P. J. and Howes, L. S. "Opera-tional trial of superheater steels in C.E.G.B. pulverized-fuel-fired boilers burning East Midlands coal", *J. Inst. Fuel*, Jan. 1962.

8   Foster, G. G. and Toft, L. H. "Wastage trials of superheater steels in C.E.G.B. power stations at Westwood (Wigan) and Bromborough (Birkenhead)", *J. Inst. Fuel*, January 1962.

9   Edwards, A. M., Evans, G. J. and Howes, L. S. "Operational trial of superheater steels in a C.E.G.B. pulverized-fuel-fired boiler burning Yorkshire coal", *J. Inst. Fuel*, March 1962.

10   Asbury, F. E., Mitchell, B. and Toft, L. H. *British Welding J.*, November 1960.

11   Baker, R. A. and Soldan, H.M. "*Service experiences at 1050° and 1100°F of piping of austenitic steels*". Paper 71, Joint International Conference on Creep, 30 September– 4 October 1963 (Inst. Mech. Eng.).

12   Straub, F. G. "Blue blush characteristics", *Proc. Amer. Power Conf.*, 30 March–1 April 1955, **17**, 511–525.

13   Baker, D. W. C. and Eaton, J. L. "Steel to combat turbine blade erosion". *Engineering*, 22 February 1963.

14   Bates, H. G. A. and Ridal, K. A. *Factors governing the creep properties in large diameter 1% Cr—Mo–V rotor forgings.* Paper 72, Joint International Conference on Creep, 30 September—4 October 1963 (Inst. Mech. Eng.).

15   Burgess, N. T. "Automatic tungsten-arc welding of heat exchangers (especially feedwater heaters)", *British Welding J.*, April 1961.

16   "Dry cooling tower and jet condensing plant". *The Engineer*, 4 December 1959, pp. 729–731.

17   Waters, T. C. and Barrett, N. T. "Prestressed concrete pressure vessels for nuclear reactors", *J. Brit. Nuclear Energy Soc.*, 1963, **2**, 3.

18   Smith, E. J. D. "The corrosion of semi-conducting glazes", *Trans. Brit. Ceramic Soc.*, 1959, **58**, 5.

19   Matthewman, W. "The use of platinised Titanium in a new form for marine cathodic protection". *Corrosion Prevention and Control*, 1962, **9**, 11.

MATERIALS REQUIREMENTS FOR AIRCRAFT TURBOJET AND RAMJET ENGINES

By A. B. P. BEETON*

SYNOPSIS

The aero engine as a type is peculiar in demanding the maximum power output per unit weight, and in being able to afford the best materials to achieve this result. In a typical case weight saving is shown to pay off at a rate of about £200 per lb wt. Maximum operating temperatures are also essential in order to reduce the size and weight for a given output, and the limit in this direction is set by material properties.

As an example of new fields being opened up, the problems of the hypersonic ramjet are discussed. It is explained that the lack of cooling air, the inadequacy of the engine fuel as a coolant, and the necessity for running up to chemically correct mixtures can only be faced by operating at temperatures considerably higher than the maximum set by engineering standards of today. Exact material requirements for this application cannot be formulated yet, but work is in hand which should lead to a better understanding of these requirements.

Finally reference is made to the special requirements of pebble-bed fillings for simulating on the test bed the air intake conditions corresponding to hypersonic flight speeds.

LIGHT structures are required for nearly all aeronautical purposes: in the aero-engine (or in parts of it, at least), the particular requirement is one of lightness coupled with high temperature operation, and the present paper attempts to explain just how these material requirements arise, and why it is so important to push technology to the limit in order to develop materials with mechanical properties of the very highest order. The point of view expressed herein is therefore that of the user endeavouring to say what he wants and why: the complementary exposition of what existing materials can do and how they may possibly be improved is left to the materials experts.

Compared with power plants constructed for other purposes, the aircraft propulsion engine is required to place special emphasis on certain design features, and to pay rather less attention to others. The greatest importance, for instance, is placed upon the attainment of maximum possible power output (in terms of bhp or thrust) for a given engine weight. This is because a given required flight range to be covered by a given aircraft specifies a certain weight margin (on top of the aircraft structure, fixed equipment and fuel) which can be allocated between engines and payload. Any saving in engine weight will therefore appear directly as an increase in the potential payload. Specific fuel consumption is of course also important, not so much because the fuel has to be paid for, but because it reflects directly in the available range for a given payload, other factors being equal. This emphasis on fuel weight rather than fuel cost does mean that aircraft engines can afford the luxury of a distillate fuel which is substantially free from vanadium and other substances responsible for high temperature corrosion of turbine blades.

Reliability must also be high, but relatively frequent and extensive maintenance can be permitted in order to achieve this. Furthermore the cost of the engine itself is quite a small quantity in comparison with the gains likely to result from small improvements in performance or reductions in weight: this point is examined in more detail later.

One obvious way in which the aero-engine designer can avoid unnecessary weight is by getting to know very exactly the operating temperatures and the stresses (thermal and mechanical) in all the major components—in fact in all

components which are sufficiently heavy to contribute appreciably to the total weight of the engine. Accurate stressing then enables load factors to be kept down, and hence also the component weights. Such an intimate knowledge of working temperatures and stresses throughout the engine is also essential in selecting the best material for a particular job—e.g. dural, titanium or stainless steel for the end stages of a high pressure ratio compressor.

To reduce weight to a minimum, the designer must know not only precisely what his loads are, but just as precisely what his chosen materials will stand. For this reason it is important to use a material with consistent properties, as well as one with high strength, low density, etc. For instance if a number of specimens are tested, and the stress to failure is determined for each specimen, the results may be plotted against the stress in terms of the number of specimens failing below this stress. Fig. 1 shows the form of typical curves for two different materials both having the same mean strength, $\bar{S}$. Clearly, however, the important stresses from the design point of view are the minimum values, S' and S'', and it is these rather than the mean stress, $\bar{S}$, which should be used as the basis for

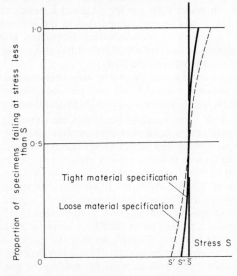

Fig. 1.—*Typical analysis of identical tests on a number of specimens*

* National Gas Turbine Establishment, Pyestock, Farnborough, Hants.

calculations. This underlines the importance of tight material specifications for all aero-engine work.

Although the sort of curves given in Fig. 1 may be obtained experimentally in many cases, so that minimum properties within a certain specification can be determined, this may not always be practicable in the case of creep tests when testing times of 1000 h or even 10 000 h are involved. Material specifications for components subject to creep must therefore be more than usually strict, since there may be only a single test result to base calculations on, and it must therefore be ensured that this value contains the smallest possible statistical error.

Materials for high temperature service have in general to be designed for a certain finite life. In highly stressed components in which only very small dimensional changes can be tolerated, the creep rate is perhaps the most important material property. The best material would then be that permitting the highest possible working temperature at some nominal condition which might typically be specified as 0·1% creep strain in 1000 h at a stress of 15 ton/in². In components operating at maximum material temperatures, where stresses and strains may be less important, it again becomes necessary to specify the life both because of the general degradation of mechanical properties with time (recrystallization) and because of the progressive attack of engine gases (notably oxygen) upon exposed hot surfaces. It might be possible to accept a 10 h life for such components.

Hot aero-engine components are also liable to be subjected to considerable thermal shock every time the engine is started or shut down, which is relatively frequently. It is chiefly for this reason that many otherwise quite promising high temperature materials have not yet replaced the conventional steels and nickel alloys.

It is interesting to put some rough figures to the premium placed upon lightness in the particular case of the turbojet engine as used in modern jet airliner service. First of all the cost of passenger transport by air: based upon a one-way transatlantic ticket price of £60 for a 3000 mile flight at say 500 mile/h, this works out at £10 per hour. Taking the average passenger and luggage to weigh 200 lb, the cost is just 1s./h per lb wt. If it is now assumed that engine and payload weights are interchangeable (i.e. 200 lb saving in engine weight permits one extra passenger to be carried without affecting performance in any way), the value of reducing engine weight can also be put at 1s./h per lb. Now the statistical life expectancy of such an engine is certainly not less than 4000 h, and the payoff resulting from saving engine weight therefore amounts to about £200 per lb. Against a premium of this magnitude, it will be appreciated that in the aero-engine all sorts of complicated manufacturing techniques and exotic materials can be justified which would be totally uneconomic in engines for most other purposes.

Enough has been said about why aero-engines have to be as light as possible. A few words must now be added to explain why they have to operate at very high temperatures as well.

First of all, let us return to the case of the simple jet engine. Fig. 2 plots the specific fuel consumption and the specific thrust (per unit air flow) against the combustion temperature. The values given refer to a fairly typical cruising condition of $M = 0·75$ in the stratosphere, with a compressor temperature rise of 225°C. While it will be seen that optimum fuel economy occurs at quite a low temperature of around 850°K, the rise in specific consumption is only about 20% if the temperature is pushed up to 1300°K. On the other hand the specific thrust is then doubled, so that the engine size (and therefore weight) can be halved. This is the basic reason why there is such a powerful incentive for putting the combustion temperature—and with it also the temperature of the hot parts

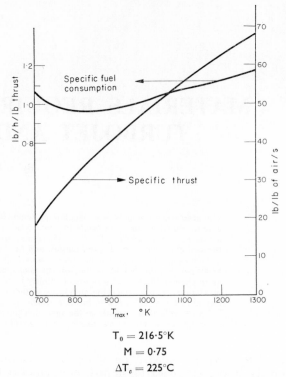

$$T_0 = 216·5°K$$
$$M = 0·75$$
$$\Delta T_c = 225°C$$

Fig. 2.—*The effect of combustion temperature on simple jet engine characteristics*

of the turbine—up to the maximum set by the strength of available materials at these temperatures.

It is therefore almost entirely material limitations that govern the size and weight of turbojet engines. The word " almost " is inserted here in order to recognize the existence of the noise nuisance, which many will agree is bad enough already, and would only be aggravated by any increase in engine temperatures. Hence there is a continuing quest for ever stronger and more refractory materials for turbine components, in order to bring down engine weight for a given required thrust, and therefore to increase aircraft range and/or payload.

Some mention may perhaps be made at this point of the material requirements for turbine blades. In order to keep down the number of stages, and hence the turbine weight for a given output, blade tip speeds have to be as high as possible. This means that the blades are necessarily very highly stressed by centrifugal loading. Since for a given tip speed and blade height the root stress is proportional to blade density, it is specific strength (i.e. stress ÷ density) that is the important property of a turbine blade material. The blades therefore have to work both at the maximum possible temperature and at the maximum possible level of stress: moreover, the tip clearance must be kept small for reasons of efficiency, which explains why creep is another very critical parameter for this application.

All air-breathing aero-engines rely to some extent on atmospheric air for cooling purposes. In the case of the conventional piston engine, the air acts either directly upon the cylinder fins or indirectly through a liquid-coolant heat exchanger. Rather less obviously, perhaps, the gas turbine needs secondary air from the compressor to cool its primary flame tubes, and also smaller quantities of ram air are needed for cooling the lubricating oil through a heat exchanger. Then again the usual variety of ramjet, flying at $M = 2$ to 3, utilizes intake air to cool both the flame-holding tinware and the containing walls of the combustion chamber and propelling nozzle, which are necessarily subjected to gas temperatures of around 2000°C. Since, however, the kinetic temperature rise of the intake air is proportional to the square of the flight speed, it rapidly becomes virtually useless as a coolant at speeds much above $M=5$, which corresponds to an inlet air temperature of about 1000°C. Fortunately no flame-holders are required to stabilize combustion above this level of inlet temperature, but the problem remains of cooling the combustion chamber and nozzle walls. In spite of this formidable cooling difficulty, there is considerable interest at present in the possibilities of the " hypersonic " ramjet flying at a speed of about $M=6$, or 4000 mile/h.

At $M=6$ burning a chemically correct mixture, the theoretical gas temperature is about 2500°C. It might be thought that some relief for the temperature problem should be possible by running at a weaker fuel–air ratio: this is, however, ruled out on performance grounds by the following considerations. Firstly, specific thrust would clearly be reduced, since less energy is being put into the same quantity of air. This means a larger engine for the same duty, just as in the case of the simple turbojet referred to previously. Then as regards the specific fuel consumption, there is one effect which results in a general deterioration as specific thrust (or fuel–air ratio) increases. This is just the Froude efficiency factor coming in:

$$\eta_F = \frac{2uv}{u+v},$$

where $u =$ flight speed, and $v =$ propulsive jet velocity with respect to the aircraft. On top of this, however, it must be remembered that there is a virtually constant intake loss (per unit air consumption) to be carried by the thermodynamic cycle. Weakening of the fuel–air ratio reduces the heat input and consequently it also reduces the proportion of this heat converted into useful work after allowing for the fixed intake loss. These two effects are therefore always working against each other to produce the sort of minimum shown in the s.f.c. curve in Fig. 2. In the particular case of the hypersonic ramjet, however, the intake losses are vastly greater, and the theoretical minimum point for best economy is moved right over to a temperature much higher than can in fact be generated even with combustion at chemically correct mixture. Consequently it becomes imperative to operate right up to the maximum 2500°C gas temperature both to keep the engine size down and to ensure reasonable economy of fuel.

To a very limited extent, the hypersonic ramjet may be able to use the fuel as a coolant, in the same way as a liquid rocket engine does. However, the fuel quantities involved in air-breathing combustion are very much less than in the rocket case, and kerosine is not a particularly good coolant. Moreover the engine is not the only part of the aircraft which is going to need cooling at $M=6$, and the covetous eyes of the structures people and of those responsible for the cooling of crew and equipment are also cast upon the engine fuel as a prospective heat sink.

It is therefore necessary to examine other methods of handling combustion gases which do not require large quantities of liquid cooling. The most obvious direction in which to proceed is to run the hot engine parts even hotter than they do at present. In this way not only can the cooling requirement (roughly proportional to the difference between the gas temperature T_G and the wall temperature T_w) be reduced, but the heat that it is possible to radiate away directly (proportional to $T_w{}^4$) will be greatly increased.

It is here that the use of special materials must be considered. Existing nickel-based alloys (which incidentally owe their present highly developed state very largely to the demands of the gas turbine aero-engine) run out of strength at about 1200°C. For operation at higher temperatures, one thinks of the refractory metals (W, Ta, Nb and Mo) and their alloys, and also of ceramics (e.g. AlO_2 and ZrO_2).

Refractory metal alloys for hypersonic ramjet use will probably not be very highly stressed, and they will be mainly needed in sheet form. They will have to operate in an oxidizing atmosphere, and will therefore require an effective coating to resist oxidation. A high thermal conductivity and a low expansion coefficient should also be beneficial in reducing distortion.

Ceramic materials are generally thought of more as heat insulators, i.e. for operation with a considerable temperature gradient normal to the surface. Mechanical properties under these conditions have to be carefully examined, and it is important not to let the weight become excessive.

It has been mentioned that external radiation is relied upon for cooling a considerable proportion of the hypersonic ramjet engine surface. The rate of heat loss, and therefore the equilibrium wall temperature also, can be controlled to some extent by the surface emissivity. There may therefore be considerable scope for the development of special coatings on these refractory materials which will endow the surface with either a high or a low emissivity.

The situation is rather different compared with the state of development of the turbojet engine, in which design techniques and operating conditions are fairly well established, and for which desired material specifications for particular components can quite easily be drawn up. Before we can make a hypersonic ramjet which could hope to compete with other forms of high speed propulsion (e.g. the chemical rocket), considerable research will have to be undertaken into manufacturing techniques for existing refractory materials, and into engineering design methods which result in satisfactory light structures at very high temperatures. Until we have gone some way down this road, it is really not possible to specify material requirements except in the very broadest of terms. There is no doubt at all, however, that success will only be achieved by stretching the high temperature capabilities of materials to the utmost. It is, of course, realized that this vague sort of utterance offers little guidance to the materials manufacturer, and it is largely for this very reason that we are attempting to design and test typical hypersonic ramjet components in advance of any detailed project incorporating this type of propulsion. As a result of such work, it is hoped to sort out the important from the unimportant material properties for different components, and to pinpoint any really critical areas which look like making the whole concept impracticable unless considerable improvement in properties can be obtained.

A further instance demanding high material temperatures in the aero-engine field concerns the ground test facilities which became necessary for providing large quantities of air at temperatures of 1500–2000°C, such as are needed for simulating flight conditions in the $M=6$ to 7 region. Such temperatures are beyond the scope of conventional types of heat exchanger, but they can be contained quite economically in a pebble bed such as is shown diagrammatically in Fig. 3. The pebbles are first of all heated by passing hot combustion gases down through the bed. When the whole bed is up to temperature, the heating flow is turned off and fresh air is blown through in the reverse direction, coming off the top substantially at the temperature of the pebble filling. It is therefore essentially a cyclic process, and the pebbles have to withstand a certain amount of thermal shock—otherwise they will disintegrate rapidly and be blown off as dust, which is a most undesirable contaminant for engine test work. It is necessary to maintain a fairly high air velocity up through the bed in order to keep the vertical temperature profile reasonably " square ", so that as much as possible of the stored heat can be extracted before the outlet temperature begins to drop off.   Because of this high flow velocity, it is necessary to have pebbles of as dense a material as possible, and to specify a certain minimum pebble size which will prevent the whole bed " lifting ".   A mean diameter of 1 to $1\frac{1}{2}$ in. is typical.

Alumina and zirconia are the most popular materials used for this purpose at the present time: the latter can be run up to a higher temperature, but it is of course quite a lot more expensive when it comes to ordering up something like 10 tons for a medium-sized pebble bed filling.   There is no doubt that in years to come air-breathing engines will be required for operation at air inlet temperatures of 2500° or even 3000°C, and there is therefore going to be considerable scope for improving the temperature capability of such pebble beds.

It is, however, emphasized that this is not an immediate requirement.

Finally it will be as well to summarize the main points that this paper has attempted to put over.   Firstly, reasons have been given for the insistence on minimum weight for all types of aero-engine, and also why the cost involved is relatively unimportant.   When some of the slack in the system has been taken up by the introduction of accurate stress analysis and strict material specifications, it is ultimately material properties that limit the specific weights that can be achieved in practice. As an example of new problems being tackled in this field, the particular requirements of the hypersonic ramjet are discussed.   Mention is also made of the material requirements for the pebble beds which are coming into use for testing this type of engine.

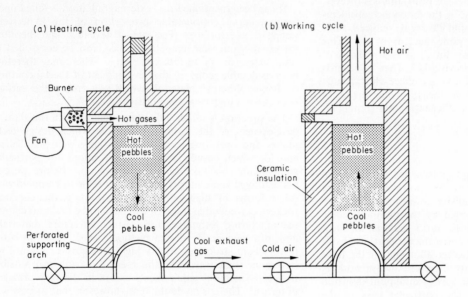

Fig. 3.—*Diagram showing operation of pebble bed heater*

DISCUSSION OF PAPERS PRESENTED AT THE SECOND SESSION

In introducing the authors, the CHAIRMAN (Professor R. W. CAHN) said that the papers were a very varied group. They had perhaps in common the generation of power of one kind or another, and the control of power. They were a useful group of papers in that they demonstrated the wide variety of properties and the criteria one had to bear in mind in choosing the right materials for that kind of application. To choose one topic at random out of the papers, he picked on the importance of weight. Mr. Beeton had been able to put a specific figure of pounds sterling against the value of weight in an aero-engine. He also emphasised the great importance of uniformity of properties if a designer were to know what he was working with. Several speakers had emphasised the importance of different forms of compatibility, which was a useful word which the atomic energy people had introduced to represent the ability of one material to stand up to the contact of another. Such things as caesium and the flow of hot gases and hot water all entered into the group of papers. Obviously, the importance of strength at various temperatures and under various conditions entered into it, and there were a number of purely theoretical criteria in connection with arc initiation. This was only a proportion of the problems that arose in the field of power generation. Nothing had been said about thermoelectric heating or cooling, or about the field which had suddenly come into the news, the magnetohydrodynamic power generation, which had its own associated materials problems.

Another point about the papers was that they gave a fine illustration of the great variability of the rate at which things developed. For example, the development of permanent magnets spread over many decades, and yet the development of the hard super-conductors had taken only about two years from their first introduction to widespread technological application.

What the symposium heard about the developments in the last decade in the electrical power generation industries was a wonderful example of Arnold Toynbee's principle of challenge and response, the challenge of atomic energy having produced a sustained improvement in the non-atomic sectors of power generation at a rate which would never have come about if it had not been for that challenge.

In spite of the fact that they had the matter of power generation and control in common, he felt that the papers were sufficiently diverse in their topics for it to be desirable that each one be discussed after its presentation.

Dr. J. K. BEDDOW asked Mr. Dugdale if the number of arcs given in Fig. 1 was the total number of arcs per centimetre.

Mr. DUGDALE replied that it was the total number of arcs on a specimen which consisted of 2 or 3 cm².

The CHAIRMAN said that earlier work had established fairly closely the mechanism of action of insulating impurities in causing an arc. He asked if Mr. Dugdale had similar ideas as to the corresponding role of surface organic contamination of the sample.

Mr. DUGDALE said he thought that organic contamination behaved in the same manner as an insulating inclusion, and the process was believed to be important as any insulating body of sufficient dimensions on the surface could be charged up by ion bombardment, like an electrical capacitor, and when the field inside was sufficiently high it underwent an electrical breakdown. The energy liberated, which would be liberated very quickly, would be sufficient to vaporise an appreciable quantity of inclusion or, for example, grease or whatever it was on the surface. This diffused away into the plasma sheath and, in the absence of ionisation, no arc started, but if there was a manner for releasing electrons on the surface, and this was the way inorganic contamination might play a part, there was a possibility that the vapour might become ionised and a multiplicative process would take place causing intensive local bombardment by ions, and hence the sort of regenerative process which could then lead to an arc. It was very interesting. The initiation of arcs became severe when one reached a field of about 10^5 V/cm, and this was a result which had been found for electrical breakdown under other circumstances. For example, Llewellyn Jones had made a fairly thorough study of this and it was very difficult to account for the process. One would appear to require a very low work function but it was quite a marked phenomenon in many electrical breakdown processes, and he thought it was an important factor in this case also.

Dr. EDELEANU asked whether careful metallography had been carried out in the studies. Very short-term heat-treatments, especially when coupled with rapid quenching, could produce very interesting structures with possibly useful properties. There was perhaps some capital to be made from the work described in the paper.

Mr. DUGDALE said he thought one might expect an increase in hardening. Presumably, the thermal fatigue process which operated was not very different from thermal fatigue as usually found. The strain rates were possibly higher. He did not think they were high enough to complicate the process. He imagined that one might obtain a harder surface.

Mr. D. W. C. BAKER referred to Fig. 8 in Dugdale's paper with regard to the angle of incidence to erosion depths. He was interested in erosion and puzzled to find that as the angle changed from normal the depth of erosion increased. What was the explanation for that? It seemed odd that an ion moving parallel to the surface should produce more erosion than one striking at the normal angle.

Mr. DUGDALE said that it was found generally that sputtering increased as the angle of incidence deviated from the normal. This was usually explained by saying that the collision processes were formed nearer the surface and one had a greater probability of an atom being directed out from the surface. However, the temperature effect had to be explained, and the only reasonable explanation for the experimental results described was that the thermal spike was different when there was a glancing attack, and in fact, a larger surface area was heated. Geometrically, it seemed reasonable that if one had an ion running in, in a perpendicular fashion, it would be expected that the volume to be heated would be about 100 Å dimension with the path of the ion roughly along the diameter. With a glancing angle one would get the same sort of volume, but because there was a surface there, one tended to get a larger area of surface heated, possibly to a higher temperature, and hence, more evaporation per event than in the other case.

The CHAIRMAN asked if it would be right to say that when the angle of incidence was more oblique, the total angle through which the incident momentum vector had to turn for an atom to escape from the surface was less.

Mr. DUGDALE said that this was certainly so for ordinary collision processes but thermal spikes had to be considered. Until recently their contribution to sputtering had been overlooked. The reason was interesting. There was quite a lot of work on sputtering, but mainly in metals. Work at Harwell showed that the dimension of thermal spikes would be greater in many metals than in glasses and ceramics because focussed collision sequences dissipated the energy of the incoming particle over a larger volume. Hence temperatures would be lower and evaporation insignificant. But in glass one could not have these focus collision sequences, and presumably in alumina, which was a very complicated structure, roughly the same restriction would apply.

Dr. R. N. HAWARD said that if a pane of glass were broken under a central load, a tension was built up, which increased until fracture occurred. The number of cracks which formed subsequently depended on the strength of the particular piece of glass. He then referred to slide 3, which was Fig. 5 on page 28 of Dugdale's paper. The diagrams could be identified as a series of such cracks fitting together into a kind of pavement. There were several apparent points of initiation of fracture. If there had been a tension build-up, quickly leading to fracture from several points of initiation, then the sort of structure that was shown in the slide should follow.

Mr. DUGDALE said that experiments were now being done with electron bombardment and one could often identify a single initiating centre in those circumstances. It was possible with the plasma experiments that there might be a little contamination which produced initiation at several places at about the same time. With electron bombardment under cleaner conditions, only one place started to crack as a rule, and the whole pattern developed from it.

Mr. J. A. WILLIAMS said that in Fig. 3 of Dugdale's paper it was stated that the arc rate went off on a prepared specimen. He believed that the author had said that the inclusions were vaporised, inclusions in the surface were gradually lost, and the surface was cleaned up. He asked if it would not be quicker to clean up the surface chemically. The method of pickling metal surfaces was well known. Would not this give the same effect, and would not the same result be achieved?

Mr. DUGDALE said that various chemical treatments had been tried without success. He had wanted to get over the point that conditioning was not primarily due to the removal of inclusions although this had been thought to be the case originally. What conditioning was due to was removal of external contamination, particularly inorganic contamination, and this had been demonstrated by deliberately making contact of the specimen with a very dilute solution of sodium chloride, and what was a previously non-arcing surface, yet full of inclusions, now became an arcing surface again. It was the inorganic contamination which was thought to produce the electrons, and which it was important to remove.

Dr. J. K. HIGGINS said that it might be interesting to look at electropolishing in that connection. Also, in Fig. 3, on the sapphire single crystal which had cracked, had the author noticed any difference in the shape of the crack when he exposed the different crystallographic phases to the discharge? Was there any spalling in the discharge of these fine-grained materials?

Mr. DUGDALE said that with sapphires of different orientation there was an orientation dependence on both the type of deformation which took place and also the crack pattern which developed. Although rhombohedral twinning seemed to be the main deformation mechanism, one could choose an orientation where this was difficult to bring about, and then both prismatic slip and basal twinning were found. Spalling of polycrystalline alumina took place.

Dr. HIGGINS asked Mr. Dugdale if there were different types of cracking with the different crystallographic orientation. Did it reflect on the thermal-spike theory? Dugdale had stated that he had had a similar dissipation of heat and therefore obtained the same mechanism on the same crystallographic phase.

Mr. DUGDALE said there were a number of factors involved in the cracking process. There had to be an initiating centre, and the energy required to form a new surface in the crack might vary with orientation. Crack orientation effects also governed the crack pattern. This was obvious from study of glasses where the crack did not release all the elastic energy. When a crack was formed in a glass surface a certain amount of elastic energy was still retained. Yet it should in principle be possible to remove all the elastic energy by crack pattern.

Mr. A. E. S. WHITE asked about the surface condition of the sapphire crystal that was exposed to thermal shock. It might be expected that if the surfaces were chemically polished, just as improved tensile strength could be obtained, better thermal shock-resistance might be obtained.

Mr. DUGDALE said that chemical polishing of magnesia surfaces had been tried once, but in this experiment it was very difficult to avoid an occasional particle of contamination from the electrode settling on the surface of the specimen which could act as an initiating centre. It was difficult in these experiments to avoid some sort of initiation of the cracks.

Dr. HIGGINS asked if Dr. Adam was worried about the fission gas release in the high-density uranium–zirconium carbide compacts. He realised that it was only a short run, but he thought that higher burn-ups might raise a problem, and it might be a good idea to have some slightly lower densities.

Dr. ADAM said that this might very well be so. Experiments conducted so far had shown only about 20% gas release from UC/ZrC fuel, which was surprising considering the very high operating temperature. 80% of the gas remained within the material and fairly rapid swelling may occur at comparatively low burn-up. If that was the case, lower density material may possibly have a lower rate of swelling initially but high density fuel has greater strength, and its resistance to swelling may be more valuable at high burn-up than the porosity of low density material. Present research programme includes irradiation of both low and high density materials to much higher burn-up than that obtained in our experimental diodes, but it may be necessary to operate the fuel at somewhat lower temperatures because only a small range of temperature control will be available in the rigs used in these experiments.

The CHAIRMAN said that as he understood it the device, even in full operating condition, would actually have to be put into the reactor to work. If that was the case he presumed there was a limitation in the choice of materials on a commercial basis, at least of things with a small neutron absorption. Did that involve further restrictions beyond those to which the Authority was being subjected at the moment?

Dr. ADAM said that detailed selection of structural materials, *etc.*, was really the next stage in the development. One had to ask a question now : what use is to be made of the device? If it was going to be used in a satellite there need not be undue worry about neutron economy because enrichment can be used to compensate for the parasitic absorption. On the other hand, if it was to be used as a topper for an AGR type of reactor one had to consider neutron economy very seriously. We have reached a point in this work when one had to stop and decide which application is most important, because otherwise a great deal of time and money can be spent in following various development lines. It is hoped that perhaps a practical application for a diode reactor would emerge soon in this country. In America with a large space programme supported by the Government a case for nuclear thermionic generators is fairly clear. In this country, however, it is necessary to consider whether the additional efficiency offered by thermionic type topper is adequate to justify the cost of the rather complicated fuel element and further development costs.

The CHAIRMAN asked how it would be used in a satellite.

Dr. ADAM replied that a small reactor can be constructed with the thermionic converters either inside the core as fuel elements or outside the core in *e.g.* a heat exchanger. The great advantage of this sort of device in space application was the high heat rejection temperature, which can be in excess of 650°C.

Dr. L. M. NŸLAND said that Dr. Adam had mentioned the promotion of caesium on the silicon dioxide and of aluminium oxide. Perhaps he knew something about the layers of some material, for example boron nitride, which could be used for protection on silicon dioxide against sodium and perhaps also for caesium vapour at elevated temperatures.

Dr. ADAM replied that it was probably quite feasible to produce protective coatings. One always tries, however, to make things as simple and robust as possible, and protective layers on insulators had not been considered though protective layers on metals have been used. Alumina was really quite resistant to caesium corrosion provided one could get it pure enough, and this was not very difficult. 99·5% purity could quite easily be produced nowadays, and good ceramic to metal seals have been made with high purity alumina.

Dr. NŸLAND said that it had already been mentioned that it was possibly difficult and expensive. Other people sometimes had difficulties with price, and others perhaps tried to find simpler metals to obtain the same results.

Mr. B. W. WILKINSON asked Dr. Adam if he had looked at the effect of caesium impurity on the corrosion of the seals, or if he had observed a difference in the corrosion rate as the corrosion proceeded and the caesium became more contaminated.

Dr. ADAM said that experiments performed so far have been very limited and were really sorting out tests. Further more detailed studies are being carried out now. Not very much is known about the effect of impurities in caesium on corrosion and reliable methods for determining oxygen content in caesium have only recently been developed.

Dr. N. B. W. THOMPSON said that in Birmingham some experiments had been carried out on crystal growing. It had already been seen from the paper by James that there were very considerable problems of crystal growing when relatively high-temperature materials were considered in semi-conductor work. The ordinary methods of heating were not very satisfactory. In another field, the field of masers and lasers, again the problem had to be faced of getting energy into the material. In the wider field of ceramic research, single crystals were of interest for people working in the fundamental properties of ceramics. One of the methods used for crystal growing had been the carbon-arc-image method. The energy was inserted optically by having a source, usually a carbon arc, on a mirror elliptically giving a magnification of the focus. That was not what was wanted, so one had a symmetrical system. The great problem of carbon-arc-image furnaces was that of the carbon arc. Carbon arc tended to be very unstable. In addition, there was raw carbon, which lasted if it was being pushed at the maximum rate, which was never what one wanted; it was about 20 minutes. Stability of the arc could be treated by servo systems but none of them seemed to be very satisfactory, so at Birmingham they had been experimenting with the use of high-pressure xenon-discharge tubes which had a small arc, and that facilitated the placing of the xenon tube. The effect of the geometry of the arc was very different from an arc image. It enabled one to have a spherical mirror, thus avoiding the majority of the wasted radiation obtained from the carbon-arc-image furnace. The high-pressure xenon-discharge tubes had a spectrum similar to daylight, and were

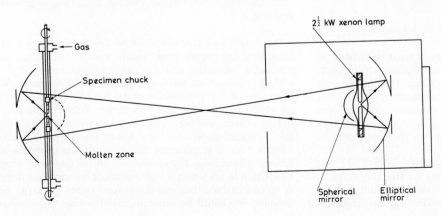

Fig. 1.—*Xenon-arc-image crystal-growing apparatus, Department of Physical Metallurgy, University of Birmingham.*

consequently used for melting materials which had appreciable absorption in the optical ultra-violet and infra-red. The placing of the spherical mirror would assist in the absorption of energy, and to date they had been able to grow rutile crystals one centimetre long and a few millimetres in diameter. A conventional crystal grower was used in which a floating-zone technique was employed. The method offered considerable prospects of being useful for materials which had a reasonable absorption. It was quite good for sapphire, but ruby had been melted and consequently he thought that perhaps some of the high-melting-point materials, perhaps not the very highest, could be grown in a single crystal form by that type of apparatus.

Mr. J. A. WILLIAMS asked Dr. James if he could tell him anything about materials that poisoned semi-conductors. The reason he asked was because from time to time he had queries from makers of semi-conductors and they put an almost impossible purity specification on the acids and chemicals they required. He asked the speaker if he could divide them into metals that poisoned and also organic materials that poisoned.

Dr. D. W. F. JAMES said he could not give a straight answer. Groups three and five are the impurities which must be added to silicon and germanium to obtain controlled n-type or p-type conductivity, therefore very low levels of these elements are required initially. Many other elements may produce extra levels in the forbidden gap and in consequence influence the lifetime. For example, nickel has a very marked effect. Oxygen is also a most undesirable impurity. While some impurities were desirable for some purposes but undesirable for others, the philosophy of the device manufacturer seemed to be that of keeping all possible impurities to as low a level as possible in order to give adequate control over subsequent doping. One might almost say it was a case of keeping the whole of the periodic table out. The presence of carbon or organic matter on silicon for example might produce silicon carbide on melting the semiconductor, and this would interfere with crystal growth producing twinning.

Mr. WILLIAMS said he gathered that they specified almost every single metal one could think of, but they said nothing about organics. He wondered whether they could possibly be made in plastic plant containing plastic containers.

Dr. JAMES said that perhaps plastics were all right. It probably depended upon which were used. If the plasticiser was one which leached out then carbon could get into the semiconductor and produce twinning during crystal growth. P.V.C. was known to be troublesome in this way. If one could use a plastic from which the plasticiser did not leach out one was probably safe. P.T.F.E. was certainly the most reliable material.

Mr. WILLIAMS said he was thinking of polythene.

Dr. JAMES said it might be all right from what he knew of it. As a further example of organic contamination which might be relevant, many people had encountered difficulty with deionised water used in washing semiconductors. Resin from the deionising column deposited on the semiconductor only to cause trouble at some later stage in production. Perhaps Mr. Robinson might like to comment on these problems.

Mr. J. S. ROBINSON said that he might answer the last question to some extent by saying that for studying some of the growth processes one of the best ways of producing the defects was to dirty the surface by taking " pure " chemical solvents and chemically cleaning the surface. That produced a uniformly dirty surface for initiating growth features.

He wished to comment on the broad implications of the vapour process which Dr. James had mentioned. He had referred to the epitaxial approach to silicon semiconductors. Diborides and boron nitride had been mentioned earlier; he could add, for example, oxides and many of the metals. Vapour transport and deposition for coating processes, single crystal growth, *etc.*, was a tool which had become increasingly important and would become more so as a materials-handling process. It could provide a means of preparing material specimens of high chemical purity and high crystal perfection for determination of properties. That was particularly valuable where, for example, high melting-point or reactivity with crucible materials precluded traditional techniques. He thought it was unfortunate that there were not papers at the symposium dealing with the application of vapour transport and deposition to protection of devices and component making, and preparation of the raw material for subsequent fabrication processes.

Dr. JAMES suggested that it was a suitable subject for another conference.

Mr. F. ROBERTS said that one of the problems seemed to be concentrating energy into very small specimens. One of the speakers had said that it was difficult to use high-frequency techniques because semi-conductors had not the right electrical properties, but it was possible to get energy into small specimens using RF heating techniques if a susceptor with the right electrical characteristics were used. There were certain types of carbon and graphite that could be made available, which could be used as secondary transformers, and these could direct the energy where it was wanted on the small samples. The other possibility was to use an electron-bombardment furnace. One had been developed at Harwell for heating tiny graphite specimens for thermal-expansion measurements with temperatures up to 2000°C.

With regard to vapour deposition on silicon carbide, it had been said that it was not possible to make large specimens by such a technique. The atomic energy industry had used the vapour deposition of carbon, as pyrographite, and also silicon carbide in the development of coated-particle fuels. That was as a coating on spherical particles about 2–300 microns in diameter; and very good films had been produced; but he knew that silicon carbide had also been produced in laminate form—flat, slab-like—by plating out on to certain substrata. He knew this had been done at RAE, Farnborough, and by the British Ceramic Research Association at Stoke on Trent. He was surprised to know that it was not possible to get silicon-carbide deposits, which approximated to single crystal characteristics, by vapour-deposition techniques. One could get large pieces of pyrographite which had electrical properties approximating to a single crystal of graphite.

Dr. JAMES said that the electron bombardment and radio frequency techniques were widely used for handling semiconductor materials and for single crystal production. A 4 Mc/s induction set was a standard piece of equipment. Some years ago, A.E.I. produced a puller for silicon which worked on electron bombardment. A large variety of these techniques existed, and were engineered to suit particular materials. Nevertheless, with the newer materials, particularly when a volatile component was involved, the problems were severe. Concerning the second part of the question, what he had meant to say was not that one could not get large deposits of silicon carbide, but one could not readily get large single crystals. It should be remembered that one was ultimately interested in a single crystal of very high purity which was big enough to put contacts on and to do something with electrically. To the best of his knowledge nobody had, in fact, had very much success in doing this by direct deposition. He knew about the work mentioned being carried out by the British Ceramic Research Association. He had been there and seen the work. While they were certainly producing a very interesting and useful material, semiconductor-wise it was a very dirty material. It was heavily contaminated with silicon, and his point still stood.

Mr. ROBERTS said that he would comment only on theoretical grounds. He could not see why silicon carbide should not form itself regularly in the form of a crystal by vapour deposition, by analogy with what happened to carbon. He did not see why it should not come down in a regular lattice structure.

Dr. JAMES said this was what he thought two years ago. That is why his organisation was working on it. They had not succeeded in producing anything of reasonable size although some epitaxial deposition on commercial single crystal substrates of SiC, obtained accidentally in the production of abrasive material, had been obtained at high temperatures.

Dr. EDELEANU was in general agreement with Mr. Baker with only one exception, and there was probably agreement even on that point. There were many established codes and practices which were out of date and which created material problems unnecessarily. A typical one was the sight glass mentioned in the paper, and he felt that when such problems arose it was profitable to put more effort in establishing a better code than solving a problem which should not exist.

One point which was not clear from the paper was the justification for thinking in terms of 20-30 years for power-stations. As pointed out in the paper, there had been great advances in the past 15 years, and in part the present very high cost of down time of a modern station was due to the inefficiency of the old stations which had to be brought on line. Presumably the next 15 years would also see great progress and perhaps it would pay to think in terms of shorter lives. That was important because the CEGB attitude had led to a great deal of the available effort on creep to be expended on establishing the long-term properties of steels and, since the available facilities were limited, it had slowed down the development of new improved steels. The first question was, " What is the extra present-day value, if any, of a superheater which is likely to last 20+1 years instead of 20 years ? ". The second question, " What is the justification for the request for accurate long-term creep data when fluctuation in service conditions introduce a much greater degree of uncertainty than extrapolation from say 10 000 h ? ".

Mr. BAKER, referring to Dr. Edeleanu's comment on the boiler sight glass problem, said that while it might appear unnecessary to have a visual indication of the boiler water level if other methods were available, it was a statutory requirement which had arisen historically from the time when the boiler drum was visible from the firing floor. Ultimately, modified legislation would probably be introduced in the light of changed circumstances, but that did not resolve the present problem.

Mr. Baker agreed that more attention should be given to the establishment of rational design codes rather than attempting to resolve artificial problems which inadequate codes presented. It was always difficult to change codes quickly and one could only hope that by persistent effort more realistic criteria would gradually evolve. He found it difficult to understand the reasoning which led to the same factors being applied to a large component rotating at high speed, the failure of which could devastate a large area, and to a pipe conveying water under pressure.

With regard to the length of time for which generating stations should be designed to last, the greater part of the plant was not subject to serious time-dependent deterioration; the civil engineering works, for example, could easily be built to last 30 years, and a shorter life would require repeated capital investment. However, a case might be made for designing certain components for a shorter life, if by so doing there was an economic return. For example, if the attainment of a higher operating steam temperature necessitated the repeated replacement of the superheater within the life of a station, it would be acceptable only if the savings arising from improvement in efficiency outweighed the extra cost. The replacement of superheaters in modern plant would be a very expensive undertaking and the present view was that the superheater and high temperature piping should be desinged to last the full life of the plant. It was for that reason that 100 000 hour data was required. The fact that fluctuations in service conditions give rise to uncertainty in predicting life can hardly be used as justification for accepting imprecise materials data. Extrapolation from 10 000 hour data, in Mr. Baker's opinion, could lead to errors at least comparable with those arising as a result of departures from design conditions.

Mr. F. S. DICKINSON said that transition pieces were detailed by Baker as having been made by either flash-butt welding or by fusion methods with nickel-based material. Was there a set temperature above which one system was preferred ? Without the nickel barrier would welds be restricted to lower-temperature operation than the others?

Mr. BAKER, in reply to Mr. Dickinson, said that a nickel barrier was not used in superheater transition pieces, they were either flash butt or fusion welded using a nickel alloy electrode. An electrodeposited nickel barrier had been used in the past for a certain type of large section pipe transition piece.

Mr. DICKINSON said that in the information presented on the welding techniques applied to type 347 stainless steel, and due to the unfortunate occurrences that everybody knew about, Baker had said that the need to avoid stress raisers had led to careful weld dressing. This, he would think, really referred to type 347 and would not be necessary in type 316 fabrication.

Mr. BAKER said that he would advocate dressing where there was any possibility of failure although he agreed that the benefits of dressing were likely to be more marked in the case of Type 347 than in Type 316 steel.

Presumably Mr. Dickinson was familiar with B.W.R.A. ring test in which a stub tube was welded on a massive block under condition of restraint and the assembly heat-treated under specified conditions normally without prior dressing to reveal susceptibility to heat-affected zone cracking. The tendency to crack increased with increase in strength of the welding electrode material used to effect the weld and it had been shown that dressing before heat treatment permitted a stronger electrode to be used before cracking was encountered.

Mr. J. A. FENDLEY mentioned Baker's reference to the limit of working temperature imposed by lack of corrosion resistance of the materials used. Could the performance of the superheater be isolated from that of the rest of the plant sufficiently to estimate the economic consequences of an increase in working temperature; and how far was the engineer prepared to go in the introduction of expensive materials to achieve such an increase?

Mr. BAKER said, in reply to Mr. Fendley, that it was difficult to isolate the superheater from the remainder of the plant in order to estimate the benefits of an increase in steam temperature. A complete design study would be needed to resolve the matter, but in any event the only criterion was the economic return, and this was a function of capital and operating costs. From the technical standpoint the removal of one barrier to advancement, such as the solution of the superheater corrosion problem, would only permit an advance to a point where another barrier appeared, such as lack of availability of H.P. rotor materials capable of operating at significantly higher temperatures.

Mr. S. A. GREGORY said that he wished to make one quick point about the pebble bed in the paper by Beeton. He was anxious to know why the specification put forward stated that the pebbles should be heavy because air had to be blown upwards. Why could not air be blown downwards?

Mr. BEETON said that this was because the pebbles had to be supported somehow. They could not very well be restrained by anything working at 2000°C. If it were possible to make a material which would support pebbles to 2000°C, the job could certainly be done that way.

Mr. J. A. WILLIAMS said, continuing with the regenerators, that it was, of course, the coke-oven regenerator used also on open-hearth furnaces. When he had been with the North Thames Gas Board they had tried filling the coke-oven regenerators with round packing, which was hardly any good at all. It had been put down to the fact that it was thought that there was a good deal of laminar flow round the pebbles. When they had gone back to the old checkers, they got flow round the corners of the checkers and had achieved the very effect that Beeton was seeking, which was the progressive cooling upwards in a cooling cycle.

Mr. BEETON said that the pebbles were made spherical in order to minimise the effects of thermal shock.

Mr. WILLIAMS said that he thought the point Beeton was looking for might be lost by choosing the shape of the pebbles. The Gas Board had probably not used it at the same temperature that Beeton had. Theirs were only running at 900°C.

Mr. BEETON said that the minimum pebble size always had to be considered in relation to the operating gas conditions. The pebbles had to be big enough to prevent fluidisation at the maximum dynamic pressure likely to be encountered.

Mr. H. REITER said that there was a statement in Beeton's paper about which he was not too happy. The author had said, " reliability must also be high, but relatively frequent and extensive maintenance can be permitted in order to achieve this ". He did not equate them together. Poor maintenance could probably mean shorter life of a component, but had nothing to do with reliability. He would like Mr. Beeton to enlarge on that point. Surely one of the aims was to get constantly longer life between servicing?

Mr. BEETON agreed that this was so, but not at the expense of extra weight. It paid to overhaul an aero-engine at relatively short intervals so that any components found to be deteriorating could be replaced. That way massive safety factors could be pared down, and the weight thus saved more than paid for the cost of the extra maintenance work. To this extent maintenance had a lot to do with reliability.

Mr. G. SANDS said that while he was fully aware of the toxicity hazard associated with the use of beryllia, nevertheless he wondered if consideration had been given to the possibility of using it as a pebble material. Hot-pressed BeO had a very high thermal conductivity and, although lower in density than sintered alumina, it was still a relatively heavy material compared with many conventional high-temperature refractories.

Mr. BEETON thought that this material had not been seriously considered. Good conductivity was certainly a very important property, but if it was accompanied by a low density this might be offset by the larger pebble size which would then be dictated.

THIRD SESSION

NEW ASPECTS OF DISLOCATION THEORY

By A. J. KENNEDY*

SYNOPSIS

The basic dislocation concepts are briefly reviewed. Some of the characteristics of dislocation behaviour in crystalline materials are examined, and notably their elastic interaction mobility, and network formation, together with some established features of their role in such processes as crack formation and thermal ageing. Recent evidence relating to more detailed dislocation events, such as loop-formation, is reviewed, and the extension of dislocation concepts to non-metallic crystals examined, covering both the (brittle) ceramic type, and crystalline polymers. The concept of a continuous distribution of dislocations is considered, and the possibilities opened up by this important branch of the subject are generally assessed. The aim of the review as a whole is to demonstrate the degree of correlation which has been achieved between theory and experiment (particularly with work in electron microscopy), and to give an indication of the way in which the subject is developing at the present time.

Introduction

Knowledge of the structure and properties of imperfections in crystal lattices has increased rapidly in recent years, due mainly to the wider use of electron microscopy, coupled with the development of more powerful theoretical methods. Before embarking on any closer examination of the current situation, it would be as well (particularly in a general conference of this kind) to survey briefly some of the fundamental tenets of dislocation theory.

Let us consider first of all an isotropic, homogeneous, elastic continuum. Suppose we wish to introduce internal stresses into the material without the application of external forces. This may be achieved by any cutting and re-sealing operation by which strains are introduced and retained. We might, for example, cut the block in half, deform one piece, and then glue it to the other half while it is still in the strained state. On removing the external forces, a state of internal strain will exist in the re-assembled material. The sequence is illustrated by Fig. 1, which demonstrates a simple form of

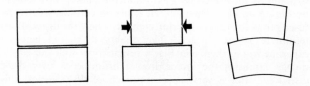

Fig. I.—*The creation of a state of internal stress in a cube by cutting, straining one of the cut pieces, and rejoining. The magnitude of the stress in such a case is uniform along the boundary, falling off with distance from this boundary*

this operation. Alternatively, the half-block could have been subjected to shear by stresses lying in the plane of the cut, and an internal shear stress would have been retained when the two pieces were reassembled. In both cases, the state of strain is uniform over the plane of the cut, falling off in magnitude with distance from this plane. We could, however, cut and rejoin the block in such a way that the state of stress is localized around a line (rather than around a plane). We shall consider this situation first, returning to that represented by Fig. 1 later in the paper. Consider, then, the operation illustrated by Fig. 2, where a cut has been made over *ABCD*, the two

* Professor of Materials, The College of Aeronautics, Cranfield, Bedford.

faces being displaced by a distance, *b*, as indicated, and then rejoined. The cylindrical hole at the edge of the cut is introduced merely to avoid the problem of the (infinite) high stresses at the edge of the cut. The axis of the cut (the centre line of the cylinder shown) is a dislocation with a vector, **b**. At any point on the line of the dislocation (see Fig. 2) the component of *b* resolved in a direction normal to the dislocation line is an *edge* component (*E*-direction), and that parallel to the line is a screw component (*S*-direction). A segment lying normal to *b* is therefore wholly edge, while a segment lying parallel to *b* is wholly screw. A general dislocation has components of both types. The continuum operations which introduce dislocations are extensively dealt with in all the standard texts, and we shall not take these considerations any further here.

So far we have dealt with a simple elastic continuum. When we come to deal with a real three-dimensional lattice, an *arbitrary* strain cannot be introduced by the theoretical operation described above. The amount of strain must be compatible with the reassembly of the pieces to form a single crystal, admittedly with a zone of imperfection in the immediate region of the dislocation. For the retention of perfect (if strained) crystallinity in the matrix, the vector describing the strain must coincide with a simple lattice vector, or with a vector sum of such vectors, otherwise crystal registry, in the bulk of the block, cannot occur. The case of a perfect dislocation is exemplified, for example, by a slip displacement

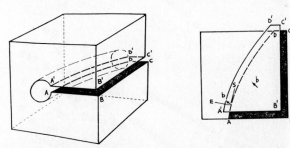

Fig. 2.—*A cut made in a block of elastic material, the (internal) boundary being along AD. The cut surfaces ABCD and A'B'C'D' are displaced relatively by the vector b and re-joined. The elastic stresses in the block are those set up by a dislocation with a vector b lying along the axis of the cylinder indicated. This cylinder of material is removed merely to avoid the problem of stress concentration at the edge of the cut in the case of a continuum: there is no such problem in the case of a dislocation introduced into an array of discrete objects, such as atoms*

69

F*

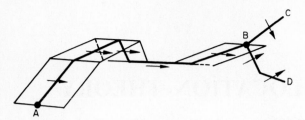

Fig. 3.—*A general dislocation line, showing the slip planes of its different segments*

equal to a simple interatomic spacing. Other vectors may be possible, in that the faults they introduce may be stable, and physically plausible in real crystals: nevertheless, the dislocations represented by such vectors are not *perfect* ones. We term them *imperfect* or *partial* dislocations.

In order to pass on as rapidly as possible to a discussion of some of the basic features of dislocations it would be as well to emphasize certain necessary generalities. A dislocation line (that is, the axis of the deformation zone which surrounds a dislocation) must be continuous; it can terminate only at a phase boundary, and in particular, at the surface. It can, however, branch into two or more dislocations, with the restriction that the vector sum of the constituent dislocations remains equal to the parent vector. In three dimensions, then, we can have the situation represented by Fig. 3. *AB* is a dislocation with a vector, **b**, *BC* and *BD* dislocations with vectors **b**$_1$ and **b**$_2$. The vector sum **b**=**b**$_1$+**b**$_2$ must be satisfied. Considering the length, *AB*, we see that the segments of the dislocations form, with the vector (which is fixed in space for the whole, unbranched, dislocation), a series of planes, which are the *slip planes* of the different segments. In real crystals, some of the dislocation segments will possess a much higher energy per unit length than the others, and may not appear at all—obviously the detailed arrangement of the atoms along the dislocation axis will differ with the crystallographic direction of this axis. In principle, however, a quite arbitrary sequence of dislocation directions may be applied and fulfilled crystallographically. We see, then, that in all cases where the vector is not parallel to the dislocation line, a unique plane is defined, and slip of the whole dislocation will take place by the composite slip of the segments on their associated planes. In the particular case where the vector and the line are parallel, no such plane is defined. Physically, this segment, which is a screw dislocation, may slip on any crystallographically suitable slip plane which contains it. If there exists more than one such plane, then the direction and

the magnitude of the applied stress will dictate which one operates. We have not here dwelt on the slip mechanism as such, but it needs to be emphasized, perhaps, that the sensitivity of dislocations to an applied shear stress makes the plastic deformation of crystals possible under relatively low stresses, a fundamental requirement of any theory which is to accord with the experimental observation.

The necessary association of edge components with specific slip planes, and the lack of such an association in the case of perfect screw dislocations, which have radially symmetrical stress fields associated with them, are facts which profoundly affect the deformation characteristics of crystals. In the case of imperfect or partial screw dislocations—that is dislocations whose lines lie parallel to the vector, but for which the vector does not correspond with a vector of the lattice—a fault must exist in the crystal structure, and the radial symmetry of the perfect screw dislocation is violated. *Partial* dislocations in the screw orientation do not, then, possess the slip possibilities of perfect screw dislocations. We shall now go on to consider the extent to which these basic ideas have been developed, and their correlation with the experimental evidence.

Some Correlations Between Dislocation Theory and Experiment

Elastic Interactions

The stress fields surrounding dislocations give rise to two important classes of effect: the first concerns the forces between dislocations, and the influence of these on the physical properties, while the second relates to the influence of such fields on the possible processes of diffusion. We shall consider the second question later, and consider first the dislocation interaction forces.

The theory predicts that edge dislocations of the same sign will tend to align into planes perpendicular to their common vector. This process (polygonization) is well established. It also predicts that a group of similar edge dislocations on a common slip plane will, under stress, pile-up against an obstacle in such a way that their distances (x) from the leading dislocation vary as n^2, where n is the number of the dislocation, taking $n=0$ for the leading dislocation. The alignment of edge dislocations to form sub-boundaries in a polygonized structure is illustrated by Fig. 4 and the pile-up distribution by Figs. 5 and 6. The material is silicon carbide, treated by fused borax in order to develop etch pits where the dislocations terminate at the surface. The quality of the fit between experiment and theory in Fig. 6 reveals how well the elastic theory expresses the interaction of dislocations over these distances. For a very close approach of dislocations, this extension of the continuum theory naturally breaks down.

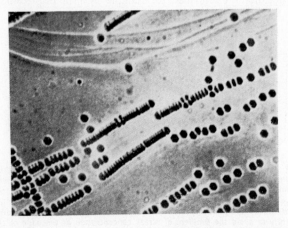

Fig. 4.—*Edge dislocations forming sub-boundary walls in silicon carbide. Note that some of the dislocations in the wall are double dislocations (Amelinckx and Strumane)*

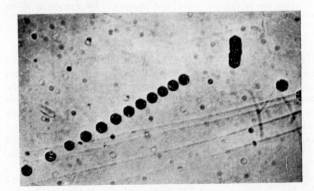

Fig. 5.—*A pile-up of glissile dislocations in silicon carbide against a sessile group of dislocations acting as a barrier (After Amelinckx and Strumane)*

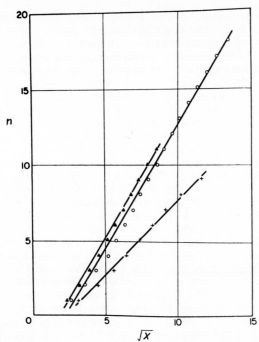

Fig. 6.—*The variation of $\sqrt{x}$ with n, the position of the dislocation in the group (n = 0 for the leading dislocation), where n is the distance from the leading dislocation. Taken from results on silicon carbide, of the type shown in Fig. 5 (Amelinckx and Strumane)*

The movement of simple dislocations; climb and cross-slip

As has been stated in the Introduction, the edge components of dislocations are restricted to slip on a single plane, defined by their line and their vector. The addition or subtraction of atoms to the edge of the " extra " plane which terminates at an edge dislocation makes it possible, however, for segments to move into other (parallel) planes, a process termed dislocation *climb*. Pure screw dislocations are not associated with any such " extra " plane, and cannot climb, but they can, as has been said, slip on other equivalent planes, a process termed *cross-slip*. Both of these features of crystalline behaviour are well established, and we shall not dwell on the experimental evidence here. The first, being diffusion-controlled, is thermally activated, and constitutes the major mechanism of softening (recovery) after previous work-hardening. The second is, for perfect screw dislocations, mechanically activated. We shall see that a thermal effect arises where such dislocations have split into partials to form what is known as an *extended dislocation*.

We can take these basic possibilities further by considering the case of a dislocation which is predominantly screw, but

which possesses an edge component, and is hence subject to climb. If we treat the problem as one of equilibrium between the line tension of the dislocation and the chemical stress acting normally to the vector (as a result of the supersaturation of vacancies), then the form of the dislocation can be derived as a helix of constant angle and radius. The direct observation of helices in electron micrographs, particularly in conditions where a high concentration of point defects exists, supports the theory (Fig. 7).

A further important aspect of dislocation geometry concerns the formation and movement of dislocation loops. A dislocation loop with a vector lying in the plane of the loop expands (or contracts) under a shear stress with a resolved component in the crystal slip direction, that is, parallel to the dislocation vector. The possible generation of such loops by particular segments of a general dislocation network was indicated in the classic proposition of Frank and Read, and such a process (that is, generation from Frank–Read sources)

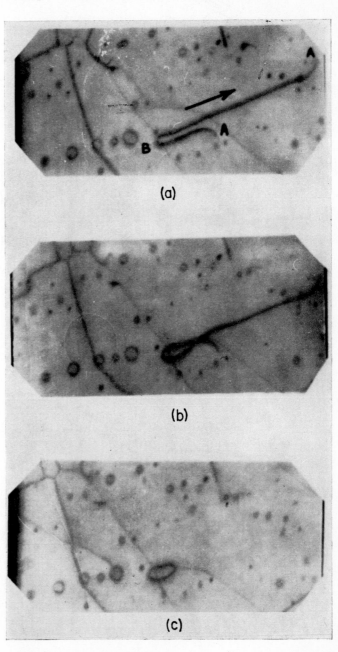

(a)

(b)

(c)

Fig. 8.—*The formation of a dislocation loop on a basal plane in cadmium*
(Price)

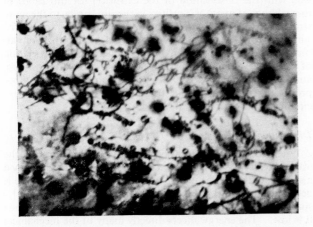

Fig. 7.—*Dislocation helices and loops in a quenched aluminium alloy*

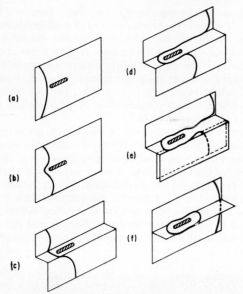

Fig. 9.—*Illustrating the mechanism of formation of the loop in Fig. 8 (Price)*

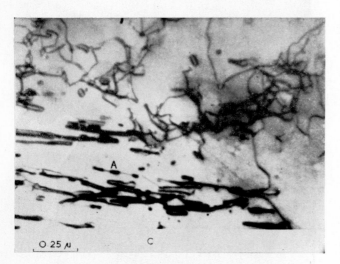

Fig. 10.—*Dislocations in polycrystalline nickel after $1 \cdot 6 \times 10^6$ cycles of fatigue, followed by a subsequent annealing treatment (Segall, Partridge and Hirsch)*

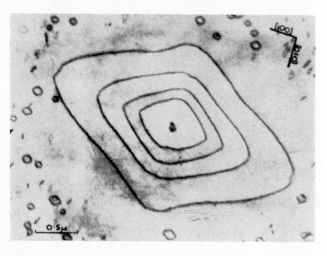

Fig. 11.—*Concentric dislocation loops in an aluminium $3 \cdot 5 \%$ magnesium alloy oil-quenched from 550°C (Westmacott, Barnes and Smallman)*

certainly occurs, though less—according to experimental observations—that might be expected. Again, this mechanism is well covered in the texts. The case of a dislocation loop with a vector possessing a component normal to the plane of the loop is important: such loops may form, for example, as a result of the collapse of a disc of clustered vacancies, and have been observed in irradiated and annealed metals, as well as in fatigued material. The properties conferred on the structure by the presence of such loops may provide a major lead towards a better appreciation of the fatigue-hardened state and the development of incipient cracks. One mode of formation of a loop (on a basal plane in an hexagonal metal, cadmium) is illustrated by Fig. 8 (Price, 1961). The process is interpreted in Fig. 9. While such loops may be formed by unidirectional stressing, they are more evident (Segall, Partridge and Hirsch, 1961) in fatigued metal (see Fig. 10), and they may, indeed, be eliminated (or partly so, at least) by the plastic deformation of pre-fatigued material. It may be assumed that for any given metal, at a selected temperature and fatigue stress level, some steady state density of loops exists characteristic of the conditions. The establishment of such loops makes it possible to appreciate the possible hardening developed (although a wholly convincing mechanism has not yet emerged in detail), as well as the characteristics of stored energy release, and to see why little X-ray asterism is developed. Loop dislocations in a wholly edge orientation (vector normal to the plane of the loop) may expand by climb, and a pinned segment of edge dislocation may develop in a *geometrically* similar way to that of the dislocations from a Frank–Read source, but by diffusion, as distinct from slip. Such sources have been observed recently, and are illustrated in Figs. 11 and 12: they are believed to be associated with precipitates. The interaction of the set of concentric loops with the loop generated from a neighbouring source (Fig. 13) reveals that the vectors of consecutive loops differ: to be specific, this arises from the splitting of the parent dislocation a [001] into $(a/2)$ [011] and $(a/2)$ [0$\bar{1}$1]. Alternate loops have the same vector, and as Fig. 13 demonstrates, the reaction with the external loop differs at A and at B. This is another example of the discrimination which is made possible by electron microscopy.

The stresses developed by differential volume expansions in a matrix can also generate dislocation loops by punching-out prismatic dislocations. The quenching of alloys containing inclusions or precipitates can lead to such a process, as Fig. 14 reveals, and other (shear type) dislocations can be generated as well. The actual initiation of a surface crack by fatigue stresses has received considerable attention, and several plausible mechanisms have been advanced, varying from special dislocation-circuiting models, which correlate very well with the observation of the extrusion (or intrusion) of thin ribbons of metal at localities in the slip bands, to the more straightforward notch-formation by non-cancelling to-and-fro surface slip. No clearly-favoured model has emerged, although there is good experimental evidence for the association of fatigue development with the ease of dislocation cross-slip, and hence, as far as crack initiation is concerned, with those propositions which invoke the circuiting (or the effective circuiting) of screw dislocations.

Dislocation Networks

Where a perfect dislocation splits into two partials, the associated lattice fault, which connects the partials, is termed a stacking fault. The extent to which the partials separate is determined by the stacking fault energy; they are closely-spaced when this energy is high, and more widely spaced when it is low. The energy affects directly many of the mechanical properties, and bears on several of the issues already discussed.

Fig. 12.—*Multiple closely-spaced dislocation climb sources in an aluminium 3·5% magnesium alloy (Westmacott, Barnes and Smallman)*

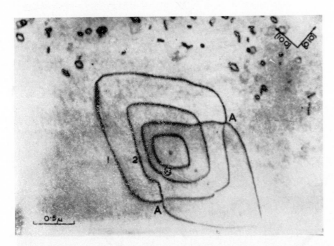

Fig. 13.—*The interaction between a group of concentric loops from a single source with a dislocation loop from another source. The interaction with one loop of the group at A differs from that with the next loop of the group at B, revealing that the Burgers vectors of consecutive loops differ (Westmacott, Barnes and Smallman)*

Fig. 14.—*Electron micrographs of a quenched copper foil showing the prismatic punching of dislocation loops, with ⟨110⟩ directions as axes. The long rows A, B and C lie in the only ⟨110⟩ direction in the plane of the foil. D is a dislocation entanglement (Barnes and Mazey)*

Fig. 15.—*A network of screw dislocations in talc; the ribbons are stacking faults*

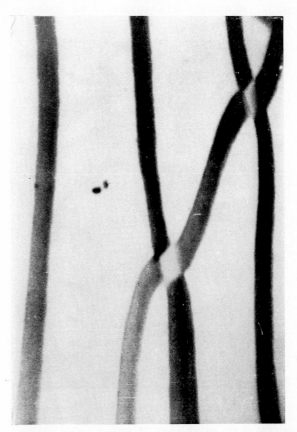

Fig. 16.—*A detail of the contrast in the overlap of screw dislocations in talc*

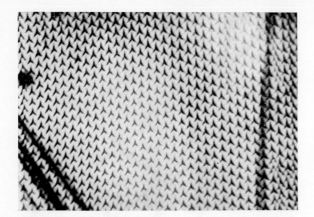

Fig. 17.—*Three sets of partial dislocations in nickel bromide*

We cannot take this question too far in a general review, but will briefly consider some illustrative examples.

It is difficult to derive good theoretical estimates of the stacking-fault energy for different metals; this is a serious limitation to the development of the subject as a whole at the present time. One approach has been that of determining the twin-boundary energy in the metal, treating each of the interfaces between the stacking fault and the matrix as a twin-boundary, and hence doubling the energy to obtain that for the stacking fault. Some recent work by Hirsch and his associates on the shapes of dislocation nodes in face-centred cubic metals reveals that the energy is in fact much lower than the twin-boundary model predicts. A crossed grid of screw dislocations in talc, and a detail of the contrast at the overlap, are shown in Figs. 15 and 16. A remarkably uniform network of three sets of partials in nickel bromide is shown in Fig. 17. A beautiful demonstration of the capabilities of

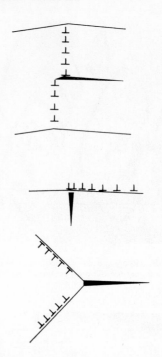

Fig. 19.—*Possible dislocation crack-forming mechanisms*

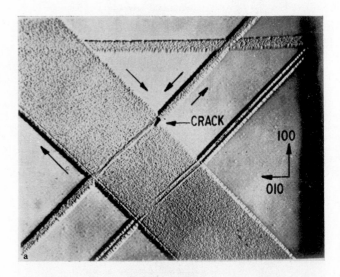

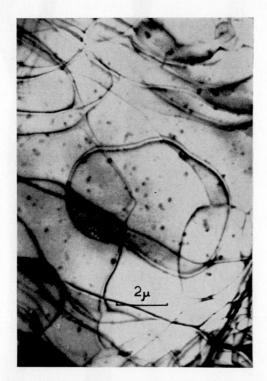

Fig. 18.—*An electron transmission micrograph of irradiated graphite showing a dislocation loop with its vector in the basal plane. The separation of the partials where the total dislocation has an edge orientation is nearly double that of the separation where the orientation is screw (Baker, Chou and Kelly)*

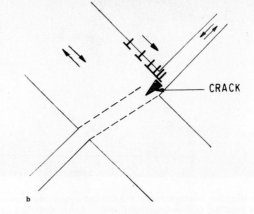

Fig. 20.—*Cracks formed at the intersection of glide bands in a MgO single crystal. The arrows indicate the shear (Johnston)*

a

electron microscopy in resolving an extended dislocation is provided by Fig. 18 which shows a dislocation loop in graphite with a vector in the basal plane. The separation of the two partials varies around the loop with dislocation orientation, being a maximum of 1500A in the edge orientation and 800A in the screw orientation. These values make it possible to compute the stacking fault energy (in this case 0·51 ergs cm^{-2}).

Fracture and Crack Propagation

From the earliest days of dislocation theory, the crack-forming potentialities of dislocation groups has been evident enough. A few of the elementary possibilities are illustrated in Fig. 19. The question is whether or not such mechanisms are physically important in real materials. There is direct evidence for the formation of cracks by piled-up groups of dislocations, as exemplified by Figs. 20 and 21 for example. The factors which determine crack instability are highly important in engineering, but there is little quantitative guidance from dislocation theory at the present time, although the microstructural features of the propagation processes have

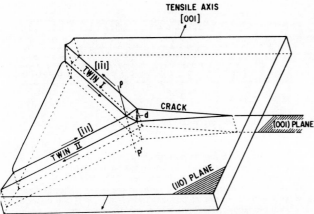

b   Microcrack formation at intersection of twins.

Fig. 21.—*A cleavage crack formed at the intersection of deformation twins in a silicon iron crystal at 77°K (Hull)*

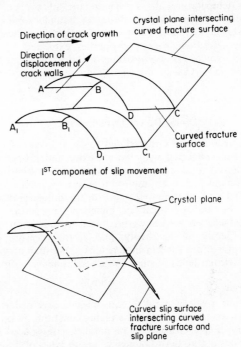

Fig. 23.—*An interpretation of Fig. 22 in dislocation terms (Forsyth)*

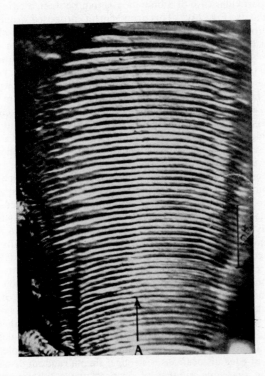

Fig. 22.—*Ductile striations in an aluminium alloy. The crack propagated in the direction of the arrow (Forsyth)*

become clarified. In fatigue, cracks initially develop along the plane of maximum resolved shear stress (usually a crystallographic plane), eventually changing over to a plane normal to the stress axis (the tensile mode) in which the fracture surface is characterized by striations. These markings (extensively examined by Forsyth and his colleagues) are due to successive composite fractures, partly ductile parallel to the tensile plane, and partly brittle on other intersecting planes. The fracture striations are illustrated by Fig. 22 and interpreted in dislocation terms in Fig. 23.

Diffusion Interactions

One of the earliest quantitative successes of dislocation theory was the treatment of strain-ageing in iron by Cottrell and Bilby. This relates to the recovery of a yield point, after plastic deformation, when the metal is subjected to a period of anneal at a temperature sufficiently high for a significant diffusion of carbon and nitrogen to occur. The possibility of solute atmospheres forming at dislocations, or at stacking fault boundaries, follows from a consideration of the stress fields.   Where the local strain energy is reduced by the acquisition of a solute atom, the probability of diffusional escape is lower than the probability of capture, and an atmosphere builds up which reduces the stress field, and hence the sensitivity of the dislocation to an applied stress.   Stacking faults may be extended by a similar mechanism.

In the case of extended screw dislocations a lowering of the stacking-fault–matrix interfacial energy makes the recombination of the partials more difficult, and hence cross-slip more difficult (an extended screw dislocation is confined to slip in the plane of its associated fault).

The thermodynamic aspects also bear upon the interaction of dislocations with point defects; the energies derived for the identifiable processes of climb, polygonization, and high temperature creep (taking these as examples) are generally reconcilable, and the physical models are reasonably persuasive.   The interactions between solute atoms and dislocations, and the reduction in dislocation mobility brought about, are key processes in the achievement of creep resistance in high temperature alloys.   There are, of course, other contributions from boundary sliding or boundary migration, or from crystallographic transformations, but nevertheless the generally useful engineering properties exhibited by these materials would not be possible without the continuous operation in service of diffusional interactions of the type discussed.

Some Recent Developments

The foregoing was not intended to be a review of all the phenomena connected with the existence and properties of dislocations: no discussion was given of work-hardening, for example, which is an important aspect of dislocation behaviour, nor of crystal growth, nor of the influence of dislocations on the electrical or magnetic properties.   The examples selected will, however, given an indication of the detailed nature of the theory, and of the measure of its agreement with the experimental results.   We shall now select a few particular fields of study for special note and comment.

Boundaries

A planar array of parallel, equi-spaced, edge dislocations with their vectors normal to the plane, constitutes a pure tilt boundary, and a crossed net of parallel, equi-spaced screw dislocations a pure twist boundary.   Both types of boundary are well-established.   A general boundary may be formed by a suitable combination of dislocations, and a new approach to the analysis of such networks has recently been advanced by Bollman (1962), which makes the dislocation reactions involved easier to appreciate.

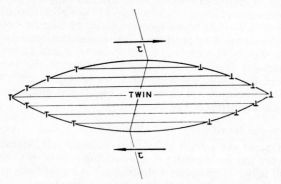

Fig. 24.—*Model of twin of finite extension, which has twin dislocations on every habit plane in its non-coherent boundaries.   The twin grows in volume by the movement of the boundaries under stress (Orowan)*

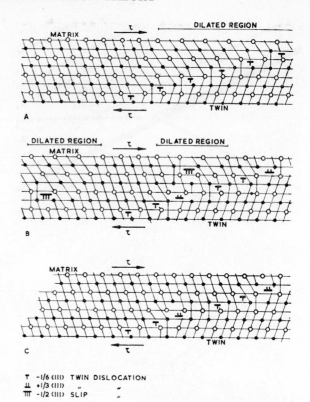

T   −1/6 ⟨111⟩   TWIN DISLOCATION
⊥⊥ +1/3 ⟨111⟩   „
TTT −1/2 ⟨111⟩   SLIP   „

Fig. 25.—*Dissociation of a non-coherent twin boundary in the b.c.c. lattice.   Two layers of atoms are projected on a (110) plane of a slice of material consisting of eight horizontal (112) planes.   A gives the non-coherent boundary between a twin, in the lower right-hand corner, and the matrix as a row of partial dislocations.   In B the dissociation has produced slip dislocations which move away from the boundary under influence of the stress.   The final situation is shown in C, where a residual boundary is shown composed of one complemetary dislocation to every two twin dislocations*

A particular case of a boundary is that between a twin and the matrix (Fig. 24).   This arrangement, proposed originally by Orowan (1954), is such that under an appropriate shear stress the volume of the twin increases by dislocation slip. There are theoretical reasons for believing that this arrangement cannot be valid as it stands in body-centred cubic lattices, mainly because of the very high stresses which would exist near the non-coherent boundaries.   The problem has been resolved by Sleeswyk (1962) by invoking what are called " emissary " dislocations.   The detailed argument cannot be reproduced in a short space, but essentially, one out of every three of the twin partials which form the non-coherent (Orowan) boundary dissociate to yield two dislocations, one a slip dislocation $\frac{1}{2}$[111] and the other a partial, which, in combination with the other twin dislocations, makes up a low-energy boundary.   The situation is exemplified by Fig. 25.   The emissary dislocations associated with a twin in a molybdenum–rhenium alloy are reproduced in Fig. 26.

More detailed theoretical studies of dislocation walls are also going forward successfully.   Chalmers and Li (1963) have considered the case of a tilt boundary of extended (dissociated) dislocations, and this makes it possible to estimate the stacking fault energy from the dependence of the boundary energy on the angle of tilt.   The calculation avoids many of the difficulties and assumptions which are inherent in the other methods.   The elastic properties of such a dislocation wall are better established (Li): for example, an array of edge dislocations is stronger than a random distribution of the same number of dislocations; a " horizontal " edge dislocation array is stronger than a " vertical " array in

Fig. 26.—*Twins and emissary dislocations created in a molybdenum-rhenium alloy by bending (Votova and Sleeswyk)*

Fig. 27.—*Electron micrograph of the initial stage of network formation of imperfections from a collapsed vacancy type disc in cadmium (Crump and Mitchell)*

resisting the glide of edge dislocations, but weaker in resisting climbing dislocations. The deduction is that the " vertical " arrays contribute predominantly to creep hardening, and the " horizontal " arrays to cold-work hardening.

Networks Derived from Vacancy Loops

Recently, Crump and Mitchell have drawn attention to the sudden changes which occur in the development of vacancy loops in cadmium in the electron microscope, due to vacancy clustering under the action of the beam.   Lines at first appear (Fig. 27) and develop in a matter of seconds to a hexagonal network (Fig. 28).   Their general appearance suggests that these lines are stacking fault ribbons, but there are reasons why this interpretation is difficult to accept—notably the retention by the bands of a uniform narrow width.   Nor can the source of the energy associated with the transformation from the original loop be identified.   The effects are not properly interpreted or substantiated at present.

The Extension of Dislocation Theory to a Wider Range of Structures

The concept of a dislocation is applicable to any crystalline matrix, and in recent years a great deal has been done in making sense of some, at least, of the properties of non-metallic materials in dislocation terms.   As an example, theories of deformation and twinning in graphite have been evolved successfully in dislocation terms, replacing the older approaches which required the introduction of unrealistic defects into the structure.   Graphite is a material of singular interest, because the partly-graphitic stage in the conversion of carbon to graphite is characterized by a structure of bent and partially-aligned planes which possess both metallic and polymeric features.   Some note has already been taken of dislocations in graphite, and these are now well established. The question of dislocations in truly polymeric materials is less well resolved, however.   The most interesting contribution to date is probably that of Zaukelies.   He reports observing crystalline slip in nylon 66 and 610, and interprets the findings in terms of dislocations.   Fig. 29 shows the edge dislocation form, and Fig. 30 the screw form; it is these imperfections which are taken to be responsible for the broad diffractions, and not the existence of amorphous material. Another approach to the intermediate, part-ordered state, is that of Hosemann, who refers to such structures as *para-crystals*.   The slip directions determined in these nylons were [1, 3, 14] for 66 and [1, 3, 18] for 610, the directions of closest packing on the (010) plane, the plane of closest packing. This development opens the door to a vast new study, and must have important repercussions on polymer physics as a whole.

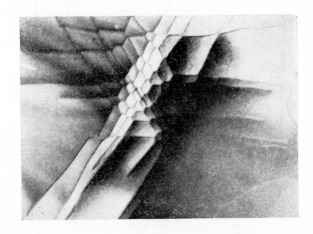

Fig. 28.—*Electron micrograph of the feature revealed in Fig. 27 some ten seconds later (Crump and Mitchell)*

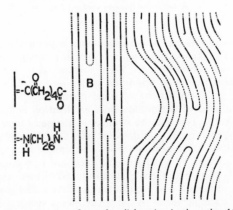

Fig. 29.—*Representation of an edge dislocation in the nylon 66 crystal lattice.   The broken line represents hexamethylene diamine portions of the molecules.   The continuous line represents adipic acid portions of the molecules.   Site marked A represents a lattice vacancy due to chain ends.   Site marked B represents a lattice vacancy due to a chain fold (Zaukelies)*

The working-out of the dislocation implications in super-lattices, that is, ordered configurations of atoms of different elements, is another subject which is advancing. The vector of a perfect dislocation in the (ordered) superlattice is greater than in a disordered structure: such a dislocation may be regarded as being formed by two ordinary dislocations (that is, dislocations in the disordered matrix) connected by an antiphase boundary (this is virtually equivalent to saying that it may be regarded as two partial dislocations in the super-lattice connected by a stacking fault). In the face-centred cubic lattice, the two constituent dislocations of the super-lattice dislocation may themselves extend, and the geometry of the whole group (four in all) depends on the energies of the stacking fault and the antiphase boundary. In the case of the $AuCu_3$ type lattice, taking this as an example, we have the arrangement shown in Fig. 31 for the [01$\bar{1}$] dislocation. A theoretical treatment of this problem by Marcinkowski, Brown and Fisher (1961) yields a value for the partial spacing

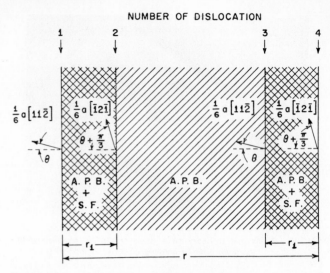

Fig. 31.—*The structure of the a* [01$\bar{1}$] *superlattice dislocation in* $AuCu_3$

intrinsic dislocation mobility is very restricted anyway at low temperatures. A general change of shape demands the operation of five independent (dislocation) slip systems, and in crystals where this is not fulfilled, ductility is necessarily limited. The question has been considered in detail by Groves and Kelly (1963). Face-centred cubic and body-centred cubic metals both exhibit sufficient systems; the NaCl type structure does not, nor does the CaCl structure, nor the rutile (TiO_2) structure. There is good evidence to support the relevance of this approach to the question of limited ductility. In MgO bicrystals, for example, cracks are initiated at boundaries by slip: this is to be expected with $\{110\} \langle 1\bar{1}0 \rangle$ type slip which offers only four independent slip systems (two in each crystal) for boundary accommodation. However, a restricted number of slip modes need not necessarily imply limited ductility in a polycrystalline matrix, because the easy modes may continue to operate with such freedom that localities of inhibited slip may not create internal stresses sufficient to initiate fracture in the particular crystal. However, the importance of the restriction exerted is evident enough.

The practical problem in the brittle high temperature materials is, then, that of promoting slip in the more difficult systems, or (a possible solution in some cases), hardening up the primary slip modes so that these do not come into operation until the imposed stresses reach levels at which several slip

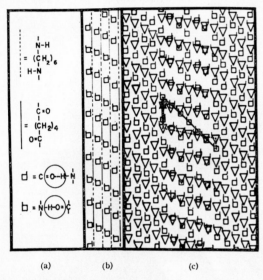

Fig. 30.—*Representation of a screw dislocation between* (010) *planes in a nylon 66 lattice.* (a) *The broken line represents hexamethylene diamine portions of the molecules. The continuous line represents adipic acid portion of the molecules. Squares and triangles represent hydrogen bond sites in the lattice. The side the tail is on represents the direction of the hydrogen atom at the site.* (b) *Illustrates the relative position of the chains to the hydrogen bond sites.* (c) *Illustrates the screw dislocation. Squares represent hydrogen bond sites in the* (010) *plane immediately above the plane whose hydrogen bond sites are represented by triangles. A Burgers circuit is drawn in. Thick portion of arrow is the Burgers vector* (Zaukelies)

(130 Å) which is in close correspondence with the observations (Fig. 32). The spacing as a function of dislocation orientation is also well substantiated. The configuration of dislocations in superlattices is an important issue, as it obviously bears directly on the plasticity of some important alloy systems. One outcome of the dislocation consideration is that alloys of the $AuCu_3$ type may be stronger in a state of intermediate ordering than the fully-ordered or fully-disordered structures.

An aspect of dislocation theory which might be emphasized in this context, as it is particularly relevant to non-metals, is that of immobile (sessile) dislocations. These occur, of course, in metals, and are characterized by a vector which is neither a simple vector of the lattice, nor a vector associated with a simple lattice fault. Even where mobile dislocations exist, unless there are sufficient of them, operating in several slip systems, a *general* deformation is not possible, and in a polycrystalline matrix very limited ductility may result. In a great many non-metallics (Al_2O_3, TiC, UC, for example) the

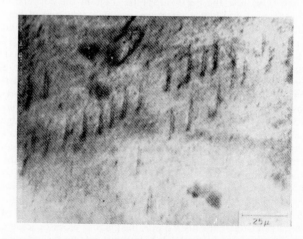

Fig. 32.—*Superlattice dislocations of nearly equilibrium spacing in fully ordered* $AuCu_3$ (Marcinkowski, Brown and Fisher)

systems operate. The strong anisotropy of deformation associated with the existence of restricted slip systems is well exemplified by beryllium: at room temperature all the slip vectors in beryllium lie in the basal plane.

Dynamic Properties of Dislocations

The stress fields of dislocations in motion, and the properties of moving dislocations generally, are subjects of some theoretical difficulty. They are, however, of immediate relevance to the technological developments in high-speed forming operations. Theoretical analysis leads to some unexpected conclusions: edge dislocations of the same sign, for example, moving on the (110) plane in body-centred cubic metals, become attractive at velocities above the Rayleigh wave velocity (~ 0.9 transverse sound velocity, c, according to Weertman (1961)). Under static or low velocity conditions, edge dislocations of the same sign, on the same slip plane, repel, of course, and their coalescence at high velocities could lead directly to crack formation. Such analyses have been extended to anisotropic crystals and the calculations show that the anomalous velocity region is decreased by a slight anisotropy. In α-iron, Cotner and Weertman (1962) calculate the Rayleigh velocity to be 0·92 c in a [111] direction on a (110) plane, and the limiting dislocation velocity to be 0·94 c. Only in this range (three times smaller than that for isotropic crystals) can similar edge dislocations coalesce under attractive forces. The situation on other planes has not as yet been established: the region may increase with increasing anisotropy.

The response of materials to high-speed deformation is again a specialist subject in its own right, but many aspects of this response are closely related to dislocation mechanisms: the propagation of the plastic wave, damping, the hardness changes induced by shock waves, and the stress-induced phase changes (such as twinning). The distribution of dislocation slip is certainly different under dynamic conditions compared with that induced by static stressing: fewer slip bands, with a larger slip in the bands is a general characteristic. The strengthening effect of shock deformation is, of course, an important practical issue. The changes developed in the dislocation structure and the associated physical properties by alternating stresses are not properly resolved. The damping increases significantly with stressing, and the dislocation distribution is strikingly modified. The appearance of surface dislocations (as revealed by etch pits) indicates (Fig. 33) that some at least of those created by the stressing may be generated in, or at, subgrain boundaries. The precise way in which an alternating stress activates a greater dislocation mobility (as exemplified by the acceleration of creep) is not understood, although some of the theoretical consequences of oscillating dislocations—loop-formation, the generation of point defects—accord well with the observed results, particularly those effects which derive from increased diffusion rates.

Continuous Distributions of Dislocations

From the foregoing we may see how, step by step, the properties of dislocations have been established, starting from simple isolated dislocations, in simple structures, thence to simple combinations of dislocations, and so on. We eventually reach a position where the behaviour of arrays of dislocations in fairly complex crystals may be seriously attacked theoretically, with, at the same time, the evolution of fundamental techniques capable of resolving the questions posed. In a real engineering material, of practical dimensions, we are dealing with a complex entanglement of dislocations, possibly exhibiting some regular features, but nevertheless in its extent and complications far removed from the small groups treated

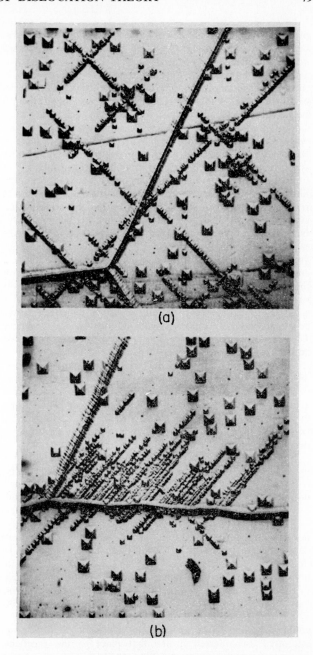

Fig. 33.—*Etch pits in sodium chloride, revealing dislocations produced (smaller etch pits) by alternating stresses. The strain amplitude is 2.7×10^{-4}. The dislocations in (b) appear to originate at a sub-boundary (Whitworth)*

by the theory. The properties of a matrix containing such a complex network are obviously not easily treated, with the exception, possibly, of certain discrete events, such as the onset of finite plastic flow, which is dictated by the slip of the weakest dislocation segments. Bulk properties in the usual sense (modulus, rate of work-hardening, and so on) cannot be quantitatively linked with the parameters of the dislocation network: indeed, the establishment of just what the significant parameters are is not easy in itself. Consequently, it must be admitted that as far as engineering is concerned, the merit of dislocation theory to date lies mainly in the qualitative understanding it brings to mechanical and thermal phenomena, coupled with the pointers it may provide for those metallurgists concerned with the evolution of new alloys and with interpretations of their behaviour.

New theoretical developments are, however, now taking place capable of handling distributions of *continuous* dislocations. We shall consider first of all what the term *continuous dislocation* means.

In the case of a discrete dislocation of the kind covered in the previous discussion, a zone (cylinder) of dislocated material exists in which the atoms occupy positions of transition between the perfect atomic arrangements on each side. Outside of this dislocated zone, elastic stresses exist, falling off with distance from the centre. We can, however (at least in theory), consider another possibility. Suppose we uniformly strain a piece of an elastic continuum and then embed it in (or attach it to) another similar piece. Taking the case illustrated by Fig. 1, we see that when the external stress is removed, a state of internal stress exists, the stress being constant over any of the planes parallel to the boundary, but changing with distance from the boundary. Any circuit taken around a point lying in the boundary will therefore yield the same displacement vector per unit length of boundary enclosed. An edge dislocation is thus uniformly spread along the boundary. If we imagine carrying out this operation on successive sheets of the material, of infinitesimal thickness, it is easy to appreciate that the zone of dislocated material may be spread, not merely along a plane, but throughout a volume. The same idea can, of course, be applied to screw dislocations, and to dislocations with a general orientation. Such a spreading may be expressed in terms of a point density of dislocations, a quantity which may vary from point to point in the material. The concept cannot be applied to atomic arrangements as such, for obvious reasons, but dislocations in weakly-bonded crystals that is, very wide dislocations, exemplify (in a limited way) what is meant by continuous dislocations.

Generalizing this approach, we may now consider a crystal in which the dislocation density and lattice strain vary continuously from point to point, and discontinuously across boundaries (such as grain boundaries). The mathematical basis for the development of continuous dislocation theory resides in Riemannian geometry and in the introduction of non-Riemannian connections such that the dislocation density tensor becomes the Cartan torsion tensor. There is thus a direct relation between dislocated crystal structures and non-Euclidean space, and hence with relativity theory. Much of the theory already worked out for other physical systems may therefore be taken over and applied to dislocations. The theory is specialized and difficult mathematically and I could not claim to be an adequate exponent of it. Those interested are referred in the first place to the excellent reviews of Eshelby (1956) and Bilby (1960).

The behaviour of a continuous distribution of *moving* dislocations has been considered by Muro (1963) and this leads to expressions relating plastic strain and the dislocation density tensors, and plastic strain rates and velocities. These offer the possibility of creating direct links with generalized plasticity theory, and it may well be that this type of correlation between an originally discrete (atomic) approach to plastic flow, and that of continuum plasticity, may prove the most important contemporary development in solid mechanics.

Whiskers

The mechanical properties of very small crystals, and in particular, of fine fibre-like metal crystals, with diameters of the order of microns, have aroused much interest in recent years, as they appear to offer a means of obtaining useful materials of much greater strength than those available at the present time. Whatever the possibilities may be in this direction, measurements on whiskers are of fundamental value as they enable some of the propositions of dislocation theory to be directly tested. The lattice of a whisker containing an axial screw dislocation is twisted by an amount which can be calculated, and its stability under shear stress determined. The predictions are confirmed by experiment, although the great majority of whiskers appear to be essentially dislocation-free. On the other hand, some whiskers certainly contain a dislocation network and the stress required to activate a Frank–Read source in a crystal of such small dimensions is very high: piled-up groups at the surface must be small and the stress at the head of the group may well be too low to force them through the surface—particularly if this has been oxidized. The general behaviour in such cases has been confirmed (see, for example, Cabrera and Price, 1958), and the results fit in also with the slow creep behaviour of such whiskers. Once creep has ceased at some stress level, it is not re-instituted by raising the stress. This is explained by the thermally-activated escape of dislocations from pinned points, and hence by the actual disappearance of effective sources. A great deal of information is now available on a variety of whiskers, covering both growth characteristics and properties, and much of this lends support to the theoretical propositions. Whether it will be possible to exercise a more precise control over the dislocation networks grown into whiskers is an open question: it is certainly an aspect of importance in the evolution of high-strength reinforced materials.

The number of features of dislocation behaviour I have touched upon is large, but even so, as any text on the subject will reveal, much has had to be omitted. A very great deal remains to be done both experimentally and theoretically. We do not as yet understand fully the factors which limit dislocation mobility in the more brittle materials, nor the precise nature of the interactions with solute atoms. Some of the properties of oscillating dislocations seem clear enough, but many questions are still unresolved, and these are very relevant to the practical issues raised by the utilization of materials in conditions where dynamic stresses are imposed.

References

Amelinckx, S. and Delavignette, P. *J. App. Phys.*, 1961, **32**, 341.
Amelinckx, S. and Strumane, G. "*Proc. Conf. on Silicon Carbide*", 1959, p. 162 (Pergamon Press 1960).
Baker, C., Chou, Y. T. and Kelly, A. *Phil. Mag.*, 1961, **6**, 149.
Barnes, R. S. and Mazey, D. J. *Acta Met.*, 1963, **11**, 281.
Bilby, B. A. "*Progress in Solid Mechanics*", 1961, **1**, 331 (North-Holland).
Bollman, W. *Phil. Mag.*, 1962, **7**, 1513.
Cabrera, N. and Price, P. B. "*Growth and Perfection of Crystals*", 1958, p. 204 (Wiley).
Chalmers, B. and Li, J. C. M. *Acta Met.*, 1963, **11**, 243.
Cotner, J. and Weertman, J. *Acta Met.*, 1962, **10**, 515
Crump, J. C. and Mitchell, J. W. *Phil. Mag.*, 1963, **8**, 59.
Eshelby, J. D. "*Solid State Physics*", 1956, **3**, 79 (Academic Press).
Groves, G. W. and Kelly, A. *Phil. Mag.*, 1963, **8**, 877.
Hull, D. *Acta Met.*, 1960, **8**, 11.
Johnston, W. G. *Phil. Mag.*, 1960, **5**, 407.
Li, J. C. M. *Acta Met.*, 1960, **8**, 563.
Marcinkowski, M. J., Brown, N. and Fisher, R. M. *Acta Met.*, 1961, **9**, 129.
Muro, T. *Phil. Mag.*, 1963, **8**, 843.
Orowan, E. "*Dislocations in Metals*", 1954, p. 69 (New York: Amer. Inst. Min. (Metall.) Engrs.).
Price, P. B. *J. App. Phys.*, 1961, **32**, 1750.
Price, P. B. and Nadeau, J. S. *J. App. Phys.*, 1962, **33**, 1543.
Segall, R. L., Partridge, P. G. and Hirsch, P. B. *Phil. Mag.*, 1961, **6**, 1493.
Sleeswyk, A. W. *Acta Met.*, 1962, **10**, 705.
Votava, E. and Sleeswyk, A. W. *Acta Met.*, 1962, **10**, 965.
Weertman, J. "*Response of Metals to High Velocity Deformation*", 1961 (P. G. Shewman and V. F. Zackey, editors) (New York: Interscience).
Weertman, J. *Phil. Mag.*, 1962, **7**, 617.
Westmacott, K. H., Barnes, R. S. and Smallman, R. E. *Phil. Mag.*, 1962, **7**, 1585.
Whitworth, R. W. *Phil. Mag.*, 1960, **8**, 425.
Zaukelies, D. A. *J. App. Phys.*, 1962, **33**, 2797.

PARACRYSTALLINE LATTICE DISTORTIONS IN Fe-Al ALLOYS

By R. HOSEMANN, D. BIALAS, A. SCHÖNFELD, W. WILKE and D. WEICK*

SYNOPSIS

It is well known that so-called "paracrystals" can be found in solid high polymers, β-keratin, polyethylene, polyacrylonitrile, etc. In solids with three-dimensional lattices built up by atoms such distortions following the theory of paracrystals should be found, if the atoms have different sizes. The diffraction pattern of an ideal mixed crystal is calculated for the one-dimensional case. Besides, of well-known components calculated in a similar way for crystal lattices by von Laue, Huang, Warren, Averbach et al.[36] two new paracrystal components are found. The integral widths of the paracrystalline reflections increase in a parabolic manner with $\sin \theta/\lambda$, from which the paracrystalline g-value can be calculated. The X-ray diffraction patterns of Fe–Al alloys give evidence of such lattices. The results agree within the errors of experiments with the paracrystalline theory of semi-rigid atoms. Hence the conventional assumption of r^{-2} distance law (equation (81)) contradicts the experiments.

Historical Aspect

Matter nowadays is classified into crystals with more or less pronounced distortions, liquids and amorphous materials and gases. It is said that crystals give rise to Bragg reflections, which mathematically are defined by the Laue factor. Between these reflections one finds more or less modulated diffuse scattering. At the feet of the reflections there are extra-Laue spots, thermal diffuse scattering (Laval[35]) or in mixed crystals intensity humps calculated by Huang.[28]

In the theory of liquids and amorphous materials in general the concept of three-dimensional lattices cannot be found. Instead of this spherical symmetric a priori probability functions (Zernike-Prins (1927)[1], Debye-Menke (1930)[2]) and radial density distributions collect the experimentally observable material. There seems to be no smooth transition from the crystalline to the liquid state of matter.

However, from the mathematical point of view it is possible to postulate a structure and an interference theory which possesses a much more general form and includes the crystals and liquids as special well-defined degenerate cases. This theory of paracrystals (Hosemann (1949, 1950) and Hosemann and Bagchi (1962))[3,4] is built up on at least 18 new statistical structure parameters which define the so-called coordination statistics.

The first paracrystals in nature were found in 1952 in the macrolattices of natural proteins. Fig. 1a shows the small angle pattern of the β-feather-keratin of a seagull,[5] Fig. 1b a two-dimensional paracrystalline lattice and Fig. 1c its Fraunhofer pattern. In the direction of the fibre axis there are Bragg-like reflections (0 k 0), but all other reflections are more and more broadened with increasing scattering angles. Some years later paracrystalline macrolattices were found in stretched linear polyethylene.[6]

Fig. 2a shows the small angle scattering of hot stretched linear polyethylene with a diffuse long-period meridianal reflection (Hess-Kiessig (1943)[7]), Fig. 2b a model, and Fig. 2c its Fraunhofer pattern.

Together with Lindenmeyer (1960)[8] we could prove that even in atomic dimensions paracrystalline lattices exist in single polyacrylonitrile crystals, which give interesting inform-

ation about the conformation and configuration of the molecular chain in the molecular lattice.

Recently we found paracrystalline lattices in atomic dimensions also in hot stretched linear polyethylene.[9]

Now, we must ask, why should it not be possible to find out paracrystalline structures even in inorganic crystals or metals? In this case the number of atoms in a lattice cell is very small, and hence many degrees of freedom are lost which are possible in high polymers. However, looking carefully for line-broadening effects of the type shown in Figs 1–3, we found them in alloys. For the first time results are given here of (Fe–Al) mixed crystals.

In Fig. 4 an atom with a larger diameter is inserted into a crystalline lattice. The conventional concept is schematically drawn on the left-hand side. All neighbouring atoms are displaced in a radial direction from the centre of the big atom following a r^{-2} distance law. In such a case the atoms have a zero compressibility, and at least the neighbouring atoms are strongly deformed three-dimensionally.

As the consequence of the r^{-2} distance law the polycrystalline solid solution material changes its shape as shown schematically in the left lower side of Fig. 4.

If on the other hand we do not introduce deformable atoms, the solid solution gets an arrangement similar to that shown in the upper right side of Fig. 4. The crystalline order of the lattice is lost since a new type of lattice distortion arises. They destroy the long-range order of the lattice (see Fig. 1b) and can be calculated by means of the theory of the paracrystal (Hosemann (1949, 1950)).[3]

To facilitate the understanding of the theory, the next section deals with some mathematical background, especially convolution integrals, which in crystallography are helpful, and for paracrystals indispensable. In another section the intensity function of a one-dimensional mixed crystal is calculated. It contains three intensity components well known in literature from three-dimensional crystallographic work and two new paracrystalline components. A further section deals with some instructive experiments with two-dimensional models, and the following gives some aspects of the background of the three-dimensional theory as far as is needed here, while another part gives some first results of X-ray diffraction of Fe–Al alloys and their analysis.

* Fritz-Haber-Institut der Max-Planck-Gesellschaft, Berlin.

G

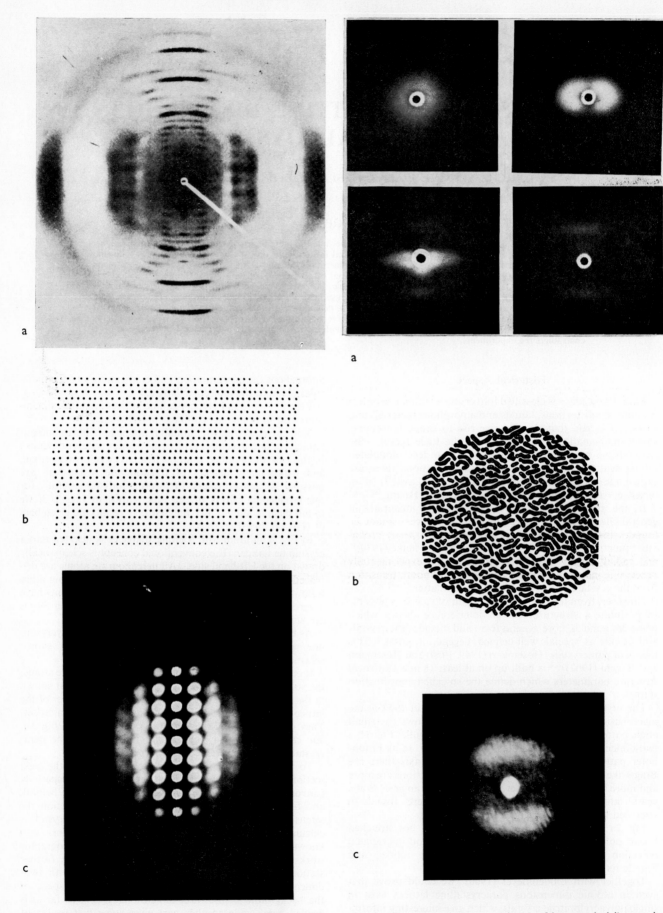

Fig. 1.—*The paracrystalline macrolattice of β-feather keratin from the sea gull. Fibre axis vertical. (a) X-ray small angle pattern (Bear, Rugo (1951)), (b) model of the lattice, (c) Fraunhofer pattern*

Fig. 2.—*The paracrystalline macrolattice of hot stretched linear polyethylene. Fiber axis vertical. (a) X-ray pattern (Hess, Kiessig (1943)), (b) model of the colloidal structure, (c) Fraunhofer pattern*

Mathematical Introduction

The platonic idea of an ideal crystal implies that the position of each atom k of the sort r can be described by three integer parameters k_1, k_2, k_3 so that each atom knows its ideal position $\mathbf{x}_{kr}$:

$$\mathbf{x}_{kr} = k_1 \mathbf{a}_1 + k_2 \mathbf{a}_2 + k_3 \mathbf{a}_3 + \mathbf{z}_r \quad . \quad . \quad (1)$$

$\mathbf{a}_1$, $\mathbf{a}_2$, $\mathbf{a}_3$ are the vectors of a lattice cell and $\mathbf{z}_r$ gives the position of the atom of the sort r in the lattice cell k. Introducing thermal vibrations, the positions of the centres of the atoms are given by:

$$\mathbf{z}_{kr} + \delta_k \mathbf{x}_r \quad . \quad . \quad . \quad (2)$$

where the time average over each $\delta_k \mathbf{x}_r$ is zero.

Studying the X-ray diffraction pattern of atomic structures, we know the diffracted intensity $J(\mathbf{b})$ is proportional to the square of an amplitude function $R(\mathbf{b})$, which is the Fourier transform (symbol $\mathscr{F}$) of the electron density distribution $\rho(\mathbf{x})$ of the structure:

$$J(\mathbf{b}) = R(\mathbf{b})\, R^*(\mathbf{b}) \quad . \quad . \quad . \quad (3)$$

$$R(\mathbf{b}) = \mathscr{F}(\rho) = \int \rho(\mathbf{x}) \exp\left[-2\pi i(\mathbf{bx})\right] dv_x, \quad . \quad (4)$$

$$\rho(\mathbf{x}) = \sum_k \sum_r \rho_{kr}(\mathbf{x} - \mathbf{x}_{kr} - \delta_k \mathbf{x}_r) \quad . \quad . \quad (5)$$

$$\mathbf{b} = (\mathbf{s} - \mathbf{s}_0)/\lambda \quad . \quad . \quad . \quad (6)$$

$\rho_{kr}(\mathbf{x})$ is the electron density distribution of an atom of the sort r, whose centre lies at $\mathbf{x} = 0$. $\mathbf{b}$ is the so-called reciprocal vector expanding the three-dimensional Fourier space, in which $I(\mathbf{b})$ and $R(\mathbf{b})$ are defined. $\mathbf{s}$ and $\mathbf{s}_0$ are unit vectors in the direction of the diffracted and primary beam, λ the wavelength of the X-rays. Equation (6) defines the surface of the so-called Ewald sphere in the $\mathbf{b}$-space. Equation (3) holds only for unifold diffraction processes, not for multiple scattering, and defines the so-called kinematical interference theories.

If we knew the complex function $R(\mathbf{b})$, we could easily derive from $R(\mathbf{b})$ the density distribution $\rho(\mathbf{x})$ by an inverse Fourier transformation (symbol $\mathscr{F}^{-1}$):

$$\rho(\mathbf{x}) = \mathscr{F}^{-1}(R) = \int R(\mathbf{b}) \exp\left[2\pi i(\mathbf{bx})\right] dv_b \quad . \quad (7)$$

dv_b is a volume-element in the $\mathbf{b}$-space, dv_x one in the $\mathbf{x}$-space. The convolution theorem of Fourier transformation[10] states that:

$$\mathscr{F}(g_1 g_2) = \widehat{G_1 G_2}, \quad \mathscr{F}(\widehat{g_1 g_2}) = G_1 G_2 \quad . \quad (8)$$

where:

$$G_1(\mathbf{b}) = \mathscr{F}(g_1), \quad G_2(\mathbf{b}) = \mathscr{F}(g_2)$$

The folding or convolution products $\widehat{g_1 g_2}$ and $\widehat{G_1 G_2}$ are defined by:

$$\left. \begin{aligned} \widehat{g_1 g_2}(\mathbf{x}) &= \int g_1(\mathbf{y})\, g_2(\mathbf{x} - \mathbf{y})\, dv_y \\ \widehat{G_1 G_2}(\mathbf{b}) &= \int G_1(\mathbf{c})\, G_2(\mathbf{b} - \mathbf{c})\, dv_c \end{aligned} \right\} \quad . \quad (9)$$

Taking into account that:

$$\mathscr{F}^{-1}(R^*) = \rho(-\mathbf{x}) \quad . \quad . \quad (10)$$

one obtains by Fourier inverse transformation of the observable intensity function $J(\mathbf{b})$ from (3):

$$\mathscr{F}^{-1}[J(\mathbf{b})] = Q(\mathbf{x}) = \int \rho(\mathbf{y})\, \rho(\mathbf{x} + \mathbf{y})\, dv_y \quad . \quad (11)$$

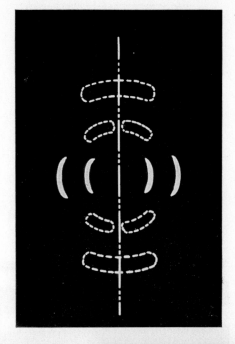

a

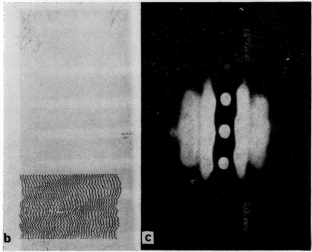

b

c

Fig. 3.—*The paracrystalline molecular lattice of a single polyacrylonitrile crystal. Chain-axes vertical. (a) electron diffraction (schematical), (b) point model of the lattice, (c) Fraunhofer pattern*

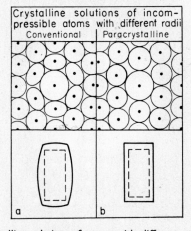

Fig. 4.—*Crystalline solutions of atoms with different radii. (a) Conventional theory, (b) paracrystalline theory, if atoms are rigid compounds*

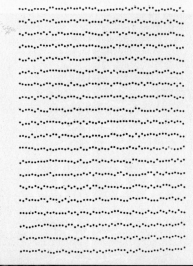

a

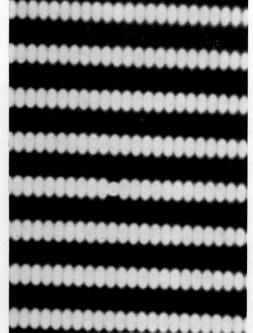

b

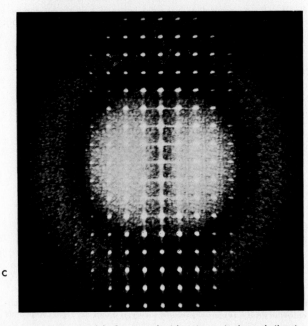

c

Fig. 5.—(a) Point model of a crystal with anisotropic thermal vibration (frozen) without any statistical correlation, (b) its Q-function, (c) its intensity function

For an infinitely large ideal crystal this Q-function is nothing else than the Patterson function of crystallography.[11] Convolution integrals of the form (11) are called " folding-squares " or " convolution-squares " (symbol $\overset{2}{\sim}$):

$$\overset{2}{\widetilde{g}}(\mathbf{x}) = \widehat{g(\mathbf{x})\,g(-\mathbf{x})} \qquad . \qquad . \qquad . \quad (12)$$

They are nothing else than the folding product of a function $g(\mathbf{x})$ with its inverse symmetric $g(-\mathbf{x})$.

For non-platonic real atomic structures $Q(\mathbf{x})$ offers many new, experimentally observable, details, which in many cases can most elegantly be calculated by means of convolution integrals (8), (11), (12).

Now let us first discuss the Q-functions of some crystalline structure, so that we may clearly find out what is the idea of a paracrystal.

A special crystal may consist of N atoms of the same sort $r=0$, only one atom in each lattice cell ($\mathbf{z}_r=0$). No statistical correlation may exist between the instantaneous displacements $\delta_k\mathbf{x}$ of the atoms (*cf.* (2)). Fig. 5a gives a two-dimensional model of such a structure, Fig. 5b its Q-function. From (1), (5) and (11) it follows that the positions of the centres of the different humps of the Q-function are given by:

$$\mathbf{x}_p = p_1\,\mathbf{a}_1 + p_2\,\mathbf{a}_2 + p_3\,\mathbf{a}_3, \qquad . \qquad . \quad (13)$$

(p_1, p_2, p_3 integers). If $\rho_0(\mathbf{x})$ is the electron density distribution of one atom lying at $\mathbf{x}=0$, the $(0, 0, 0)$-hump of the Q-function is given by $N.\overset{2}{\widetilde{\rho}}_0$, all other humps having a density distribution proportional to :[12]

$$\overset{2}{\widetilde{\rho}}_r = \overset{2}{\widetilde{\rho}}_0\,\overline{(\mathbf{x}-\delta_k\mathbf{x}+\delta_i\mathbf{x})} \qquad . \qquad . \quad (14)$$

If $P(\mathbf{x}-\mathbf{a})$ is a point function[13] at $\mathbf{x}=\mathbf{a}$ and $H_0(\mathbf{x})$ the probability of finding a certain vector $\delta_k\mathbf{x}=\mathbf{x}$ in the structure, we have :

$$H_0(\mathbf{x}) = \overline{P(\mathbf{x}-\delta_k\mathbf{x})} \qquad . \qquad . \quad (15)$$

Equation (14) can be rewritten as :†

$$\overset{2}{\widetilde{\rho}}_0(\mathbf{x})\,\overline{\widehat{P(\mathbf{x}-\delta_k\mathbf{x})}\,P(\mathbf{x}+\delta_i\mathbf{x})}.$$

Since in our model there is no correlation between the single displacements, the average of a folding product is identical with the folding product of the two averages. From (12), (14) and (15) one obtains :

$$\overset{2}{\widetilde{\rho}}_r = \overset{2}{\widetilde{\rho}}_0\,\widehat{\overset{2}{\widetilde{H}}_0}. \qquad . \qquad . \quad (16)$$

The larger x_p, the smaller the number of coinciding atoms in (11). Its number is given by :[14]

$$\overset{2}{\widetilde{s}}(\mathbf{x})/v_r. \qquad . \qquad . \quad (17)$$

$s(\mathbf{x})$ is the regular shape function of the crystal and has the value $1(0)$ for all $\mathbf{x}$-vectors ending in (outside of) one of its lattice cells, v_r the volume of one lattice cell. Hence the Q-function of Fig. 5b is given by :[15]

$$Q(\mathbf{x}) = N(\overset{2}{\widetilde{\rho}}_0 - \overset{2}{\widetilde{\rho}}_0\,\widehat{\overset{2}{\widetilde{H}}}_0) + \overset{2}{\widetilde{\rho}}_0\,\widehat{\overset{2}{\widetilde{H}}_0(z_c\overset{2}{\widetilde{s}}/v_r)} \quad . \quad (18)$$

$z_c(\mathbf{x})$ is the lattice-point function of Ewald (1940)[16] and has points with the weight one at the corners of each lattice cell :

$$z_c(\mathbf{x}) = \sum_{p_1}\sum_{p_2}\sum_{p_3} P(\mathbf{x}-\mathbf{x}_p) \qquad . \qquad . \quad (19)$$

† $f(x-a) = \widehat{f(x)\,P(x-a)}$

If the Fourier transforms of ρ_0, H_0, s, z_c are given by:

$$f_0(b)=\mathscr{F}[\rho_0(\mathbf{x})], \quad D_0(b)=\mathscr{F}[H_0(\mathbf{x})]$$
$$S(b)=\mathscr{F}[s(\mathbf{x})], \quad Z_c(b)=\mathscr{F}[z_c(\mathbf{x})] \qquad . \quad (20)$$

we immediately get from (18) by Fourier transformation with the help of equations (8)–(12) the intensity function (3):

$$J(\mathbf{b})=|f_0{}^2|(1-|D_0{}^2|)+|f_0{}^2||D_0{}^2|\frac{1}{v_r}Z_c\widehat{|S^2|} \quad . \quad (21)$$

According to its Fraunhofer-pattern in Fig. 5c each reflection has the same shape, given by the " shape-factor " $|S^2|$. Its position is given by the " reciprocal lattice factor " (Ewald, (1940)):[16]

$$Z_c(\mathbf{b})=\mathscr{F}(z_c)=\frac{1}{v_r}\sum_{h_1}\sum_{h_2}\sum_{h_3}P(\mathbf{b}-\mathbf{b}_h) \quad . \quad . \quad (22)$$

with: $\qquad \mathbf{b}_h=h_1\mathbf{A}_1+h_2\mathbf{A}_2+h_3\mathbf{A}_3$

$\mathbf{A}_1$, $\mathbf{A}_2$, $\mathbf{A}_3$ are the edge-vectors of the reciprocal lattice cell and given by $\mathbf{A}_1=\mathbf{a}_2\wedge\mathbf{a}_3/v_r$, $\mathbf{A}_2=\mathbf{a}_3\wedge\mathbf{a}_1/v_r$, $\mathbf{A}_3=\mathbf{a}_1\wedge\mathbf{a}_2/v_r$.

The whole intensity is proportional to the " atom factor " $|f_0{}^2|$. But the " Bragg reflections " must be multiplied by the " Debye factor " $|D_0{}^2|$, which damps their intensity. The first term of (21) gives rise to a diffuse background. Since in the model Fig. 5a we have thermal oscillations only in the horizontal direction, the background is quite anisotropic too and shows maxima near the reflections $(3, 0)$, $(\bar{3}, 0)$ but is zero along the vertical axis $(0, h_2)$.

Fig. 6 gives the structure, Q-function and Fraunhofer pattern of an ideal mixed crystal without any displacements $\delta_k\mathbf{x}$. In each lattice cell we have again only one atom, but now two different sorts r with the electron clouds ρ_A and ρ_B. If $N\alpha$ atoms of the sort A are randomly distributed over the different lattice points, the rest occupied by $N(1-\alpha)$ atoms of the sort B, the hump $(0, 0, 0)$ of the Q-function now has the density distribution:

$$N\overline{\tilde{\rho}_r^2}=N[\alpha\,\tilde{\rho}_A^2+(1-\alpha)\,\tilde{\rho}_B^2] \quad . \quad . \quad (23)$$

All other humps are proportional to:†

$$\overline{\tilde{\rho}_r^2}=\overline{[\alpha\rho_A+(1-\alpha)\rho_B]^2}$$
$$=\alpha^2\,\tilde{\rho}_A^2+2\alpha(1-\alpha)\widehat{\rho_A\rho_B}+(1-\alpha)^2\,\tilde{\rho}_B^2 \quad . \quad (24)$$

Hence the first difference-hump at $(0, 0, 0)$ in (18) must be replaced by the difference of (23) and (24) and we obtain:

$$Q(\mathbf{x})=N\alpha(1-\alpha)\widehat{(\rho_A-\rho_B)^2}+\overline{\tilde{\rho}_r^2}(z_c\,\tilde{s}^2/v_r) \quad . \quad (25)$$

If f_A, f_B are the Fourier transforms of ρ_A, ρ_B from (25) immediately follows:

$$J(\mathbf{b})=N\alpha(1-\alpha)|f_A-f_B|^2+|\alpha f_A+(1-\alpha)f_B|^2\frac{1}{v_r}Z_c\widehat{|S^2|} \quad (26)$$

The first term again gives rise to a diffuse background (first calculated by von Laue (1926)).[17] Contrary to Fig. 5c, at zero angles it has values different from zero, too.

† If the electron clouds have no centre of symmetry, $2\widehat{\rho_A\rho_B}$ must be replaced by

$$\rho_A\widehat{(\mathbf{x})\rho_B}(-\mathbf{x})+\rho_A\widehat{(-\mathbf{x})\rho_B}(\mathbf{x}).$$

G*

Things become much more complicated if correlations exist between adjacent atoms with respect to their displacements and sorts. The single humps of the Q-function now have different shapes. Then the $I(b)$-function no longer has a smooth background but intense accumulations occur, mostly near to reciprocal lattice points, but outside the Bragg reflections. It is interesting to note that in all crystallographic theories the shape of the kernel is unchanged and proportional to the last term in (21) and (26). The Laue factor governs all calculations. Crystalline long-range order of the lattice peak function (19) remains untouched from all these distortions and no phenomena similar to Figs. 1–3 can be handled.

In the following sections we will discuss whether this long-range order in mixed crystals can be destroyed in a similar fashion to the high polymer lattices, if the atoms have different radii. Fig. 7 gives such an example. Now the cell edge-vectors vary from cell to cell. Let us for convenience assume again that no correlation exists between neighbours. If $H_k(\mathbf{z})$ is the probability distribution function, to find a special cell edge-vector† $\mathbf{a}_{k+1}=\mathbf{y}$ in the neighbouring cell has the probability:

$$H_k(\mathbf{y})\,H_k(\mathbf{z}).$$

To calculate the distance statistics between one lattice point and its second neighbour one must collect all combinations of $\mathbf{y}$, $\mathbf{z}$ with a constant vector sum

$$\mathbf{y}+\mathbf{z}=\mathbf{x}.$$

† $\mathbf{a}_k=\mathbf{z}$ in a lattice cell, then the combination with a cell edge vector.

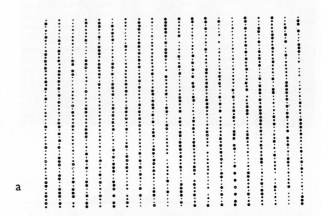

a

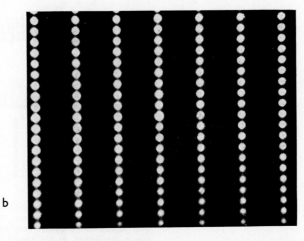

b

Fig. 6.—(a) *Ideal mixed crystal with two sorts of atoms*, (b) *its Q-function*

Since we are interested in the value of the second neighbour statistics $H_{2k}(\mathbf{x})$ at this point $\mathbf{x}$, we must integrate over all possible **z**-values. Hence we obtain

$$H_{2k}(\mathbf{x}) = \int H_k(\mathbf{y})\, H_k(\mathbf{x}-\mathbf{y})\, dv_y = \widehat{H_k\, H_k} \qquad (27)$$

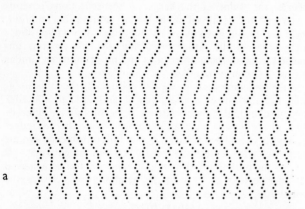

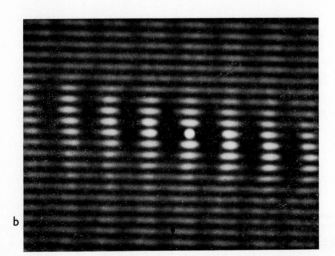

Each hump of the Q-function Fig. 7b in the direction k is given by:

$$H_{nk}(x) = \overbrace{\widehat{H_k\, \widehat{H_k\, H_k} \ldots \widehat{H_k\, H_k}}}^{(n-1)\ \text{times}} \qquad (28)$$

The average cell edge vector $\overline{\mathbf{a}_k}$ is given by $\int x H_k(\mathbf{x})\, dv_x$.

The square of the standard deviation of H_k in the direction of the unit vector $\mathbf{s}_t$ is defined by:

$$\Delta_t^2\, \mathbf{a}_k = \int (\mathbf{x}-\overline{\mathbf{a}_k},\, \mathbf{s}_t)^2\, H_k(\mathbf{x})\, dv_x,\quad \overline{\mathbf{a}_k} = \int \mathbf{x} H_k(\mathbf{x})\, dv_k \quad (29)$$

The humps on the negative k-axis are given by

$$H_{-nk}(\mathbf{x}) = H_{nk}(-\mathbf{x}). \qquad (30)$$

In the same way the hump $p_1\, p_2\, p_3$ of the Q-function is given for positive p_k-integers (*cf*, 13) by:[18]

$$H_{p1,\, p2,\, p3}(\mathbf{x})$$
$$= P(\mathbf{x}-0)\, \overbrace{H_1 H_2 \ldots H_1}^{|p_1|\ \text{times}} \overbrace{H_2 H_2 \ldots H_2}^{|p_2|\ \text{times}} \overbrace{H_3 H_3 \ldots H_3}^{|p_3|\ \text{times}} \quad (31)$$

Its centre of gravity lies at:

$$\overline{\mathbf{x}}_p = p_1\, \overline{\mathbf{a}}_1 + p_2\, \overline{\mathbf{a}}_2 + p_3\, \overline{\mathbf{a}}_3. \qquad (32)$$

Its squared standard deviation in the direction of the unit vector $\mathbf{s}_t$ is given by:

$$\Delta_t^2\, \mathbf{x} = p_1\, \Delta_t^2\, \mathbf{x}_1 + p_2\, \Delta_t^2\, \mathbf{x}^2 + p_3\, \Delta_t^2\, \mathbf{x}_3. \qquad (33)$$

All these relations are verified in the Q-function of Fig. 7. With the help of (30) and (31) the Fourier transform can be easily calculated. It is called " paracrystalline lattice factor $Z(\mathbf{b})$ ". If:

$$F_k(\mathbf{b}) = \mathscr{F}[H_k(\mathbf{x})], \quad k = 1, 2, 3 \qquad (34)$$

are the " statistic amplitudes " of the paracrystalline lattice one obtains :

$$Z(\mathbf{b}) = \prod_{k=1}^{3} (1 + F_k + F_k^2 + \ldots + F_k^* + F_k^{*2} + \ldots)$$

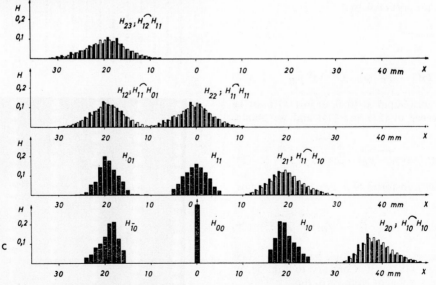

Fig. 7.—(a) *Model of a paracrystalline lattice, whose correlation statistics are rods parallel to the abscissa, (b) its Q-function. One can recognize with regard to horizontal neighbours an elliptic zone of interaction, where the humps do not merge one into the other. In the vertical direction the zone of interaction is unbounded, (c) Calculated (black) and observed (white) humps of the Q-function*

Taking into account that :

$$1+F+F^2+F^3+\ldots+F^{n-1}=(1-F^n)(1-F)^{-1}$$

one obtains with $n \to \infty$:[19]

$$Z(\mathbf{b})= \frac{1}{v_r}\, P(b-0)+\prod_{k=1}^{3} \mathrm{Re}\, \frac{1+F_k}{1-F_k} \quad . \qquad . \quad (35)$$

If all three H_k are point functions (35) degenerates into the crystalline lattice factor Z_c (*cf.* equation (22)).

In the paracrystalline lattice of Fig. 8 the two H_k's have globular shapes. The Fraunhofer pattern Fig. 8b divided through N is its lattice factor. One can transform (35) to:

$$Z(\mathbf{b})= \prod_{k=1}^{3} \frac{1-|F_k|}{1+|F_k|} +\text{peaks.} \qquad . \qquad . \quad (36)$$

The first term gives a diffuse background, and the second more and more broadened peaks. The integral width of the reflections $(h_1, 0, 0)$ in the direction $\bar{\mathbf{a}}$, for instance, is given by:[20]

$$\Delta b_1 = \frac{1}{2\bar{a}_1}\,[1-|F_1(h_1,0,0)|]=\frac{1}{\bar{a}_1}\,\pi^2 g_{11}^2\, h_1^2, \quad . \quad (37)$$

where :

$$g_{11}^2=\Delta_1{}^2\,\bar{a}_1/\bar{a}_1{}^2 \qquad . \qquad . \qquad . \quad (38)$$

is the square of the relative statistical fluctuation of the vector $\mathbf{a}_1$ in the direction 1. In the three-dimensional paracrystal there exist nine such independent g_{st}-values, which define many different types of distorted lattices. The "mesophases" of Hermann (1931)[21] for instance are special degenerate cases where some $g_{st}=0$, the rest larger than $0\cdot3$. In a crystal all $g_{st}=0$.

Strictly speaking, (36) is valid for an "ideal paracrystal" whose cells have all the shapes of parallelepipeds. If the cells are more deformed, correlation correction terms occur. In many practical cases they can be neglected.[21]

The intensity function of a paracrystal is just the same as (21) and (26), if one replaces Z_c by $Z(\mathbf{b})$ from equation (35). By the folding process with $|S^2|$ the width (37) of a peak increases. If N_1 is the weight averaged number of reflecting lattice planes one obtains as a first good approximation:

$$\Delta b_1 = \frac{1}{\bar{a}_1}\, \sqrt{[(\pi g_{11}\, h_1)^4+N_1{}^{-2}]} \qquad . \quad (39)$$

If the first summand is small (large) compared to the second, the reflections are Bragg-like (totally diffuse), hence their maxima are proportional to $N_1{}^2(N_1)$. Their integral intensities are proportional to :

$$D_k{}^2=2|F_k|(1+F_k)^{-1} . \qquad . \qquad . \quad (40)$$

These $D_k{}^2$ are Debye-like damping factors, but are derived from the paracrystalline distortions. Substituting (40) into the first term of (36), the paracrystalline diffuse background scattering can be rewritten as:

$$J_2(\mathbf{b})= \prod_{k=1}^{3} (1-D_k{}^2) \qquad . \qquad . \quad (41)$$

which has some similarity with the diffuse Debye scattering (first term in (21)).

The One-dimensional Mixed Paracrystal

As in the example of Fig. 6, $N\alpha$ atoms of the sort A statistically are intermixed with $N(1-\alpha)$ atoms of the sort B. Atoms A have a radius $R+dR$, atoms B a radius R. All atoms are placed on one straight row, the one touching the next. This one-dimensional structure for constant R and dR is again totally incompressible.

The probability distribution function to find an atom with radius x is given thus by a double-point function:

$$H_{1/2}(x)=(1-\alpha)\,P(x-R)+\alpha P(x-R-dR) \qquad . \quad (42)$$

Here P is a one-dimensional point function of the scalar variable x. According to (27) the distance statistics between the centres of adjacent atoms is given by the folding product of (42) with itself :

$$H_{2/2}=\widehat{H_{1/2}\,H_{1/2}}$$

$$=(1-\alpha)^2\,P(x-2R)+2\alpha(1-\alpha)\,P(x-2R-dR)$$

$$+\alpha^2 P(x-2R-2dR). \quad (43)$$

But this is not a coordination statistic, since the distance statistics of the centres of second neighbours is not given by folding $H_{2/2}$ with itself. To understand this we must bear in mind that between these two centres lie the radii of two different atoms and the diameter of a third atom. The diameter-probability distribution is given by :

$$H=(1-\alpha)\,P(x-2R)+\alpha P(x-2R-2dR) \qquad . \quad (44)$$

Hence the distance statistics of second neighbours are given by:

$$H_2=\widehat{H_{1/2}\,H\,H_{1/2}}=\widehat{H_{2/2}\,H.} \qquad . \qquad . \quad (45)$$

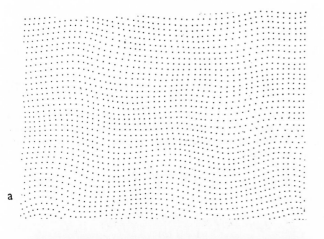

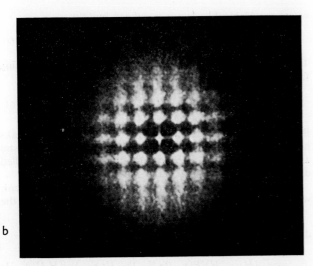

Fig. 8.—*Paracrystalline lattice with globular shaped coordination statistics and its Fraunhofer pattern*

For the distance statistics between nth neighbours one obtains:

$$H_n = \overbrace{H_{2/2} H H \ldots H}^{n-2 \text{ times}} \qquad . \qquad . \quad (46)$$

Hence $H(x)$ are the coordination statistics which build up the one-dimensional mixed paracrystal.

Fig. 9 shows the different statistics. $H_{2/2}$ and H have the same first momentum, which according to (29) is the averaged lattice constant $\bar{a}$:

$$\bar{a} = \int x H(x)\,\mathrm{d}x = \int x H_{2/2}(x)\,\mathrm{d}x = 2R(1+\alpha\delta),\ \ \delta = \frac{\mathrm{d}R}{R} \quad (47)$$

This is nothing but Vegard's rule. The standard deviation Δa of the coordination statistics H is given by (*cf.* (29)):

$$\Delta a = 2R\delta \sqrt{[\alpha(1-\alpha)]} = 2\mathrm{d}R\sqrt{[\alpha(1-\alpha)]} \quad . \quad (48)$$

Hence the one existing g-value is the quotient of (47) and (48):

$$g = \frac{\delta\sqrt{[\alpha(1-\alpha)]}}{1+\alpha\delta} \qquad . \qquad . \qquad . \quad (49)$$

Since the standard deviation of $H_{2/2}$ is $1/\sqrt{2}$ of the value (48), the humps of H_n have positions of their centres equidistant as in (32), but their widths do not follow the simple law (33). Moreover, to calculate the Q-function of the structure, one must take into account that strong correlations exist here between distances of atoms and their structure.†

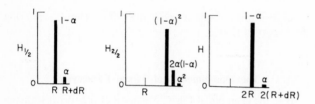

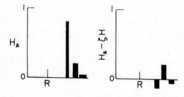

Fig. 9.—*The one-dimensional point coordination statistics $H_{1/2}$, $H_{2/2}$, H, H_A and $H_A - \zeta H$*

Let us suppose, for convenience, that atoms of sort B have the electron density distribution $\rho_0(x)$, those of sort A the distribution $\rho_A(x) = A\rho_0(x)$.‡

Then the hump (0) of the Q-function according to (23) is given by:

$$N\overline{\overset{2}{\rho_r}} = N\overset{2}{\rho_0}(1-\alpha+\alpha A^2) \qquad . \qquad . \quad (50)$$

the next hump by:

$$(N-1)\overset{2}{\overbrace{\rho_0}} H_A \text{ with } H_A$$

$$= (1-\alpha)^2 P(x-2R) + 2A\alpha(1-\alpha) P(x-2R-\mathrm{d}R)$$

$$+ A^2 \alpha^2 P(x-2R-2\mathrm{d}R) \quad (51)$$

† In equations (21) and (26) this correlation was neglected, since Z_e was the Laue factor. Replacing it by the paracrystalline lattice factor $Z(b)$, things become more complicated.

‡ At the end of this section we will replace $A\rho_0$ by a folding product $\widehat{\rho_A \rho_0}$. The following calculation is valid for both cases.

the nth hump by:

$$(N-n)\overset{2}{\overbrace{\rho_0}} \overbrace{H_A H \ldots H}^{n-1 \text{ times}}. \qquad . \qquad . \quad (52)$$

Introducing the shape function $s(x)$ of the linear paracrystal the factor $(N-n)$ can be replaced by (17), where $v_r = \bar{a}$. (50) agrees with (23). Subtracting $\overline{N\overset{2}{\rho_r}}$ we again obtain the first term of (25), which gives rise to the diffuse Laue scattering J_1 [first term of (26)]:

$$J_1(b) = N f_o^2\, \alpha(1-\alpha)(A-1)^2 = N\alpha(1-\alpha)|f_A - f_B|^2 \quad . \quad (53)$$

the hump at 0 is then reduced to $N\overset{2}{\rho_r}$. Now H_A has the integral value:

$$\int H_A(x)\,\mathrm{d}x = \zeta = (1-\alpha+\alpha A)^2 \quad . \qquad . \quad (54)$$

Hence $\overset{2}{\rho_r}$ and $\overset{2}{\rho_0} H_A$ have the same weights and therefore besides the factor $(N-n)$ the same is true for all remaining humps of the Q-function. Replacing H_A in (52) by:

$$H_A(x) = \zeta H(x) + [H_A(x) - 2H(x)] \qquad . \quad (55)$$

the first term produces humps of the Q-function, which are of type (31) and all inclusively the 0-hump folded with:

$$\overset{2}{\overline{\rho_r}} = \overset{2}{\rho_0}\, \zeta \qquad . \qquad . \qquad . \quad (56)$$

If:

$$f_0(b) = \mathscr{F}(\rho_0), \quad F(b) = \mathscr{F}(H), \quad F_A(b) = \mathscr{F}(H_A)$$

we get from the first term in (55) analogous to (35) and (26):

$$J_o(b) = \frac{1}{\bar{a}}\,|\bar{f}_r|^2\, Z\,\widehat{|S|}^2\,. \qquad . \qquad . \quad (57)$$

According to (36) it can be separated into a diffuse component J_2 and peaks of the character discussed in (39), (40). Since $|S|^2$ is point-like compared with the first term of (36) and has the weight:

$$\int S(b)^2\,\mathrm{d}b = N\bar{a} \qquad . \qquad . \qquad . \quad (58)$$

one obtains:

$$J_2(b) = N|\bar{f}_r|^2\,\frac{1-|F(b)|}{1+|F(b)|} = N|\bar{f}_r|^2 (1-D_1^2), \qquad . \quad (59)$$

where the Debye-like factor is defined by (40):

$$D_1^2 = 2|F|(1+|F|)^{-1}. \qquad . \qquad . \quad (60)$$

The term with the peaks J_4 is then proportional to the damping factor (61):

$$J_4 = J_0 - J_2 = \frac{1}{\bar{a}}\,|\bar{f}_r^2|\,[Z - \widehat{(1-D_1^2)}]\,|S|^2 \quad . \quad (61)$$

But contrary to the second terms in (21) and (26) the peaks have widths (39), which depend on the size of the paracrystal and the g-value (49) of the paracrystalline distortion (called distortion of the second kind).

Now we must calculate another intensity-component, which is produced by the second term of (55). Along the $+x$-axis from the Q-function we had left a remainder:

$$\mathrm{d}Q(x)$$

$$= \overset{2}{\rho_0}\,(H_A - \overbrace{\zeta H})[P(x-0)(N-1) + H(N-2) + \widehat{H\,H}(N-3)$$

$$+ \ldots]. \quad (62)$$

TABLE I.—*Intensity Components of the One-dimensional Mixed Paracrystal*

Comp.	Equations	Formula	Author
J_0	(57)	$\dfrac{1}{a}\mid\alpha f_A+(1-\alpha)f_B\mid^2\mid Z\mid\mid S^2\mid = J_2+J_4$ total paracryst. intensity	
J_1	(53)	$N\alpha(1-\alpha)\mid f_A-f_B\mid^2$	V. Laue (1926)
J_2	(60)	$N\mid\alpha f_A+(1-\alpha)f_B\mid^2(1-\mid D_1^2\mid)$	Huang (1947)
J_3	(73)	$N2\alpha(1-\alpha)\mid(f_B-f_A)[\alpha f_A+(1-\alpha)f_B]\mid\pi h\delta\sin 2\pi h$	Warren, Averbach and Roberts (1951)
J_4	(62)	J_0-J_2 even component of paracryst. peak	
J_5	(74)	$\dfrac{1}{a}\mid f_0^2\mid Re\left[(F_A-\zeta F)\dfrac{1+F}{1-F}\right]\mid S^2\mid$ odd component of paracryst. peak	

On the $-x$-axis lie the corresponding humps (see (30)). At $x=0$ no hump remained.

The Fourier transform of (62) analogous to the derivation of (35) contains a geometric series. One obtains:

$$\mathscr{F}(dQ)=\mid f_0^2\mid 2Re[(F_A-\zeta F)\overline{(1-F)^{-1}}]\mid S^2\mid/\overline{a} \quad . \quad (63)$$

Since:

$$\frac{2}{1-F}=1+\frac{1+F}{1-F} \quad . \quad . \quad . \quad (64)$$

it can be split into two components:

$$\mathscr{F}(dQ)=J_3+J_5. \quad . \quad . \quad (65)$$

The first one gives a background, the second contributes to the peaks. Let us calculate J_3 firstly:

From (54) we know that $H_A-\zeta H$ has the weight zero. Hence we get from (44) and (51) after a short calculation:

$$H_A-\zeta H=-C_1 P(x-2R)+(C_1+C_2)P(x-2R-dR)$$
$$-C_2 P(x-2R-2dR) \quad (66)$$

$$C_1=\zeta(1-\alpha)-(1-\alpha)^2$$
$$=\alpha(1-\alpha)[1+2(A-1)+\alpha(A-1)^2] \quad . \quad . \quad (67)$$

$$C_2=\zeta\alpha-\alpha^2 A^2=\alpha(1-\alpha)[1-\alpha(A-1)^2] \quad . \quad (68)$$

Hence:

$$C_1+C_2=2\alpha(1-\alpha) A>0 \quad . \quad . \quad (69)$$

$$C_1-C_2=2\alpha(1-\alpha)(A-1)[1+\alpha(A-1)]. \quad . \quad (70)$$

The real part of the Fourier transform of (66) is given by:†

$$Re(F_A-\zeta F)=(C_1+C_2)\cos 2\pi\ddot{h}\left(1+\frac{\delta}{2}\right)$$
$$-C_1\cos 2\pi\ddot{h}-C_2\cos 2\pi\ddot{h}(1+\delta) \quad (71)$$

with:
$$2Rb=\ddot{h}$$

Since:

$$\ddot{h}=\ddot{h}\left(1-\frac{\delta}{2}+\frac{\delta}{2}\right)\text{ and }\ddot{h}(1+\delta)=\ddot{h}\left(1+\frac{\delta}{2}+\frac{\delta}{2}\right)$$

from the cosinus theorem we obtain:

$$Re(F_A-\zeta F)=(C_1+C_2)\cos 2\pi\ddot{h}\left(1+\frac{\delta}{2}\right)\left(1-\cos 2\pi\ddot{h}\frac{\delta}{2}\right)$$
$$-C_1\sin 2\pi\ddot{h}\left(1+\frac{\delta}{2}\right)\sin 2\pi\ddot{h}\frac{\delta}{2}$$
$$+C_2\sin 2\pi\ddot{h}\left(1+\frac{\delta}{2}\right)\sin 2\pi\ddot{h}\frac{\delta}{2} \quad . \quad (72)$$

† $\mathscr{F}[P(x-x_0)]-=-\exp(2\pi i x_0 b)^{23}$

Since δ is a small quantity, the first term can be neglected and $\sin\gamma$ can be replaced by γ. Taking into account that $\mid S^2\mid$ is point-like compared with (72), we obtain for the component J_3 after substitution of (70) from (63), (64), (65) and (72):

$$J_3(b)=-N\mid f_0^2\mid 2\alpha(1-\alpha)(A-1)[1+\alpha(A-1)]\pi h\delta\sin 2\pi h \quad (73)$$

$J_5(b)$ produced by the second term of (64) is given by:

$$J_5(b)=\frac{1}{a}\mid f_0^2\mid Re\left[(F_A-\zeta F)\overline{\frac{1+F}{1-F}}\right]\mid S^2\mid \quad . \quad (74)$$

The diffusion component J_3 was first calculated by Warren, Averbach and Roberts.[24] If:

$$\delta(A-1)>0 \quad . \quad . \quad . \quad (75)$$

e.g. the heavier (lighter) atoms have the larger (smaller) diameter, J_3 near each reciprocal lattice point increases with decreasing and decreases with increasing scattering angle and is zero in the reciprocal lattice point. Together with the other diffusion components J_1 and J_2 the total background is higher at each reflection on this side towards larger $\mid b\mid$-values. If, on the other hand, the lighter atoms have larger diameters we have the contrary case.

The same tendency can be found in the peak-like component (74), which also is zero in the centre of the reflection. It produces an odd component in the paracrystalline reflections, whose component J_4 according to (62) is always even. Toman[25] has observed an odd component in Guinier–Preston zones of Al–Cu alloys, and from this Doi[26] calculated the displacements $\delta_k x_r$ of the lattice planes near the centre of such zones. Gerold[27] also discussed such phenomena.

If we finally replace the assumption:

$$\rho_B=\rho_0, \quad \rho_A=A\rho_0$$

and introduce the atomic scattering factors f_A^2 and f_B^2, we get the results laid down in Table I.

The total intensity function is given by:

$$J=J_1+J_2+J_3+J_4+J_5 \quad . \quad . \quad (76)$$

The three first components are diffuse, the other two peak-like. Introducing the products (35) and (41), expressions for the three-dimensional mixed paracrystal can be obtained which at least are first approximations. Introducing the Guinier approximation[29] for a statistics amplitude (34) one obtains with (29):

$$\mid F_k(\mathbf{b})\mid\sim\exp(-2\pi^2 b^2\Delta_b^2 a_k), \quad . \quad . \quad (77)$$

where $\Delta_b a_k$ is the standard deviation of $H_k(\mathbf{x})$ in the direction of the vector $\mathbf{b}$. Then (41) is approximately given by:

$$2\pi^2 b^2(\Delta_b^2 a_1+\Delta_b^2 a_2+\Delta_b^2 a_3) \quad . \quad . \quad (78)$$

For many crystals all three summands in the bracket are equal and given by (48). Hence the damping factor D_1^2 in the

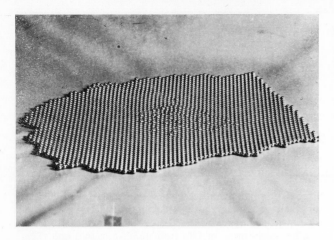

Fig. 10.—*Model of a two-dimensional crystal. In the central region some larger steel balls*

Fig. 12.—*The central region has become paracrystalline*

one-dimensional case, given by:

$$D_1{}^2 = \exp\left[-8\pi^2\,\alpha(1-\alpha)(\mathrm{d}R)^2\,b^2\right]. \qquad . \quad (79)$$

in a three-dimensional paracrystal must be replaced by:

$$D^2 = \exp\left[-24\pi^2\,\alpha(1-\alpha)(\mathrm{d}R)^2\,b^2\right]. \qquad . \quad (80)$$

Huang[28] found nearly the same factors.†

Two-dimensional Models

As shown below, experiments demonstrate that atoms in paracrystalline structures behave much more as rigid spheres than as liquid-like deformable clouds. The following experiments give a first rough picture of what could occur in atomic dimensions if rigid atoms of two different sizes were mixed.

In Fig. 10 about 3000 steel balls of 4 mm diameter are laid down on a foil so that they crowd together without being attached by surface conditions. They build up one single two-dimensional crystal. In the central region about 40 balls are carefully replaced by spheres with 4·5 mm diameter. They cannot touch the foil at this moment.

By shaking the drum they begin slowly to obtain more room for themselves. Step dislocations grow from the central region to the boundary of the crystal (Fig. 11). More shaking brings the thick balls into equilibrium also. In the central

† See for further details the following section on the three-dimensional problem. A complete discussion will be given in another paper.

region the crystallographic lattice planes are replaced by paracrystalline bent rows of spheres (Fig. 12).

If, on the other hand, the thick balls are arranged regularly in superstructures, no changes occur with further shaking (Fig. 13). Only one superstructure on the right-hand side has not, at this moment, obtained the necessary space for itself. Two-step dislocations go to the boundary of the surrounding crystal. Short-range order is established.

Some Remarks on the Three-dimensional Problem

In a previous section the condition of incompressibility automatically yielded paracrystalline distortions. This same condition according to Huang (1947)[28] *et al.*[36] in the three-dimensional case does not introduce paracrystalline displacements, the atoms in a similar way as in an ideal crystal know their crystalline lattice points and are displaced by thermal vibrations as in the case of (14). Hence the Huang factor (*cf.* (79), (80)) acts as a Debye factor H_0, defined by (15) and (20). The Q-function is of the type of Fig. 5b and is different from Fig. 7b.

If compressibility is zero, from Hooke's law follows a possible solution for the displacement $\delta_s x_k$ of an atom at $\mathbf{x}_k$, if at $\mathbf{x}_s$ lies an atom of the sort A:

$$\delta_s\,\mathbf{x}_k = c\,\frac{\mathbf{x}_k - \mathbf{x}_s}{|\mathbf{x}_k - \mathbf{x}_s|^3}\,; \quad c = R^2\,\mathrm{d}R . \qquad . \quad (81)$$

All $N\alpha$ disturbance centres produce effects which can all be added without any interference. Hence the total shift $\delta\mathbf{x}_k$ of the atom k is given by:

$$\delta\mathbf{x}_k = \sum_{s=1}^{K}\delta_s\,\mathbf{x}_k,\ \text{if}\ \alpha \ll 1;\quad N\alpha = K. \qquad . \quad (82)$$

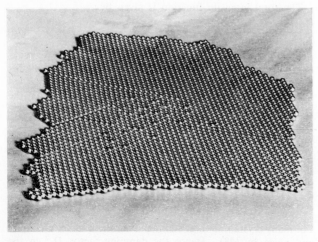

Fig. 11.—*Step dislocations arise after shaking*

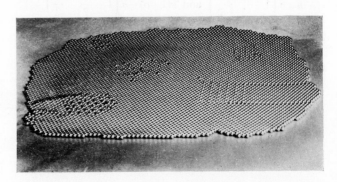

Fig. 13.—*Short range order of different superstructures*

The sum has to be taken over all K atoms of the sort A with $s \neq k$. Let us for convenience discuss a single crystal with the shape of a sphere of radius r_0 and whose centre lies at $x=0$. For large crystals we can replace the summation in (82) by an integral and get from (81) for the averaged shift:

$$\overline{\delta x_k} = \frac{Kc}{4\pi r_0^3/3} \int' \frac{x-x_k}{|x-x_k|^3} \cdot 4\pi x^2 \, dx \quad . \qquad . \quad (83)$$

$\int'$ means that the integral is to be taken over the entire r_0-sphere except for a R-sphere around $x=x_k$. Since the K atoms A are randomly distributed in the solid solution, we know that in the statistical average the sphere remains a sphere with an increased radius $r_0(1+\alpha\delta)$. Hence for the averaged displacement of an atom at $x=x_k$ we get:

$$\overline{\delta x_k} = \alpha\delta \cdot x_k \qquad . \qquad . \quad (84)$$

For the average of the square displacement one obtains from (81):

$$\overline{\delta x_k^2} = c^2 \sum_{s=1}^{K} \sum_{t=1}^{K} \frac{x_k - x_s}{|x_k - x_s|^3} \frac{x_k - x_t}{|x_k - x_t|^3}$$

The $K(K-1)$ summands with $s=t$ give the result:

$$(1 - K^{-1})(\overline{\delta x_k})^2.$$

Hence the standard deviation of the displacement of an atom for $K \gg 1$ is given by the K summands with $s=t$. Replacing the sum by an integral again one obtains:

$$\Delta^2 = \overline{\delta x_k^2} - \overline{\delta x_k}^2 = \frac{Kc^2}{4\pi r_0^3/3} \int' \left[\frac{x-x_k}{|x-x_k|^3} \right]^2 4\pi x^2 \, dx$$

specially for $x_k = 0$ one obtains:

$$\Delta^2 = \frac{3Kc^2}{Rr_0^3} = 3\alpha(dR)^2 \qquad . \qquad . \quad (85)$$

In a similar way for two-dimensional structures of incompressible atoms with a radial r^{-1} distance law one obtains:

$$\Delta^2 = 2\alpha(dR)^2 \cdot \ln(r_0/2R). \qquad . \qquad . \quad (86)$$

Finally from (33) and (48) we find for one-dimensional incompressible structures with an r_0-distance law:

$$\Delta^2 = 4\alpha(1-\alpha)(dR)^2 (r_o/2R). \qquad . \qquad . \quad (87)$$

This one-dimensional case, which according to the section on p. 87 gives rise to paracrystalline distortions, appears in solid solutions, where the atoms A aggregate in plate-like zones: for example, Guinier–Preston zones in Al–Cu alloys. But according to Figs 10–13 the one dimensional statistics (42)–(44) of p. 87 here must be replaced by three-dimensional functions which take into account the curvature of the rows of atoms. The two-dimensional case (86) occurs if the precipitations of the A-atoms inside the solid solution are rod-like. Since Δ^2 again is a function of r_0 we are also here in the case of paracrystalline distortions.

If on the other hand the atoms of the sort A are randomly distributed over the lattice points x_k and show no clustering effects, according to (85) paracrystalline distortions cannot occur. Nevertheless we must not forget that this only happens if the radial r^{-2}-law (81) holds. Insofar Huang's calculation is correct. However, Huang's calculation does not hold for non-spherical crystals, since the lattice in the statistical average is deformed (see Fig. 4 left-hand side at the bottom). Moreover, the atoms in this case suffer tremendous deformations, which in reality would not happen.

If, for instance, $\delta = dR/R$ is positive, the neighbouring atom is shifted and deformed markedly: its one surface is shifted by an amount dR, the opposite surface by $dR/9$ (see Fig. 4). It suffers in radial direction, hence a relative contraction of about $4\delta/9$, orthogonal to this a relative dilatation of $2\delta/3$. Hence it is deformed to an ellipsoid of revolution, whose quotient of axes length is about $1-\delta$. If, moreover, the crystal without atoms of the sort A has the shape of a rod, after inserting the thicker atoms A it becomes a barrel. (81) hence leads to some results which in the atomic and macroscopic scale do not satisfy. Recently Doi[†] evaluated experimental data of Toman (1955),[25] who had investigated Guinier–Preston zones in Al–Cu alloys. He found an odd component in the reflections (*cf.* (74)) which leads to δx_k-values appreciably different from the quadratic law (81). For the case of one substitutional impurity in an f.c.c. lattice Flinn and Maradudin[30] have shown theoretically that essential deviations occur from equation (81).

The above authors assume that the electrical potential around a single atom is spherically symmetric and rigid, and calculate the equilibrium positions of atoms surrounding a thicker atom of the sort A. In the case of a f.c.c. lattice, appreciable displacements in the radial direction occur mostly in the directions 110, 101, ..., where adjacent atoms are in touch with each other. Here the constant c of (81) is large: in the directions 100, 010, ..., c is very small. But the atoms in the direction 210 suffer a displacement, which is not radially directed but more parallel to the neighbouring direction 110.

Introducing the polar coordinates r, θ, ϕ and denoting the three polar coordinates of δx_k by δ_r, δ_θ, δ_ϕ one obtains:

$$\frac{\partial}{\partial r} r^2 \delta_r = -\frac{r}{\sin\theta} \left[\frac{\partial}{\partial\theta} \sin\theta\delta_\theta + \frac{\partial}{\partial\phi} \delta_\phi \right] - \gamma k \quad . \quad (88)$$

k is the isothermal compressibility and γ a constant only, if (81) holds. By putting $\theta=0$ for the 110-direction, and $\phi=0$ for a plane containing the 110 and 210 directions from Flinn's calculation we obtain that $\partial/\partial\theta \sin\theta\delta_\theta < 1$ for small θ and hence:

$$\frac{\partial}{\partial r} r^2 \delta_r + \gamma k > 0. \qquad . \qquad . \quad (89)$$

Assuming a distance law $\delta_r = c(\theta, \phi) r^n$ we obtain for $k=0$ for all directions 110, 101, ..., with large c-values, $n > -2$. For the directions 100, 010, ..., with small c-values:

$$n < -2.$$

Hence the atom A in 12 directions 110 displaces the neighbouring atoms markedly over larger distances. Though this effect is not so pronounced as in the case of rigid balls (Figs 10–13), paracrystalline distortions would also occur.

Experimental Results on Fe–Al Alloys

We have investigated a series of Fe–Al alloys with different atom percentage 100α of Al.[‡] However, this material offers some difficulties (microstrains, for instance, which cannot be removed so easily, since at higher temperatures the Al-atoms begin to migrate). Nevertheless, we think that the following results can give some evidence of paracrystallinity. At least these experiments (and others not yet published) can be more conveniently understood by means of the concept of para-crystals.

† Private communication.

‡ Prof. Oelsen and Dr. Möller from the Max-Planck-Institut Düsseldorf kindly assisted us in preparing the samples.

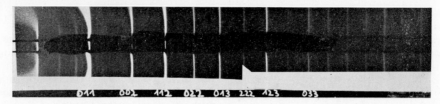

Fig. 14.—*X-ray pattern of Fe–Al alloy with 12·6 at. % Al, 15 h annealed in H_2 at 450°C. MoK_{α_2} and fine focus tube. In the central region one layer of the two-layered X-ray film is removed to obtain undistorted line profiles*

All the samples under investigation have b.c.c. lattices. Hence, according to Flinn and Maradudin, the displacements δx will be most pronounced in the directions 111, $^+\bar{1}11, \ldots$. We have investigated the integral widths Δb of the reflections (110), (220), (330), (440) of alloys with $\alpha=0\%$ and $=12·6\%$ Al. Since the netplanes ($hh0$) have an angle of 33° with the 111-directions sufficiently large paracrystalline distortions are to be expected. Mo–$K\alpha_2$-radiation[†] and a high-precision Guinier–AEG double-cylinder diffraction camera were used. In combination with a fine-focus X-ray tube,[‡] a bent Johann-crystal gave with $CaWO_4$-powder Debye–Scherrer lines of 0·2 mm width ($2\theta=0·1°$). Since the observed Fe–Al patterns had at least four times wider reflections collimation errors were not to be taken into account.

Fig. 14 shows an X-ray pattern with $\alpha=12·6\%$ Al annealed for 15 h at 450°C. The microphotometer curves give Gaussian-like reflections (110) and (220), while (330) and (440) have a faint tail at larger scattering angles. Since at 700°C Al markedly evaporates, we think that this tail is produced by regions with smaller α-values and, hence, a smaller lattice constant. This is the main reason why the errors of the experimental results are relatively high at this moment ($\sim 10\%$).

The line widths are given by the last term of (26), which for Gaussian-like profiles yields an integral width (39). In Fig. 15 the squared integral widths of the observed reflections ($hh0$) are plotted against h^4.

We see that the line widths of the unannealed powder with $\alpha=0\%$, which was obtained by filing the metal from the bulk, does not fulfil (39). The full line drawn through the experimentally measured points ● ● is calculated by:

$$(\Delta b)^2 = G^2 h^2 + L^{-2} \qquad . \qquad . \quad (90)$$

showing that microstrains are responsible for the line broadening with increasing scattering angle. After annealing for 15 h at 450°C this broadening effect is drastically reduced, proving that most of the microstrains have been removed. The full line is again calculated with (90) and shows that the G-value by annealing drops down from $1·2\times10^{-3}$ Å^{-1} to $0·35\times10^{-3}$ Å^{-1}.

Both curves with $\alpha=0\%$ Al intersect the ordinate at the same point $(\Delta b)^2\times10^6=2$ and show that the mean size of the crystallites:

$$L=\frac{1}{\Delta b}\cong 710 \text{ Å}$$

does not change by annealing for 15 h at 450°C. This agrees well with the fact that 450°C lies far below the temperature of recrystallisation.

On the other hand, the sample with 12·6% Al after the same annealing process shows a broadening not removable and of the type given by equation (39). The full line corresponding to this sample, drawn in Fig. 15 through the measured widths

† See for details Hofmann and Jagodzinski.[31]
‡ See for details Hosemann[33] and Hosemann and Hoeft.[34]

Δb were analysed numerically by means of equations (39) and (90) and gave the following parameters:

$$L=580 \text{ Å}; \quad G=0·5\times10^{-3} \text{ Å}^{-1}; \quad g=0·6\% \quad . \quad (91)$$

The dotted line which fits also within the errors with the experimental data is given by:

$$L=500 \text{ Å}; \quad G=0; \quad g=0·8\%$$

From these results we can draw the conclusion that again most of the microstrains are removed by annealing. However, paracrystalline distortions along the (110) netplanes occur with a g-value (*cf.* (38)) of:

$$g_{110}=0·7\% \qquad . \qquad . \qquad . \quad (92)$$

From the observed positions of the ($hh0$)-reflections one obtains by means of (47) the δ-value of the Al atoms in the Fe lattice of (*cf.* (47)):

$$\delta=0·059.$$

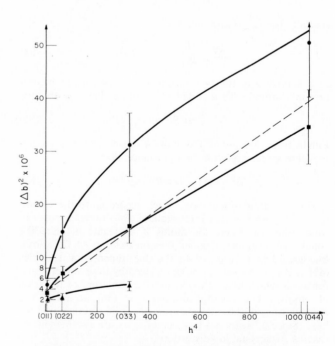

● *no Al and not annealed*
——— *theoretical curve* $(\Delta b)^2 = G^2 . h^2$ *pure (microstrains)*
▲ *no Al, annealed 15 h at 450°C, practically no microstrains*
■ *12·6 at. % of Al, 15 h at 450°C annealed in H_2-atmosphere*
- - - - *theoretical curve according to equation (39), showing pure paracrystalline distortions*
——— *theoretical curve with paracrystalline distortions and a small amount of microstrains (see (91))*

Fig. 15.—*Observed integral widths Δb of ($hh0$) reflections of Fe–Al samples*

This result agrees well with the lattice constants published by Taylor and Jones.[32] If the atoms would behave like rigid balls, from (49) with $\alpha = 0.12$ we would get:

$$g = 1.9\%.$$

Furthermore, if the atoms would follow the distance law (81) and behave like liquid droplets, we would according to (85) obtain:

$$g = 0\%.$$

The experimentally observed value (92) lies in between these two extreme cases and proves that according to the calculations of Flinn and Maradudin (who proposed rigid electrical potentials) the nearest neighbours of an Al atom are only so much deformed, that an effective δ-value in the 110-direction of:

$$\delta \sim 0.03 \qquad . \qquad . \qquad . \quad (93)$$

arises. In the case of liquid-like atoms according to (81) the centre of the next nearest neighbours of Al atoms are shifted by $dR/4$, hence $\delta \sim 0.015$.

More detailed work, both theoretically and experimentally, must be done, to describe the phenomenon of paracrystallinity in metallic alloys adequately.

References

1 Zernike, F. and Prins, J. A. *Z. Phys.*, 1927, **41**, 184.
2 Debye, P. P. and Menke, H. *Z. Phys.*, 1930, **31**, 797.
3 Hosemann, R. *Z. Phys.*, 1949, **127**, 16. *Z. Phys.*, 1950, **128**, 1 and 465.
4 Hosemann, R. and Bagchi, S. N. " *Direct Analysis of Diffraction by Matter,*" 1962, (Amsterdam: North-Holland).
5 Bear, R. S. and Rugo, H. J. *Ann. N.Y. Acad. Sci.*, 1951, **53**, 627.
6 Hosemann, R. and Bonart, R. *Mark. Chem.*, 1960, **39**, 105.
7 Hess, K. and Kiessig, H. *Nat. Wiss.*, 1943, **31**, 171.
8 Lindenmeyer, P. H. and Hosemann, R. *J. Appl. Phys.*, 1963, **34**, 42.
9 Hosemann, R. and Wilke, W. *Faserstoffe u. Textiltechnik*, 1964 (in press).
10 Reference 4, p. 87.
11 *Ibid.* p. 269.
12 *Ibid.* p. 245.
13 *Ibid.* p. 160.
14 *Ibid.*, p. 218.
15 *Ibid.*, p. 246.
16 Ewald, P. P. *Proc. Phys. Soc.*, 1940, **52**, 167.
17 Laue, M. v. *Ann. Phys.*, 1962a, **81**, 877; *Z. Krist.* 1926b, **64**, 115.
18 Reference 4, p. 139.
19 *Ibid.*, p. 310.
20 *Ibid.*, p. 325, 334.
21 *Ibid.*, p. 310.
22 *Ibid.*, p. 325.
23 *Ibid.*, p. 165.
24 Warren, B. E., Averbach, B. L. and Roberts, B. W. *J. Appl. Phys.*, 1951, **22**, 1493.
25 Toman, K. *Act. Cryst.*, 1955, **8**, 587.
26 Doi, K. *Act. Cryst.* 1960, **13**, 45.
27 Gerold, V. *Z. Met. Kde.*, 1954, **45**, 599.
28 Huang, K. *Proc. Roy. Soc.*, 1947, **190A**, 102.
29 Reference 4, p. 308.
30 Flinn, P. A. and Maradudin, Z. A. *Ann. Phys.*, 1962, **18**, 61.
31 Hofmann, E. G. and Jagodzinski, H. *Z. Met. Kde.*, 1955, **46**, 601.
32 Taylor, A. and Jones, R. W. *J. Appl. Phys.*, 1958, **29**, 522.
33 Hosemann, R. *Z. Angew. Phys.*, 1955, **7**, 532.
34 Hosemann, R. and Hoeft, J. *Z. angew. Phys.*, 1959, **11**, 365.
35 Laval, J. *J. de Phys. et Rad.*, 1954, **15**, 545 and 657.
36 Borie, B. *Act. Cryst.*, 1957, **10**, 89; *Act. Cryst.*, 1959, **12**, 280.

THE STRUCTURE AND PROPERTIES OF COMPLEX AND HETEROPHASE MATERIALS

By L. HOLLIDAY, M.A., B.Sc., F.R.I.C., M.I.Chem.E.,* and J. MANN, M.A., D.Phil., A.R.I.C.*

SYNOPSIS

Complex heterophase materials (sometimes called composites) fall within the province of materials technology rather than materials science. Materials as diverse as fibre-glass resin systems, rubber reinforced with carbon black, expanded thermoplastics, asphalt aggregates and concrete are included in this class. Some typical examples will be described.

The study of these materials is complicated by geometrical and topological factors which are a consequence of their structure. These variables, and the various phase relationships which are possible, will be discussed together with the concept of the representative cell. In addition, some problems involved in calculating the physical properties of the system from the geometry of the system and the physical properties of the components will be outlined.

Introduction

The class of materials which has variously been described as complex, heterophase, or composite is so vast that some explanation is required for any attempt to deal with it in a single paper. Our justification is that the study of such materials is at a very early stage of development, and there is a need for generalizations. We shall attempt to show the advantages of the generalized approach, and to indicate some of the gaps in our knowledge and how these may be overcome.

To begin with, it is necessary to start with a working definition of a complex material. Such a definition is bound to be arbitrary, since there are many points in common between a steel (which would not normally to considered a complex material) and a cermet, or between a crystalline polymer and a rubber which is reinforced with carbon black. We shall define a complex material as a solid which is made by physically combining two or more existing materials to produce a multiphase system with different physical properties from the starting materials. Some chemical interaction often occurs in the process, but in most cases at least one phase remains substantially unchanged. We shall not attempt a more rigorous definition at this stage.

The Variables Which Define a Complex Material

In order to describe a complex material fully, it is necessary to deal with (1) the geometrical variables and (2) the composition variables. Since this involves the frequent use of the word " phase ", it is necessary to point out that we frequently use the word in a descriptive rather than a " Gibbsian " or thermodynamic sense when dealing with complex materials. The Phase Rule is valid for phases which are in equilibrium, and is derived by assuming that the chemical potential of a particular component in each phase is the same. The Phase Rule, therefore, applies to many phases in complex materials, as for example in alloys. It does not apply, however, to all those classes of complex materials where one material is deliberately added to another. Since these systems are not in equilibrium, they have additional degrees of freedom (e.g. the nature and amount of

the added phases), which are of great importance in the development of complex materials.

There are clearly a large number of possible phase relationships, which fall into two broad classes:

(1) One continuous phase—one or more disperse phases.

(2) Two or more continuous phases—each continuous phase may contain one or more disperse phases.

This then raises the question—what size does a phase have to be before it becomes a separate phase. This is merely a question of definition, because there is no sharp dividing line at which a heterogeneity or region of inhomogeneity becomes a second phase. In the case of added disperse phases (as opposed to disperse phases which are formed in situ) the lowest size depends mainly on the lowest size in which solid particles are manufactured and can be handled. Carbon black is near the lower limit, with a diameter which may go down to 0.01μ.

If a gas is the disperse phase (as in an expanded thermoplastic) the dividing line between homogeneity and heterogeneity is even more difficult to draw. The inherent voids or holes in a glassy or crystalline polymer may themselves be of much greater than molecular dimensions. It is necessary to postulate such voids in order to explain the difference between the theoretical and the actual strength of some materials, e.g. ceramics. This concept goes back to the work of Griffith.[1] The voids may not be much smaller than the particles of carbon black of 0.01μ mentioned above. They may contain air or water which has diffused into the material. Recent work on gas solubility in polymers[2] shows that the total volume of free space is of the order of magnitude of 3% by volume of material. Voids in the range 15–200Å in diameter have been reported in monofilaments.[3] On the other hand, when holes or cells are deliberately introduced into a material such as polystyrene by gassing and subsequently expanding, they are very much larger than the natural voids or holes and are of the order of 100μ in diameter. It is difficult to produce cells which are much smaller than this.

To describe a system with one or more disperse phases in a continuous phase, we have to consider the following four features:[4, 5]

(a) The geometry of the disperse phase(s):

(1) Shape of particles.

(2) Size and size-distribution of particles.

* Carrington Plastics Laboratory, Shell Chemical Co. Ltd., Urmston, Manchester.

(3) Concentration and concentration-distribution of particles.

(4) Orientation of particles.

(5) Topology of particles.

(b) The state of matter of the disperse phase(s).

(c) The composition of the disperse phase(s).

(d) The composition of the continuous phase.

The geometry of complex materials

SYSTEMS WITH ONE CONTINUOUS PHASE

It will be seen that to describe the geometry of the disperse phase is a complicated task, since we have to consider the geometry of the individual particles, as well as the arrangement in space of the particles in relation to each other. Shape, size, and size-distribution are properties of the particles whilst orientation, concentration, and topology are features of the system. These geometrical variables are well recognized in metallography, but outside the field of metals they have been paid little attention. However, even though metallurgical phases are usually Gibbsian, the same geometrical and morphological factors are important in metals and in complex materials.

The shape of most disperse phases encountered in materials technology can be considered as approximating to spheres or cylinders. Depending on the height : diameter ratio, the cylinders may in turn be platelets at one extreme or rods at the other. For example, the gas cells in an expanded material can be regarded as spheres. Below a certain volume fraction they are true spheres, but above the volume fraction at which they are close packed they become polyhedra (which can be regarded as spheres to a close approximation). Examples of platelets and rods are metal flitters and glass fibres.

The size and size-distribution are important variables since they basically control the texture of the material. Together with volume fraction, they also determine the interfacial area, which plays a large part in determining the magnitude of the interaction between the disperse phase (or phases) and the continuous phase.

Concentration is usually measured in terms of volume or weight fraction. The concentration distribution describes the extent to which the phases are mixed and is the most important single measure of the homogeneity of the system. It is not the sole measure of the homogeneity of the system, however, since every independent geometrical variable which can be

described by a distribution function (as for example size-distribution) is independently affected by mixing and is a separate criterion of homogeneity. This point will be discussed further below. The concept of homogeneity is naturally of great importance, since it determines the extent by which a representative volume of material differs in physical properties from the bulk of the material.

The orientation of the particles affects the isotropy of the systems. With non-spherical particles there is a possibility that the processing steps by which the material is manufactured (e.g. mixing or extrusion) will induce orientation of the particles and hence produce some anisotropy.

By topology of the particles, we mean their spatial relation to each other. For example, it is possible to imagine a dispersion of spherical particles so arranged that they form a network in which the particles are touching. This may happen at a much lower concentration than that at which the close packing of spheres becomes possible. An interesting example of this is the dispersion of carbon black in rubber. Above a concentration of about 10%, the electrical conductivity increases markedly. This has been attributed to the formation of filaments of spheres of carbon black. An example of this type of phenomenon is shown in Fig. 1, which is an electron micrograph ($\times 4000$) of a rubber latex.

TWO OR MORE CONTINUOUS PHASES

The problem of producing a material which is made up of two or more continuous phases is an interesting one. The simplest example is a sponge or a sintered metal. A sintered metal can be made with a wide range of porosities. It has a continuous metal phase and sometimes a continuous air phase. By impregnation, the air phase can be replaced by lubricating oil (as in a self-lubricated bearing), by a thermoplastic, or by a second metal. Alternatively, two materials may be mixed as powders, and the mixture may be sintered as in the cermets, where one component is a ceramic and the other a metal. These two methods are virtually the only techniques available for producing two continuous phases, and this imposes limits on the volume fraction of each phase which can be introduced.

If the two materials A and B have melting points T_A and T_B where $T_A > T_B$ and the phases are produced sequentially, then phase A will be made by sintering at $T < T_A$ and phase B will be introduced as a liquid at T_B. The volume fraction of $A(V_A)$ will depend on the shape of the particles and their packing, and on the pressure and temperature of the sintering operation.

Assuming that the particles of A are equal spheres, then the range of V_A for symmetrical arrangements of the spheres are:

Co-ordination number	Arrangement	V_A
6	Cubic	0·53
8	Body-centred cubic	0·59
12	Face centred cubic	
	Hexagonal close packed	0·75

A random packing of equal spheres would give V_A in the order of 0·6–0·63. With a random packing of unequal spheres V_A may be increased to 0·85–0·9. The effect of sintering is to raise this figure slightly, but at the same time the balance $(1 - V_A)$, which may be of the order of 0·1, will now be made up of a mixture of closed and open cells, of which only the open cells will accept phase B.

If the particles have a very irregular shape, for example if they are flakes, they may pack initially in a much more open way (V_A as low as 0·1). After sintering the packing density

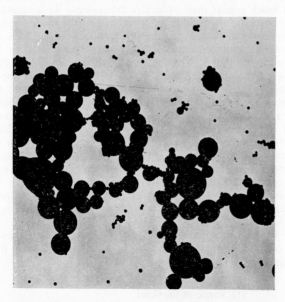

Fig. 1.—*Cluster formation in synthetic rubber latex* ($\times 4000$)

(a)	(b)	(c)
1-Dimensional continuous phase A in continuous phase B	2-Dimensional continuous phase A in continuous phase B	3-Dimensional continuous phase A in continuous phase B

Fig. 2.—*Model geometry of systems containing two continuous phases*

will increase and V_A will be >0.1. Thus, considering both spherical and non-spherical particles, the extreme ranges for V_A will be >0.2 say and <0.9. The most normal range will be >0.5 and <0.9. The extreme ranges of V_B will, therefore, be 0.1–0.8 and the normal range 0.1–0.5. This indicates the geometrical factors which limit the phase ratio which is possible. This is illustrated below in the system MgO–Mg_2SiO_4.

It will further be appreciated that the geometry of systems which are made up of two continuous phases is exceedingly complex. Simple examples of two-continuous phases are shown in Fig. 2.

We have taken a cube as the shape of the solid, and for descriptive purposes call the rod-like continuous phase " 1 "-dimensional and the sheet-like continuous phase " 2 "-dimensional, even though phase A must have a definite thickness and must in fact be 3-dimensional.

Diagram (*b*), which shows a 2-dimensional continuous phase A, is similar to laminated and sandwich structures, and to structures which include a surface coating as one phase. This is a special form of two-continuous-phase systems, since the continuity of phase B is interrupted in the dimension normal to phase A. If phase A in this example contains discrete holes, then B may exhibit normal 3-dimensional continuity. Diagrams (*a*) and (*b*) also illustrate the fact that if one phase is effectively 1- or 2-dimensional, the system will normally be anisotropic. 3-dimensional two-continuous-phase systems, of which (*c*) is a simple example will normally be isotropic although it is easily possible to visualize anisotropic versions of this type of system.

The Representative Cell Concept

In order to look for the generalizations which will facilitate the study of complex materials, it is necessary to describe the systems in a quantitative way. We have already mentioned the geometrical factors which are involved, and since these are independent of the nature of the materials, they form a suitable starting-point. We also need some measure of the scale and order (or texture and homogeneity) of the system. One of us has recently proposed for this the concept of the representative cell.[6]

To date, the only unit which has been available to materials scientists has been the crystallographic unit cell. Whilst this is the ultimate basic unit, it does not describe completely either polycrystals (which have an additional degree of disorder stemming from the relative orientation of the individual crystals) or complex materials which may contain crystalline or amorphous phases. For these materials we need to consider—in addition to the unit cell—an additional larger unit which describes the " texture " and order of the material as a whole. We have called this larger unit the representative cell, which is an imaginary volume representing to a defined and arbitrary probability the heterogeneity of the actual material.

In the general case, the heterogeneity cannot be uniquely described by a single geometrical variable. For example, concentration distribution and particle-size distribution are independent variables, each of which independently affects the heterogeneity. Thus, if n geometrical variables are required to describe the system, there will be n different sizes of the representative cell. In this case the representative cell can be described as the largest of these, since this will embrace the others.

We shall now illustrate how the principle works by applying it to a simple example. Consider a system in which equal spheres are randomly distributed in a matrix. The concentration of spheres may be measured as a volume fraction or in terms of numbers per unit volume. Since the spheres are equal these units are equivalent, but since they are randomly distributed the concentration varies from point to point in the system. This is the only geometrical variable. If the average volume concentration is 1%, the local concentrations will fall above or below this figure. Imagine that 100 equal samples of size v_1 are taken, and that 99 samples fall within the concentration range 0.9–1.1% volume. If 100 equal smaller samples of size v_2 are taken, imagine that 99 samples fall within the concentration range 0.8–1.2%. We must now produce a criterion by which a small volume of material is judged to be representative. If the criterion is that the concentration should be between 0.9 and 1.1%, then volume v_1 is the smallest volume with a 99% probability of representing the material. If the criterion is that it should be between 0.8 and 1.2% then volume v_2 has a 99% probability of representing the material, v_1 is, of course $>v_2$. For the same concentration, as the diameter of the spheres increases, then v will increase.

Let us now introduce a second geometrical variable, and imagine that the spheres are not equal. To begin with, assume for simplicity that they are made up of 50% diameter d_1 and 50% of diameter d_2. The criterion by which a small volume of material is judged to be representative could be that it should contain between 45% and 55% of particles of diameter d_1 and between 55% and 45% of particles of diameter d_2. The volume could then readily be found which had a 99% probability of meeting this criterion. This volume would be different from volumes v_1 and v_2 in the preceding paragraph. This concept is applied to a real system in the paper referred to above.[6]

Properties of Complex Materials

Turning to the properties of complex materials, these are determined by the properties of the individual phases and the geometrical arrangement of these phases in the material. However, consideration of complex materials in this light is frequently not necessary. In the field of mechanical properties for example, we can study the properties of complex materials phenomonologically. In this approach, which has been termed " macrorheology ", we are concerned only with the relationships between the various properties of the complex material which is treated as though it were a single-phase material. This method of approach is extremely useful and is often appropriate to engineering uses of complex materials. However, in this approach we ignore the structure of the material and do not attempt to answer the question why a complex material shows a particular set of mechanical properties.

The answer to this question is of interest not only to the materials scientist, whose goal is to understand the properties of complex materials, but also to the manufacturer of complex materials, since this understanding enables him to see ways in which materials can be improved. The ultimate objective

H

of this type of work is to be able to calculate the properties of a complex material from the properties of the individual phases and the geometrical arrangement of the phases in the material.

Much diverse effort has been devoted to the calculation of the properties of complex materials and the subject has a long history; one of the earliest studies is that of Lord Rayleigh[7] who in 1892 investigated the conductivity of a cubic array of spheres in a continuous matrix. However, the work is scattered over many different materials and fields of activity, and it seems opportune to try to make an overall assessment of the present position.

In discussing the calculation of the properties of complex materials we can distinguish three distinct classes of properties. These are:

(a) Properties which can be calculated from the properties of the constituent phases without a knowledge of structure.

(b) Properties which can be calculated from the properties of the constituent phases together with a knowledge of the geometry of the phases.

(c) Properties which can be calculated only if an intimate knowledge of the complex material is available, since the properties of the individual phases are modified in the complex material.

In this classification, we include complex materials in which there is chemical interaction between the two phases and regard such materials as being composed of new phases which differ in chemical composition from the original materials from which the composite is made.

Structure-independent properties

In the absence of chemical reaction between the component phases of a complex material, both density and heat capacity can be calculated simply from the densities and heat capacities of the individual components. This calculation is independent of the structure of the composite provided only that its components fill space completely. This is frequently not the case in complex materials, and density measurements, therefore, provide a useful tool for investigating whether a material contains occluded air or voids.

Structure-dependent properties

Most of the properties of a complex material are structure-dependent and can be calculated in principle from the properties of the individual phases and the structure of the material. However, there are few properties for which such calculations can be made rigorously. Because of this fact, most of the theoretical equations which have been derived for complex materials require testing with a well-defined experimental system.

Optical properties

In principle the optical properties of a complex material can be calculated from the properties of the individual components and a knowledge of structure, though these calculations would be extremely tedious in many cases. The optical property which is of most interest practically is the transparency of the material. Fortunately in this case detailed calculations are not necessary.

Alumina is usually an opaque material due to the fact that it contains voids which cause the scattering of light. Thus transparent alumina can only be made by eliminating the voids or by reducing their size sufficiently so that they no longer cause appreciable scattering of light. This is the way in which the transparent alumina " Lucalox " has been developed.

A similar phenomenon is encountered in the sphere of rubber-reinforced thermoplastics. Here the scattering of light is caused by the presence of small rubber particles which have a different refractive index from that of the surrounding matrix. By matching the refractive index of the matrix with that of the rubber, transparent materials of this type have been developed, e.g. " Plexigum " S70 which is a methyl-methacrylate-based impact-resistant thermoplastic.

Elastic moduli

There are many theories which allow the moduli of two-phase complex materials to be calculated. Most of these theories relate to a structure involving a dispersion of spheres in a continuous matrix. The calculation for other geometries is more difficult, but calculations can be made for two limiting cases in which the two components are arranged either in series or in parallel.[27]

Several theories have been worked out for the case of a dispersion of spheres in a continuous matrix.[8-14] The systems to which these theories apply are listed in Table I.

TABLE I.—*Theories of elastic moduli*

Author	System	Comments
Hashin[8]	Rigid spheres in soft matrix	Accurate. Valid only at low volume concentrations
Reiner[9] and Hashin	All systems	Accurate. Valid only at low volume concentrations
Kerner[10]	All systems	Approximate. Applicable at high volume concentrations
Mackenzie[11]	Air bubbles in matrix	Accurate. Applicable only at low volume concentrations
van der Poel[12]	All systems	Approximate. Applicable at high volume concentrations
Guth[13]	Rigid spheres in soft matrix	Approximate. Applicable at high volume concentrations
Hashin[14]	All systems	Sets upper and lower bounds for modulus

The theories which were developed for application at high volume concentrations are only approximate, since they all involve arbitrary assumptions. Calculations for two of these theories and an exact theory which is applicable only at low volume concentrations for the case of rigid spheres in a soft matrix are presented in Fig. 3, where it can be seen that they predict substantially different moduli. In the same figure experimental results are also given for a suspension of bitumen in water.[12] The theory of van der Poel is in good agreement with these results, suggesting that this theory is the most suitable for application to systems composed of a dispersion of rigid spheres in a soft matrix.

A comparison of the relevant theories for a case representing soft spheres in a rigid matrix is given in Fig. 4. This refers to acrylonitrile–butadiene–styrene polymers which consist of a dispersion of soft polybutadiene rubber spheres in a styrene/acrylonitrile copolymer matrix which has a high modulus. It will be seen that the agreement of the theory of Kerner and that of Reiner and Hashin with the experimental results is quite good. However, the Kerner theory, which is supposed to be applicable at high volume concentrations, gives no better agreement with the experimental results than does the accurate theory of Reiner and Hashin, which is valid only at low volume concentrations. Van der Poel's theory was derived for use with a dispersion of hard spheres in a soft matrix. However, there is nothing in its derivation which restricts it to such systems. We have, therefore, calculated the moduli predicted by van der Poel's theory for the ABS polymers and the results are also shown in Fig. 4. We can see that the theory is not in agreement with experiments and we must conclude, therefore, that, although the theory gives excellent agreement for hard spheres in a soft matrix, it is nevertheless basically unsound.

The theory of Mackenzie has been tested by Coble and Kingery[15] for aluminas of varying porosity. Their results are reproduced in Fig. 5, where it can be seen that the theory is in excellent agreement with experiment. This is surprising since the theory should only be accurate at low volume concentrations. The theory of Kerner, on the other hand, which purports to be applicable at high volume concentrations, is in fact in less good agreement with experiment. As with the polymer system described above Kerner's theory predicts moduli which are higher than the experimental values.

We can see from these comparisons of theory and experiment that the present position is far from satisfactory. The theory of van der Poel which is excellent for one system fails spectacularly on a different system. The theories which are intended to be applicable at high volume concentration are no better than the accurate theories which are applicable only at low volume concentrations.

Hashin[14] has recently applied an exact theory to the problem of the calculation of the elastic moduli of systems

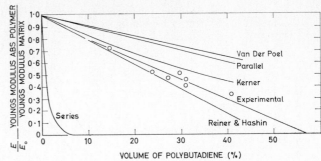
Fig. 4.—Relative Young's moduli of ABS polymers

composed of a uniform dispersion of spheres in a matrix. He concludes that the best that can be done with existing methods is to calculate upper and lower bounds for the moduli. In the case of the bulk modulus the upper and lower bounds coincide, showing that the solution is exact for bulk modulus. The upper and lower bounds do not coincide, however, for the shear modulus and Young's modulus. Moreover, the bounds get further apart as the ratio of the moduli of the two phases increases. For an infinitely rigid component in a soft matrix the upper bound lies at infinity and for a dispersion of air in a rigid matrix the lower bound lies at zero. Thus, while the upper and lower bounds calculated in this way may be useful for some systems (as will be shown below) they are too far apart to be of use in many systems of practical interest.

The question naturally arises as to whether the bounds for shear and Young's moduli can be improved and brought closer together. Although the answer to this question is not known from the theoretical standpoint, experimental results on ABS polymers suggest that this may not be possible. Thus, we have found that two ABS polymers made from polybutadiene lattices of different particle sizes but otherwise identical have shear moduli which are 30% different. McIntyre[16] has also found that dynamic mechanical properties are dependent on particle size in systems consisting of dispersions of rubber in polystyrene. The experimental evidence suggests, therefore, that the shear modulus is indeterminate in terms of volume concentration and properties of the constituent phases, and that exact solutions can only be

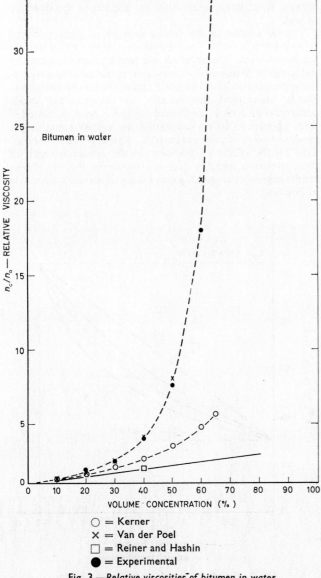

○ = Kerner
× = Van der Poel
□ = Reiner and Hashin
● = Experimental

Fig. 3.—Relative viscosities of bitumen in water

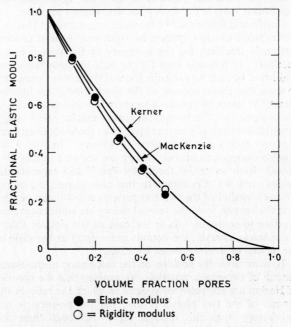

VOLUME FRACTION PORES

● = Elastic modulus
○ = Rigidity modulus

Fig. 5.—Relative elastic moduli of alumina versus porosity

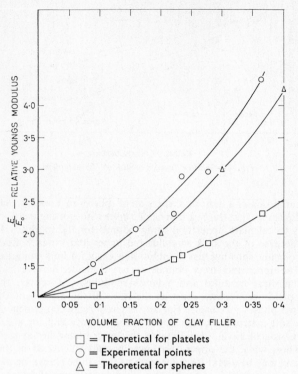

□ = Theoretical for platelets
○ = Experimental points
△ = Theoretical for spheres

Fig. 6.—*Relative elastic moduli of clay filler in polythene*

expected when the particle size of the spheres and possibly particle-size distribution are defined.

When we turn to systems involving dispersions of non-spherical particles in a matrix the problem becomes even more complicated. Guth[17] has presented approximate formulae for hard particles of various shapes in a soft matrix and we have previously shown[18] that his equation for spherical particles is in reasonable agreement with experiment for a dispersion of carbon black in polyethylene. We show in Fig. 6 a comparison of predictions from the Guth theory with experimental results on a polyethylene containing a dispersion of a clay filler, consisting of particles which are disc shaped. It can be seen from the figure that the Guth theory for spherical particles is in better agreement with experiment than is the theory for disc-shaped particles.

Hashin and Shtrikman[19] have recently generalized Hashin's earlier work to cover systems in which only volume concentration is specified, *i.e.* the geometry of the system is not specified. In this case even for the bulk modulus the upper and lower bounds do not coincide and the authors were able to show that this is because all the elastic moduli are indeterminate in terms of volume concentration and properties of the two phases. The bounds for shear modulus and Young's modulus are naturally further apart than those obtained from Hashin's theory for dispersions of spheres. In Fig. 7 the bounds obtained from their theory are shown together with bounds from an earlier theory by Paul[20] and experimental results on a WC–Co alloy. In this case where the ratio of Young's moduli of the two components is 3·4 it can be seen that the bounds from the general theory are sufficiently close together to be useful. As in the case of the simpler theory for spheres, however, the bounds move apart as the ratio of the moduli of the two phases increases.

To summarize the position on the calculation of the elastic moduli of two-phase materials, we can say that the theories of Hashin are adequate for systems in which the ratio of the moduli of the two phases is low, but the position is not satisfactory when this ratio is high. Although there are theories which give good agreement with experiment for

individual cases, the discussion above shows that the value of a theory should not be judged by this criterion. We are in agreement with the statement made by Hashin: " Expressions for the effective elastic moduli or other physical constants of multiphase materials will be of lasting value only if, besides agreeing with experimental results, they are based on exact theory ". There is clearly a need for further theoretical work in this field.

The parallel and series models mentioned earlier are also useful in considering the moduli of complex materials, since they give extreme values between which the modulus of a real system must lie. The parallel model is particularly useful since it gives an accurate prediction of the moduli of continuous-filament reinforced materials.[21] Further reference to the parallel and series models will be made later in the section on thermal conductivity.

Tensile strength

Some progress has been made on the calculation of tensile strengths of complex materials. Perhaps the most striking example, though one of the simplest, is the calculation of the tensile strength of copper reinforced with continuous parallel tungsten wires.[22] A comparison of theoretical predictions with experiment is shown in Fig. 8. The most significant feature in this work is that the theory also applies to discontinuous short fibres when these are aligned in the direction of test.

The calculation of the tensile strength of materials containing pores presents a more difficult problem which has not yet been solved. Pores reduce the tensile strength, partly by reducing the load-bearing cross-section, but also by acting as stress concentrators. The latter factor appears to be incompletely understood theoretically, for whereas the stress-concentration around a spherical cavity has been calculated,[23] there appears to be no calculation for a body containing a random system of spherical cavities. Kingery[24] has presented data on the effects of porosity on the tensile strength of three materials and his data are shown in Fig. 9. These results suggest that useful general theories should be possible in this field.

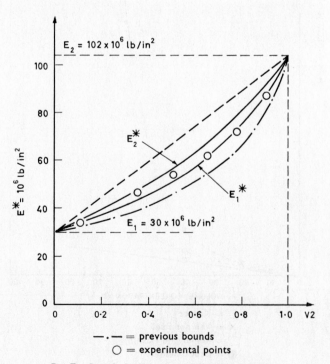

—·— = previous bounds
○ = experimental points

Fig. 7.—*Bounds for Young's modulus, Wc–Co Alloy*

An analogous problem occurs in the case of high-impact polystyrenes.   These materials consist of a dispersion of soft rubber spheres in a hard polystyrene matrix.   Polystyrene is a brittle material which has a linear stress–strain curve and which fractures at a low elongation.   The high-impact polystyrenes, however, show a yield point (using the terminology of polymer physics) and will extend some 30% after yield.   The yield point and further extension of these materials is due to the production of microcracks at the rubber/matrix interface.   This does not lead to catastrophic failure, however, since the rubber particles dissipate the stresses at the tip of some cracks and crack–crack interaction stablizes other cracks.[25]   The yield point of these materials, *i.e.* the stage at which microcracks begin to form, occurs at an elongation which equals the fracture elongation of pure polystyrene.   Using the experimentally-determined fracture elongation of pure polystyrene, it is possible to calculate the yield stress via a calculation of modulus, when the stress–strain curves of the rubber reinforced polymers are linear.   It would seem that this theory cannot be applied to the effect of porosity on tensile strength, since it can be seen from Figs. 5 and 9 that porosity has a greater effect on tensile strength than on modulus.

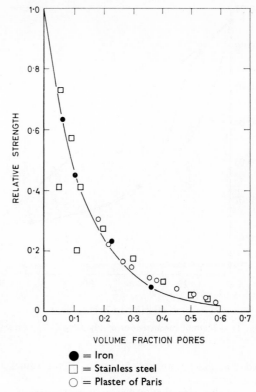

Fig. 9.—*Effect of porosity on tensile strength*

- ● = Iron
- □ = Stainless steel
- ○ = Plaster of Paris

and this component dominates the calculated conductivity of a parallel model.   At high volume concentrations the Mg_2SiO_4, which has the lower conductivity, is the continuous phase.   The conductivity of the composite then approximates to that of the series model, since the lower conductivity component dominates the conductivity of the series model.   At intermediate compositions there is a transition from one type of behaviour to the other as contacts increase between particles of the dispersed phase.

The calculation of the thermal conductivity of a dispersion of air bubbles in polystyrene played an important part in the development of foamed polystyrene as an insulant.[23]   The early foamed polystyrenes had thermal conductivities which were too high for many applications.   Theoretical calculations

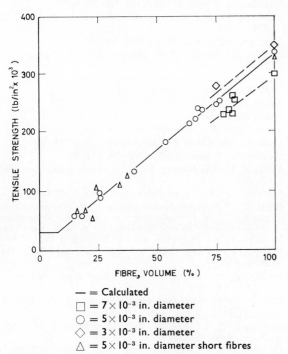

Fig. 8.—*Tensile strengths of copper reinforced with tungsten wires*

- — = Calculated
- □ = 7×10^{-3} in. diameter
- ○ = 5×10^{-3} in. diameter
- ◇ = 3×10^{-3} in. diameter
- △ = 5×10^{-3} in. diameter short fibres

Thermal conductivity

Theoretical equations for the thermal or electrical conductivity of a dispersion of spheres in a continuous matrix have been derived by Kerner[26] and others.[27]   Similar expressions for the parallel and series models can be derived readily.

The form of the theoretical relations which are given by these theories are shown in Fig. 10.   The authors have not been able to find data to test the theory for a dispersion of spheres, but Fig. 11 presents some experimental results for the system MgO–Mg_2SiO_4[27] together with theoretical curves for the series and parallel model.   The sigmoid shape of the experimental curve can be understood in the following way. At low volume concentrations of Mg_2SiO_4, the MgO is the continuous phase and the conductivity of the composite approximates to that of the parallel model.   This is because the higher conductivity component is the continuous phase

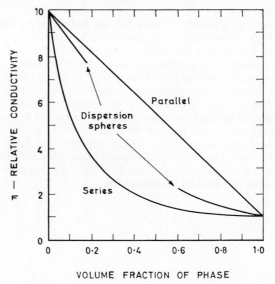

Fig. 10.—*Thermal conductivities of model systems*

H*

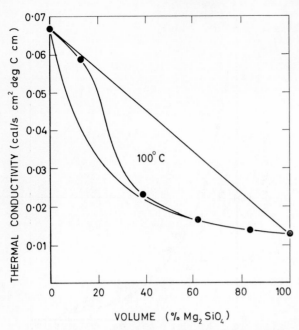

Fig. 11.—*Thermal conductivities of MgO-Mg$_2$SiO$_4$ mixtures*

showed that these were well in excess of the values to be expected from the conductivities of air and polystyrene. The reason for this was that radiative heat transfer and heat transfer by convection within the air cells were appreciable, and it was concluded that the way to improve the materials was to reduce the size of the air cells. In this work it was not necessary to have an accurate theory for conductivity since the discrepancies between theory and experiment were large.

Modification of Properties of Consituent Phases

Some properties of complex materials cannot be calculated simply from a knowledge of the properties of the constituent phases, since these are modified in the complex. The calculation of this type of property demands a more detailed understanding of materials than the properties which have been discussed above. It is doubtful whether useful generalizations applicable to a variety of materials can be made in this field. We have chosen, therefore, merely to outline two problems of this type.

The first problem concerns the age hardening of alloys through the formation of precipitates of a dissolved metal or of an intermetallic compound,[29] *e.g.* aluminium containing 4% copper. Two mechanisms seem to be at work here, and theoretical treatments have been given. In alloys which are near the maximum hardness, the critical resolved shear stress for flow is higher than that for the unaged material. This appears to be due to a higher force being required to enable dislocations to pass through the material of the precipitate. In over-aged alloys, where the precipitates are fewer in number but larger in size, the increased flow stress is believed to be necessary in order to force the dislocations between the obstacles provided by the precipitates.

An even more dramatic change in the properties of a phase of a complex material is shown by acrylonitrile-butadiene-styrene (ABS) polymers. The styrene–acrylonitrile copolymer matrix of these polymers is a typical brittle, glassy polymer. The ABS polymers, on the other hand, show a yield point at which they neck and cold draw. During this process the brittle matrix cold draws and the molecules of the matrix orient. No adequate theory has been presented to account for this behaviour, though heating of the polymer during extension has been suggested as a contributory factor.[25] It is quite clear that this phenomenon could not be predicted from the stress-strain curves of the two components, and that even a qualitative theory will have to be based on a detailed understanding of the mechanisms of tensile elongation.

References

[1] Griffith, A. A. *Phil. Trans.*, 1921, **221**, 163.
[2] Iager, A. A., and Isilipotkira, M. V. *Polym. Sci. U.S.S.R.*, 1962, **3**, 1142.
[3] Statton, W. O. *J. Polym. Sci.*, 1962, **58**, 205.
[4] Holliday, L. *Nature, Lond.*, 1963, **197**, 222.
[5] Holliday, L. *Chem. & Ind.*, 1963, No. 20, p. 794.
[6] Holliday, L., and Thackray, G. *Nature, Lond.*, 1964, **201**, 270.
[7] Lord Rayleigh. *Phil. Mag.*, 1892, **34**, 481.
[8] Hashin, Z. *Bulletin of the Research Council of Israel*, 1955, **5C**, 46.
[9] Reiner, M. " *Deformation, Strain and Flow* ", 1960 (London: H. K. Lewis & Co. Ltd.), p. 214.
[10] Kerner, E. H. *Proc. phys. Soc. Lond.*, 1956, **69B**, 808.
[11] Mackenzie, J. K. *Proc. phys. Soc. Lond.*, 1950, **63B**, 2.
[12] van der Poel, C. *Rheologia Acta*, 1958, **1**, 198.
[13] Guth, E., and Simha, R. *Kolloidzschr.*, 1936, **74**, 266.
[14] Hashin, Z. *J. appl. Mech.*, 1962, **29**, 142, 765.
[15] Coble, R. L., and Kingery, W. D. *J. Amer. ceram. Soc.*, 1956, **29**, 377.
[16] McIntyre, A. D. *J. Appl. Polym. Sci.*, 1963, **7**, 1291.
[17] Guth, E. " Hydrodynamical theory of the viscosity of suspension ", *in*, " *Proceedings of the Fifth International Congress on Applied Mechanics* ", p. 448, Cambridge, Mass., 1938. (Published, Wiley, Chapman & Hall, 1939.)
[18] Haward, R. N., and Mann, J. *Proc. Roy. Soc. Lond.*, 1964, **282A**, 120.
[19] Hashin, Z., and Shtrikman, S. *J. Appl. Mech. and Phys. of Solids*, 1963, **11**, 127.
[20] Paul, B. *Trans. Amer. Inst. min. metall. Engrs*, 1960, **218**, 36.
[21] Hibbard, W. R. *Chem. Engng*, 70, **24**, 203.
[22] McDanels, D. L., Jech, R. W., and Weeton, J. W. *Metal Progr.*, 1960, **78**, 118.
[23] Goodier, J. N. *Trans. Amer. Soc. mech. Engrs*, 1933, **55**, 39.
[24] Kingery, W. D. " *Introduction to Ceramics* ", 1960 (London: John Wiley & Sons Ltd.), p. 622.
[25] Nielsen, L. E. " *Mechanical Properties of Polymers* ", 1962 (New York: Reinhold).
[26] Kerner, E. H. *Proc. phys. Soc. Lond.*, 1956, **69B**, 802.
[27] Kingery, W. D. *Idem. ibid.*, 501.
[28] Stochdopole, R. E. *Chem. Engng Progr.*, 1961, **57**, No. 10. p. 55.
[29] Kelly, A. *Proc. Roy. Soc. Lond.*, 1964, **282A**, p. 63.

The manuscript of this paper was received on 5 February, 1964.

THE NATURE OF THE GLASSY STATE

By R. W. DOUGLAS*

A TECHNOLOGICAL definition of glass might be " an inorganic product of fusion which has cooled to the solid state without precipitating crystals ". Scientifically this is satisfactory, but it is too restrictive; it is satisfactory in relating the definition of the glassy state to the liquid state but a better definition would be " a glass is a substance which has cooled from the liquid state below its liquidus temperature without precipitating crystals and has then continued as a super-cooled liquid until a temperature range is reached in which the normal processes of relaxation in the liquid become so slow that they may be considered inoperative ". In a glass the atoms remain disposed with respect to one another as in a liquid but there is no continuous translation of the atoms with respect to one another; they vibrate about fixed positions.

Whether a liquid forms a glass or not, at and below the freezing point, or the liquidus temperature, there must be a tendency for crystals to grow in the liquid. However, a crystal can only grow if it is bigger than a certain minimum size for if it is too small the contribution of the surface energy to the energy per unit volume of the small crystal will be so large as to raise the effective free energy of the crystal above that of the liquid and it will therefore redissolve. A process of nucleation thus has to be recognized and the conditions for glass formation must be related to the probability of nucleation and the rate of crystal growth. Glass formation is thus a kinetic problem.

Super-cooling can indeed take place in all liquids. This presumably means that nucleation can be prevented, as for example by keeping the liquid very pure, and also by dealing only with very small quantities so that the probability of nucleation in that particular volume becomes very small indeed. Liquid metals, for example, when in the form of finely divided droplets can, in general, be cooled to a temperature T such that the ratio T/T_m where T is the normal melting point is about 0·8. Even so it is thought that the nucleation is not homogeneous, *i.e.* it only takes place when the liquid is in contact with some other phase and does not take place homogeneously in the liquid itself.[1] Only a few liquids, however, form glasses. In the non-glass-forming liquids it appears that when super-cooled the occurrence of a nucleus is followed so rapidly by crystal growth that there is almost explosive conversion of the super-cooled liquid into the crystal. The glass-forming material thus has to have both rare nucleation and slow crystal growth. Important contributions to the theory of nucleation in ordinary liquids and in glass-forming liquids have been made by Turnbull and his collaborators.[2]

The second kinetic process in the attainment of the glassy state occurs in the temperature region in which the relaxation times associated with the various degrees of freedom become so slow as to be negligible in their effect, that is, they become frozen out. This region is appropriately described as the transformation range and in this region the physical properties of a glass may easily be observed to change with time. The properties of a glass below the transformation range thus depend upon its thermal history, that is, the rate at which it

has been cooled through the transformation range. It will be noticed that these definitions have no restriction as to the composition of the substance and indeed they have been shown to apply perfectly satisfactorily to organic glasses such as glycerol, to single component glasses such as selenium, and to all inorganic glasses of the types envisaged in the technological definition with which this introduction commenced.

Glasses of commerce have to satisfy technical and economic requirements and by weight the vast majority of the glass produced consists principally of a mixture of the oxides of silicon, sodium and calcium and is prepared from indigenous raw materials. Demand for glasses of special properties, optical glasses, glasses for the electronics industry, glasses of low thermal expansion for cooking ware, to mention a few, leads to a very wide range of chemical compositions being produced commercially. More than sixty of the elements have been used in commercial glass compositions. A few examples of common commercial glass compositions are given in Table I.

Kinetic Processes

Nucleation and Crystallization

The pioneer work in this field was done by Tamman[3] in the early years of this century and he showed quite clearly that the process of nucleation could be separated from that of crystal growth. Moreover, he recognized quite clearly that a glass would be formed *in principle* in any liquid if heat could be removed fast enough to avoid crystal nucleation and growth. More recently it has been recognized that with some substances it may be impossible to attain a sufficient rate of cooling to form a glass even if it is very finely divided.[2]

Traditionally the glass industry has used controlled crystallization of minor components of the glass to produce, for example, opal glass which may contain up to 5 % of CaF or mixed NaF CaF.[4] Selenium ruby glass[5] owes its colour to the precipitation of about 0·1 % by weight of mixed CdSe CdS crystals; in gold and copper rubies the colour is due to the precipitation of metallic particles in even smaller amounts. In normal glasses precipitation of crystals, or devitrification as it is usually described, must be avoided and the composition of the glass must be chosen so that, in the forming operations, the glass is not held for long just below the liquidus temperature. It is for this reason that flat glass usually contains MgO, and CaO, while container glass in this country which passes through different time temperature cycles in the forming operations can be made without MgO. The addition of 2 % of MgO to a typical soda–lime–silica glass can lower the liquidus temperature by 200°C without greatly altering the viscosity at that temperature.

In the last twenty years or so a team at the Corning Research Laboratories under the leadership of Dr. Stookey[6] has made notable contributions in the study of nucleation and crystallization in glasses which have led to important commercial developments. These developments have sprung from the discovery of a photo-sensitive glass; this was a glass containing a small amount of dissolved metal such as gold or

* Department of Glass Technology, the University of Sheffield.

TABLE I.—*Typical Commercial Glass Compositions*

	SiO$_2$	Al$_2$O$_3$	CaO	MgO	Na$_2$O	K$_2$O	PbO	B$_2$O$_3$	BaO	ZnO
Container glass	73·0	2·0	10·4	—	14·0	—	—	—	—	—
Window glass	72·0	1·3	8·2	3·5	14·3	—	—	—	—	—
Lead table ware	56·0	1·3	—	—	4·7	7·2	29·5	—	—	—
Cooking-ware	81·0	2·0	—	—	4·5	—	—	12·0	—	—
Fibreglass	54·5	14·5	16·0	4·4	0·5	—	—	10·0	—	—
Optical flint	49·8	—	—	—	1·2	8·2	18·7	—	13·4	8·0
Borosilicate crown	69·6	—	—	—	8·4	8·4	—	9·9	2·5	—

silver which, after exposure to ultra violet radiation and subsequent heat treatment, developed a colour due to the growth of small metallic particles in the glass.   It is said that, quite by accident, a sample of this glass was overheated during the heat treatment when it was found that the devitrification product of the glass was precipitated on the metallic particles so that where the glass has been exposed to ultraviolet light it had now become opalescent.   This discovery itself had important technological applications for it was found that the opal regions so formed were more resistant to chemical attack than the parent glass, so that the parent glass could be etched away leaving pieces of the desired shape in the opal glass

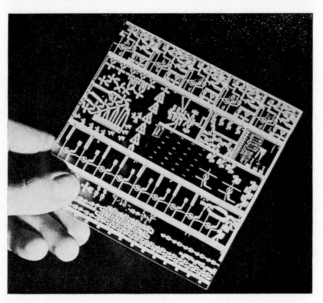

Fig. 1.—*Fluid amplification elements made of photo-sensitive glass. (Courtesy of Corning Glass Works, Corning, New York)*

(Fig. 1). Subsequent development produced a glass which could be changed almost completely into crystalline material, and a new series of materials was created called by Corning—glass-ceramics. In this way ceramic-like products consisting of 90 to 98% crystal can be produced by normal glass blowing techniques, the glass article being subjected to the appropriate heat treatment in order to convert it into a ceramic (Fig. 2). This would be of little importance were it not for the many special physical properties which can be made available in this way. For example, the material is extremely inert chemically and can be designed to have either zero or very small coefficient of expansion. Some typical properties are given in Table II.[7]

Tashiro[8] has reported that the mechanical strength varies inversely as the square root of the particle size of the crystals in glass ceramics. However, the fracture of glass is a complicated phenomenon: the strength is extremely sensitive to the condition of the surface and it should be emphasized that the strengths recorded in Table II refer to " abraided " samples.

These developments have given rise to an intense interest in the process of nucleation and crystallization. No evidence

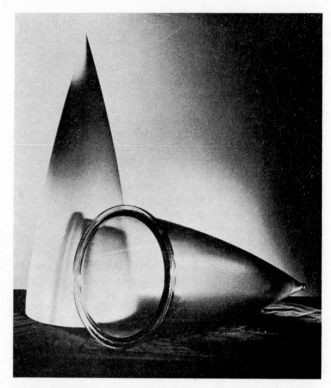

Fig. 2.—*Code 9606—Pyro-Ceram material. Shown in the glassy form and after conversion to ceramic by heat treatment.   (Courtesy of Corning Glass Works, Corning, New York)*

has yet been obtained of homogeneous nucleation and it has been found that one of the most efficient nucleating agents is titanium dioxide, at least when present in the lithia–alumino–silicate glasses which have been found particularly useful for this application.   The details of the process of nucleation are not yet completely established but it looks very much as though it can depend upon a region of liquid immiscibility in the material which only occurs when the substance has super-cooled; thus these particular glasses have what might be described as second degree metastability.   They are metastable in the sense that they have super-cooled below the liquidus temperature and secondly, while in this metastable state, they have entered a region of immiscibility which is

TABLE II.—*Some Typical Glass-Ceramic Properties*

	Corning Pyroceram Code 9608	Borosilicate glass Code 7740
Softening temperature °C	1250	820
Coefficient of thermal expansion $\times 10^{-7}$ per °C	7–20*	32
Modulus of rupture abraided specimens lb/in$^2 \times 10^{-6}$	12·5	9·5
Knoop hardness 500 g	588	442

* According to heat treatment

only accessible if the glass fails to crystallize and enters the first metastable state.

Glasses are substances in a metastable state; but these new developments emphasize that there are many possible additional metastable states between a glass and the stable phases recorded in the usual phase diagram. It is perhaps instructive to look at this behaviour in the same terms as are used when deriving a phase equilibrium diagram from curves showing how the free energy of system varies with composition for various phases. Fig. 3 shows for an hypothetical

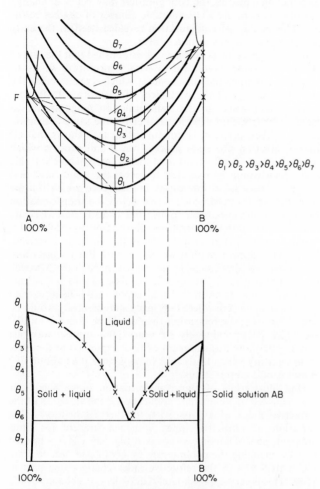

$\theta_1 > \theta_2 > \theta_3 > \theta_4 > \theta_5 > \theta_6 > \theta_7$

Fig. 3.—*Derivation of phase–equilibrium diagram for binary system from free energy diagram*

mixture AB the way in which the free energy varies with composition; for the liquid phase this variation is shown by the parabola-like curves which rise up the free energy scale as the temperature falls. The two small curves show the free energy of crystalline phases, A with a small solid solubility of B, and B with a small solid solubility of A. When the temperature falls so that part of the curve for a solid phase lies below the liquid curve (θ_3 for example) some compositions can reduce their free energy by separating into liquid and solid of the compositions given by the common tangent to the liquid and solid free energy curves. In this way the phase equilibrium diagram can be derived as indicated in the figure.

To demonstrate how metastable liquid immiscibility can arise it has to be assumed that the barrier to the crystallization of Fig. 3 is so great that it does not take place. At some lower temperature the free energy curve of the liquid may then develop a hump as shown in Fig. 4. This will arise when the mean of E_{AA} and E_{BB} the energies of atoms A in contact with like atoms and atoms B in contact with like atoms is less

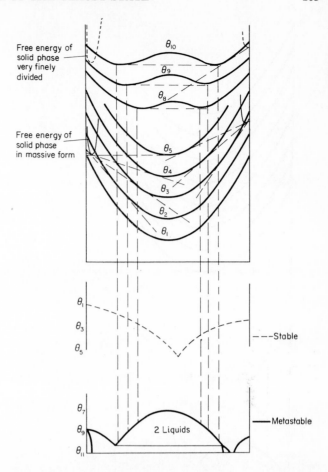

Fig. 4.—*Derivation of metastable arrangements in binary systems*

than E_{AB}, the energy of a pair of unlike atoms A, B in juxtaposition. The two liquid regions will then develop as shown for compositions when the hump develops. The possible existence of metastable crystalline compounds can also be envisaged as shown in Fig. 5 where the full line in the bottom half of the figure represents the equilibrium of a metastable phase formed after the failure of the primary phase to precipitate.

These new developments in the control and use of metastable states open up vistas of ever-increasing interest in the theory and practice of these non-metallic materials.

Kinetic Processes

The Transformation Range

Here again the pioneer work in the transformation range dates from the early 1920's when anomalous absorption of heat was observed in heating a piece of glass and the pattern of the heat absorption was found to depend on the previous thermal history of the sample.[9] There is no difficulty at all in interpreting this work now in terms of the relaxation times of the various processes of configuration change and their relation to the temperature, and it can now be said that the transformation range phenomena provide us perhaps with the strongest evidence for insisting that glasses are liquid-like substances. This has been discussed in considerable detail[10] in many places and it probably suffices now to summarize the situation briefly in the following words.

It is easy to recognize that the density of the liquid and the corresponding crystal are of the same order, that is to say, the difference in the densities is rarely as much as 10%. The atoms in the liquid and in the crystal are therefore at about

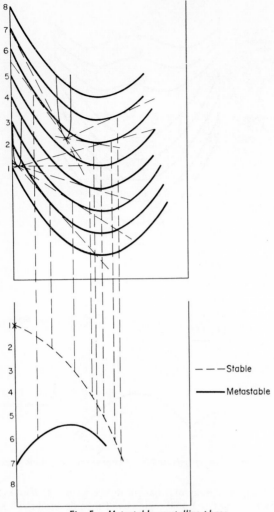

Fig. 5.—*Metastable crystalline phase*

now that this distribution function varies with temperature and that following a sudden change of temperature a certain time must elapse before the configuration reaches its new equilibrium value. In the transformation range the time for this process becomes long compared with the experimental time so that it can be observed easily in the course of its evolution. At even lower temperatures the rate is so slow as to be negligible and the configuration can be referred to as frozen-in. It is possible, for example, by quick cooling to freeze-in a configuration appropriate to some temperature θ such that on reheating the configuration may begin to change at some temperature a considerable number of degrees below θ. This change of configuration revealed itself in the early experiments as an absorption of heat.

In recent years it has become well established that the rate of change of configuration varies with temperature so as to reveal an apparent activation energy which is the same as the activation energy of the coefficient of viscosity. In fact all relaxation processes in the transformation range appear to have, at least within experimental error, the same activation energy. This, perhaps, is not surprising as it shows that all these relaxation processes proceed via a unit process which must of course be a fluctuation of the thermodynamic variable and which would be expected to reveal the same activation energy. There is an interesting consequence which follows from this observation which is that below the transformation range it is quite impossible to measure a steady state viscosity of a glass, for as the temperature falls the time to reach equilibrium increases at the same rate as the viscosity increases. To a rough approximation we may regard the viscosity and the time to equilibrium as being related through the Maxwell expression $\eta = G\tau$. Taking G to be about 3×10^{11} dyne/cm^2 and making the assumption that an experiment is being carried out at a temperature where the steady state viscosity would be say 10^{25} poises, the relaxation time would be about $3 \cdot 3 \times 10^{13}$ sec which is approximately 10^6 years. Put another way one can say that any measurement of flow expressed as a steady state viscosity which leads to a value greater than about 10^{16} poises is of doubtful status.

One illustration of this transformation range behaviour which has led to commercial application is the variation of the refractive index of a glass with its thermal history. The variation of refractive index with temperature for three different rates of cooling is shown in Fig. 6.[11] It will be seen that by changing the cooling rate by about one decade from 1°C/h to 9·87°C/h the refractive index changes one part in 1500. This is very approximately equivalent to a change of 1%

the same distances apart. In the crystal, however, the order of the arrangement of the atoms on the points of the crystal lattice continues over long distances. No such long distance order exists in a liquid and the arrangements of the atoms in a liquid can only be described by means of a distribution function which expresses the probability of finding an atom at a given distance from another atom. It is well established

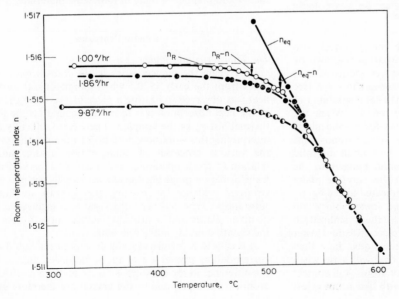

Fig. 6.—*Variation of refractive index during cooling at constant rates. The refractive index is measured at room temperature on quenched samples. (Glass 8370)*

in the silica content of glasses cooled at the same rate; thus some control of commercial value of the refractive index can be obtained by selective heat treatment. The room temperature refractive index for different rates of cooling is shown in Fig. 7[11] which also indicates how the limits of the transformation range vary with the time taken to make a particular

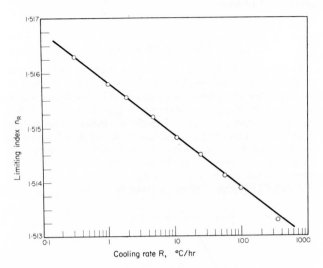

Fig. 7.—Final limiting index n_R as a function of constant cooling rate R. (Glass 8370)

experiment. The maximum rate of cooling shown is about 350°C/h which gives a room temperature refractive index of 1·5133; this corresponds with the equilibrium refractive index at about 550°C.

The lowest cooling rate shown is about $\frac{1}{3}$°C/h and this leads to a refractive index of 1·5162 which corresponds to the equilibrium refractive index at 500°C. In this particular experiment the transformation range is limited to about 50°C. If on the other hand the specimens instead of being cooled at different rates are soaked for a long time in the transformation range and then cooled quickly so as to freeze in the configuration reached during the soak the transformation range can be doubled. Densities obtained by soaking of the same glass are shown in Fig. 8[12] where it will be seen that the range covered is 100°C in temperature and 0·03 g/cm³ in density, this corresponds approximately to 0·006 in refractive index.

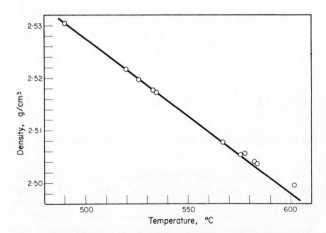

Fig. 8.—Equilibrium density versus temperature. The density is the room-temperature density of samples quenched from equilibrium at the temperatures shown

Glass articles are normally annealed by cooling slowly after fabrication to minimize permanent stresses which are set up because at high temperatures the viscous flow enables temperature gradients to exist without any strains. On cooling, the different total contractions give rise to permanent internal stresses. Fine annealing of optical glass, however, requires slower cooling than that which would reduce these stresses suitably, for only if each part of the glass has the same thermal history will it have the same refractive index. This is accomplished by ensuring that from the temperature at which strains are no longer released sufficiently quickly the rate of cooling is constant for both the inside and outside of the glass. (See Fig. 9.)[13]

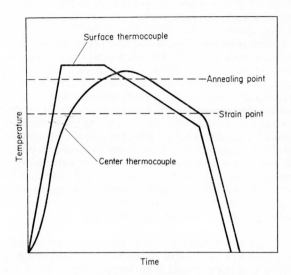

Fig. 9.—Annealing cycle for large masses of glass

This temperature from which the cooling rates must be equal of course depends upon the time scale of the experiment, and by soaking for long enough at constant temperature, so that the whole of the glass is brought to the same configuration, the cooling process can be started from various temperatures in the transformation range and in this way the refractive index of a melt of glass can again be subject to slight adjustment at room temperature.

The Physical and Chemical Properties of Glasses

By varying the chemical composition of inorganic glasses it is possible to produce a range of materials in which the chemical and physical properties vary over enormous ranges; glasses with absorptions in the ultraviolet or in the visible spectrum at convenient wavelengths—glasses which transmit infrared—glasses of low expansion to withstand thermal shock—glasses of higher expansion to match the coefficient of expansion of metals—glasses which dissolve in water—glasses which are very inert chemically—glasses which soften at 100°C to fused silica glass which is still extremely viscous at 2000°C.

In applying science to the understanding of these materials as distinct from applying science in their manufacture we wish to relate these properties to the atomic arrangements and the interatomic forces. In some ways this task for the glassy state is one of tremendous difficulty because the atomic arrangement must be described by a distribution function which has only been established theoretically for the simple rare gas liquids and which experimentally is extremely difficult to determine with any satisfactory accuracy. Although in the past it has been the custom to interpret the macroscopic properties in terms of a crude description of the arrangement of atoms in the glass it is abundantly clear that the only direct information that can be obtained about the structure is by the use of phenomena on the appropriate scale, that is, for the interaction of the glass with radiation of the right wavelength or energy. X-ray and neutron diffraction show that the near neighbour configuration is exactly that which would be expected from the known crystal chemistry of the atoms concerned. For example, in silicate glasses the silicon is always surrounded by 4 atoms of oxygen while in sulphide glasses there is the tendency to find the sulphur present in long chains and in phosphate glasses the presence of phosphate chains has been established. It is interesting to note that in phosphate glasses it has been possible by solution into water and subsequent chromatography to demonstrate the existence of these chain polymers of various lengths.[14]

Silicon, selenium, phosphorus, have often been referred to as the network formers. The interatomic bonds which they form are more or less directional in character and, by and large, the information available about their arrangements in glass is that which would be predicted from their behaviour in crystalline substances. It is much more difficult to obtain information about the alkali or alkaline-earth ions which were normally regarded as being situated in spaces left amongst the network forming atoms. In recent years considerable progress has been made with one particular class of ions that is, the transition metal ions with their incomplete 3 d-shells and the rare earth ions with their unfilled f-shells.[15] Increasing interest is growing around the discovery that neodymium in certain glasses provides an excellent laser material.

The energy levels of the 4 f-ions are little affected by the host glass; by contrast the 3 d-ions are much more affected but nevertheless it is possible to understand their absorption spectra in terms of ligand field theory which in recent years has been so successful in dealing with the chemistry of these ions. Although these ions behave much as they do in aqueous solution the chemistry of the ions in solution in glasses is rather more complex. This is because of the possibility of the entry of oxygen into the glass; although it is well-known that in aqueous solution, ferrous chloride can be slowly oxidized to ferric chloride by oxygen from the air, this process is normally of far less consequence than it is in the glass. Two extreme cases have to be considered, the first—the states of oxidation of the ions when the glass containing them has been brought to equilibrium with a known atmosphere and the second—the states of oxidation of the ions when the melt approximates to the condition of no interchange with the atmosphere during the preparation of the glass. The time to reach equilibrium in a silicate glass even at 1400°C is very long; for example, it may take as long as 100 h to bring a melt of 30 g of glass into equilibrium with the atmosphere. In commercial practice the state of oxidation is somewhere in between the two extremes. By controlling these processes many interesting coloured glasses can be produced; indeed one problem on which the flat glass industry in America is prepared to spend money is the possibility of producing a glass which on exposure to ultraviolet light darkens sufficiently rapidly to keep the intensity of radiation transmitted constant and independent of the incident intensity. This means putting into the glass a pair of redox oxides so that one of them on exposure to ultraviolet light can release an electron which can be trapped by the other oxide, the ion which has released the electron thus becoming coloured. This is a well known phenomenon in glasses containing manganese which in the reduced form does not cause absorption in the visible part of the spectrum. On exposure to ultraviolet light manganese is oxidized and the oxidized form has a fairly strong absorption in the visible spectrum giving the familiar violet colour which can often be observed in old glasses which have been exposed to the sun's radiation. After this purple colour has been developed removal

of the ultraviolet radiation results in a very slow fading of the colouration. This fading can be much accelerated by heating to high temperatures but at room temperature the decay time is very long indeed. To meet the requirement of the self-adjusting glass a process like this with much shorter decay times is necessary and it is in this direction that the experimentation must proceed.

Electrical Properties

In the ordinary silicate glasses of commerce the electrical properties are determined primarily by the alkali content of the glass, for these ions have considerable mobility even at temperatures where the glass configuration is fixed, *i.e.* below the transformation range. The glasses behave then as unipolar electrolytes and the conductivity is roughly proportional to the content of alkali ions. Oxides such as alumina may have a specific effect as in the soda–alumina–silicate glasses where the alkali ion is exceptionally mobile. Some typical resistivity temperature plots are given in Fig. 10.

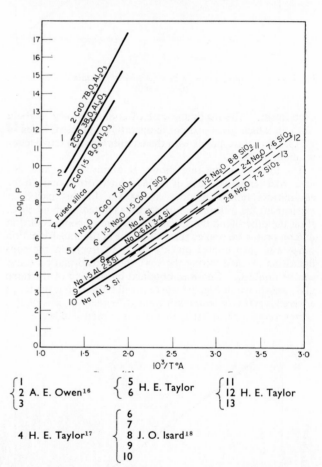

{ 1	
{ 2	A. E. Owen[16]
{ 3	

{ 5	
{ 6	H. E. Taylor

{ 11	
{ 12	H. E. Taylor
{ 13	

4 H. E. Taylor[17]

{ 6	
{ 7	
{ 8	J. O. Isard[18]
{ 9	
{ 10	

Fig. 10.—*Typical electrical resistivity temperature relations for some simple glasses*

The desire for infrared transmitting windows led to investigations of the properties of sulphide glasses. One development of this work was the family of glasses suggested for potting the transistor devices. These glasses consisted of mixtures of arsenic, sulphur, selenium and tellurium and were notable for their high electrical resistivity. The addition of other ions such as the halides produces considerable conduction which appears to be electronic. Already from such devices an electrical switching device has been made which has an excellent memory.[19] A typical current voltage curve for a point-contact on a piece of arsenic–tellurium–iodine glass is shown in Fig. 11.   However, the best understanding of this phenomenon at the moment suggests that what really happens

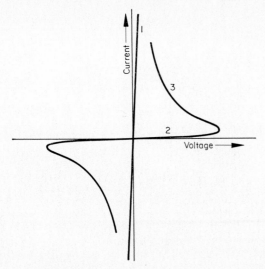

Fig. 11.—*Current-voltage characteristic of semiconductor glass diode*

under the contact is that when a current is passed the material warms up sufficiently to cause devitrification; the crystalline material so formed is much more conducting than the glass with the consequent remarkable change in characteristic. If the load is removed quickly the crystalline material remains until the glass under the contact is reheated sufficiently to cause it to fuse into a glass again.

Conclusion

This brief review of a few topics of more recent interest has, I hope, demonstrated the new possibilities that can be found by the scientific study of a class of materials which is most familiar through a technology which has existed for thousands of years.

The glass industry has, in fact, changed in the last 40 years or so from a craft to a very fully mechanized industry, but, in addition there are many products now made in the glass industry which were not in existence 40 years ago. The demands of the electrical and optical industries for special glasses have stimulated much research and development. Now new materials are appearing such as the glass-ceramics and the chalcogenide glasses. The scientific study of glass has many difficulties which arise from the randomness of the atomic arrangement of the glassy and liquid states, but fortunately progress in accurate quantitative studies is putting the phenomenological descriptions on a sound basis.

References

[1]   Turnbull, D.   *J. Appl. phys.*, 1949, **20**, 817.

[2]   Turnbull, D., and Cohen, M. H.   " *Modern Aspects of the Vitreous State* ", 1960, **1**, 38 (Butterworth).

[3]   Tamman, G.   *J.S.G.T.*, 1925, **9**, 167.

[4]   Ryde, J. W. and Doris E. Yates.   *J.S.G.T.*, 1926, **10**, 274.

[5]   Rooksby, H. P.   *J.S.G.T.*, 1932, **16**, 171T.

[6]   Stookey, S. D. and Maurer, R. D.   *Progress in Ceramic Science*, 1962, **2**, 78 (Pergamon Press).

[7]   News Item   *J.S.G.T.*, 1960, **1**, 1, 9.

[8]   Tashiro   *J. Ceram. Ass. Japan*, 1960, **68**, 6, 158.

[9]   Tool, A. G. and Eichlin, C. G.   *J. Amer. Ceram. Soc.*, 1931, **14**, 276.

[10]   Douglas, R. W.   *J.S.G.T.*, 1947, **31**, 50.

[11]   Lillie, H. R. and Ritland, H. N.   *J. Amer. Ceram. Soc.*, 1954, **37**, 466.

[12]   Ritland, H. N.   *J. Amer. Ceram. Soc.*, 1954, **37**, 310.

[13]   Tooley, F. V.   " *Handbook of Glass Manufacture* ", **1** (Ogden, New York).

[14]   Westman, A. E. R.   *Glastech. Ber.*, 1962, **35**, 500.

[15]   Bates, T. and Douglas, R. W.   *J.S.G.T.*, 1959, **43**, 289 and Bates, T.   *Modern Aspects of the Vitreous State*, 1962, **11**, 193 (Butterworth).

[16]   Owen, A. E.   *Phys. & Chem. Glasses*, 1961, **2**, 87.

[17]   Taylor, H. E.   *J.S.G.T.*, 1955, **39**, 193.

[18]   Isard, J. O.   *J.S.G.T.*, 1959, **43**, 113.

[19]   Pearson, A. D., Northover, W. R., Dewald, J. F. and Peck, W. F.   *Advances in Glass Technology*, 1963, **1**, 357.

FIBRE REINFORCED METALS

By J. G. MORLEY*

SYNOPSIS

For any considerable improvement in the properties of structural materials in terms of increased operating temperatures, higher elastic moduli, and lower densities, ceramic materials such as metallic oxides, nitrides, and carbides must be used for structural purposes in place of metals. The factors affecting the strength of these materials are examined and their possible technological application as strong load bearing fibres embedded in a metal matrix is discussed.

The aluminium–silica fibre system is an example of a ceramic fibre reinforced metal. Silica fibres have been found to have tensile strengths enormously greater than aluminium alloys and these high strengths are maintained up to temperatures considerably above the maximum usable temperatures for these materials. A detailed examination of the effect of various factors on the strength of fused silica fibres has been made and fabrication of silica-fibre aluminium composites is described.

Experimental results obtained so far indicate that this material is much stronger and retains its strength to much higher temperatures than do aluminium alloys.

General Considerations

If we are to achieve the full potential of structural materials we must be prepared to discard the ways of thinking which tie us to the gradual evolution of the popular materials of today and see if we can evolve new and superior lines of development by starting again from first principles. There are two main requirements which an engineering material must fulfil—it must carry a load and it must be tough. A load can only be carried by reason of the restoring force generated by elastic deformation of the material, but there are two mechanisms which can produce toughness—the biological one of two-phase materials (wood, bone, *etc.*) and the metallurgist's mechanism, ductility. In a sense the latter can also be regarded as a type of two-phase system since the second phase, that is the plastic material, is generated just where and when it is needed. For example, a small flaw producing local high stresses at a crack tip will normally be rendered harmless in a metal by local plastic deformation leading to energy absorption and to a change in crack geometry so reducing the stress.

Both the metallurgical and biological toughening mechanisms have their limitations. The biological one deals only with materials which have rather low stiffness and poor temperature capability. The ductility mechanism leads to unfortunate side effects: fatigue is one, and the problem of achieving high strength at high temperatures whilst avoiding brittleness at low temperatures is another.

For any radical improvements in terms of increased operating temperatures, lower densities and higher elastic moduli we must be prepared to consider using brittle materials such as metallic oxides, nitrides, borides and carbides for structural purposes in place of metals. The relevant mechanical properties of three examples of these materials compared with iron and aluminium are shown in Table I.

Although brittle materials in general have much higher specific moduli and higher temperature capabilities than metals they have, so far, been of little practical value for engineering purposes because of their brittleness and low usable strength.

We have long known that the strength of a solid deduced from reasonable assumptions about the nature of interatomic forces is enormously greater than the strengths of materials we normally encounter in nature. Theoretical estimates of

the strength of a solid give values of the order of 1000 ton/in² corresponding to elastic strains of about 10%, and this value is between 10 and 100 times greater than those of normal structural materials. These calculations apply to brittle materials as well as to metals.

For many years now fine glass fibres have been known to be exceptions to the general rule, having strengths approaching the theoretical estimates. Despite considerable variability very fine glass fibres appeared to have much higher tensile strengths than thicker ones, and this marked dependence of strength on fibre size was accepted until quite recently when it was found that the strength of glass was not dependent on the physical dimensions of the specimen but only on the degree of perfection of the surface. (Thomas,[1] Green,[2] Proctor,[3] Morley *et al.*[4]). Bulk specimens can now be prepared which show the same strength as the thinnest specimens. The apparent effect of size previously observed can be explained by the much greater experimental difficulty in producing and maintaining a surface of the required perfection in a large sample. The presence of a surface flaw (which can be caused by mechanical damage, thermal and other effects) produces high local stresses which cause premature failure of the specimen. So far flaws in glasses seem to be exclusively a surface phenomena except where they are caused by the presence of inclusions of undissolved foreign material.

Over the last 10 years or so fine crystalline filaments of various materials known as whisker crystals have been observed to have strengths approaching the theoretical estimates (see for example Brenner,[5] Webb and Forgeng,[6] Bacon[7]). Again, a size effect has been apparent, measured strengths of whiskers increasing rapidly as the diameter falls below about 2 μ. It is now beginning to look as if the effect of size on the strength of brittle crystalline materials may also be a second order effect. Flaws in the form of surface steps

* Rolls-Royce Ltd., Old Hall, Littleover, Derby.

TABLE I.

Material	Modulus lb/in² × 10⁻⁶	Specific gravity	Specific modulus
Iron	30	8	3·75
Aluminium	10	2·7	3·7
Sapphire (Al₂O₃)	67	3·9	17·0
Silicon Carbide	100	3·2	31·0
Graphite	140	2·2	63·0

have been observed on the surfaces of whisker crystals (Marsh[8]) and bigger crystals have on average bigger steps. Large crystals of silicon with carefully polished surfaces have been observed by Dash[9] to have strengths comparable with silicon whiskers and more recently Morley and Proctor[10] have observed that quite large single crystals of sapphire with carefully polished surfaces show strengths comparable with strong sapphire whisker crystals. It will be interesting to see if comparable results can be observed in large crystals of other brittle materials.

Although it now looks as if high strengths may be attained in a large number of brittle materials they will still fail catastrophically if the stress exceeds a critical value and they will also be susceptible to surface damage leading to serious degradation of their strengths. There may be applications where these unfortunate characteristics can be tolerated but for general applications a structural material must have adequate toughness.

In structural use these materials cannot be loaded by any means which produces high local stresses to their surfaces or stress raising flaws would be generated leading to a catastrophic loss of strength. At the same time the material has to be protected from accidental damage and provision has to be made for the occasional presence of a stress raising flaw. All these requirements can be met if the strong brittle load-bearing material is used in the form of a large number of fibres embedded in a matrix as glass fibres are used to reinforce a synthetic resin matrix. The principle here is to distribute a large number of strong fibres in a matrix of relatively low modulus, which therefore deforms easily. An applied load will, therefore, be carried by tensile stresses in the fibres and transmitted from one fibre to the next by shear stresses in the matrix. If the fibres are very long compared with their diameters then the shear stresses in the matrix and at the interface between the fibres and the matrix can be very small, except at the ends of the fibres. In this way the fibres can be loaded up to their breaking stress by small shear forces acting over a large surface area and these forces, therefore, do not produce local surface damage with associated stress raising flaws. Because of the relatively low modulus of the matrix it is under quite low overall stress and under these conditions it is difficult for cracks to spread through the material. In this way failure of a few fibres can be tolerated since the fracture of one fibre does not spread into the lightly stressed matrix around it and so the damage is localised. As there is a very large number of fibres the material as a whole maintains its integrity.

The high-temperature capabilities of ceramic fibres cannot be realised if they are used in conjunction with epoxy or phenolic resins of the type used in glass fibre reinforced plastics but metals or ceramics can be considered as possible matrix materials for use over a wide range of temperatures.

The use of ceramics as matrix materials seems attractive because of their high melting temperatures and generally low densities, but it seems probable that they will always have low failing strain as a result of the inevitable presence of stress raising flaws. These could be produced as a result of mechanical damage to the surface as well as being present at grain boundaries and other discontinuities within the body of the material. Preferential load sharing by the fibres, due to the modulus difference between the fibres and the matrix, seems very difficult to arrange with these materials and other means of preventing crack propagation might have to be evolved if composites of this type are to be of technological value.

Metals are rather more convenient as matrix materials in that, as a group, they tend to have rather lower moduli than ceramics and this gives some possibility of a limited amount of preferential load-sharing by the fibres due to a modulus difference between the fibres and the matrix. An applied load will also be preferentially transferred to the fibres by plastic deformation of the matrix and this property can also be expected to enhance the toughness of composites of this type. If by these mechanisms the fibres can be made to carry the greater portion of an applied load a fibre reinforced metal will be of structural value at higher temperatures than those reached by the matrix metal alone and, providing the known high strengths of the fibres can be retained under these conditions, the composite material will have strengths much higher than those of conventional alloys.

This line of argument leads to the conclusion that ceramic fibre reinforced metals are potentially materials of considerable engineering significance and an attempt has been made to gain some initial experimental information on the properties of materials of this type.

Fibre Reinforced Metals

There are a number of topics which seem to require consideration in any experimental investigation of the properties of fibre reinforced metals and these are discussed below.

Factors Affecting Fibre Strength

A thorough investigation of all factors affecting fibre strengths seems to be a necessary preliminary to the choice of a suitable fibre metal system and appropriate fabrication techniques.

Wetting and Bonding to Possible Matrix Metals

There must be adequate wetting and bonding between the fibres and the matrix metal but at the same time chemical reactions leading to degradation of fibre strengths must be avoided.

Elastic Matrix

The behaviour of composites when both the fibres and the matrix are behaving in a purely elastic manner seems to correspond quite closely to that of glass fibre reinforced plastics. In these materials load transfer to the fibres takes place by reason of the large modulus difference between the fibres and the matrix. In the case of ceramic fibre reinforced metals this modulus ratio will not in general be so large and the topic has been investigated theoretically by Arridge.[11]

Plastic Matrix

The fibres can be loaded up by plastic deformation of the metal matrix and this mechanism should be independent of any preferential load-sharing due to modulus differences.

Influence of Fibres on Matrix Metallurgy

It might be expected that the presence of the fibres might influence the physical metallurgy of the matrix quite apart from any preferential load-sharing by the fibres. Some points for consideration here are the effects of interfibre distances, particularly if these are very small; the nature of the fibre matrix interface and the effect of stresses on the matrix, produced by differences in Poisson's ratio and different thermal expansion coefficients between the fibres and the matrix.

Failure Mechanisms

Failure mechanisms and flaw propagation in ceramic fibre reinforced metals are likely to be complex phenomena because of the different modes of failure of the twin types of materials. Brittle fibres probably do not suffer from oscillating load fatigue as do metals but may well suffer from static fatigue as do glasses.

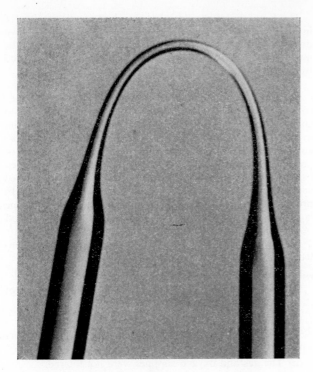

Fig. 1.—*Silica rod showing 8% elastic strain*

Fabrication

Successful fabrication of experimental composite materials requires an adequate quantity of fibres having as nearly uniform properties as possible, and it is also necessary to be able to control such factors as the size and aspect ratio of the fibres, the interfibre spacing and degree of fibre alignment.

Available Experimental Materials

Three types of fibres, metal wires, glass fibres and whisker crystals are available for experimental work. The availability and uniformity of metal wires make them very attractive for model work. (Jech,[12] Tyson and Kelly,[13] Cratchley.[14])

Whisker crystals are clearly much superior in the technological sense but are not available in technological quantities. Experimental work with individual whiskers appears to be a formidable but necessary task if a complete understanding of all factors affecting whisker strengths is to be obtained.

Glass fibres are easy to produce in quantity and have high strength-to-weight ratios, but they suffer severe loss of strength at quite modest temperatures. However, silica fibres can be very much stronger and also retain their high strengths to temperatures far above the limit of commercial aluminium alloys. It therefore seemed worthwhile to investigate the possibility of using strong silica fibres to reinforce an aluminium matrix.

Properties of Fused Silica Fibres

Over a number of years various investigators, including Boys,[15] Schurkow,[16] Reinkober,[17] Anderegg[18] and Eberhardt *et al.*[19] have made measurements of the tensile strengths of fused silica fibres produced in various ways. Very high tensile strengths were observed and Anderegg reported a maximum value of about ($3 \cdot 5 \times 10^6 \, lb/in^2$). The results were very variable and there was poor agreement between the different observers but all reported that very fine fibres tended to have much higher average strengths than thicker ones. On the other hand Griffith[20] working with very much thicker specimens and estimating strengths in bending reported strengths comparable with the highest observed by other workers for thin fibres in tension. More recently Hillig[21] also working with relatively massive specimens, has observed similar strengths in bending at room temperature and considerably higher strengths when the specimens were immersed in liquid nitrogen.

Morley, Andrews and Whitney[4] have made an extensive study of some of the factors affecting the strengths of fused silica fibres and also of quite massive specimens. Summaries of the experimental procedures used and the results obtained are given below.

Four millimetre diameter fused silica rods were heated in an oxy-coal gas flame and drawn down so as to form a test section about one millimetre in diameter. Several minutes after manufacture, when the silica was quite cold, the specimens were bent by hand to fracture and the behaviour of the

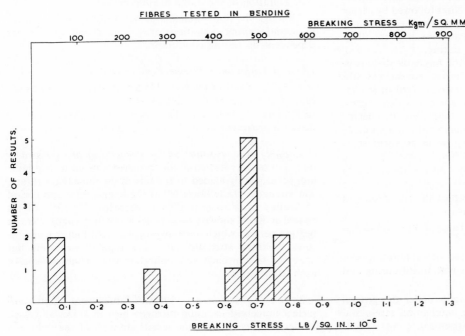

Fig. 2.—*Strengths of silica rods approx. 1 mm diameter (Histogram)*

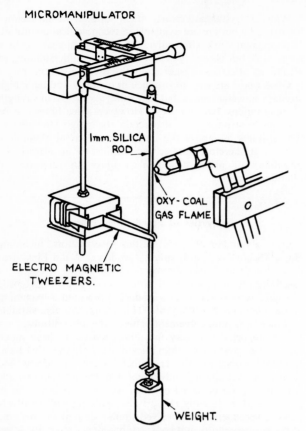

MICROMANIPULATOR

Imm. SILICA
ROD

OXY - COAL
GAS FLAME

ELECTRO MAGNETIC
TWEEZERS.

WEIGHT.

Fig. 3.—*Apparatus used for the manufacture of experimental silica fibres (after Morley, Andrews and Whitney)*

sample was recorded using a cine camera. The maximum strain reached in each specimen was then computed from measurements taken from the last frame of the cine film before fracture occurred. (Fig. 1.) The maximum stresses were computed from these values, it being assumed that Hooke's law was obeyed and the experimental results are given in Fig. 2. The results obtained confirmed Griffith's earlier observations and showed that any dependence of fibre strength on size must be due to second order effects and, from the description of the experimental procedures followed by earlier workers, it appeared very likely that the fibres tested contained stress raising surface flaws produced as a result of the fibres suffering mechanical damage during testing.

In order to avoid the possibility of mechanical damage Morley *et al.*[4] produced their test specimens from short lengths of 1 mm dia. silica rod which had previously had their ends heated in an oxy-coal gas flame to form spherical beads. These short lengths of rod, about 4 in. long, were then heated in the centre over a length of a few millimetres in a specially designed apparatus and drawn down so as to form short fibres having a diameter of about 10^{-3} in.

The factors which seemed likely to influence the strengths of the fibres were:

(1) The time and temperature to which the silica rod was heated before the fibre was drawn.

(2) The chemical condition of the flame and the impurities present in it.

(3) The thermal history of the cooling of the fibre together with its physical and chemical environment during that period.

(4) Subsequent treatment of the fibres under the general headings of temperature, time, mechanical stress and the physical and chemical environment.

The 1 mm diameter silica rods were hung vertically, heated in an oxy-coal gas flame for a known time and then drawn down by a known weight. During the heating period the lower part of the rod and the attached weight were supported by electromagnetically operated tweezers (Fig. 3).

The flame was fed from cylinders of coal gas and oxygen —the pressure and flow being carefully controlled. The silica rods were carried on a micromanipulator, care being taken to ensure that the rods were always placed in the same position in the flame. In this way the rods experienced reasonably constant temperature and chemical conditions. The period of heating of the rod and the release of the weight were controlled by a two-channel electronic timer and solenoid operated valves were used to cut off the gas and oxygen supplies. In order to produce a fibre it was necessary to have a small time lag, *t*, between the opening of the tweezer and the switching off of the flame.

By use of the apparatus the following factors were controlled.

(1) The duration of the initial heating period.

(2) The temperature and overall chemical composition of the flame.

(3) The weight applied and the small time interval, *t*.

There remained, however, some important parameters which were not under control, notably:

(*a*) The gas and oxygen supplies were not filtered.

(*b*) The atmosphere surrounding the fibres as they were drawn down was not subject to control.

(*c*) The silica used was commercially available Vitreosil and was not specially selected in any way.

Breaking strengths of fibres made with the apparatus described and tested in air at room temperature are shown in Fig. 4. Average strengths of about 850 000 lb/in² are observed under these conditions.

The following factors were found to have no detectable effect on fibre strengths.

1. Variations in oxygen and gas flow rates.

2. Variations in the position of the silica rod in the flame.

3. Variations in rod thickness.

4. Variations in the applied weight and the small time interval, *t*.

5. Duration of the initial heating period.

Although the fibre strengths proved to be quite insensitive to manufacturing conditions they were found to be very dependent on testing conditions.

Effect of Variation in Testing Conditions

1. *Effect of rate of loading.* Under standard conditions the rate of straining of the fibres was 0·17 cm s, giving a time to fracture of about 1 s. The fibre strengths were found to decrease progressively as the rate of straining was decreased.

2. *Effect of temperature on the strengths of fibres tested in air.* Fibres were heated in air for periods of up to one hour and subsequently loaded to fracture at the same temperature. The strengths of the fibres fell as the temperature and period of heating prior to testing were increased (Fig. 5). Fibres heated at 300°C showed no noticeable fall in strength over the heating periods which were investigated. At higher temperatures the fibre strengths fell quite rapidly with time but appeared to approach an equilibrium value characteristic of each temperature.

3. *Tensile strengths at* −196°C. Fibres were tested completely immersed in liquid nitrogen held in a Dewar vessel. Under these conditions the tensile strength of the fibre was

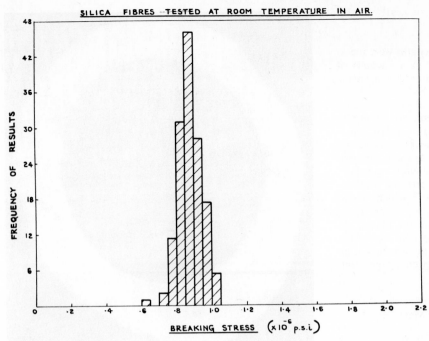

Fig. 4.—*Strength of silica fibres in air (Histogram)*

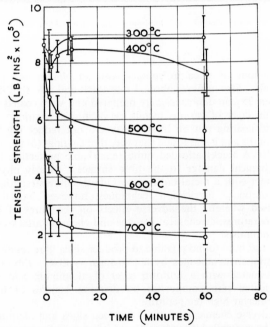

Fig. 5.—*Silica fibre strengths as a function of temperature and time*

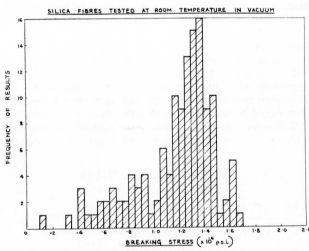

Fig. 7.—*Strength of silica fibres at room temperature in vacuum (Histogram)*

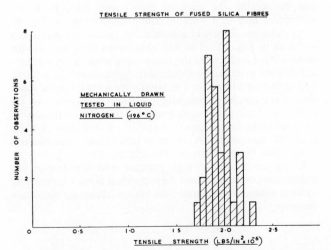

Fig. 6.—*Strength of silica fibres immersed in liquid nitrogen (Histogram)*

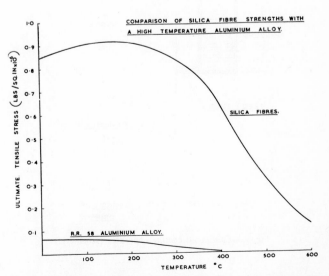

Fig. 8.—*Comparison between strengths of silica fibres and a commercial aluminium alloy*

considerably increased, average strengths of nearly 2×10^6 lb/in^2 being observed (Fig. 6).

4. *Tensile strengths in vacuum.* Fibre strengths were measured at room temperature and at 700°C in a vacuum of between 10^{-4} and 10^{-5} mmHg. Much higher fibre strengths were observed under vacuum conditions (Fig. 7).

Although fibre strengths were not much affected by manufacturing conditions they were very much affected by testing conditions and results indicated that two types of flaw generating processes were present—apart from flaws produced as a result of mechanical damage to the surface. At room temperature and below the observations were in qualitative agreement with the development of flaws by a stress corrosion mechanism, as suggested by Charles and Hillig,[22] which would develop flaws by chemical processes under the action of the applied stress, thus reducing the strength of the fibres. At temperatures in excess of 300°C a second type of weakening process was observed which took place in the absence of an applied stress but which was time and temperature dependent.

Silica Fibre Aluminium Composite Materials

As a result of the study of the strength of fused silica fibres it was apparent that this material was many times stronger than commercial aluminium alloys and that its high strength was maintained up to temperatures far beyond the usable limits for this material (Fig. 8). It was also appreciably lighter than aluminium.

It seemed reasonable to suppose that composites of aluminium reinforced by silica fibres would be much stronger than aluminium alloys and that they would be of structural value at temperatures much nearer the melting point of aluminium than would be reached by commercial aluminium alloys.

This argument was supported by some simple experiments[23] which were carried out in an attempt to learn something of the

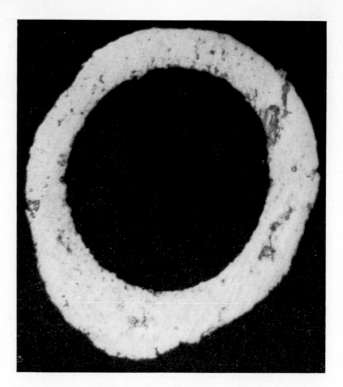

Fig. 10.—*Cross-section of aluminium coated silica fibre (diameter 50 microns)*

behaviour of silica in contact with aluminium and other metals. Strong fibres about 1 mm thick and also thin ones, about 25 μ in diameter, were prepared and were coated with a thin layer of various metals by vacuum deposition. The metal coating put on in this way did not reduce the fibre strengths and it was found that very thin coatings (of the order of 100 Å thick) afforded quite remarkable protection from mechanical damage to the fibre surface. Clearly physical contact with a metal did not degrade the fibre strengths.

Composite fabrication techniques, however, had to be devised whereby the adverse effects on the fibres of high temperatures, mechanical damage and chemical attack could be minimised.

It has been found possible to produce silica fibre reinforced aluminium composites by a two-stage process. Fibres are first coated with a uniform layer of aluminium and then fabricated into composites by pressing bundles of fibres together at high temperature.

Adverse chemical reactions between silica and aluminium can be controlled (Standage[24]) and it has been found possible to coat continuous silica fibres with a uniform layer of aluminium by passing the fibre at high speed through molten aluminium held in a suitable container (Arridge[25]) (Fig. 9). A typical cross-section of a coated fibre produced in this way is shown in Fig. 10. The soft aluminium layer protects the silica surface and makes the fibres quite resistant to mechanical damage in marked contrast with conventional glass fibres. The technique allows for the possibility of varying the inter-fibre distances by controlling the fibre diameters and the thickness of the aluminium coating, whilst the uniformity of the aluminium layer leads to a uniform distribution of fibres within the composite. At the same time the use of continuous fibres eases the problem of fibre alignment.

Under conditions of high pressure and temperature the aluminium coatings around the individual fibres fuse together to form a continuous aluminium matrix having no significant porosity (Fig. 11).

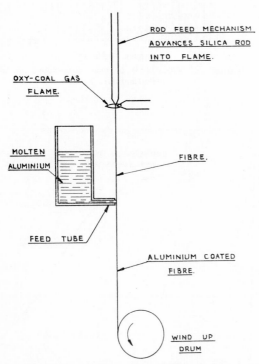

CONTINUOUS COATING APPARATUS.

ROD FEED MECHANISM
ADVANCES SILICA ROD
INTO FLAME.

OXY-COAL GAS
FLAME.

MOLTEN
ALUMINIUM

FIBRE.

FEED TUBE.

ALUMINIUM COATED
FIBRE.

WIND UP
DRUM

Fig. 9.—*Continuous coating apparatus (schematic)*

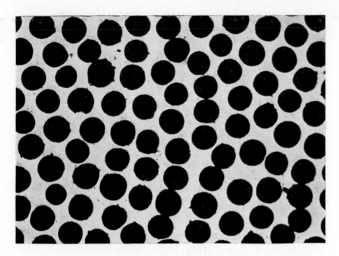

Fig. 11.—*Cross-section of aluminium silica fibre composite*

Preliminary fabrication studies using hot pressing techniques, and an investigation of the tensile strength of the material as a function of temperature have been carried out by Cratchley and Baker.[26]

These authors suggest that the fabrication conditions affect the strength of the composites produced in two ways. Fibre strengths will be degraded by high temperatures and pressures, but these factors will promote better bonding between the aluminium coatings around adjacent fibres. For a given temperature, therefore, there will be an optimum pressure at which composites having maximum strengths will be produced. The results of Cratchley and Baker shown in Fig. 12, in which composite strengths are plotted against pressing pressure, support this hypothesis.

Composite strengths have been measured, in the direction of fibre alignment, at room temperature and at elevated temperatures and compared with aluminium alloys and S.A.P. The fibre reinforced system is much stronger than the other materials over the whole of the temperature range (Fig. 13).

In aluminium based materials, therefore, it seems that relatively simple fabrication techniques can be used to produce a

ceramic fibre reinforced system which has much higher strengths over the whole temperature range than can be obtained by hardening the metal by a dispersed particle phase. At the same time the fabrication techniques used open up the possibility of producing complex shapes to final size in one pressing operation.

Conclusions

There is now some evidence from model systems (Jech *et al.*,[12] Kelly and Tyson,[13] Cratchley[14]) and from ceramic fibre metal systems (Sutton[27] and Cratchley and Baker[26]) that fibre-reinforced metals are materials of some interest. Work at

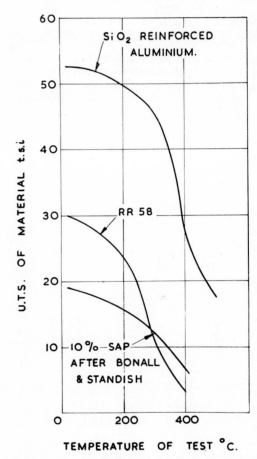

Fig. 13.—*Effect of temperature on the ultimate tensile strengths of aluminium silica fibre composites, aluminium alloy and S.A.P. (after Cratchley and Baker)*

Rolls-Royce has been concentrated on the silica fibre aluminium system which is not only of interest as a model material but even at this early stage of development shows promise of being a valuable technological material. However, an extensive research programme will have to be carried out before the general characteristics of the silica fibre aluminium system can be understood and its potential importance verified.

There seems good grounds for believing that this system is merely one selection from a large number of possible fibre-reinforced metal systems which could cover a wide range of operating requirements and have higher strengths and higher operating temperatures than more conventional metal alloys.

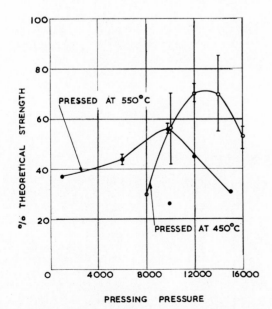

Fig. 12.—*Effect of fabrication pressure on strength of aluminium silica fibre composites (after Cratchley and Baker)*

J*

Acknowledgments

The author is indebted to Rolls-Royce Limited for permission to publish this paper and to Mr. R. G. C. Arridge and Dr. A. E. Standage for permission to quote from their unpublished work. Thanks are due to them and also to Dr. A. M. Smith, Dr. D. Cratchley and Mr. B. A. Procter for helpful discussions.

References

1. Thomas, W. F. *Phys. Chem. Glasses* (1960), **1**, 4–18.
2. Green, C. H. *J. Amer. Ceram. Soc.* (1956), **39**, 66–72.
3. Proctor, B. A. *Phys. Chem. Glasses* (1962), **3**, 7–27.
4. Morley, J. G., Andrews, P. and Whitney, I. *Phys. Chem. Glasses*, Feb. 1964.
5. Brenner, S. S. *J. Appl. Phys.* (1962), **33**, 33–9.
6. Webb, W. W. and Forgeng, W. D. *J. Appl. Phys.* (1957), **28**, 1449–54.
7. Bacon, R. *J. Appl. Phys.* (1960), **31**, 283.
8. Marsh, D. M. *Phil. Mag.* (1960), **5**, 1197.
9. Dash, W. C. *Growth and Perfection in Crystals*, p. 189, ed. R. H. Deremus *et al.* Cooperstown Conference (Wiley) 1959.
10. Morley, J. G. and Proctor, B. A. *Nature* (1962), **196**, 1082.
11. Arridge, R. G. C. *Proc. 18th Conference Reinforced Plastics Division S.P.I.* (Chicago), Feb. 1963.
12. Jech, R. W., McDanels, D. L. and Weeton, J. W. *Proc. 6th Sagamore Conf.*, p. 116. ASTIA 161443.
13. Tyson, W. and Kelly, A. " *Royal Society Discussion Meeting* ", June 1963, paper B.
14. Cratchley, D. and Baker, A. *Metallurgia*, Jan./Feb. 1964.
15. Boys, C. V. (1890). *Phil. Mag.*, **30**, 116–8.
16. Shurkow, S. *Phys. Z. Sow.* (1932), **1**, 123–31.
17. Reinkober. *Phys. Zeit.*, **38**, 112–122, 1937; **33**, 32–38, 1932; **32**, 243–250, 1931.
18. Anderegg, F. O. *Industrial & Engineering Chemistry* (1939), **31**, 290–298.
19. Eberhardt, E., Kern, H. and Klumb, H. *Z. angew Phys.* (1953), **3**, 209.
20. Griffith, A. A. *Phil. Trans.* (1920), **221(A)**, 163–198.
21. Hillig, W. B. *Florence Conference, Union Scientifique Continentale du Verre* (1961), p. 295.
22. Charles, R. J. and Hillig, W. B. *Florence Conference, Union Scientifique Continentale du Verre* (1961), p. 511.
23. Whitney, I. and Morley, J. G. Unpublished work.
24. Standage, A. E. Unpublished work.
25. Arridge, R. G. C. Unpublished work.
26. Cratchley, D. and Baker. A. A. *Metallurgia*, Jan/Feb. 1964.
27. Sutton, W. H. " *General Electric Research Report* ", R62 SD 65, June 1962.

DISCUSSION OF PAPERS PRESENTED AT THE THIRD SESSION

The CHAIRMAN (Professor J. G. BALL) said that there were five papers to be presented during the morning. They were continuing the tradition of being thoroughly interdisciplinary. That meant that they covered a wide field, and it was interesting to see the impact of one way of thinking on another. That fact should be very well exemplified during the morning's activities.

Mr. J. A. FENDLEY questioned the advantages of the correlation of so diverse a range of systems as undertaken by Mr. Holliday. The merits of heterophase systems depended predominantly on their physical properties and more especially on the nature of the interaction between the phases, which a purely geometric classification must necessarily leave out of consideration. Thus, among systems involving metals, restriction to geometric considerations failed to take into account the differences in principle between dispersion hardening and fibre reinforcement. Among polymer systems, resin-rubber blends were a useful illustration. The production of a technically useful material depended on a chemical bond between components, or on the common presence of a highly polar link. Without them, a composite of identical structure had no thermoplastic proportion at all. Such examples of the dominance of physical characteristics could easily be multiplied. They suggested that the utility of concepts of the kind discussed by Mr. Holliday was limited to variations in composition of systems of otherwise strict physical similarity.

More specifically, Mr. Fendley enquired whether any correlation had been established between the nature of the dispersed phase in ABS polymers and the physical properties of the composite—by analogy to observations on metallurgical systems similarly involving dispersed phases.

Mr. HOLLIDAY said the question was rather a large one. What was meant by " interaction " was the key to this. It was being used to describe many different things. An attempt was being made to introduce system into the field of complex materials. It was not claimed that geometrical parameters were the sole variables required to describe such systems. Many more parameters had to be invoked. Nevertheless, an attempt was being made to describe complex materials as completely as possible.

The interphase had not been dealt with, and the interphase or interface was one of the factors involved in interactions in multiphase systems. In most of the correlations between structure and properties, one assumed perfect adhesion between the dispersed phase and the matrix. This assumption was of doubtful validity. For example, if there was a third phase present at the interface (e.g. an impurity) the adhesion at the interface might be imperfect.

Mr. Holliday said that on the one hand there are disordered systems showing regions of order; on the other hand there exist highly ordered systems containing regions of disorder; and in the middle there was Professor Hosemann, who was trying to generalise in this field. He asked Professor Hoseman, with a material which was capable of being either glassy or crystalline and which could transform itself from the glassy state to the crystalline state readily, as with a sugar glass where the transformation was quick and easy, could he find evidence for paracrystallinity between these two extremes? Was there one material which could show both short range order and long range order, and could he find paracrystalline order in the middle?

Professor HOSEMANN said that in all high-polymer fibres there exist so-called " crystalline " and " amorphous " phases. Careful line profile analysis of cold and hot stretched linear polyethylene shows that at room temperature these crystallites in reality are paracrystalline microfibrils with a g-value of $\sim 3\%$ (for definition, see Hosemann's paper, eqn. 38). This paracrystallinity also plays an important role in the structure of liquids and molten metals (cf. Hosemann-Bagchi (1962), " Direct analysis of diffraction by matter ", North Holland Publ. Comp., Amsterdam).

Dr. N. B. W. THOMPSON asked if Dr. Morley could take up the problem of interfacial bond because the strength of the bonding between the metal and an amorphous or glassy face was obviously of great importance. As a metallurgist, he had a certain amount of understanding of the bonding between metallic faces and the nature of a grain boundary, for example the coherent boundaries that sometimes existed between precipitates and matrix materials, and it was known that quite a lot of the properties depended on the strength of the interfacial bond. But he found it rather difficult to understand the nature of the bond that might exist between a metal and a glass. In the one case there was an ordered structure—a regular crystalline structure—and in the other, a glassy structure. Was there any theoretical background for understanding the strength of the bond between those faces, or was it just a matter of empiricism?

Dr. MORLEY agreed that it was an important factor, but it was too early to say anything of any significance about the subject at this stage.

Dr. I. L. HEPNER asked Dr. Morley if he had carried out any experiments using that very interesting and revolutionary material in fabricating plant, e.g. pressure vessels. What were the economics of the material, particularly compared with the highly alloyed steels?

Dr. MORLEY said that with regard to pressure vessels for chemical engineering, the answer was that nothing had been done. This was experimental material to enable something to be learnt about the nature of reinforced metals. As far as costs were concerned, he did not know how these would eventually work out, but a speaker yesterday had pointed out that it did not matter if materials cost £200 a pound for certain applications. This material would cost less than that, but it was a factor which had not been considered in any detail.

Dr. J. MANN referred to the question of the previous speaker (Mr. J. A. Fendley) on ABS systems. A good account of that could be found in a paper by Dr. Haward and himself (given at a Royal Society's symposium the previous year), which was soon to be published.

He had a question for Professor Kennedy. Professor Kennedy, in his printed paper, had given an example of slip in a polymer system, interpreted in terms of dislocations. As someone experienced in metals, how convincing did Professor Kennedy find the experimental evidence in the nylon polymers that dislocations were at work there?

Professor KENNEDY said that he found it completely convincing. The surface features were entirely reconcilable with crystallographic directions. Once a formalism of imperfections had been established in this way, good reasons would have to be found to explain why crystals should not conform. He would ask what evidence we have of perfect crystallinity in any crystalline structure.

A SPEAKER said that Dr. Morley's material was a very interesting one. Its obvious application was as an engineering material. Looking through all the curves given by Dr. Morley, he noticed that he gave tensile strengths but said nothing about Young's modulus. Being chemical engineers, they used it not only as bolts but also as shafts, and that was where stiffness counted. To develop the theme further, he had actually used SAP as a chemical engineering material. He had had the same problem some time ago of designing submerged pumps for pumping high-test peroxide. A very high-purity aluminium was the only thing that could be used. He had had to design the bolts and the shafts. The bolts were no problem at all because they had only to have tensile strength, but the shaft had not only to have tensile strength but also stiffness and therefore to have a good Young's modulus. The Young's modulus of SAP was virtually that of aluminium. He had made experiments to try to increase the Young's modulus by preferentially etching away the aluminium and leaving aluminium oxide behind. The attempt was to stiffen the shaft by increasing the ceramic content. That had not been very successful. Was it possible to stiffen a shaft by preferentially removing the aluminium?

Dr. MORLEY said that as the silica and the aluminium had about the same elastic modulus (10 million p.s.i.) then the composite material had the same modulus—at least up to the yield point of the aluminium matrix. There might be applications for a material of this stiffness, but he would still regard it as an experimental material. As far as the designing of components requiring materials of high stiffness was concerned, the silica fibre aluminium system would not offer more than conventional materials in this respect. One would not get a higher modulus unless you put fibres of a higher modulus than silica in the matrix. A higher modulus fibre would of course increase the modulus of composite proportionately.

Dr. EDELEANU said that a question of the boundary between two different materials was a fascinating one and little seemed to be known about it from a theoretical point of view. He said that perhaps progress could be made by reducing the problem to a two-dimensional one to allow fundamental studies to be made. A method which could be used was described in the *Philosophical Magazine*,[1] although it was only applicable to a very limited range of material combinations.

Mr. J. S. ROBINSON asked whether any work had been done in which the fibre was replaced by a fibrous hole totally eliminating the fibre material itself, where the plastic flow was reduced by the interference of dislocations and where

there was no actual fibre strength, as with Dr. Morley's case. He asked for comments on the introduction of holes to improve creep resistance.

Professor KENNEDY said that it had not been done, as far as he knew.

The CHAIRMAN said he thought the papers during the afternoon showed that it was done to lower the modulus or resistance to deformation by introducing porosity.

Dr. MORLEY said that he knew that this had been suggested at various times, but knew of no work which had been done to demonstrate its validity.

Mr. E. RAVOO said that he thought the topic of physical properties in heterogeneous materials was fascinating. It was an old topic, perhaps older than most people were aware. No less a person than Sir James Maxwell had dealt with it in a quantitative manner in his treatise on electricity and magnetism, where he was considering the electrical conductivity in dispersed systems. His equation was valid only in the case of low concentrations of the dispersed phase. More recently, Tobias and Meredith,[2] at the University of California, had extended the theory and modified it somewhat, and the theory was in very good agreement for a wide range of conductivities in both the dispersed and the continuous phase, and also in a large range of volume fractions. It seemed to him that that theory should also apply to conductivity other than electrical, such as thermal conductivity. Perhaps Holliday and Mann might find it a helpful working hypothesis for correlating their data.

Dr. MANN said that he did not know of such work.

Mr. HOLLIDAY said that whether one was talking about electrical conductivity, thermal conductivity, or modulus, there was no difference between the formulae for series and parallel models.

Professor R. W. CAHN referred to the question about the possible effect of holes for strengthening a material. It was a very interesting field. Work had been done on it over ten years ago, when it was found that the properties of platinum made either by normal casting followed by wire-drawing or else by sintering followed by wire-drawing, were different. There was no micrographic distinction to be seen between the materials in the as-drawn condition, but if they were subjected to heating to try to recrystallise them then the material made by powder metallurgy was much more reluctant to recrystallise than the material originally cast. At that time, electron-microscopy was not normally used, but the assumption was that pores that were present in the material after sintering had survived in an attenuated form, and the process of wire-drawing prevented the growth of crystals at a nuclear stage during crystallisation.

Holes did not appear to have much direct effect on the strength of the material. They made it stable against crystallisation at a higher temperature, and in that sense improved its high-temperature characteristics.

Mr. A. E. S. WHITE said that the question about the application of the Maxwell equation for thermal conductivity was treated in W. D. Kingery's book, "*Introduction to Ceramics*".[3]

He had a question for Professor Douglas, who had said that if sodium silicate glass, which dissolved in water, had calcium oxide added to it, it prevented dissolving. It seemed curious; there seemed no very good reason why it should make any difference, calcium oxide being readily soluble in water.

Professor DOUGLAS said that the attack of water on glass was a very complicated process, one part of which was a diffusion of sodium ions to the surface to be replaced by ions of like charge from the water. This left a highly siliceous layer on the surface and in turn some of this silica was removed into the solution. The addition of lime certainly lowered the mobility of sodium ions in the glass and presumably also in the siliceous layer that was formed during the reaction.

Dr. E. R. PETTY said that Professor Cahn had mentioned the platinum-void dispersion. It had been done also for nickel by Dennison and Davies[4] at Swansea, but he could not remember the exact details.

Surprisingly little emphasis had been laid on the dispersion of phases; that is the size as well as the volume fraction. He asked if Dr. Morley had studied the effects of various amounts and different lengths and thicknesses of fibres in such materials. What was the brittleness of the materials?

Dr. MORLEY said that it would be very nice to look at things like the effects of differences in fibre thickness and inter-fibre distances. This would have to be done, but involved a large amount of work.

As far as brittleness was concerned, the materials were tough in the sense that they had quite good impact strengths.

Mr. C. R. SHAKESPEARE referred to bonding. He said that it was worth noting that Petrasek and Weeton[5] had worked on tungsten fibres in copper and had found that if elements which alloyed to the tungsten were added, the strength was greatly reduced, because the tungsten fibres were embrittled at the interface. He thought that that might apply in Dr. Morley's case. If an attempt was made to achieve better bonding by reaction between fibres and matrix, flaws in the surface of the fibres might result, which would drastically lower their strength.

Mr. A. H. COLLINS said that his remarks were again on bonding, and might comply with the request to bring the subject of glass into the discussion. He wondered if there was any analogy in the aluminium and silica to glass to metal seals.

Perhaps Professor Douglas could comment, in that there might be some interaction at the molten aluminium temperature between aluminium and the silica.

Professor DOUGLAS said that in fact aluminium stuck very hard onto glass. Aluminium and silica liked to react very much indeed, and presumably there was a layer of oxide which could accommodate the change. The problem was to get the oxide layer in the right condition.

Dr. P. HANCOCK said that he wished to make a brief comment with particular reference to Morley's Fig. 13, where he had plotted UTS against the tensile-testing temperature for SAP, RR58, and silica-reinforced aluminium. It would seem that with SAP the fall of the ultimate tensile strength with temperature followed a rather ordered sort of curve, as would be expected, whereas with RR58, once solution began a very rapid fall of the UTS was observed at about 300°C. It seemed to him very noticeable that the silica-reinforced aluminium results also showed a rapid fall in the UTS values between about 300 and 400°C, whereas one would expect that material to follow the SAP behaviour, assuming that there was no interaction between the silica and the aluminium. He suspected that the sudden fall at about 300°C meant that there was some change in the bonding properties between the silica and the aluminium in that temperature range and wondered whether such a possibility was being investigated.

Dr. MORLEY said that it might well be, and that it was under investigation.

References

1   ——, ——. *Phil. Mag.*, 1962, **7**, 573.
2   Meredith, R. E., and Tobias, C. W. *Trans. Electrochem. Soc.*, 1961, **108**, 286.
3   Kingery, W. D. " *Introduction to Ceramics* ", 1960 (New York; John Wiley & Sons, Inc.).
4   Davies, P. W., and Dennison, J. P. *J. Inst. Met.*, 1959–60, **88**, 471.
5   Petrasek, D. W., and Weeton, J. W. *Nasa Tn*, 1963, D1568.

FOURTH SESSION

THE INFLUENCE OF ENVIRONMENT ON THE DEVELOPMENT OF MATERIALS FOR NUCLEAR REACTORS

By R. W. NICHOLS, B.Met., F.I.M.

SYNOPSIS

The selection and development of materials is as much decided by the chemical and physical environment as it is by the need to carry out a particular engineering function. With regard to nuclear reactors, the important points have been that reactor components are bombarded by fast neutrons and that they are subjected to high temperatures in oxidising coolants. The necessity to meet these requirements is discussed in terms of reactor structural and canning materials.

For the reactor pressure vessel steels, the effect of irradiation gave emphasis to the development of notch ductile steels and weld metals, and later to the development of higher strength steels with good notch ducility. For gas-cooled reactors it was necessity to develop finned tubing which gave satisfactory performance in the heat exchangers. The particular corrosion requirements in these heat exchangers have directed attention to the use of high chromium ferritic steel.

In pressure tube reactors the need for neutron economy, strength and corrosion resistance led to the development of Zircaloy-2. More recent work has aimed at the development of zirconium/niobium alloys to give better strength, corrosion resistance and hydrogen pick-up. Other current work is aimed at the assessment of the important modes of failure, with special attention to the effects of irradiation and of hydrogen on properties.

Turning to canning materials, the choice of Magnox for the current power reactors arose from consideration of oxidation resistance and ductility, whereas in the Dounreay Fast Reactor, compatibility requirements with the metallic uranium fuel led to the selection of niobium. More recently, the good high temperature strength and corrosion resistance of stainless steel and nickel alloys have led to them being considered for a number of high temperature systems, *e.g.* in the Fast Reactor, Gas-Cooled Reactors and High Temperature Steam-Cooled Reactors. In the Advanced Gas-Cooled Reactor the primary problem was resistance to corrosion by the carbon dioxide coolant, and a 20% Cr–25% Ni steel was developed to meet this requirement with satisfactory structural stability, whilst some effects of irradiation on the properties of this material are reported.

Introduction

Over the past few years, advancing nuclear technology has demanded many advances in materials. The use of higher temperatures and higher pressures has led to search for stronger materials, whilst at all times the need for neutron economy has restricted the choice of base or alloying elements for in-core components to those elements with low neutron absorption. Additional requirements result from the effects of the service environment. The materials currently used as coolants in nuclear reactors—carbon dioxide, water or steam, helium, and sodium containing various impurities—all show some degree of reaction or interaction with structural materials. Considerable effort has thus been devoted to developing materials with increased resistance to particular coolants, and at the same time with improved properties. The other special feature of the environment in which nuclear reactor components must work is the continuous bombardment by neutrons of a wide range of energies, and by gamma radiation. The effect of such radiations has been studied in considerable detail, and these studies have affected the selection of materials. In the past the understanding of irradiation effects has not in general been sufficient to allow much development of materials specifically to reduce such effects. The work is now approaching the stage where such development may be possible and the more important findings are summarized in this paper to indicate such possibilities. To cover satisfac-

torily the whole field of reactor materials development in a paper of this length is impossible and discussion will be limited to the metallic structural components—such as the reactor pressure vessel, heat-exchanger tubes, and pressure tubes—and the fuel element canning materials.

Reactor Pressure Vessel Materials

The design of a virtually leak-tight pressure vessel to contain a large gas-cooled reactor poses a number of material problems. The economic savings resulting from increase in size and pressure have led to the progressive increase in thickness of the plates making up a steel vessel and, because of steel manufacturing factors, it becomes increasingly difficult with increasing thickness of plate to maintain the high standards required for tensile strength, notch ductility, cleanliness, and weldability. It has only been by progressive extension of the steel manufacturing, welding, and inspection techniques that the thickness of steel for power-reactor construction has been extended from 2 in. to about 5 in.[1] The use of even greater thicknesses is undoubtedly possible, although this may intensify supply and manufacturing difficulties. The current extensions to gas-cooled reactor technology make use of pre-stressed concrete pressure vessels, but the potentialities of steel vessels are still kept in mind, particularly as further experience is gained in the construction of thick-walled vessels for smaller water-cooled reactors which work at even higher pressures. Such vessels are demonstrating

* United Kingdom Atomic Energy Authority, Reactor Materials Laboratory, Calcheth, Warrington, Lancs.

the possibilities of the use of higher-strength, low-alloy steels. Further increase in reactor size for a given steel thickness could result from using the steel more efficiently. To this end, the possible modes of failure of a steel vessel have been studied in detail, to provide evidence on the safety of operation with stresses higher than those permitted by B.S. 1500 : 1958, on which previous designs have been based. Some work of this type has been described by Cowan and Nichols[2] and will not be discussed further in the present paper. It is of interest to note, however, that the gains that can result from a better understanding of an existing material can be as substantial as those arising from the development of new materials.

Irradiation effects

In pressure-vessel steels it has been shown that the major changes in properties result from the lattice defects produced by displacement of atoms from their equilibrium positions by neutrons with energies greater than about 400 eV. The effects on tensile properties are an increase in yield strength and ultimate strength, and at higher doses a reduction in tensile ductility:

TABLE I.—*Tensile Properties of ASTM A 212 B Steel Irradiated at 95°C 0.24% C, 0.81% Mn, Normalized 1040°C, Grain Size ASTM 5*

Dose, (n/cm² >1 MeV)	Strain rate, (min⁻¹)	Yield stress, (10³ lb/in²)	UTS (10³ lb/in²)	R of A, (%)
0	0.05	47.3–51.6	75.0–76.1	62–67
10¹⁹	0.05	65.4	80.8	68
10²⁰	0.05	92.6–94.9	97.0–97.1	24–28
0	0.5	50.7–52.6	76.7–76.8	58–64
10²⁰	0.5	94.5–98.5	97.8–100.1	32–35

With the neutron doses found at the pressure vessel in present designs, such changes are not important from a design aspect. More significant changes occur in notch ductility, the temperature for transition from brittle to ductile behaviour increasing, and the energy level for ductile behaviour in the Charpy test decreasing with increasing irradiation (Fig. 1). The degree of embrittlement is not linear with dose but over the range of practical interest shows a square root relationship[3] as indicated in Fig. 2. Whilst the degree of embrittlement is somewhat sensitive to the detailed neutron energy spectrum, it does not appear to be affected by dose-rate variation in the practical range. It is, however, markedly temperature dependent, and increase in irradiation temperature above 250°C produces smaller damage for a given dose, as a result of thermal annealing effects. For most steels this type of embrittlement is not important at irradiation temperatures above 350°C.

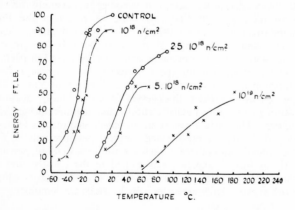

Fig. 1.—*Effect of irradiation dose on ductile–brittle transition temperatures of Conlo 1 temperature of irradiation 130°–150°C*

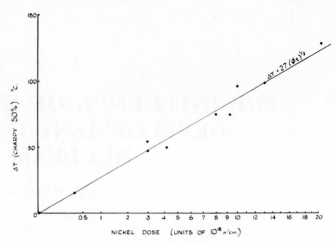

Fig. 2.—*0.13%C Aluminium-treated pressure vessel steel irradiated 130°–150°C in Calder R.C.C.*

The influence of material variables on the degree of embrittlement is less understood than that of irradiation variables. Whilst there is considerable variation in the embrittlement resulting in different samples from the same irradiation, especially at irradiation temperatures around 300°C, the factors leading to this difference have not yet been isolated. Composition, at least in terms of the major alloying elements, does not appear to be important since the whole spread of results shown in Table II is almost encompassed by those from two samples of a silicon-killed pressure-vessel steel of similar composition. Consideration of the levels of impurity elements which may be thought important in this respect (*e.g.* boron) shows these also are not the controlling factor. The effect of prior mechanical and thermal history on embrittlement also appears to be unimportant.[3] There is some indication in Table II, however, that manual weld metal shows a low irradiation effect, possibly as a result of its fine metallurgical structure. The superior resistance of fine-grained material was predicted by Cottrell[4] and has been shown experimentally by Mogford *et al.*[5] Trudeau[6] found a contrary effect in a 3¼% nickel, but this material is metallurgically rather different from the current pressure-vessel steels. More recent results[3] which confirm the beneficial effect of fine-grain size are shown in Table III.

Pressure-vessel Material Development

The increase in brittle fracture transition temperature on irradiation and the relative lack of dependence of this effect on material variables has directed attention to using a material with an initially low transition temperature, as indicated by a test such as the crack-arrest test.[7] Such tests have

TABLE II.—*Comparison of Embrittlement in Different Materials*

Steel		ΔT for 2×10¹⁹ n/cm² at 140–160°C (°C)
Cu–Mo low alloy steel		174
Silicon-killed P.V. steel	(a)	165
Al-treated P.V. steel		130
Silicon-killed P.V. steel	(b)	87
0.5 Cr 0.25 Mo steel		71
Machine Weld Metal	(a)	166
	(b)	153
	(c)	139
	(d)	101
Manual Weld Metal	(a)	84
	(b)	76
	(c)	55

TABLE III.—*Effect of Ferrite Grain Size on the Radiation Embrittlement of Steels.*

Irradiation temperature, 150°C; integrated neutron dose, 7.0×10^{17} neutrons per cm² (fission)

Steel (a)	Heat treatment	Ferrite grain size, (grains per mm²)	Increase in transition temperature, (°C)		
			35 ft lb	25% fibrous fracture	50% fibrous fracture
Aluminium grain size controlled mild steel (1)	1000°C for 1 h; transferred to 900°C, cooled 40°C per h to 650°C, held 16 h, furnace cooled.	523	50	40	55
	930°C for ½ h; cooled at 40°C per h to 650°C, held 16 h, furnace cooled.	6 890	5	5	10
Silicon-killed mild steel (2)	1100°C for 8·5 h; transferred to 930°C; cooled 12°C per h to 650°C, held 16 h, furnace cooled	76	65	50	55
	930°C for ½ h; cooled at 40°C per h to 650°C, held 16 h, furnace cooled.	842	45	40	40
	930°C for ½ h; air cooled to room temperature, 650°C for 16 h, furnace cooled.	4 130	30	30	30
Experimental nickel–molybdenum–vanadium steel (3)	930°C for ½ h; cooled at 40°C per h to 650°C, held 16 h, furnace cooled.	5 060	40	50	45
	930°C for ½ h; air cooled to room temperature, 650°C for 16 h, furnace cooled.	36 500	10	5	5

(a) Analysis of Steels:—

(1) 0·13% carbon;   0·12% silicon;   1·19% manganese;
0·08% nickel;   <0·05% chromium;   0·06% molybdenum;
<0·03% vanadium;   0·19% copper;   0·012% aluminium;
0·004% oxygen.   0·005% nitrogen.

(2) 0·12% carbon;   0·09% silicon;   1·26% manganese;
0·07% nickel;   <0·05% chromium;   <0·05% molybdenum;
<0·03% vanadium;   0·19% copper;   0·005% aluminium;
0·013% oxygen;   0·005% nitrogen.

(3) 0·11% carbon;   0·12% silicon;   1·05% manganese;
1·04% nickel;   0·07% chromium;   0·24% molybdenum;
0·17% vanadium;   0·08% copper;   0·007% aluminium;
0·003% oxygen;   0·006% nitrogen.

indicated the beneficial effects of low carbon content (Fig. 3)[8] and of high manganese content (Fig. 4). Complete deoxidation (" fully-killing ") and low soluble-nitrogen contents can also be beneficial. The beneficial effect of fine grain size on initial transition temperature and on irradiation embrittlement can be achieved by normalizing treatment (Fig. 6) provided that care is taken to avoid excessively high normalizing temperatures which can lead to large grain sizes. The materials so far used have for these reasons been low carbon (up to 0·15%) high manganese (about 1%) fully-killed mild steel used in the normalized condition.

The earlier work on improving these steels was aimed at increasing creep strength in the 300–500°C range. Whilst this work was successful,[9] change in design towards cooled pressure vessels made it inapplicable. Later work was aimed at increasing the tensile strength. Low-alloy steels with good notch ductility and good weldability have been achieved which give a minimum UTS of 36 ton/in², as compared with the 28 ton/in² of the mild steel. Such steels also maintain their properties to somewhat higher temperatures as indicated in Table IV. One such steel, a low carbon, Mn–Cr–Mo–V steel, has been used successfully by Babcock & Wilcox Ltd. in the site construction of the heat exchangers at the Sizewell reactor, each heat exchanger approaching the size of the reactor pressure vessel at Calder. Similar lines of development have been followed with respect to weld metal. The welding techniques and electrodes developed and those used

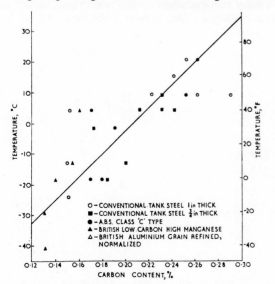

Fig. 3.—*Crack-arrest temperature and carbon content*

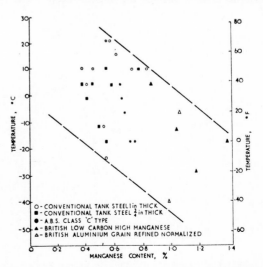

Fig. 4.—*Crack-arrest temperature and manganese content*

TABLE IV.—*Comparison of Pressure Vessel Steels (Normalised and Stress-relieved Conditions)*

Steel	Min. UTS (ton/in²)	Temp. for 35 ft lb Charpy value (°C)	Robertson Crack arrest temp. (°C)		Creep limit at ¼ TS, (°C)
			Gradient	Isothermal	
Silicon-killed	28	+20	+20	+40	350
Al grain-refined	20	−10	−20	+20	320
0·02% Nb	28	−40	−50	−50	~330
Grain refined+Mo	28	0	−10	...	>350
1·5% Ni–0·3% Cr–Mo–V	36	−20	−20	− 6	~400
Low C Mn–Cr–Mo–V	36	+ 0	−20	− 5	400
1·5% Ni–0·5% Cr–Mo–V	40	+20	− 8	+45	~400
QT, Cr–Mo–V	38	0	−40	0	420

on current reactor vessels have given initial notch ductilities at least as good as those in the reactor plate (Table V). Similarly, higher-strength weld metals with good notch ductility have been developed for use with the higher-strength steel plates.[10]

TABLE V.

Charpy V-notch temperature for

Sample	20 ft lb (°C)	25% Fibrosity (°C)	Isothermal crack arrest (°C)
Electrode *W*	−35	−21	0
Electrode *X*	−50	−25	−20
Al-killed Steel Plate	−40	−19	− 5

Heat-exchanger Tubing

A feature of the current gas-cooled reactor designs is that the hot gas coming from the reactor at temperatures up to about 575°C is used to raise superheated steam for driving the turbines. The heat-transfer properties of the gas make it desirable that tubing used in the heat exchanger is provided with extended surfaces, on the hot gas side of the tube. Several processes have been developed in which fins or studs are welded on to the external tube surface or in which external fins are raised by rolling. The requirements for the heat-exchanger-tube steel thus differ considerably from those of the reactor pressure-vessel steel. Unlike the latter, the heat-exchanger steel is not subject in current designs to damaging neutron flux. However, the material is subject to higher temperatures than the pressure vessel and so must have good high-temperature strength and resistance to corrosion by both the external coolant gas and the internal steam. The condi-

tions inside the tube are similar to those in a conventional boiler, and the temperature limits for various materials under such conditions are well established by practical usage (Table VI). The corrosion conditions on the coolant-gas side are peculiar to the reactor application and may impose more severe temperature limitations.

The oxidation of structural steels in carbon dioxide has been investigated collaboratively in a number of laboratories, and this work has been reviewed by Moore and Raine.[12] In dry carbon dioxide, or in dry carbon dioxide containing small additions of carbon monoxide, the oxidation of reactor-quality mild steel at 400°C follows a parabolic law and would give rise to only about 2×10^{-3} in. of oxide thickness in 20 years. The addition of small amounts of moisture to the gas, particularly at high pressures, can lead to higher corrosion rates and even to accelerating attack. Fig. 6 shows the effect of moisture at 450°C on the oxidation of mild steel by carbon dioxide; non-parabolic oxidation has also been found under some test conditions at 400°C and has been accompanied by local excrescences in the scale. The effects are found in low-alloy as well as in mild steels. For example, tests on $2\frac{1}{4}$ Cr–Mo steels in dry carbon dioxide and CO/CO_2 at 550°C have given weight gains of *ca* 20 mg/cm² max after 22 000 h[13] whereas rates of *ca* 50 mg/cm² 1000 h have been observed at this temperature in CO/CO_2 at reactor pressures in the presence of 500 ppm (wt) of moisture. In the Advanced Gas-cooled Reactor, additions are made to the carbon-dioxide coolant to reduce its radiolytic attack on the graphite. The coolant composition is thus likely to favour the accelerated attack found in moist gas. Additional corrosion allowances cannot easily be provided on the heat-exchanger fins, and excessive corrosion with the risk of detached scale being swept into the circuit must in any case be avoided. The solution is to develop heat-exchanger tubing with higher resistance to coolant oxidation. One approach has been to increase the

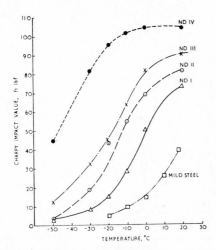

Fig. 5.—*Effect of metallurgical factors on Charpy V-notch transition curves of low-carbon high-manganese plate steels*

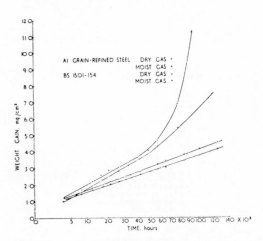

Fig. 6.—*Oxidation at 450°C of selected steels in dry and moist carbon dioxide containing carbon monoxide (0·8 vol %) at 200 lb/in² gauge*

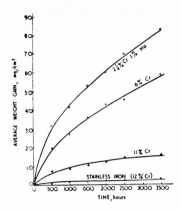

Fig. 7.—*The oxidation of chromium steels at 550°C in carbon dioxide containing carbon monoxide (0·3 wt. %) and moisture (0·03 wt. %) at 150 lb/in² gauge*

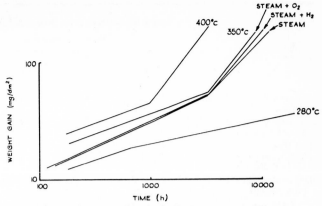

Fig. 9.—*Corrosion of Zircaloy-2 (Z105) in steam at 800 lb/in²*

TABLE VI.—*Temperature Use Range (°C) for Alloy Steels in Conventional Superheaters (after Brister and Bressler)*

		For pressures below 900 lb/in²	For pressures above 1200 lb/in²
Carbon steel		up to 510	up to 450
Carbon Molybdenum		475 to 530	up to 490
½ Cr	½ Mo	480 to 530	470 to 520
1¼ Cr	½ Mo	510 to 560	470 to 560
2½ Cr	½ Mo	550 to 600	550 to 600
5 Cr	½ Mo	590 to 615	—
9 Cr	1 Mo	590 to 650	—
18 Cr	8 Ni	610 to 700	590 to 700

chromium content of the steel and Fig. 7 shows that the oxidation resistance, even in moist gas, improves progressively with increase of chromium content. For the higher temperatures, the well-established austenitic steels can be used, but it is desirable to avoid these in regions of the heat exchanger near to where boiling of the water occurs because of the risk of stress corrosion occurring from the inside of the tube. The present experimental results suggest that a 9% Cr–1% Mo steel would be suitable for this critical temperature range. Such a steel shows a weight gain of only 8 mg/cm² after 7000 h at 550°C and reactor pressures in CO_2/CO containing 500 ppm moisture. Tube fabricators are now developing methods of finning such tubes, and the present results are most promising.

Pressure tubes

In the past, the development in the U.K. of thermal reactors for power generation has been concerned entirely with gas-cooled reactors. In order to broaden the basis of reactor development, the U.K.A.E.A. has recently started to build at Winfrith Heath a prototype steam-generating, heavy-water-moderated reactor (S.G.H.W.) with an electrical output of 100 MW. The design chosen is shown diagrammatically in Fig. 8 and makes use of 112 pressure tubes through the core of the reactor, each of which contains the pressurised light-water coolant, and in which steam is generated which passes directly to the turbine. The problems in design and manufacture of a large pressure vessel are thus avoided, but other problems are intensified. Since the pressure tubes pass through the core, they must be made of materials of low neutron absorption, and be kept as thin as possible. These factors, together with the need for mechanical strength and corrosion resistance in boiling water at about 300°C, has limited the choice of pressure-tube materials to zirconium and its alloys.

The best-known zirconium alloy for reactor use is Zircaloy-2, and most of the pressure tubes in the prototype S.G.H.W. will be made from this material. This alloy (which contains about 1·5% Sn, 0·12% Fe, 0·1% Cr, 0·05% Ni and not more than 100 ppm N_2) was developed to give improved and more consistent oxidation resistance in high-temperature water than is found for unalloyed zirconium. During its initial corrosion, the oxide film on unalloyed zirconium is tightly adherent and black, but after a certain weight gain has been reached, the corrosion rate increases and the film becomes white and less adherent. Impurities, particularly

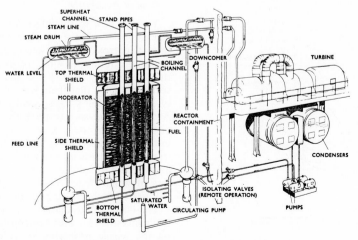

Fig. 8.—*Schematic coolant circuit—S.G.H.W.*

K

TABLE VII.—*Mechanical Properties of Zirconium Alloy Pressure Tubes**

		Room Temperature					300°C			
		U.T.S. (lb/in²×10⁻³)	0·2% proof stress (lb/in²×10⁻³)	Elong. (%)	Red. in area (%)	Burst stress (lb/in²×10⁻³)	U.T.S. (lb/in²×10⁻³)	Appx. 0·2% proof stress (lb/in²×10⁻³)	Elong. (%)	Red. in area (%)
20% cold-worked Zircaloy-2 (autoclaved)	L	86	82	15–20	50	58–65	50	47	15–20	50
	T	81	70	20	50		45	42	20	50
20% cold-worked Zr–2½% Nb alloy (autoclaved)	L	105	70	20	50	83–84	68	65	20	50
	T	115	100	20	50		72	70	20	60–75
Heat treated Zr–2½% Nb alloy (880°C water quenched) (24 h at 500°C)	L	110	85–90	22–25	55–60	—	80–82	—	21–25	60–65
	T	120	100–105	20	50–55	—	84–90	—	18–20	60
30% cold-worked Zircaloy-2 (autoclaved)	L	90	66	15–20	30–35	—	60	—	18	40
	T	90	75	15–20	30–35	—	54·5	—	18	35–40

* The tubes were heated for three days in steam at 400°C to simulate the autoclaving treatment which may be applied in service.

nitrogen, reduce the time to transition, whereas tin additions, such as those in Zircaloy-2, increase the time to transition. Even after transition the corrosion film on Zircaloy-2 remains adherent and gives a reasonable post-transition oxidation rate (Fig. 9).[34]

The desirability on neutron economy grounds of reducing the pressure tube thickness in the first instance suggests the development of materials with higher strength. The strength of Zircaloy 2 at the operating temperatures of 280–300°C can be significantly improved by cold work, and U.K. experience has shown that pressure tubes 5·14 in. int. dia. × 18 ft long can be produced successfully with up to 30% residual cold work. Even higher strengths can be obtained with other alloys in the cold worked condition. The selection of alloying elements is again limited by neutron economy and corrosion conditions (Fig. 10) and zirconium–niobium alloys, which were first studied in Russia,[15] are of particular interest. On the basis of these results, the U.K.A.E.A. has recently investigated in more detail the properties of Zr–2½% Nb alloy. This alloy in the annealed condition has similar strengths to the cold-worked Zircaloy-2. Production trials have demonstrated the practicability of producing pressure tubes in this alloy in the cold-worked condition and the significantly improved strengths which were obtained are shown in Table VII. Zirconium, like iron, shows a phase transformation on cooling down from 1000°C, and in the Zr–2½% Nb alloy it is possible to use this phase transformation, together with an age-hardening effect, to produce higher strengths. The procedure is to quench from temperatures exceeding 850°C and then to temper at about 500°C for times over 5 h.

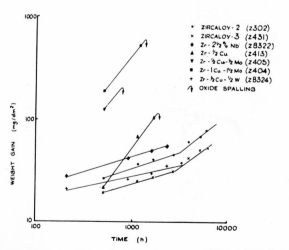

Fig. 10.—*Corrosion of zirconium alloys in steam at 350°C and 800 lb/in²*

The mechanism of hardening is now understood and the treatment temperatures, times, and alloy compositions have been optimized.[35] Reactor-size tubes have recently been treated giving the excellent mechanical properties shown in Table VII.

The corrosion behaviour of the Zr–2½% Nb alloy in high-temperature water and steam has been found to vary with heat-treatment conditions. The resistance to oxidation is reduced by quenching, but is restored by the tempering treatment, so that in the final condition the corrosion resistance is only slightly inferior to that of Zircaloy-2. At temperatures of current interest (~300°C) the cold-worked Zr–2½% Nb alloy has a rate of oxidation in steam similar to that of the quenched and tempered alloy, but at higher temperatures the former is superior. The corrosion rate of the cold-worked Zr–2½% Nb alloy before transition can be up to twice that for Zircaloy-2, but the post-transition rates are more similar, especially at higher temperatures. Unlike the case for Zircaloy-2, however, the corrosion rate of Zr–2½ Nb alloy is markedly increased by oxygen additions to the steam. In such an atmosphere, as in moist air, the rate of corrosion is very dependent on the heat treatment, the longer tempering times (~24 h) giving better corrosion resistance. This may necessitate a compromise between strength and corrosion resistance in selecting the heat-treatment conditions. The reduced resistance to oxidation is believed[14] to result from the local disruption of the protective oxide film by the preferential oxidation of the Nb-rich particles to Nb_2O_5. The addition of tin to the alloy has been found to increase the time to transition in air.[14]

Effects of Irradiation

Turning now to the effects of irradiation, theoretical considerations[16] suggest that fast neutrons may accelerate the rate of corrosion. Dawson et al.[14] studied such effects in steam and found no effect of irradiation at temperatures at or above 450°C. At 400°C the results were varied, but it seems probable that there was no effect at a fast neutron flux of 3×10^{13} n/cm² s⁻¹, especially in the pre-transition region. At 340°C there was a considerable increase, particularly in the post-transition rate. Transition occurred at about 30 days in-pile as against 200 days out-of-pile, and the in-pile post-transition rate was up to eight times that of out-of-pile. Even allowing for a factor of 8 on the out-of-pile results, the actual loss of weight from S.G.H.W. pressure tubes by corrosion will not be embarrassing during a reactor lifetime.

The effect of irradiation on mechanical properties is also being investigated. Fast neutron doses up to $2·7 \times 10^{20}$ n/cm⁻² on the tensile properties of cold-worked Zircaloy-2[17] and heat-treated Zr–2½% Nb alloy[18] increase the tensile strength

TABLE VIII.—*The Effect of Irradiation to 2×10^{20} n/cm² on Impact Properties*

Material	Nominal Hydrogen content (ppm)		Test Temperature			
			20°C (ft lb)	100°C (ft lb)	200°C (ft lb)	300°C (ft lb)
Cold-worked Zircaloy-2	20	Control	1·5	2·8	3·9	4·5
		Irrad.	1·5	2·8	3·9	4·5
	120	Control	0·7	1·0	3·6	5·4
		Irrad.	0·2	0·2	0·8	2·8
	300	Control	0·3	0·3	0·7	4·5
		Irrad.	0·2	0·2	0·4	1·7
	500	Control	0·3	0·3	1·0	4·0
		Irrad.	0·1	0·2	0·3	0·8
Cold-worked Zr–2½% Nb alloy	20	Control	2·5	3·7	5·5	5·8
		Irrad.	0·8	1·5	3·0	4·7
	120	Control	0·6	0·8	2·9	4·8
		Irrad.	0·3	0·3	0·9	2·8
Annealed Zr–2½% Nb alloy	20	Control	2·7	3·5	5·3	6·4
		Irrad.	1·1	1·8	3·0	4·0
	120	Control	0·9	1·2	2·8	6·1
		Irrad.	0·3	0·4	1·3	4·1
	300	Control	0·5	0·7	1·7	4·0
		Irrad.	0·2	0·3	0·5	3·2

and decrease the ductility. No irradiation results are available for the cold-worked niobium alloy, but the same general effect should be observed. Although irradiation reduces the uniform ductility to very low values, tensile and fatigue tests on notched Zircaloy-2 specimens irradiated to 6×10^{21} n/cm² show that the material behaves in a ductile manner.[19] At hydrogen contents below 50–60 ppm irradiation of cold-worked Zircaloy-2 has no significant effect on impact properties.[20] The combined effect of hydrogen and irradiation is being investigated at Culcheth, using miniature notch-impact specimens. Some preliminary results are presented in Table VIII which is taken from graphs of impact energy against temperature. Hydrogen has the same general effect as irradiation in lowering the impact energy at any given test temperature. The effects of hydrogen content and irradiation appear to be to some extent additive, and for cold-worked Zr–2½% Nb alloy containing 20 ppm hydrogen the impact energy–temperature curve after irradiation at 300°C to a dose of 2×10^{20} n/cm² is equivalent to that of the unirradiated material containing 120 ppm of hydrogen. The same conclusion applies to cold-worked Zircaloy-2 with hydrogen contents above 100 ppm.

Hydrogen Absorption

It would thus appear that the eventual life-limiting feature of zirconium pressure tube may well be the combined embrittling effects of hydrogen and fast neutron irradiation, and much work is being concentrated on determining the amount of hydrogen which will enter the zirconium alloy from the corrosion process and assessing the effect of this on the tube behaviour. Zircaloy-2 absorbs about 100% of the hydrogen produced by corrosion up to a weight gain of about 10 mg/dm². The rate of absorption subsequently decreases to almost zero, and then rises after transition so that for long exposures about 50% of the hydrogen produced enters the metal. There also appears to be a reduction in the rate of absorption when the solubility of hydrogen in the specimen is exceeded.[6,7] Large amounts of hydrogen (up to 3000 ppm) added prior to oxidation have little effect on the rate of oxidation of Zircaloy-2. Cold-worked Zr–2½% Nb alloy absorbs only about 10% of the hydrogen produced both in the pre- and post-transition regions, and heat treatment does not appear to produce major changes. The amount of hydrogen absorbed by the metal usually increases under irradiation in the same proportion as the amount of oxidation; there is normally no change in the *percentage* of corrosion hydrogen absorbed by the metal, although in some instances the absorption has been lower than expected.

Consideration of the predicted in-pile rates of corrosion and the corresponding hydrogen pick-up, suggests that after some

TABLE IX.—*Oxidation* of Stainless Steels in CO_2–5% CO by Volume at 300 lb/in² gauge*

Material		650°C			750°C			800°C		
		1000 h	3500 h	10 000 h	1000 h	3500 h	9000 h	1000 h	3500 h	10 000 h
Sheet materials:										
18/8/Nb	P	0·46	0·59	0·74	0·75	0·80	0·97	0·54	0·64	0·87
	A	0·11	0·30	0·50	0·27	0·32	2·1	0·06	0·41	0·89
20/25/Nb	P	0·16	0·22	0·36	0·21	0·25	0·39	0·26	0·35	0·51
	A	0·09	0·20	0·38	0·17	0·21	0·27	0·08	0·45	0·57
25/20/Nb	P	0·12	0·19	0·34	0·16	0·21	0·31	0·22	0·31	0·48
	A	0·10	0·25	0·46	0·18	0·24	0·14	0·25	0·39	0·51
Tube materials:										
18/8/Nb	P	0·59	0·75	0·90	1·02	1·11	1·19	0·55	0·65	0·83
19/14/Nb	P	0·30	0·40	0·55	0·50	0·58	0·74	0·37	0·52	0·80
20/25/Nb	P	0·13	0·22	0·37	0·19	0·25	0·34	0·26	0·39	0·53
20/25/Nb‡	P	0·22	0·29	0·44	0·30	0·38	0·49	0·24	0·32	0·47
25/20/Nb	P	0·21	0·31	0·46	0·30	0·33	0·51	0·27	0·39	0·62
AGR 20/25/Nb† production-type can		0·25	0·36†	0·41	0·24	0·33†	0·38	0·27	0·35†	0·47

* Weight gains expressed as mg/cm².

† Weight gains after 4500 hours.

‡ Double vacuum melted: all others single vacuum melted.

A = abraded to 600 SiC grit.

P = acid pickled.

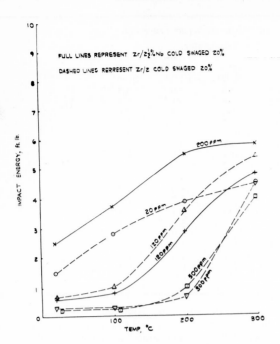

FULL LINES REPRESENT Zr/2½%Nb COLD SWAGED 20%

DASHED LINES REPRESENT Zr/Z COLD SWAGED 20%

Fig. 11.—*Avery impact showing the effect of increasing hydrogen on the transition curves*

20 years of operation the level of hydrogen in a pressure tube could exceed the solubility limit. The present data show the solubility of hydrogen in Zircaloy-2 at 300°C to be 95 ppm and that in the Zr–2½% Nb at the same temperature to be 175 ppm. It has been shown that the nature of the zirconium–hydride precipitates which form when the solubility limit is exceeded depends on the fabrication history and the applied stress during precipitation. Under some circumstances hydride platelets showing a high degree of preferred orientation, normal to the applied tensile stress, can form resulting in extremely low-tensile ductility.

The Effects of Hydrogen

In the absence of stress or deformation-orientated hydride, it has been reported that hydrogen contents up to 500 ppm have no significant effect on either the tensile strength or ductility of cold-worked Zircaloy-2.[21,22] Similarly, work at International Research and Development Ltd., Newcastle, on cold-worked and heat-treated Zr–2½% Nb alloy has shown that hydrogen up to 200 ppm does not significantly affect the tensile strength or ductility.[23]

As indicated earlier, hydrogen in excess of 10 ppm alters the resistance to fracture in the notch impact test. Typical energy–temperature curves for different hydrogen levels are shown in Fig. 11 and it will be seen that increasing hydrogen contents reduce the energy needed to produce fracture at temperatures below 300°C and increase the "transition" temperature. The actual values are very dependent on both specimen and notch orientation, but under comparable conditions at low hydrogen levels, the Zr–2½% Nb alloy in both the cold-worked and heat-treated conditions show better impact resistance than the cold-worked Zircaloy-2. Tests are being developed at the Reactor Materials Laboratory to assess the effect of hydrogen on the behaviour of actual pressure tube. In one such test, short lengths of pressure tube previously hydrided to given hydrogen levels are pressurized to working stresses at controlled temperatures and then impacted with a sharp chisel. At room temperature with very low (~20 ppm) hydrogen levels, the tube is pierced without forming a crack. Under similar conditions but with tubes containing more than 100 ppm hydrogen, a crack propagates

the full length of the tube. Increasing the test temperature produces a sharp transition in behaviour; tests at temperatures of 150°C and above do not show crack propagation even with 500 ppm hydrogen. Whilst further such tests, including those on irradiated material, are necessary it does appear that the hydrogen content can be permitted to rise above the solubility limit.

The work on the development and assessment of the Zr–2½% Nb has now reached the stage where the alloy can be considered for use. The ability to produce both cold-worked and heat-treated material has been demonstrated in full-size components. The alloy has similar neutron absorption to Zircaloy-2, but is appreciably stronger. The above discussion has indicated the importance of the effect of corrosion hydrogen entering the tube during service. For given operating conditions there is likely to be little difference in the quantities of hydrogen in the two alloys, the somewhat higher corrosion of Zr–2½% Nb being balanced by the smaller proportion of the corrosion hydrogen which enters the metal. Whether there are differences in the effect of a given amount of hydrogen on the properties of the two alloys remains to be established, but the Zr–2½% Nb alloy does show a somewhat higher solubility limit. Taking into account all aspects, it would appear that the Zr–2½% Nb alloy has important advantages as a pressure-tube material.

Fuel-element Canning Materials

The influence of environment on the development of reactor materials is particularly pronounced with respect to the metallic cladding which encloses the fissile material of the fuel element and separates it from the coolant. Whilst this is true of all reactor systems, the discussion in this paper will be limited to canning materials in gas-cooled reactors. Those in water and steam-cooled reactors are frequently of zirconium alloy for similar reasons to those discussed for pressure tubes; materials in sodium-cooled reactors are discussed in another paper to this conference.[24]

Aluminium was the first canning material to be used in gas-cooled reactors since its technology was well established and because it shows low thermal neutron absorption, high thermal conductivity, with good resistance to oxidation. With the increase of coolant-gas outlet temperatures, the interest in aluminium and its alloys diminished since their high temperature mechanical properties were not sufficiently attractive.

Magnesium has an even lower thermal neutron absorption than aluminium and is capable of somewhat better high-temperature mechanical properties under comparable conditions. Unlike aluminium, magnesium is compatible with uranium metal at all temperatures in the solid phase and a large miscibility gap exists in the liquid phase. There is thus no possibility of a damaging interaction between a magnesium can and uranium fuel under reactor conditions. Magnesium was, however, rejected for the early reactors because these were air-cooled, and magnesium has a much poorer resistance to oxidation in air than aluminium, appreciable oxidation occurring at temperatures of 350°C and above. The resistance of different alloys varies considerably; additions of aluminium, beryllium, and calcium were shown by Huddle and Wyatt[25] to increase the resistance to air oxidation.

The resistance to oxidation of all magnesium alloys in carbon dioxide is considerably superior to that in air[26] so it was natural that magnesium-alloy cans were favoured when it was decided to use carbon dioxide as coolant in the Calder reactors. The possibility of a magnesium fire, particularly under fault conditions, was of course considered and this led to the preference for an alloy which showed resistance to oxidation under a wide variety of conditions. This factor, together with consideration of the high-temperature mechanical properties and weldability, led to the development of the 0·05% Be– 0·1% Ca–1·0% Al Magnox alloy which has been the basis of the material used for the fuel-element cans in all of the current civil power reactors.

The desire for more economic power led to the design of the Advanced Gas-cooled Reactor and to the completion in 1962 at Windscale of an experimental reactor of this type generating 100 MW (heat). This reactor is also cooled by carbon dioxide but the higher gas temperatures prevent the use of magnesium alloys, which would not have sufficient high-temperature strength or oxidation resistance. In the Calder-type reactors, metallic uranium was used as a fuel and, as was indicated earlier, the possibility of reaction between uranium and the canning material must be considered in the selection of a can. Iron and nickel-base alloys react rapidly with uranium at temperatures around 740°C,[27] a fact which, incidentally, led to the preference for niobium in the Dounreay fast reactor, niobium showing no reaction at temperatures up to at least 1000°C. The selection of uranium dioxide as the fuel material for the A.G.R. removed this difficulty, since there is no reason on thermodynamic grounds to expect any incompatibility between stoichiometric uranium dioxide and stainless steels, which limited early data suggested would be suitable for use in a CO_2 coolant up to 750°C.

To be used as A.G.R. canning material, a stainless steel must have adequate corrosion resistance in the coolant, be capable of fabrication into thin walled tube (down to 0·01 in. wall thickness), have adequate strength and ductility even after exposure to prolonged heating and irradiation and have an alloy content limited to a minimum on neutron economy grounds. These factors played a prominent role in selecting the alloys during the development programme. To reduce the possibility of detrimental inclusions, a consumable vacuum-arc melting process was chosen and very high degrees of cleanliness were achieved. With regard to composition, particular attention was given to corrosion resistance, since the earlier results indicated that this increased with chromium contents from 18 to 25%. Table IX[28] lists oxidation rates determined for these steels in the form of sheet or tube in CO_2–5% CO at 300 lb/in² g in the temperature range 650–800°C, and illustrates the superior corrosion resistance of the more highly alloyed materials.

Next to corrosion resistance the effect of composition on thermal stability of the alloys was considered. The high nickel content of the 20 Cr/25 Ni/Nb alloy was selected on the basis of existing equilibrium diagrams to reduce the formation of the embrittling sigma phase. The beneficial effect was confirmed in thermal-stability tests; these consisted of 10 000 h ageing treatments at 650–750°C with subsequent room-temperature Charpy impact tests. Of the four steels tested, the most stable was found to be 20/25/Nb and the most embrittled 25/20/Nb, the latter containing 30–40% sigma phase after 10 000 h exposure at 750°C. On this basis 20/25/Nb was selected as the most promising canning material for Windscale A.G.R. Further tests where a larger number of stainless steels were tested in CO_2 at 750 and 900°C, have confirmed the choice of 20/25/Nb on the grounds of oxidation resistance even at temperatures somewhat higher than had been originally envisaged.

Tests of some 20 000 h duration have now been carried out on bright pickled, vacuum-melted 20/25/Nb sheet in CO_2 and CO_2–5% CO by volume mixtures at atmospheric pressure over the temperature range 650–800°C. More directly relevant are tests on double vacuum-melted A.G.R. production-finned tubing with either ground or machined finish, over the same temperature range in CO_2 and CO_2–5% CO by volume mixtures at 20 atm pressure, extending now to 12 000 h exposure.

K*

Results from the two series of tests are comparable. Little change in weight has been found after the initial period extending to a maximum of a few thousand hours; the total weight gain after 10 000 h at 800°C being of the order of 0·5–1·0 mg/cm². Metallographic examination of such oxidized specimens of 20/25/Nb has shown little localized or intergranular oxidation, the maximum extent of oxidation found being less than $0·4 \times 10^{-3}$ in. at 800°C. This is very different from the behaviour of an 18/8/Nb which showed local deep pits or cracks, particularly when oxidized under stress.

The effect of neutron irradiation[29,30] on the room-temperature properties is to increase the proof stress and ultimate strength and decrease the ductility. The loss in ductility is small and results from a decrease in uniform elongation, the fractures being predominantly transgranular. These changes in properties, like those referred to in the section on pressure-vessel steels, result from lattice defects produced by fast-neutron collision and become less on increasing the irradiation temperature, or on increasing the post-irradiation test temperature. For the conditions applying to the A.G.R. can, these changes have no engineering significance. Irradiation to a fast dose of 1×10^{-20} n.v.t. at high temperatures (590–750°C) has only little effect on the proof stress or UTS over the range of post-irradiation-test temperatures from 500 to 900°C.[31] The major effect of irradiation at 590 and 750°C is to reduce the ductility of all three steels, as measured by both uniform and total elongation to very low values over the temperature range 650–900°C (Figs. 12 and 13). This loss of ductility is accompanied by a change in fracture characteristics. The irradiated specimens fail with an intercrystalline fracture while the control specimens fail in a predominantly transgranular manner.

The differences observed between the effects of irradiation at 590°C and those at 750°C are also shown in Figs. 12 and 13. The only significant difference is the tensile-test temperature at which a reduction in ductility is first observed. In Fig. 12 all the steels after irradiation at 590°C show a loss of ductility of 25–45% when tested at 500°C. This loss increases with test temperature up to 650°C and remains fairly constant over the range 650–900°C. Fig. 13 shows that after irradiation at 750°C the effects on ductility at 500°C are much less than for specimens irradiated at 590°C, and for the 20 Cr/25 Ni/Nb steel no loss of ductility is observed until the test temperature exceeds 575°C. Tests on an A.I.S.I. type 316L austenitic steel show somewhat similar changes in ductility to the 20/25 steel after similar irradiations. The detrimental effect of high-temperature irradiation on the ductility when stressed at temperatures

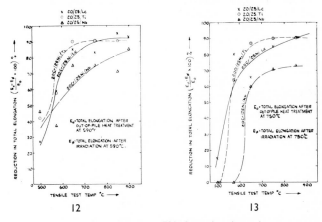

12	13

Fig. 12.—*Effect of irradiation at 590°C on the elevated temperature tensile ductility of three austenitic steels*

Fig. 13.—*Effect of irradiation at 750°C on the elevated temperature tensile ductility of three austenitic steels*

above 550°C has also been shown in in-pile tube-burst tests conducted at Oak Ridge.[32] It is clear that the mechanism of this high-temperature embrittlement is different from that of the lattice-defect, low-temperature embrittlement, and no fully satisfactory explanation can at present be given. Current tests at A.E.R.E.[33] have demonstrated the importance of thermal rather than fast neutron dose and indicate that boron content and grain size are important factors. Whilst the ductility changes are not considered likely to be embarrassing in the Windscale A.G.R., future applications for stainless-steel cans may be more demanding and it is hoped that the current work will enable the development of alloys in which this effect is much reduced.

Conclusions

The demand for increased efficiency in nuclear reactors makes increasing demands on materials to withstand higher stress levels under increasingly severe environments. The need to develop higher-strength nickel- and iron-base alloys for canning purposes, which will not show low ductilities after exposure to high thermal neutron doses has been indicated. For pressure tubes, the main interest is in increasing the resistance to boiling water corrosion at around 350°C without sacrificing strength. The development of the high-chromium heat-exchanger tubes referred to earlier will fill the present need, but more information on the conditions under which austenitic stainless steels are free from stress-corrosion effect may simplify design. With regard to pressure vessels some applications require even thicker and stronger steels than those used in the past. High-strength, highly notch-ductile steels such as the high-nickel and maraging steels may be of interest if they do not deteriorate too rapidly on thermal ageing at operating temperatures.

Acknowledgments

The author is indebted to Mr. R. V. Moore, Managing Director of the U.K.A.E.A. Reactor Group for permission to publish this paper.

Thanks are also due to colleagues in the Reactor Group and the Research Group for permission to include work not previously published at the time of writing this paper.

References

[1] Poulter, D. R. (Ed.). " *Design of Gas-cooled Reactors* ",
[2] Cowan, A., and Nichols, R. W. " *ASME Annual Meeting Philadelphia* ", 1963. (New York: American Society of Mechanical Engineers.)
[3] Nichols, R. W., and Harries, D. R. " *Fourth Pacific Area National Meeting of the ASTM* ", 1962. (New York)
[4] Cottrell, A. H. *Trans. Amer. Inst. min. (metall.) Engrs*, 1958, **212**, 192.
[5] Mogford, I. L., Churchman, A. T., and Hull, D. " *AERE Report M/R 2485* ", 1958. (London: H.M.S.O.)
[6] Trudeau, L. P. "*Iron and Steel Institute Special Report No. 69*", 1961. (London: Iron and Steel Institute.)
[7] Kehoe, R. B., and Nichols, R. W. *Nuclear Engineering*, 1961, **6**, 112.
[8] Nichols, R. W., and Watkins, B. in Poulter, D. R. (Ed.). " *Design of gas-cooled Reactors* ".
[9] Mackenzie, I. M. " *Iron and Steel Institute Special Report No. 69* ", 1961. (London: Iron and Steel Institute.)
[10] Cowan, A.
[11] Brister, P. M., and Bressler, M. N. " *Joint International Conference on Creep* ", 1963.
[12] Moore, C., and Raine, T. " *Iron and Steel Institute Special Report No. 69* ", 1961. (London: Iron and Steel Institute.)
[13] Tyzack, C.
[14] Dawson, J. K., Asher, R. C., Wanklyn, N., Boulton, J., and Watkins, B. " *Third Geneva Conference* ", 1964.
[15] Cox, B. " *UKAEA Report AERE-R 4348* ", 1963. (London: H.M.S.O.)
[16] Pensler, J. P. " *USAEC Report NMI*-1235 ", 1959. (Washington)
[17] Schwartz, C. M., and Young, A. P.
[18] Todd, A. G.
[19] Call, R. H. "*USAEC Report NMI*-1235 ", 1959. (Washington.)
[20] Asher, R. C., Cox, B., and Dawson, J. K. " *Proceedings of the IAEA Symposium on Power Reactor Experience* ", 1961. (Vienna.)
[21] Nelson, R. C. " *USAEC Report GEAP*-4089 ", 1962. (Washington.)
[22] Winton, J., and Murgatroyd, R. in " *USAEC Report GEAP*-4089 ", 1962. (Washington.)
[23] Evans, W., and Bell, L. G. " *Atomic Energy of Canada Ltd. Report AECL*-1395 ", 1961. (Atomic Energy of Canada Ltd.)
[24] Tyzack, C. This Symposium, p. 151.
[25] Huddle R. A. U., and Wyatt, L. M. " *British Nuclear Energy Conference Calder Symposium* ", 1957.
[26] Granger, L., and McIntosh, A. B. " *British Nuclear Energy Conference Calder Symposium* ", 1957.
[27] McIntosh, A. B., and Bagley, K. Q. *J. Inst. Mat.*,
[28] Tyzack, C., Campbell, C. S., and Trowse, F. W. *Journal of the British Nuclear Energy Society*, 1963.
[29] Harries, D. R. *J. Iron Steel Inst.*, 1960, 194,
[30] Schreiber, R. E.
[31] Hughes, A. N., and Caley, J. R. *Journal of Nuclear Materials*, 10, No. 1, p. 3063.
[33] Harries, D. R., " *Third Geneva Conference* ", 1964.
[34] Boulton, J. " *IAEA Conference on the Corrosion of Reactor Materials* ", Vol. II, 1962.
[35] Winton, J. in " *USAEC Report GEAP*-4089 ", 1962. (Washington.)

The manuscript of this paper was received on 26 February, 1964.

SOME EFFECTS OF TEMPERATURE AND ENVIRONMENT ON THE MECHANICAL BEHAVIOUR OF METALS

By G. C. SMITH*

SYNOPSIS

The elastic moduli of metals show only a slow decrease with increase of testing temperature and are not much altered by alloying elements. However the resistance to plastic flow and fracture depend markedly on temperature and composition and are also much less than would be expected theoretically for perfect lattices.

At low temperatures, brittle failure can occur in certain metals, with very low energy absorption, which leads to problems in connection with the working and application of these metals. Methods of improving the resistance to brittle failure are discussed, with particular emphasis on variables such as grain size, purity and microstructure, and the slowing down of crack growth by structural discontinuities. Reference is also made to fatigue behaviour at low temperatures.

At high temperatures deformation takes place readily and creep becomes a serious problem. The changes occurring during creep are outlined, in terms of the deformation within grains and at grain boundaries, and also the onset of grain boundary fracture. Methods of improving resistance to creep deformation and fracture depend upon the use of solid solution and dispersion hardening and control of grain size and shape, and the requirements are discussed.

The influence of gaseous and liquid environments at low temperatures is mentioned in connection with fatigue failure, and brittle failure induced by hydrogen. At high temperatures gaseous environments can result in serious attack and loss of metal, particularly with some of the high melting point metals, and protective coatings must be devised to overcome this problem. Cracking induced by liquid metals may also be important in certain temperature ranges.

Introduction

The use of metals in engineering depends upon many factors. Mechanical, physical and chemical properties may all be important and for some applications of the commoner metals such as mild steel, cheapness and availability must also be taken into account. However, for many purposes, mechanical behaviour is particularly significant, comprising elasticity, tensile strength, ductility, and energy absorbed in fracture, as well as resistance to fatigue and more complex forms of stressing. Such properties will govern not only the mechanical behaviour in service, but may also be relevant to the ease or otherwise of fabrication.

The temperatures at which metals are used differ widely, and may be very low or very high in an absolute sense, or in relation to the melting point of the metal concerned. In addition gaseous or liquid environments may be present which modify the mechanical behaviour. The aim of the present paper is to indicate the alterations in mechanical behaviour which changes in temperature can bring about, and the importance of the structure and composition of the metal in connection with these alterations, together with a mention of environmental effects.

Elastic Properties

Engineering structures are often designed on the assumption of elastic behaviour, and so the Young's modulus of elasticity is of some importance. The elastic moduli of a number of metals at room temperature are plotted in Fig. 1 as a function of their melting points.[1] The general increase with melting point, is an indirect reflection of the increased binding strength

between the atoms of high melting point metals. The modulus values usually fall slowly and smoothly with increasing temperature[2,3] as shown in Fig. 2, although allotropic and magnetic changes can introduce irregularities for some metals, e.g. nickel and cobalt.

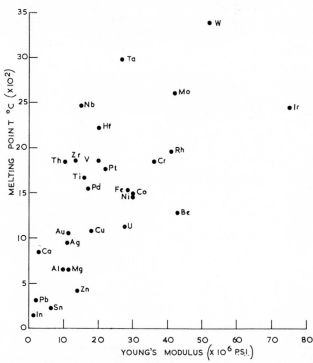

Fig. 1.—*Young's modulus of elasticity plotted against the melting points for pure metals*

* Department of Metallurgy, University of Cambridge.

135

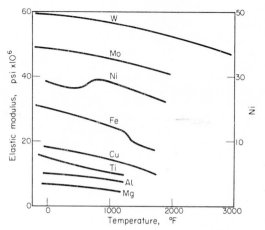

Fig. 2.—*The change of Young's modulus of elasticity with temperature for several metals*[3]

Since changes in microstructure, such as changes in grain size or size of precipitate particles, will not influence to any appreciable extent the number of bonds between different types of atoms in the structure, it might be anticipated that the modulus would depend little on heat treatments which might affect other properties considerably. Table I shows this to be true for a steel in different states of heat treatments.[4]

TABLE I.—*Effect of Heat Treatment on Hardness and Young's Modulus of a Steel* (0·97% C, 0·16% Si, 0·38% Mn, 0·26% Ni, 1·37% Cr)[4]

Heat Treatment	Hardness	Young's Modulus ton/in$^2 \times 10^3$
Oil quenched from 825°C	880	13·1
Oil quenched from 825°C and tempered 400°C	600	13·6
Oil quenched from 825°C and tempered 720°C	260	13·8

The relatively low values of moduli of some important engineering metals such as aluminium and titanium have stimulated work on means of increasing elastic moduli. The most generally effective method is the incorporation of finely dispersed oxides, carbides, nitrides, borides or intermetallic

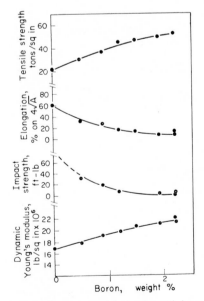

Fig. 3.—*The variation in mechanical properties with boron content for binary titanium–boron alloys*[7]

compounds, having elastic moduli higher than the matrix. The resultant increase in modulus depends primarily upon the volume fraction of the second phase, although the geometry of the dispersion also has an effect. Increases have been reported for aluminium[5,6] and titanium alloys.[7] Fig. 3 shows that in titanium alloys, particles of titanium boride can increase the modulus significantly but at the same time, the increased content of a hard second phase increases the tensile strength and lowers the ductility and impact strength. The reduction in ductility could limit the applicability of this method of increasing modulus, particularly for low temperature uses where brittle failure is more likely to occur. At high operating temperatures, the improvement in modulus would be maintained provided the second phase did not dissolve in the matrix. However, strictly elastic behaviour is much less well defined at higher temperatures, since plastic deformation due to creep becomes increasingly important even at low stresses.

If a metal is required with lower modulus of elasticity than normal, this can be achieved by the introduction of a low modulus second phase, or porosity,[8] or something which is akin to porosity such as the weakly bonded graphite in grey cast iron. Such additions will, however, reduce the strength and ductility.

Tensile Strength

The resistance of pure metals to deformation and fracture varies considerably. In general, however, strength as measured in a tensile test increases with melting point whilst ductility falls away. Thus at room temperature the ultimate tensile stress (U.T.S.) of lead (m.pt. 327°C) is about 1 ton/in^2, aluminium (m.pt. 654°C) 4 ton/in^2, nickel (m.pt. 1450°C) 20 ton/in^2 and tungsten (m.pt. 3300°C) 70 ton/in^2. The corresponding percentage elongations to fracture[9] are 64, 50, 28 and 8. The strengths may be increased by alloying or by work hardening, so that aluminium alloys are available with tensile strengths up to 45 ton/in^2 and heavily cold drawn tungsten wire has a strength of 300 ton/in^2. The elongations and work to fracture are usually much reduced by these treatments.

In tensile tests metals normally undergo necking, *i.e.* local reduction in area, before fracture, so that the true stress at fracture will be greater than the U.T.S. However even when allowance is made for this by dividing the load at fracture by the minimum area, the fracture strengths so obtained are much less than the theoretical fracture strength of a perfect crystalline lattice, which is approximately[10] $E/10$ where E is the Young's modulus of elasticity. Thus for lead, aluminium, nickel and tungsten at room temperature the theoretical fracture strengths are 100, 450, 1340, 2300 ton/in^2 respectively; values which are far above those normally found. A similar discrepancy arises in connection with resistance to initial plastic deformation. The theoretical shear strength[11] of a perfect lattice is approximately $G/30$, where G is the shear modulus of the lattice. This gives theoretical values which are much higher than the initial yield strengths in shear of bulk metals. The low values of measured yield strength are due to plastic deformation occurring not by a homogeneous shear, but by the spreading of slip by the movement of dislocations, which is a much easier process.

Ease of plastic deformation can also lead to fracture, without the stress ever rising to the theoretical value of $E/10$. The metal then undergoes 100% reduction in area at facture and this is what happens normally with high purity copper or aluminium. In other cases plastic deformation again leads to fracture, but by holes developing internally from the interfaces between the metal and weakly bonded inclusions or precipitate particles. These internal holes increase in size by plastic deformation and eventually link together to produce rupture by what is termed internal necking. In such cases the external reduction in area at fracture is considerably less than 100%, and due to the deformation being localised, the work to fracture may be reduced to a low level, giving rise to an apparently brittle failure.

In addition to ductile fractures occurring by plastic deformation, some metals are susceptible to very low energy brittle fractures, which propagate either on cleavage planes or along grain boundaries, with little plastic deformation. Such fractures are thought to be initiated by the formation of small cracks in the lattice either by particular dislocation interactions, or cracking of weak second phases or interfaces.

It is therefore clear that structural defects in a metal, either at the atomic level or in the size range of second phase particles, can modify very markedly the deformation and fracture behaviour. Direct confirmation of the importance of defects on mechanical behaviour is obtained from mechanical tests on small diameter metal whiskers which have nearly perfect crystal structures,[12] and as a result show near theoretical yield and fracture strengths.

Since the theoretical shear strength and fracture strength can be expressed approximately as fractions of the shear and elastic modulii, the change of these strength values with temperature for perfect crystals should be similar to the modulus changes shown in Fig. 2. However, bulk metals show a much greater temperature dependence for yield and and fracture strength than Fig. 2 would indicate and this is due to marked influence of temperature on dislocation movements and interactions. Since thermal activation can help dislocation movement, yield stresses would be expected to rise continuously for all metals as the testing temperature is lowered towards absolute zero, and experimental results demonstrate that this is so. However fracture behaviour is more complicated owing to different modes of fracture being possible in different temperature ranges so that although fracture strength does often rise with decreasing temperature this is not always the case.

Dislocations make metals much weaker plastically than they should be, and in order to overcome this, obstacles to dislocation movements are usually introduced into the crystal lattice. Work hardening, caused by plastic deformation, is due to an increase in the number of dislocations, so that many of these become tangled together in such a way that they cannot move easily, and also impede the movement of other dislocations. Alternatively foreign atoms in solution in the matrix lattice (solid solution strengthening) or foreign atoms forming fine second phase precipitate particles (precipitation or dispersion strengthening) may be used to form barriers. These methods enable considerable increases in strength to be obtained but it is difficult to obtain structures which will impede dislocation movement completely. As a result alloys hardened by the introduction of barriers to dislocations still have yield and fracture strengths which are below the theoretical values. Commercial aluminium alloys, can be strengthened by fine precipitates to an U.T.S. $\sim$45 ton/in^2, but this is still a long way below the theoretical strength and the same is true for even the highest strength steels, U.T.S. $\sim$280 ton/in^2.

The discrepancy between actual and calculated strengths is stimulating research into methods of achieving strengths nearer the theoretical, and currently two main lines are being investigated. The first is to extend the use of dispersion hardening. However, production problems arise in incorporating a sufficiently large volume fraction of dispersed phase with the correct size and spacing of the particles. The dispersed particles should be of high strength and as dissimilar as possible in structure from the matrix, so that dislocations moving in the matrix are halted at the particle–matrix interface, rather than penetrating through the particles. Also the nature of the interface between the precipitate and the matrix must be controlled, since such interfaces constitute potential nuclei for cracks, when a stress is applied to the alloy. Crack formation at an interface will be easier, the higher the value of the interface energy, and this will usually be high for those particles which are most dissimilar from the matrix, i.e. the ones which it is most desired to add for other reasons. Precipitation hardening is used extensively to produce dispersions, since alloys can be designed which are single phase at elevated temperatures, and therefore readily forgeable; then by quenching and subsequent heat treatment at a lower temperature the precipitate is formed. This technique may not however produce the optimum type and volume fraction of precipitate, so that further developments may have to depend upon techniques such as powder metallurgy[13] which give greater flexibility although with greater complexity and expense.

The other approach to high strength is to reinforce the metal matrix by the use of high strength fibres and to transfer most of the applied stress to the fibres by plastic flow in the metal matrix.[14] High strength is obtained in the fibres by making them of small diameter and as free from defects as possible. This method has in its favour the fact that the movement of dislocations in the matrix need not be suppressed so that the spacing of the fibres can be greater than the spacings required for effective dispersion hardening, and as a result the structures may be easier to produce. Also the toughness as measured by work to fracture, may be more readily controlled than in dispersion hardened alloys. A possible disadvantage of fibre strengthening is anisotropy since the highest strength is in the direction of the fibre axes.

Toughness and Low Temperature Behaviour

Introduction

High static strength is a useful property for a structural material, but this must be combined with some degree of fracture toughness, i.e. a significant amount of work must be absorbed in fracturing the metal. For this reason bulk metals having theoretical strengths might be of little use, because the energy to fracture would only have to equal the surface energy of the new fracture surfaces and thus be very small. A combination of lower strength with some plastic deformation before fracture, to absorb energy, is more generally satisfactory, and gives a material of the toughness which is normally required by engineers. However, even at strength levels which are well below the theoretical values, some metals fail with little overall prior deformation, as mentioned earlier. Changes in testing temperature can induce this behaviour and one of the main engineering problems currently experienced with some metals, is a lack of ductility or toughness at low temperatures, although considerable energy is absorbed when fracture occurs at higher temperatures. The tensile strength usually increases with lower testing temperatures even in the range where the ductility decreases, although when completely brittle behaviour is obtained, the strength may also start to fall off. The behaviours[15,16] of several different metals are shown in Figs. 4 and 5, and it will be seen that in tensile tests, a sudden change in toughness (ductility) occurs over a comparatively small temperature range with many body-centred cubic metals and alloys although important exceptions exist (see Fig. 5), but not with those having face-centred cubic structures.

Hexagonal metals show mixed behaviour; some like cadmium,[17] titanium and zirconium do not exhibit low temperature brittleness, whilst others do, e.g. zinc. Thus classification by structure is a useful guide to low temperature behaviour, but it must be emphasised that no general rules can be formulated.

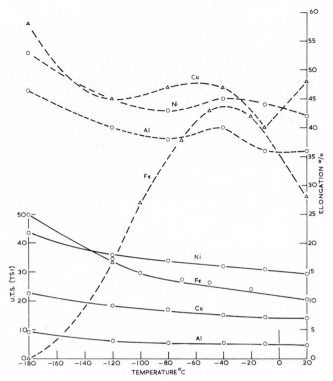

Fig. 4.—*The effect of testing temperature on the tensile strength and elongation of copper, nickel and aluminium (face-centred cubic) and iron (body-centred cubic)*

The onset of brittleness at low temperatures is accompanied by a change in type of fracture from one involving considerable plastic deformation to a cleavage or grain boundary type, with no evidence in the fully brittle state of any macroscopic deformation at all.

If specimens are notched the change in fracture behaviour occurs at higher temperatures, Fig. 6, and this is a much more serious problem from an engineering viewpoint, since it is often impossible to avoid notches or stress concentrators of some sort in actual structures.

Theory of the Transition Temperature

The sudden onset of low temperature brittleness has been extensively investigated and it is not proposed to review the many theories which have been advanced. However, the approach which is currently favoured is that in body-centred cubic metals, small amounts of plastic deformation produced by slip or twinning, result in micro-cracks in the lattice. Whether or not brittle behaviour is exhibited then depends upon whether the cracks can grow under the applied stress, into large fully developed cracks which propagate to cause rapid failure. One condition which expresses this[18] is,

$$\sigma_y k_y d^{\frac{1}{2}} = \beta G \gamma \qquad . \qquad . \qquad (1)$$

where σ_y is the yield stress, k_y is a constant which gives a measure of the strength of dislocation anchoring in the metal due to high local concentrations of solute atoms or impurity atoms in dislocations, d is the grain diameter, β is a constant which depends on the stress system and is equal to 2 for torsion, 1 for tension and $\frac{1}{3}$ for notched tests, G is the shear modulus and γ the surface energy of the crack faces. If the left hand side of (1) is greater than the right, brittle behaviour is observed, and *vice versa*.

Use of equation (1) enables several features of low temperature brittleness to be appreciated and suggests ways in which materials of greater toughness at low temperatures might be developed. The effect of testing temperature in promoting a transition from ductile to brittle fracture, is due to the relatively rapid increase in yield stress which occurs with decrease in temperature for body-centred cubic metals, and which is associated with the type of lattice, and with impurity effects which alter the k_y term. The higher ductile-brittle transition temperature found in notched-bar tests, is also explained by equation (1) due to the lower value of β when a notch is present, and the increase of yield stress due to the higher local strain rate at the base of a notch.

The effect of some structural variables will now be considered and it should be remembered that changes referred to specifically in connection with notched-bar transition temperature will be paralleled by similar changes in the tensile behaviour but in a lower temperature range.

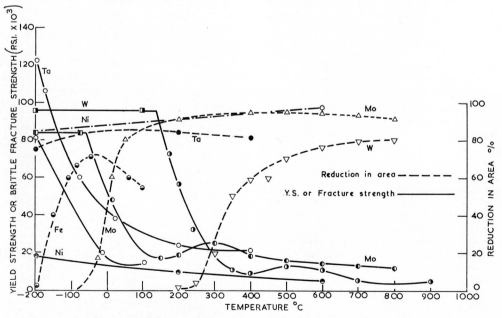

Fig. 5.—*The effect of testing temperature on the yield strength and reduction in area at fracture of iron, tantalum, tungsten and molybdenum (body-centred cubic) and nickel (face-centred cubic)*[16]

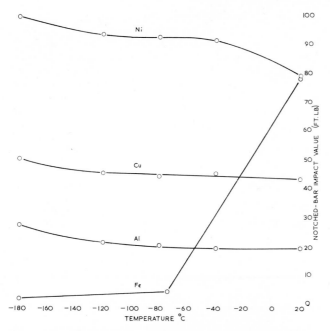

Fig. 6.—*The effect of testing temperature on the energy absorbed to fracture in notched-bar impact tests on copper, nickel and aluminium (face-centred cubic) and iron (body-centred cubic)*

Grain Size

The finer the grain size, the lower the transition temperature, as shown in Fig. 7, for a 0·11% carbon steel, where the changes in grain size were induced by changes in the normalizing temperature.[19] In low carbon steels grain size can also be reduced by the addition of certain alloying elements. Thus aluminium and nitrogen added to steel give aluminium nitride[19,20] precipitates which restrain grain boundary movement, and additions of elements such as niobium which form stable carbides, have a similar effect. Fine insoluble precipitates are the most effective means of refining grain size, but if they are completely insoluble, it is difficult to disperse them in liquid metal, due to problems of wetting and the maintenance of a uniform dispersion on solidification. Nevertheless investigations of the possibilities of doing this might be rewarding in helping to produce fine grained materials with low transition temperatures. Alternatively powder metallurgy fabrication techniques might be employed for low

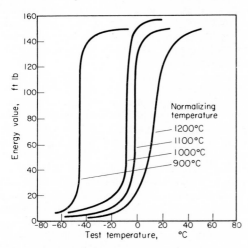

Fig. 7.—*The notched-bar impact values at various testing temperatures for a 0·11% C steel having different grain sizes produced by change of normalizing temperature*[19]

tonnage materials. A fine grain size should also increase[21] the low temperature toughness of the body-centred cubic refractory alloys, with which brittleness at low temperatures (see Fig. 5) can be very troublesome.

Deformation and Solute Effects

Plastic deformation raises the yield stress and thus usually increases the tendency for brittle behaviour. However, small amounts of plastic deformation may first reduce the transition temperature[22] in those cases where dislocations are strongly locked by solute atoms segregated to them, since the small deformation introduces free dislocations and so reduces the k_y term. Hardening by neutron irradiation also increases susceptibility to low temperature brittleness and the same is true when the yield stress is raised by alloying, due to solid solution or precipitation hardening. Thus the adverse effect of high silicon on the ductile–brittle transition temperature of mild steel is associated with the solid solution hardening it produces.[19] However, other alloying elements in solid solution such as manganese can be beneficial in lowering the transition temperature of mild steel. This effect has often been attributed to a decrease in the k_y term due to manganese scavenging nitrogen from dislocations (see below) and also a reduction

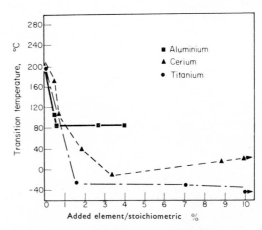

Fig. 8.—*The influence of aluminium, cerium and titanium additions on the transition temperature of recrystallised chromium*[24]

in grain size with only slight solid solution hardening. However, even at equivalent grain sizes and yield strengths manganese lowers the transition temperature without changing the value of k_y.[23] It is therefore suggested that it increases the value of the effective surface energy term γ, and so restrains potential cracks from reaching any detectable size. This influence of manganese serves to illustrate the complexity of the problem and at the same time suggests that there is still room for further developments in overcoming low temperature brittleness. However, much basic research is required before we can specify the compositions and structures required.

When impurities segregate strongly to dislocations, a reduction in brittleness can be obtained by the use of scavenging elements[24] which remove the impurity atoms from the dislocations and form insoluble precipitates. Fig. 8 shows the effect of nitride-forming elements on the transition temperature of chromium containing 0·002% nitrogen. This result also emphasises the marked embrittling influence of certain impurities in small concentrations.

Impurities may also segregate to give continuous, low surface energy fracture paths through the metal, with a resultant increase in brittleness (equation (1)). When this happens the fracture is changed from transgranular to

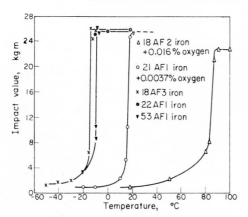

Fig. 9.—*The influence of oxygen content on the notched bar impact values at various temperatures for iron*[25]

intergranular, since segregation is most likely to occur at grain boundaries. Fig. 9 shows the influence of oxygen[25] in pure iron in raising the transition temperature; in the brittle condition, the fracture path becomes more and more intergranular, the higher the oxygen content. Small concentrations of oxygen and carbon in molybdenum[26] also result in low energy intergranular fractures, and an increase in transition temperature.

The effect of impurities is also found in more complex structures such as heat treated alloy steels,[27] and even intermetallic compounds.[28] Fig. 10 shows the improvement in impact behaviour of a chromium–molybdenum steel due to a lowering of the sulphur and phosphorus contents, the grain size being the same in each case. Temper embrittlement in steels also appears to be due to impurities,[29] and in this case considerable changes in transition temperature can be produced by altering the distribution of the impurities by heat treatment.

There is room for further improvement in the low temperature toughness of many metals, by control of the distribution and level of impurities. This requires a range of metallurgical investigations since not only must the physical metallurgy be unravelled but also the problems must be examined which arise in the production of alloys containing only the elements required, and not a miscellany of impurities in addition.

" Crack stoppers "

Further attention could also be given to the introduction of suitable "crack stoppers" into a material. The aim would be to prevent a growing crack extending rapidly either by increasing the local energy absorbed during growth or by

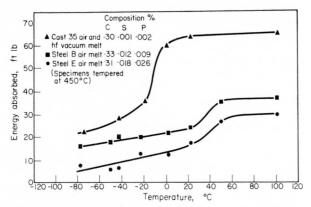

Fig. 10.—*The effect of impurities and the melting process on the notched bar impact values of a chromium-molybdenum steel of grain size ASTM 4–5*[27]

putting obstacles in its path, to deflect it into a region of lower stress.

To increase the local energy absorption it would be necessary to pin together the planes on which a crack was likely to spread, by using precipitates traversing the plane. If the precipitates were bonded to the matrix but not of themselves susceptible to brittle failure, their deformation would slow down crack propagation. Alternatively, if they were less well bonded, and so pulled out of the matrix as the crack widened, the resistance to sliding in the precipitate–matrix interface would increase the local energy absorption. Results on sodium

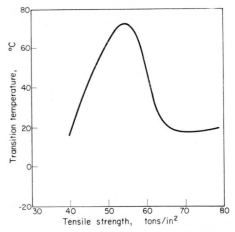

Fig. 11.—*The relationship between tensile strength and impact transition temperature for low carbon bainitic steels in the normalized condition*[31]

chloride,[30] in which precipitation of fine particles of gold slows down the rate of crack propagation and increases the work required to extend a crack are of interest in this context. Also work on bainitic steels[31] emphasizes the importance of local microstructure on the ease of crack popagation. As Fig. 11 shows, the transition temperature of low carbon steels may decrease with increasing tensile strength, over a certain strength range. This means that contrary to normal expectation higher strength bainites may have better toughness than lower strength bainites at low test temperatures. This is attributed to the higher strength bainites having structures consisting of finely divided carbide particles precipitated within ferrite grains. The carbides interrupt the fracture path of a cleavage crack so that the crack deviates from one plane to another, the different planes then being joined by local plastic deformation which increases the energy absorbed in the fracture. In the higher temperature bainites this does not happen due to fewer carbide particles being precipitated within the ferrite grains, most of the carbide now being formed at the ferrite boundaries.

The influence of "crack stoppers" has also been determined in silver chloride.[32] This has a ductile–brittle transition temperature which can be lowered by additions of alumina, although larger amounts cause an increase, Fig. 12. The yield stress is raised by the alumina. The reduction in transition temperature only occurs with spherical alumina particles and irregular ones cause an increase. It was suggested that spherical particles can reduce the triaxiality of the stress system, when a growing crack approaches a particle. This results in more plastic deformation and thus an increase in the energy absorbed in fracture. The bonding between alumina and a silver chloride matrix appears to be rather weak and this would increase the effect of the alumina since too good a bond would result in the interface being less able to relax the triaxiality around the crack tip. At temperatures above the transition temperature, the energy to fracture is reduced by the

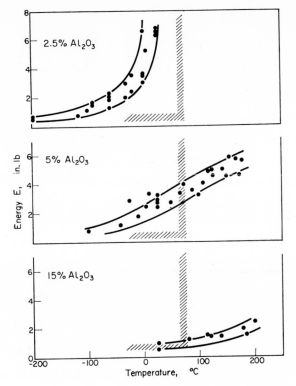

Fig. 12.—*The influence of spherical alumina particles on the transition temperature of silver chloride. Dashed lines are for pure material*[32]

alumina due to the particle interfaces acting as centres for the initiation of ductile fracture by plastic deformation and internal necking.[33,34] Once the cracks form, the overall ductility, and thus energy absorbed in fracture, will depend upon the volume fraction of precipitate.[35] The use of dispersed particles to increase energy absorption at low temperatures might therefore result in the fracture energy being reduced at high temperatures. However for small volume fractions of particles it may be possible to balance these two effects and so design microstructures which still have reasonable toughness above the transition temperature and improved toughness at low temperatures (Fig. 13).

Work of this type on metal systems would be of value since it has been reported that the ductility of tungsten can be improved by dispersions of zirconia.[36]

Laminated Structures

In connection with arresting cracks the use of laminated structures of metals, or metals and non-metals is also worth consideration. A laminated structure, of steel and copper, could be resistant to crack propagation at low temperatures due to the resistance of the copper to brittle failure. Alternatively if the laminations were of steel and a weakly bonded non-metal a crack growing across one of the steel laminations could be deflected along the weak interface at an angle to its previous path and thus possibly into a region of lower stress. It has been pointed out[37] that the behaviour of mica is similar to that of a laminated structure, in that it is very resistant to crack growth in a particular crystallographic direction due to easy cleavage on planes normal to this growth direction. This anisotropy in behaviour is so marked that if precautions are taken to avoid crack growth in other directions, very high strengths can be obtained, compared with the normal values.

Laminated structures could be built up by rolling "sandwiches" of metals or possibly by incorporating controlled amounts of suitable non-metallic material and then hot rolling to spread this into a layered structure. This would be similar to the methods used for producing wrought iron by successive "piling up" and "rolling out" operations; such techniques were used hundreds of years ago by sword manufacturers[38] to produce sharp, tough blades.

There appears to be little information on the low temperature behaviour of laminated structures. However, preliminary investigations of the resistance of laminated aluminium structures[39] to fatigue crack propagation at room temperature show an encouraging trend.

Disadvantages of laminated structures would include anisotropy, and liability to cracking along the laminations during fabrication, if suitable stresses arose, so making forging more difficult.

Fatigue Properties at Low Temperatures.

At room temperature, changes in ultimate tensile strength often result in similar changes in fatigue strength. The usual increase in ultimate tensile strength which metals show at low temperature would therefore be expected to produce an increased fatigue strength. Fatigue behaviour has been investigated for a number of metals down to $4 \cdot 2°K$[40] and Fig. 14 shows typical results. The face-centred cubic metals all show a continuous increase in fatigue strength with decreasing temperature, as also do the hexagonal metals, magnesium and cadmium. However zinc, (hexagonal), and iron, (body-centred cubic), show an initial increase, followed by a decrease, when the temperature falls to the range where brittle failure takes place in a tensile test. This could be related to growing fatigue crack acting as a notch, and promoting more rapid failure, in those metals which are susceptible to low temperature brittleness. Also the fatigue process itself appears to change in the temperature range where brittle failure occurs since fatigue failure can only be produced over a very small range of stress. Above this stress the specimens break almost immediately the load is applied, and below it, they last indefinitely, so that a normal S–N curve cannot be obtained.

For those metals which are prone to low temperature brittleness, the low temperature fatigue behaviour will therefore usually be improved by a reduction in the transition temperature. However exceptions to this can occur over certain temperature ranges, as shown by Fig. 15 which refers to a heat-treated nickel–chromium steel.[41]

For some alloys such as the high strength aluminium alloys, the increase in fatigue strength at low temperatures is greater than would be anticipated on the basis of the increase in ultimate tensile strength. This is due to the low temperature suppressing structural changes[42] which cause a lowering of the fatigue strength at room temperature, but which do not necessarily affect the tensile behaviour. An increase in the ratio of fatigue strength to ultimate tensile strength is thus found at low temperatures for such alloys.

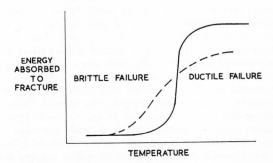

Fig. 13.—*Schematic representation of the effect of a dispersed phase (dotted curve) on the fracture energy–temperature relationship of a metal (full-curve)*

Materials available at present

The preceding sections have outlined the problems which arise with some metals due to lack of toughness at low temperatures, and it is a particularly unhappy coincidence that steels, the most widely used of engineering materials, should be affected in this way. It is obviously important that as much as possible should be done to overcome susceptibility to brittle failure, and thus extend down to lower temperatures, the safe working ranges for steels and similar metals, in the notched and un-notched condition.

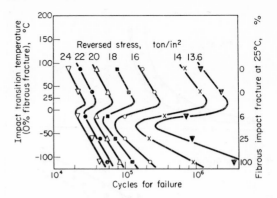

Fig. 15.—*The influence of the notched-bar transition temperature of a 3% nickel-chromium steel on the notched fatigue life at different stresses*[41]

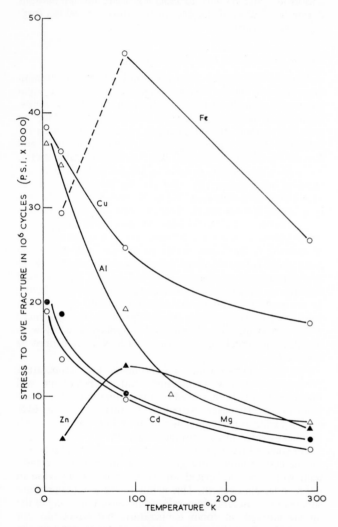

Fig. 14.—*The relationship between testing temperature and the stress required to cause fatigue failure in 10^6 cycles, for several metals*[40]

There are however some steels which can be used at low temperatures without the risk of brittle failure. These often contain considerable amounts of alloying elements which enable the austenitic (face-centred cubic) form of iron to exist at room temperature and below instead of the normal ferritic (body-centred cubic) form. The behaviour at low temperatures is then similar to that of other face-centred cubic metals *e.g.* copper and nickel. Nevertheless such steels may show lower notched-bar values at low temperatures than at room temperature due to some instability of the austenitic structure, resulting in partial transformation to brittle martensite. The extent of breakdown is increased by the combined effects of the low temperature and plastic deformation induced during testing, but the process is gradual with temperature so that there is no sudden change in behaviour over a critical temperature range. Even at liquid nitrogen temperatures the

notched-bar impact energy in typical cases may still be 50% or so of the high room temperature values, generally shown by austenitic steels (Fig. 16). There are also ferritic steels with nickel as the principal alloying element, which can retain considerable toughness at low temperatures.[43] The explanation of this effect is not clear, but such steels are an example of the fact that crystal structure alone does not determine low temperature toughness.

Nickel-base alloys also retain excellent ductility in tensile and notched-bar tests at low temperatures. For example Monel (67% nickel and 33% copper—face-centred cubic) shows no change at −250°C, in the high room temperature values of elongation, reduction in area and notched-bar energy, although the yield strength and ultimate tensile strength are increased by 100% and 60% respectively. Such a material is obviously extremely valuable to the engineer looking for high strength and high toughness at very low temperatures.

Copper alloys also give low temperature combinations of strength, ductility, and notched-bar values which are as good, if not better, than at room temperatures. In some copper–zinc alloys the microstructures may contain substantial quantities of the beta body-centred cubic phase. However although the absolute values of toughness usually decrease when the microstructure is two-phase the presence of the beta does not result in any sudden reduction in toughness at low temperatures. In fact alloys of a composition resulting in a 100% beta structure still show notched-bar values at 78°K which are only a little less than that at room temperature. The pattern of behaviour

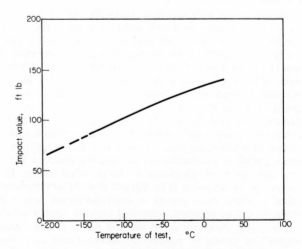

Fig. 16.—*Impact properties of an 18-8 Cr–Ni stainless steel, oil-quenched from 1050°C*

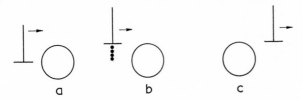

Fig. 17.—*Climb of an edge dislocation in order to by-pass a precipitate particle. The dots in (b) represent atoms removed by diffusion*

shown by nickel and copper alloys is also followed by aluminium alloys, although the absolute values of notched-bar energy are lower, particularly for the high strength age-hardened alloys.

Titanium and zirconium alloys can also give high values of notched-bar energy at −196°C with no evidence of a ductile–brittle transition behaviour. However, the energy values in some cases increase substantially around room temperature or above, an effect which appears to be associated with impurities. The toughness of titanium and zirconium alloys is also seriously reduced by dissolved hydrogen which precipitates as a separate hydride phase.

These few examples of alloys which give combinations of strength and toughness at very low temperatures, which are as good, if not better than at room temperature, illustrate that the engineer already has a selection from which to make his choice. However, there are certainly no grounds for complacency and efforts must be directed to the development of other alloys, and particularly steels, with improved low temperature behaviour.

High Temperature Behaviour

Introduction

With increase of testing temperature the yield stress of a metal decreases so that plastic deformation occurs more readily and brittleness of the type discussed in the previous section disappears. The problem which then faces the engineer at high temperatures is the ease with which deformation can occur, and which makes it difficult to operate metals under stress without plastic deformation. In addition, whereas at low temperatures a metal may elongate plastically under an applied stress and then subsequently remain of constant length by withstanding the stress elastically, at high temperatures, plastic deformation becomes time-dependent, and gives rise to what is known as creep.

Structural Instability

The reasons why deformation becomes time-dependent at temperatures which are high relative to the melting point are mainly connected with the decreased structural stability of the metal. At low temperatures dislocation barriers produced by

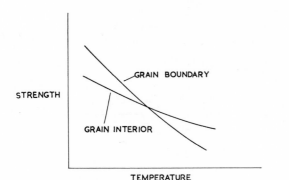

Fig. 18.—*Schematic representation of the strengths of grains and grain boundaries as a function of testing temperature*

plastic deformation are stable, and can only be overcome by increasing the applied stress. However, at higher temperatures thermally activated processes such as recovery and recrystallization become important, in which dislocations annihilate one another or become rearranged into networks which offer less resistance to further dislocation movement. Also it is easier for dislocations to by-pass precipitates and other obstacles, by gliding onto slip planes at an angle to the initial slip plane (cross slip) or climbing by self-diffusion (Fig 17).

Precipitates may also be unstable at high temperatures and grow rapidly in size, with a resultant increase in the average spacing between them; in addition the volume fraction of the precipitate may be reduced due to solution in the matrix. Both of these changes will decrease the effectiveness of the precipitate in hindering dislocation movement.

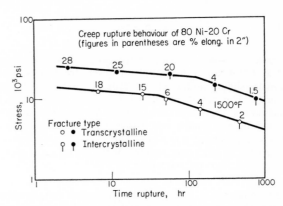

Fig. 19.—*Stress-rupture behaviour of an 80–20 nickel-chromium alloy showing the change of slope associated with a change in mode of fracture*[44]

Grain Boundary Sliding and Fracture

Another effect which becomes important at elevated temperatures, is deformation by sliding at grain boundaries, and also the onset of grain boundary fractures. At low temperatures grain boundaries exert a strengthening effect, by impeding the transfer of slip from one grain to another, so that deformation and fracture do not normally occur at the boundaries. Fine grained materials therfore show higher yield stresses at low temperatures, and as discussed earlier, increased toughness in certain temperature ranges. However, at high temperatures displacements occur between grains at their boundaries, and as a result fine grained materials may be weaker than more coarse grained ones. The behaviour of grain interiors and grain boundaries with respect to deformation reflect two different types of process. Deformation within a grain due to dislocation motion is a highly ordered crystallographic process. In contrast, deformation occurring between two grains at their boundary involves the relative motion of two surfaces each having a somewhat random arrangement of atoms arising from the disordered atomic structure which exists in most grain boundaries. Grain boundary sliding therefore resembles the deformation of an amorphous rather than a crystalline material. The stress to cause such movement will have a different temperature dependence from that relating to deformation within a grain. The situation is often represented as in Fig. 18 where the strength can be taken in general terms to refer to both the resistance to deformation and the resistance to fracture. Thus at high temperatures grain boundary sliding contributes more to the deformation, and fracture often occurs at the boundaries, with a reduction in ductility, due to the deformation becoming highly localised in the grain boundaries and contributing little to the overall deformation. The point of intersection of the curves in Fig. 18 known as the equi-cohesive temperature, alters with variables

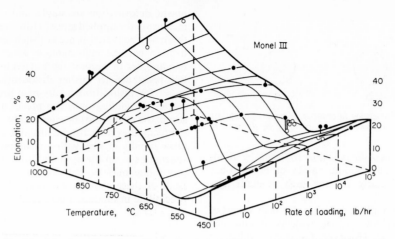

Fig. 20.—The elongation of monel as a function of testing temperature and testing rate[45]

such as strain rate. For example at lower strain rates, grain boundary sliding and fracture occur down to lower temperatures. This results in discontinuities in plots of stress versus time to rupture as shown in Fig. 19.[44] The longer time portions of the curves are associated with intergranular failures and reduced ductilities. The lives are also reduced compared with the extrapolations of the parts of the curves relating to transcrystalline failure.

Intergranular failure and low ductility may occur only in a certain temperature range, so that at higher temperatures, nearer to the melting point, although the yield stress continues to decrease the ductility rises again. This effect may also depend on strain rate as shown in Fig. 20 for monel metal.[45] It is believed to depend on the rapidity with which grain boundary migration can occur at very high temperatures. If a boundary moves rapidly by diffusion, the processes leading to fracture of the boundary are unable to develop significantly before the boundary moves on. Thus defects produced in the original boundary area are then transferred to within the body or a grain, where they are less effective in promoting failure.

Fracture at boundaries can develop in several different ways (Fig 21). Wedge shaped cracks are due to the stress concentration induced on a boundary plane by sliding occurring on intersecting grain boundaries. Such cracks tend to form in the lower temperature range of intercrystalline cracking, and require higher stresses[46] than the rounded cavities which often appear randomly along grain boundaries and are not necessarily associated with the junctions. In the case of the wedge shaped cracks, fracture occurs by progressive growth until linking takes place, whereas the rounded cavities grow slowly in size until failure occurs by the local deformation of the metal separating the cavities. The formation of the rounded cavities is thought to be due to grain boundary sliding causing decohesion at a precipitate-metal interface or by sliding taking place across ledges in the boundary. The ledges in the boundary may be pre-existing, or generated by plastic deformation within the grains.[47] Whichever mechanism operates the cavity once formed will be stable under the applied stress provided that the relationship holds that $\sigma = 2T/r$ where σ is the applied stress, T is the surface tension of the metal and r the cavity radius.[48] The applied stress is then sufficient to balance the surface tension stress in the metal which will be tending to shrink the cavity. Higher stresses will cause the cavity to grow by local diffusion processes. Alternatively the cavities may enlarge by plastic deformation. In either case coalescence of neighbouring cavities will eventually occur and cause failure.

Matrix Strengthening at High Temperatures

The designer of alloys for resisting stresses at elevated temperatures thus has two important mechanical problems. The first is to suppress deformation within the grains and at grain boundaries, and the second to make the boundaries more resistant to fracture.

To suppress deformation within grains, dislocation movement must be made more difficult and this can be done in principle by the solid solution and precipitation hardening techniques utilized at low temperatures. However, high operating temperatures increase the difficulties of doing this. Solutes which segregate to dislocations at low temperatures, and thus have an anchoring effect, become more uniformly distributed at high temperatures; also their diffusion rates become comparable with the rate of dislocation movement, which again reduces their anchoring effect on dislocations.

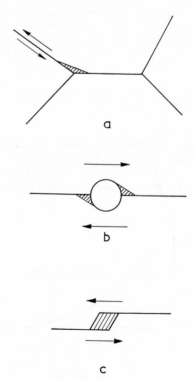

Fig. 21.—Mechanisms for producing cracks by sliding between grains at their boundaries

Nevertheless solid solution strengthening does contribute to the high temperature creep resistance of many alloys. This is particularly true in metals with face-centred cubic structures where stacking faults associated with dislocations may be stabilised by certain solute atoms,[49] and this makes cross-slip of dislocations more difficult.

The other method of controlling dislocation movement is by the use of precipitate particles as discussed earlier. The problem here is to avoid growth of the particles during exposure to temperature and stress for prolonged periods, and the two important variables[50] are the inherent chemical stability of the particles and the nature of the interface between the particles and the matrix.

The chemical stability will control the degree of dissociation of the particle at any temperature. This in turn will influence the growth rate, since growth depends on the dissociation of a particle and solution and diffusion of its constituent atoms. Therefore, the greater the chemical stability of a dispersed phase and the lower its solubility, the lower will be its coarsening rate. For this reason precipitates of oxides, carbides and nitrides should be more resistant to growth than most intermetallic compounds. However, low solubility in the solid metal at high temperatures usually means low solubility also in the liquid, which makes the manufacturing technique difficult. It is much easier to produce fine precipitates of intermetallic compounds by conventional solution heat treatments and ageing cycles but this ease of preparation inevitably imposes limitations on the stability of the dispersed phase, and also on the compositions which can be used. These limitations are removed when techniques such as powder metallurgy are utilized,[13] and in theory a structure can then be designed and produced with the correct fractions and size distributions of the most stable dispersed phases. However, much more work is required before this can be done efficiently and cheaply enough for such alloys to become fully competitive with conventional materials.

Alloys containing stable dispersed phases also have the advantage of showing considerable resistance to softening at high temperatures following cold work.[51] This arises from the strong anchoring effect which the particles have on dislocations, thus preventing the movements necessary to bring about recovery and recrystallization. Higher dislocation densities characteristic of cold worked material can therefore be retained to much higher temperatures than normal, and contribute to the creep strength.[52] Fig. 22 shows the stress–rupture behaviour of nickel containing 2% of thoria,[53] in comparison with more conventional alloys of the nimonic type hardened by intermetallics. The superior stability of the thoria dispersion is demonstrated by the low slope of its stress–life plot, compared with the nimonics; also the stability of the cold worked structure in the nickel–thoria alloy is evident. The superior behaviour of the nimonics at shorter lives is a reflection of the greater volume fraction of intermetallic precipitates in these alloys, compared with the 2% of thoria. Improvements in the techniques of dispersing oxides in metals should enable the short time strength to be improved whilst retaining superior behaviour at longer times and high temperatures. Fig. 23 shows the effect of testing temperature on the strength of a nickel–thoria[54] alloy compared with several conventional high temperature alloys and the superiority at the highest temperatures is well defined. This figure also shows that the nickel–thoria retains a useful strength even when 98% of the structure is at a temperature around 0·8 of its absolute melting point.

Dispersion strengthening is being investigated for higher melting point metals such as chromium,[76] molybdenum[55a] and tungsten.[56] For molybdenum Jaffee[55b] has reported that small amounts of titania and zirconia were particularly effective when added by powder metallurgy techniques, but not when

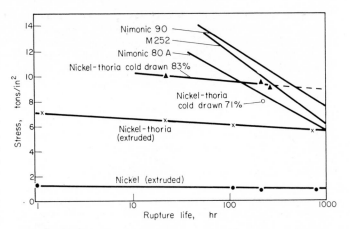

Fig. 22.—*Comparison of the stress rupture behaviour at 815°C of nickel-thoria alloys in different states of heat treatment and nimonic alloys*[53]

added to arc melted material, due presumably to the difficulty of obtaining a satisfactory dispersion in the liquid metal. The refractory metals pose greater problems in terms of finding dispersed phases which will be stable at the much higher operating temperatures which are possible with such metals. However, if these can be found dispersion strengthening will be a valuable means of further improving the high temperature strengths obtained by solid solution effects.

Interfacial Energy

An important feature of a dispersed phase, non-metallic or inter-metallic, is the nature of its interface with the matrix. This is because the driving force for growth in size of a dispersion, is the decrease in total interfacial energy which occurs when a large number of small particles changes to a small number of large particles. A small interfacial energy between precipitate and matrix will thus help to reduce the coarsening rate. The interfacial energy will be lower for those dispersed phases which have structures similar to that of the matrix, so that it is possible to maintain some degree of continuity of atomic planes across the interface. A good example of this is the Ni_3Al precipitate in nimonic alloys,

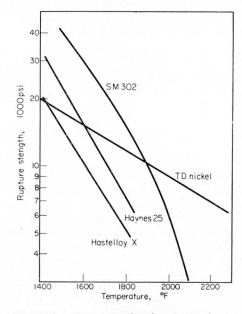

Fig. 23.—*The 100 h rupture stress plotted against testing temperature for a nickel–thoria alloy (T. D. Nickel) and three conventional creep resistant alloys. Hastelloy X (47 Ni, 22 Cr, 20 Fe, 9 Mo) Haynes 25 (51 Co, 20 Cr, 15 W, 10 Ni) SM 302 (57 Co, 22 Cr, 10 W 9 Ta)*[54]

L

which is isomorphous with the nickel matrix, and differs in lattice parameter from the matrix by only $\frac{1}{2}\%$. This results in a low interfacial energy[57] and is very important in connection with the stability of the nimonics at temperatures which are high relative to their melting points.

In the case of a dispersed phase such as an oxide the nature of the interface will depend upon how the particles are formed in the matrix, i.e. by a direct mixing technique or by some precipitation reaction. There is evidence that when oxides form by precipitation,[58] continuity of atomic planes can occur from precipitate to matrix, and this should result in a low interfacial energy. With mechanical mixing, higher interfacial energies should result due to the improbability of the mixing taking place in such a way that matching of the two lattices can occur. Information is not available on this point although the interfacial energies between bulk specimens of oxides and metals are often high.[59] The possibility exists however that small additions of specific metals may lower the interfacial energy between a precipitate, and a matrix, by forming a transition structure,[60] and thus help to maintain structural stability.

Grain Boundary Deformation and Fracture

Turning to the problem of grain boundary sliding, an effective way of reducing this is by the use of suitable grain boundary distributions of precipitates. If the precipitates are

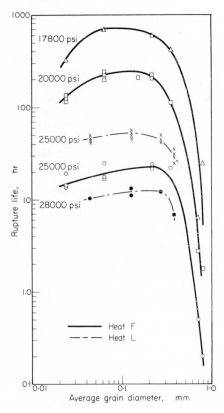

Fig. 25.—*Variation of rupture life with grain size for monel at 595°C*[63]

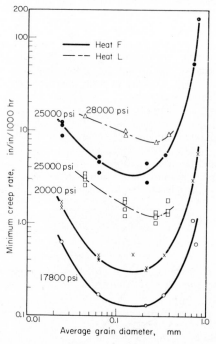

Fig. 24.—*Variation of minimum creep rate with grain size for monel at 595°C*[63]

well bonded to the matrix they can pin the grains together across the boundary and so restrict the distance over which sliding can occur. It is however important that the precipitate should be well bonded to the matrix, otherwise decohesion may occur under stress[61] and result in cavities which grow and coalesce to give failure. This emphasises again the importance of obtaining a low interfacial energy between precipitate and matrix. Since the useful life of alloys under creep conditions is often determined by the stage at which cracking starts in the boundaries,[62] there is room for further investigations to determine the optimum microstructure for resistance to grain boundary cracking. In nimonic alloys it is known that the correct distribution of grain boundary

chromium carbide precipitate is important in controlling the useful life, since with certain distributions, although the creep rate may be low, the life may nevertheless be very short due to early intergranular fracture.[62] Fig. 19 also indicates that control of the incidence of grain boundary cracking could result in longer lives at the lower stress values.

Grain size and geometry are also important in connection with the restraining of grain boundary sliding and fracture. Since grain boundaries are important in creep, it might be anticipated that an optimum grain size would exist for maximum creep resistance at a given temperature for a given metal. This size would represent a compromise between the poor resistance to creep associated with a very fine grain size, because of the large grain boundary area on which sliding can occur, and the low creep resistance associated with a single crystal due to ease of deformation within the grain. Grain size effects in creep have been reported for many alloys and Figs. 24 and 25 show results for monel.[63] Fig. 24 illustrates that the minimum creep rate shows its lowest value at a certain grain size and Fig. 25 shows a similar effect for the rupture life which goes

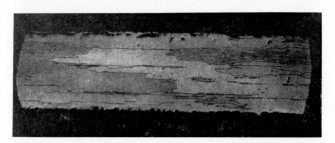

Fig. 26.—*Highly elongated grain structure developed in tungsten containing small amounts of oxides after annealing for 1 min at 2000°C × 100*[64]

through a maximum at a particular grain size. However, the same relationships as found in Figs 24 and 25 were not necessarily found to hold for all testing temperatures.

Grain shape also influences high temperature creep behaviour and a common example of this is the structure developed in tungsten wires used for lamp filaments.[64] The highly elongated grains shown in Fig. 26 are produced by the addition of small amounts of certain oxides to the tungsten, and these oxides influence the recrystallisation behaviour so that a very directional grain structure is produced instead of the more normal equiaxed arrangement. This results in a great improvement in creep resistance under longitudinal stressing, due to the lower stresses acting on the boundaries, and also the restriction of sliding by the irregular grain boundary surfaces. Heavily elongated grains are also found in nickel–thoria alloys and many other metal–oxide alloys due to the anchoring effect of the particles on the grain boundaries. This particular grain structure undoubtedly contributes to good high temperature strength, in addition to effects already mentioned. It should be noted however that this could lead to marked anisotropy in the creep behaviour although there appears to be no evidence about this.

Fatigue at Elevated Temperatures

The decrease in resistance to deformation under static stresses at elevated temperatures is paralleled by a similar decrease in resistance to fatigue stresses. In addition the mode of failure in fatigue may also change from transcrystalline to intercrystalline, as a result of extensive cavity formation at the grain boundaries. The mechanisms by which these cavities are produced appear to be similar to those operating during creep. As a result it is often found that changes in composition and structure which improve creep rupture behaviour, also improve high temperature fatigue strength. Correlations can be obtained between the fatigue strength and the creep rupture strength for failure in the same time, so that predictions about fatigue behaviour are possible using stress rupture results. In practice engineers may be confronted with the more complex problem of creep and fatigue stresses being applied simultaneously to a material at high temperatures. Interactions between the creep and fatigue processes are then possible, but even here it appears that the general principles outlined earlier in relation to high temperature strength, still apply.

Fatigue strength becomes much more sensitive at high temperatures to frequency of stressing, and the total time for which the stress is acting may now be a more important parameter than the number of cycles applied. Environment is also more important in view of the possibility of grain boundary failure being accelerated by the rapid diffusion of impurities down the boundaries. Fluctuating temperatures may also produce thermal fatigue stresses which can add on to the applied stresses and accelerate failure.

Materials Available at Present

The principles underlying the development of creep-resistant structures have been outlined in the previous sections. However, the first consideration in developing an alloy for use at a particular elevated temperature must be the melting point of the metal on which the alloy is based. There has been extensive development during the last ten years of steels, nickel-base and cobalt-base alloys for operating temperatures up to 1000°C. In particular the nickel-base nimonics retain 100 h rupture strengths at 1000°C of about 5 ton/in² and this is achieved by extensive solid solution and intermetallic dispersion strengthening. The good properties of nickel–thoria alloys at these temperatures have also been mentioned.

It is clear however that only limited increases in operating temperatures can be expected in the future with nickel, cobalt

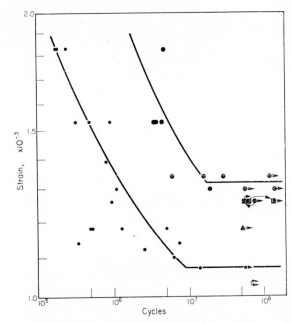

Fig. 27.—*The displacement of the fatigue S-N curve for a* 0·5% *carbon steel, caused by testing in vacuum (upper curve)*[65]

and iron-base materials in view of the decreasing gap between the melting points (1400–1500°C) and the operating temperature. Attention is therefore being directed to the higher melting point metals, and in particular chromium (m.pt. 1850°C) niobium (m.pt. 2468°C) molybdenum (m.pt. 2600°C) tantalum (m.pt. 2980°C) and tungsten (m.pt. 3380°C). Titanium and zirconium which have melting points of 1670°C and 1860°C are not being considered in this context since their alloys give inferior creep behaviour to existing materials, at temperatures around 1000°C. Other higher melting point metals such as the platinum metals are also ruled out on the grounds of scarcity and cost.

Many refractory metal alloys have been produced which give vastly superior creep behaviour at temperatures of 1000°C and above, than the best nickel-base alloys. Thus at temperatures around 1000°C the stress for 100 h rupture life is approximately 25 ton/in² for a molybdenum–titanium–zirconium alloy and this value is probably capable of being increased. Improvements over the behaviour of nickel-base alloys are also obtained with alloys of the other refractory metals. Unfortunately, however, although excellent creep resistance is obtained, which should enable significant operating stresses to be withstood at temperatures up to 1500°C or even higher, other problems are encountered which limit the current applications of these alloys. In the case of chromium, molybdenum and tungsten, brittleness at room temperature can cause serious forming problems, and it is therefore important to reduce the ductile–brittle transition temperatures, by manipulation of the variables discussed previously. Also, with the exception of chromium, oxidation rates are high for these metals so that environmental effects limit their use rather than creep strength.

The present position is therefore reasonably promising with regard to the strength of new alloys, at higher operating temperatures than at present, but how much advantage can be taken of these strengths depends critically upon other factors.

Environmental Effects

Introduction

It has been assumed so far that no interaction occurs between the metal and its surroundings. However this is not always true even at low temperatures and is rarely if ever true at high temperatures, and considerable modification of mechanical behaviour may be caused by such interaction.

Low Temperatures

At low temperatures the interaction with gaseous environments is usually very small, resulting in thin surface films of oxide, on contact of metals with air. Such films have little effect on tensile or notched bar behaviour, although a more marked effect may be found in fatigue, where a crack grows slowly through a metal. During fatigue crack growth, clean metal is continuously exposed at the crack tip and may interact with the atmosphere. This can result in fast crack propagation due to the destruction of metal by the local corrosive attack, and also the effect of gas films or thin layers of corrosion product in suppressing local rewelding at the crack tip during the compression part of a stress cycle. Fig 27 shows the displacement of the S–N fatigue curve which occurs when a 0·5% carbon steel[65] is tested in vacuum instead of air at room temperature. Other gases will exert a greater or lesser effect depending upon the extent to which they attack the metal in question. With some metals the mode of fatigue crack propagation may also be changed by gases from the normal transcrystalline type to intercrystalline.[66]

Increases in fatigue life have been obtained with aluminium alloys by decreasing the pressure of the surrounding air,[67] the increase occurring within a pressure range of 10^{-2} to 10^{-4} torr; lower pressures have no further effect.

Moisture in the atmosphere may also reduce fatigue endurance. With this a secondary effect may be involved, namely production of atomic hydrogen by metal–water vapour interaction, and the subsequent diffusion of the hydrogen into the metal, where it may then influence the rate of fatigue cracking.

The extent of gaseous interactions will become less as the testing temperature is lowered, but results on aluminium alloys show that even at liquid nitrogen temperatures they may be still sufficient for the fatigue lives to be affected,[68] although not greatly.

Gas absorbed by a metal due to interaction with an atmosphere at a high temperature may also exert an effect on subsequent low temperature behaviour. Earlier the effects were mentioned which oxygen and nitrogen, picked up by a metal at high temperatures, can have in increasing the risk of brittle failure at low temperatures. Hydrogen is another gas which can readily dissolve in metals during high temperature processing and subsequently affect low temperature behaviour.

This can be due to the formation of hydride precipitates as with titanium and zirconium, or to gas in solution. In the latter case a feature of the embrittlement is that it is more pronounced at low rates of straining. The effect is important in steels and in addition, as Fig. 28 shows, nickel which normally shows high ductility at low temperatures may suffer embrittlement in a certain temperature[69] range. At very low temperatures the embrittlement disappears and the same is true for steel, provided that the presence of the hydrogen has not previously resulted in any local cracking in the lattice.

With liquid evironments the possibilities of interaction become greater, and macroscopic effects, such as the surface roughness induced by corrosive attack, may influence the nucleation of cracks in fatigue or brittle failure. Corrosion fatigue and stress corrosion effects may also arise, so that the simultaneous application of corrosion and stress results in an accelerated rate of cracking. This may be accompanied by a change from transcrystalline to intercrystalline cracking, and the state of heat-treatment of the alloy can exert a considerable influence on the behaviour.

High Temperatures

At high temperatures general attack on a solid metal, or specific attack at grain boundaries, by gases or liquids becomes much more important. The attack may simply reduce the effective load bearing cross-section of the material or alternatively by localized penetration and diffusion, cause accelerated deformation and fracture at grain boundaries.

The problem of oxidation is particularly serious with many of the refractory metals, some of which oxidise at a high linear rate, in comparison with lower melting point metals, *e.g.* nickel, where the oxide scale formed is compact and protective so that the oxidation rate falls off with time. The situation may be illustrated by the data in Table II where comparative oxidation rates are listed.[70]

As yet it has not been possible to develop sufficiently oxidation resistant, high strength alloys of refractory metals by alloying, in the manner in which oxidation resistant steels and nickel alloys have been produced, although oxidation behaviour can be improved.

The alternative to developing inherently oxidation resistant alloys is the use of protective coatings. This, involves coating alloys of molybdenum, niobium, *etc.*, with oxidation resistant ceramic or metallic layers which form protective coatings on exposure to the atmosphere.[71] With ceramic coatings difficulties are encountered due to brittleness and expansion differences between coating and metal. Expansion problems may also occur with metallic coatings together with interdiffusion effects occurring between metal and coatings, which can result in the formation of low melting point alloys or

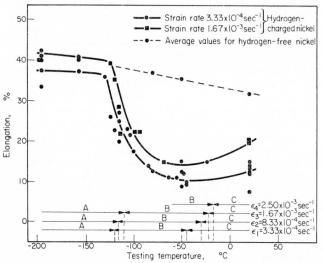

Fig. 28.—*Elongation of hydrogen-free nickel and nickel containing 40 ml of hydrogen/100 g nickel as a function of testing temperature*[69]

TABLE II.—*Oxidation of Various Materials at 1200°C in Dried, Flowing Air*

Material (wt. %)	Exposure (h)	Metal loss (in./side)	Factor by which oxidation rate is less than for Mo
Molybdenum	0·5	0·018	1
Tantalum	1·25	0·032	1·4
Niobium	1·25	0·020	2·3
95 Nb–5 Cr	18·25	0·063	10
Hafnium	18·25	0·047	14
Tungsten	4·0	0·010	14
93 Nb–7 Mo	1·5	0·003	18
Zirconium	18·25	0·024	27
Titanium	66·25	0·044	54
Chromium	66·25	0·0075	320
67 Cr–33 Ni	66·25	0·0028	850
Stainless Steel	66·25	0·0015	1600
Ni–12·5 Cr–6·5 Al	66·25	0·0006	4000
Silicon	66·25	0·0001	v. large

brittle intermetallics. In addition, with metallic coatings the operating temperature of the refractory metal will be limited by the maximum temperature the coating metal can withstand. Alternative coatings contain silicides which form glassy surface layers at high temperatures, or are based on aluminide compositions which form a protective layer of alumina, but both types have limitations.

A coating must be able to resist extensive cracking as a result of any stresses imposed on it and have some capacity for "self-healing" in the event of small discontinuities appearing during service. As a result of the coating problem there is at present no refractory metal alloy that can be used to replace nimonic alloys for prolonged operation under stress, at temperatures around 900°C, although the high temperature strengths of the refractory metal alloys are much superior. A solution to this problem would enable the engine designer to use higher operating temperatures with a resultant increase in efficiency. Alloys are also required for use in the temperature range 1500°–2000°C for ram-jet and rocket applications. The strength of the refractory metals is still high at these temperatures, but the lives are very short due to gaseous attack.

With some of the refractory metals it is necessary not only to avoid loss of metal due to direct attack, but also to prevent diffusion of oxygen and nitrogen into the metal since these gases may lead to a serious reduction in ductility, due to solid solution effects, or to the precipitation in an embrittling form, of oxides or nitrides. Since the diffusion rates of the gases concerned may be high at the temperatures involved it is difficult to devise alloys which are inherently resistant to this effect, or coatings which can act as sufficiently impervious barriers.

There are, however, some cases where creep-rupture lives can be increased by the diffusion of small amounts of reactive gases into a metal during test. With these it appears that the reaction of the gases with alloying elements leads to the production of an internal precipitate, in a form which exerts a strengthening effect due to dispersion hardening.[72,73] The quantity and form of the precipitate is thus important in controlling whether increased or decreased creep lives are obtained. The nature of a testing environment may also affect the rate at which a crack can grow in a material[72] by altering the value of the surface energy, i.e. the work necessary to grow a crack.

Liquids

It has also been suggested that crack propagation may be modified by the presence of a liquid due to a change in interfacial energy values. For example, if the interfacial energy between a liquid and metal is lower than that between air and the metal, the work involved in growing a crack will be reduced. Embrittlement can arise in this way when liquid metals are in contact with solid metals, and energetically it may also be easier for the crack to grow at a grain boundary, resulting in fracture with very little ductility. The embrittlement occurs rapidly once the liquid metal has wetted the solid metal surface, but it is only found at temperatures where the wetting agent is liquid.[74] This fast cracking rate indicates that macro-diffusion effects are not important, although it has been suggested that micro-diffusion at the crack tip may be highly significant.[75] Within the liquid temperature range for the wetting agent, it is possible for a ductile to brittle transition to be produced even in a face-centred cubic metal, and a dependence of fracture strength on grain size is found which is similar to that for body-centred cubic metals in contact with normal atmospheres. The embrittlement only occurs for certain solid metal–liquid metal combinations so that although for example molten lithium can severely embrittle copper and iron it has no effect on aluminium alloys. Since this form of embrittlement requires the wetting agent to be liquid it is not important at very low temperatures, and it also disappears at temperatures above the ductile–brittle transition temperature for the system. However, at high temperatures it is possible for a more gradual embrittlement to take place when a liquid metal is in contact with a solid, due to interdiffusion resulting in the production of inter-metallics or other precipitates, often at grain boundaries. These may then crack or pull away from the matrix under stress.

Conclusions

It has been possible only to outline the general changes in the mechanical behaviour of metals, produced by changes in temperature and environment. Also rather than giving detailed descriptions of alloys which are already in use at low or high temperatures the emphasis has been largely on the problems at present encountered. Whether or not significant developments take place in the future in the applicability of metals under extreme conditions of temperature and environment will have to depend upon how successfully these problems can be solved. This will mean following up many lines of investigation of a fundamental and development nature. There is still considerable uncertainty about the basic mechanisms of fracture at low and high temperatures. These must be elucidated so that it becomes clear where effort should be concentrated in order to design alloys with improved fracture resistance. There is also much which is still not known about the processes involved in interactions of metals with their environments, and these become of vital importance at high temperatures. In addition to fundamental work aimed at discovering mechanisms there is work urgently required on problems of a more technological nature. Thus the influence of grain size and impurities on low temperature ductility is well-established, but there are difficulties in obtaining very fine grain sizes and very high purities in alloys for commercial use. These difficulties must be carefully examined and efforts made to overcome them. Commercial application also inevitably introduces new problems which may not be encountered in the early stages of development of an alloy in the laboratory. For example, welding is becoming of ever increasing importance as a fabrication technique, but creep resistant alloys containing insoluble dispersed phases cannot be joined by conventional welding techniques due to segregation of the dispersed phase whilst the metal is molten. Also welding can introduce into an assembly residual stresses which under certain conditions can raise the ductile–brittle transition temperature. Development of new materials will therefore inevitably require developments in processing and design techniques if full advantage is to be taken of the inherent capabilities of the material. This perhaps is the theme with which to conclude. Metallurgists can vary the properties of metals over a wide range but it must clearly become more and more difficult to combine say, ease of formability at room temperature with high resistance to creep deformation at a temperature 1500°C or so higher. The use of metals at greater extremes of temperature must therefore be closely interwoven with a willingness on the part of the engineer to sacrifice, at least to some extent, the combination of strength and high ductility which he has grown accustomed to expect from metals.

Acknowledgments

The author would like to thank Professor A. H. Cottrell for helpful discussions and Mr. J. A. Charles, Dr. A. Kelly and Dr. R. B. Nicholson for reading the manuscript and making useful suggestions. Also to thank Mr. S. D. Charter for preparation of several of the line diagrams.

L*

In addition, grateful acknowledgment is made to the following for permission to reproduce figures: The Institute of Metals, Figs. 3, 8 and 26; Acta Metallurgica Figs. 5 and 28; The Iron and Steel Institute, Figs. 7, 9, 10 and 11; The American Institute of Metallurgical Engineers, Fig. 12; The Royal Society, Fig. 14; The American Society for Metals, Figs. 20, 24 and 25; Powder Metallurgy, Fig. 22; Metal Progress, Fig. 23; The Philsosphical Magazine, Fig. 27; The McGraw-Hill Co., Figs. 2 and 19; The International Nickel Co. (Mond) Ltd., Figs. 15 and 16.

References

[1] Smithells, C. J. " Metals Reference Book ", p. 614. (Butterworths).

[2] Roberts M. H., and Nortcliffe, J. *J.I.S.I.*, 1957, **157**, 345.

[3] Guard, R. W. *Product Engineering*, October 1956.

[4] Jones, F. W., and Nortcliffe, J. *J.I.S.I.*, 1947, **157**, 535.

[5] Dudzinski, N., Murray, J. R., Mott, B. W., and Chalmers, B. *J. Inst. Metals*, 1948, **74**, 291.

[6] Dudzinski, N. *J. Inst. Metals*, 1952, **81**, 49.

[7] Brown, A. R. G., Brooks, H., Jepson, K. S., and Lewis, G. I. *J. Inst. Metals*, 1963, **91**, 161.

[8] Wheatley, J. M., and Smith, G. C. *Powder Metallurgy*, 1963, **12**, 141.

[9] Smithells, C. J. " Metals Reference Book " (Butterworths).

[10] Cottrell, A. H. *Proc. Roy. Soc.*, 1963, **A276**, 1.

[11] Cottrell, A. H. " Dislocations and Plastic Flow in Crystals ", p. 9 (Oxford).

[12] Maclean, D. " Mechanical Properties of Metals ", p. 85. (Wiley).

[13] Smith, G. C. *Powder Metallurgy*, 1963, **11**, 102.

[14] Kelly, A. " Royal Society Discussion on New Materials ", 1963.

[15] Teed, P. L. " Properties of Metals at Low Temperatures ". (Chapman & Hall).

[16] Bechtold, J. H. *Acta Metallurgica*, 1955, **3**, 249.

[17] Tegart, W. J. McG. *J. Inst. Metals*, 1962, **91**, 99.

[18] Cottrell, A. H. *Trans. A.I.M.E.*, 1958, 192.

[19] Irvine, K. J., and Pickering, F. B. *J.I.S.I.*, 1963, **201**, 944.

[20] Erasmus, L. A. *J.I.S.I.*, 1964, **202**, 32.

[21] Ratliff, J. L. *et al.* Reported by Michael, A. B., and Gentry, W. O. *AGARD Conference on Refractory Metals*, June 1963. (Pergamon Press).

[22] Wain, H. L., Johnstone, S. T. M., and Henderson, F. *J. Inst. Metals*, 1962, **91**, 41.

[23] Hahn, G. T., Cohen, M., and Averbach, B. L. *J.I.S.I.*, 1962, 200, 634.

[24] Henderson, F., Johnstone, S. T. M., and Wain, H. L. *J. Inst. Metals*, 1963, **92**, 111.

[25] Rees, W. P., Hopkins, B. E., and Tipler, H. R. *J.I.S.I.*, 1951, **169**, 157.

[26] Northcott, L. *J. Less Common Metals*, 1961, **3**, 125.

[27] Cottrell, C. L. M., Langstone P. F., and Rendall, J. H. *J.I.S.I.*, 1963, **201**, 1032.

[28] Westbrook, J. H., and Wood, D. L. *J. Inst. Metals*, 1963, **91**, 174.

[29] Steven, W. and Balajiva, K. *J.I.S.I.*, 1959, **193**, 141.

[30] Forty, A. J. *Private Communication*.

[31] Irvine, K. J., and Pickering, F. B. *J.I.S.I.*, 1963, **201**, 518.

[32] Johnston, T. L., Stokes, R. J., and Li, C. H. *Trans. A.I.M.E.*, 1961, **221**, 793.

[33] Tipper, C. F. *Metallurgia*, 1949 **38**, 133.

[34] Puttick, K. E. *Phil. Mag.*, 1959, **4**, 964.

[35] Gurland, J., and Plateau, J. *Trans. A.S.M.*, 1963, **56**, 442.

[36] Chang, W. H. Contribution to " Symposium on Refractory Metals and Alloys " p. 106 (Interscience).

[37] Gordon J. *Private Communication*.

[38] Smith, C. S. " A History of Metallography ". (Chicago University Press).

[39] Forsyth, P. J. E., George, R. W., Ryder, D. A., and Vian, R. E. *Royal Aircraft Establishment, Tech. Note. Met. Phys.* 353, p. 179.

[40] McCammon, R. D., and Rosenberg, H. M. *Proc. Roy. Soc.*, 1957, **A242**, 203.

[41] Haynes, A. G. " Research Applied in Industry ", September, 1961.

[42] Broom, T., Molineux, J. H., and Whittaker, V. N. *J. Inst. Metals*, 1956, **84**, 357.

[43] Marschall, C. W., Hehemann, R. F., and Troiano, A. R. *Trans. A.S.M.*, 1962, **55**, 135.

[44] Guard, R. W. " Mechanical Behaviour of Materials at Elevated Temperatures ", p. 273 (McGraw-Hill).

[45] Rhines, F. N., and Wray, P. J. *Trans. A.S.M.*, 1961, **54**, 2, 117.

[46] Maclean, D. *J. Inst. of Metals*, 1957, **85**, 468.

[47] Gifkins, R. C., " Swampscott Conference on Fracture ", p. 579 (Wiley).

[48] Cottrell, A. H. " Structural Processes in Creep " Iron and Steel Institute Special Report, No. 70, 1.

[49] Howie, A. and Swann, P. R. *Phil. Mag.*, 1961, **6**, 1215.

[50] Cochardt, A. W. *Trans. A.I.M.E.*, 1957, **209**, 434.

[51] Gatti, A., and Fullman, R. L. *Trans. A.I.M.E.*, 1959, **215**, 762.

[52] Adachi, M. and Grant, N. J. *Trans. A.I.M.E.*, 1960, **218**, 881.

[53] Tracey, V. A., and Worn, D. K. *Powder Metallurgy*, 1962, **10**, 34.

[54] Anders, F. J., Alexander, G. B., and Wartel, W. S. *Metal Progress*, December 1962.

[55a] Nicol-Smith, A. J., and Northcott, L. " AGARD Conference on Refractory Metals ", June 1963 (Pergamon Press).

[55b] Jaffee, R. I., " AGARD Conference on Refractory Metals ", June 1963 (Pergamon Press).

[56] Atkinson, R. H., Keith, G. H., and Koo, R. C. " Refractory Metals and Alloys ", p. 319 (Interscience).

[57] Maclean, D. " Vacancies and Other Point Defects in Metals and Alloys " (Institute of Metals), 1958.

[58] Ashby, M. F., and Smith, G. C. *J. Inst. Metals*, 1962, **91**, 182.

[59] Livey, D. T., and Murray, P. " Plansee Proceedings ", 1955, (Pergamon Press).

[60] Tikkanen, M. H., Rosell, B. O., and Wiberg, O. *Powder Metallurgy*, 1962, **10**, 49, 1962.

[61] Resnick, R., and Seigle, L. *Trans. A.I.M.E.*, 1957, **209**, 87.

[62] Betteridge, W., and Franklin, A. W. *J. Inst. of Metals*, 1957, **85**, 473.

[63] Shahinian, P., and Lane, J. R. *Trans. A.S.M.*, 1953, **45**, 177.

[64] Swalin, R. A., and Geisler, A. H. *J. Inst. of Metals*, 1957, **86**, 129.

[65] Wadsworth, N. J. *Phil. Mag.*, 1961, **6**, 397.

[66] Snowden, K. U. *Nature*, 1961, **189**, 53.

[67] Ham, J. L. *National Research Corporation, U.S.A., Final Report.* Contract AF 49(638)–1005.

[68] Broom, T., and Nicholson, A. *J. Inst. of Metals*, 1961, **89**, 183.

[69] Boniszewski, T., and Smith, G. C. *Acta Metallurgica*, 1963, **11**, 165.

[70] Semmel, J. W. " Refractory Metals and Alloys ", p. 119 (Interscience).

[71] Levinstein, M. A., and Wlodek, S. T. " AGARD Conference of Refractory Metals ", June 1963 (Pergamon Press).

[72] Shahinian, P., and Achter, M. R. " High Temperature Materials ", p. 448 (Wiley).

[73] Lawthers, D. D., and Manjoine, M. J. *Ibid.*, p. 486.

[74] Rostokor, W., McCaughey, J. M., and Markus, H. " Embrittlement by Liquid Metals ", 1960 (Reinhold).

[75] Stoloff, N. S., and Johnston, T. L. *Acta Metallurgica*, 1963, **11**, 251.

[76] Ryan, N. E., and Landau, C. S. *J. Aust. Inst. Metals*, 1963 **8**, 273.

THE BEHAVIOUR OF MATERIALS IN LIQUID SODIUM

By C. TYZACK

SYNOPSIS

Elemental sodium has been known for a century and a half, but its potentialities as a cooling medium have only been fully exploited in the nuclear and space era. Its heat transport and transfer properties and its high boiling point make sodium an ideal coolant for fast fission reactors where large quantities of heat must be rapidly transported from small nuclear cores.

Experimentation has shown that the behaviour of materials in sodium at high temperatures is largely conditioned by their interaction with impurities in the liquid metal such as oxygen, nitrogen, carbon and hydrogen. It is beyond the scope of this paper to consider the effects of all these impurities on the corrosion behaviour and mechanical properties of materials of interest in sodium technology, and attention will be confined to discussing the effects of oxygen impurities on corrosion behaviour of selected metals.

The behaviour of a particular metal in sodium is largely determined by the relative thermodynamic stability of its oxide at the temperature of interest in relation to that of sodium oxide, or sodium containing sodium oxide at less than unit activity. Three types of behaviour have been distinguished. If the metal oxide is less stable than sodium oxide then any room temperature oxide existing on the metal will be reduced and the subsequent behaviour of the metal surface wetted by sodium will depend on solution processes of which two types have been distinguished, (a) a process where the slowest step is dissolution at the solid–liquid interface, (b) a process where diffusion of solute across a boundary layer is rate controlling.

If, on the other hand, the oxide of the metal exposed in sodium is of much greater stability than sodium oxide then there seems to be a tendency for simple oxides to be formed similar to those formed in the gas phase under oxidizing conditions. The detailed behaviour may, however, depend on the mechanical stability of the oxide film in the liquid metal under erosive conditions.

The third class of behaviour which has been observed is that where the oxide of the metal exposed in sodium is of comparable thermodynamic stability to sodium oxide, where there is a tendency for complex oxides containing sodium and the metal in question to be formed. Niobium is a good example of this, and the complex oxide formed appears to have poor protective properties, as the bulk of the film is lost into the sodium stream under dynamic conditions.

Introduction

Sodium has been known as a chemical element since its discovery by Davy 156 years ago, and has played an important rôle in the chemical industry. Its full potentialities as a cooling fluid, however, have only been realised and exploited within the period of the development of nuclear technology. The excellent heat transport and heat transfer properties of sodium, its high boiling point (880°C) and radiation stability permit a more efficient use to be made of nuclear fuels with high specific energy outputs than is possible with more conventional gas or steam coolants. This point is illustrated in Fig. 1 taken from a recent paper presented to the European Atomic Energy Society.[1] The Americans have also shown that liquid metals are the most attractive coolants and working fluids for space nuclear power systems where compact design is at a premium.

Basic Considerations

These points accepted, then how do we go about selecting materials for service in sodium or sodium–potassium alloy environments? Broadly we are looking for answers to the questions, (a) will the metal dissove in sodium? (b) will the metal oxidise in sodium? (c) how will the mechanical properties of the material be affected by exposure in sodium? A detailed answer to all these problems is, of course, beyond the scope of this paper, and discussion will be limited to items (a) and (b). It has rapidly become apparent to workers in the field that it is the impurities, particularly the non-metallic impurities, in the sodium which largely determine the behaviour

* Reactor Materials Laboratory, Reactor Group U.K.A.E.A., Culcheth.

of materials in the liquid metal. Properties such as wetting behaviour, solution and corrosion processes (i.e. mass transfer phenomena) and mechanical properties may be affected singly or in combination by impurities such as oxygen, hydrogen, carbon and nitrogen in the sodium.

Is it possible to make any predictions on how a particular metal will behave when exposed to sodium at temperatures of interest in reactor technology, say 200–650°C? I believe that as a result of the work done in the U.K., U.S. and France during recent years, it is now possible to see some clear cut trends. Whether or not loss of metal section from a component exposed in sodium occurs will depend on a number of factors but primarily in the first instance on thermodynamic considerations of oxide stability. If the oxide of the metal under consideration is less stable than sodium oxide at the temperature of interest, then reduction of any existing oxide film on the metal will occur, eventually exposing pure metal in the sodium where the extent of loss of metal section will depend on solution processes. These arguments are also true where any complex sodium–metal–oxide might initially exist which was less stable than sodium oxide—progressive reduction would occur. Examples of such metals are copper, iron, nickel and molybdenum.

The second class of metals is that possessing oxides of greater stability than sodium oxide at the temperatures of interest. In these cases the metal will oxidise, gettering oxygen from the sodium, and provided that the oxide film formed is mechanically resistant to erosion by sodium, it should grow by solid state diffusion controlled processes not dissimilar from those obtaining on a gaseous oxidizing environment of similar oxidation potential. Examples of this class are uranium and zirconium.

The third class of metals comprise those which have oxides of comparable stability to sodium oxide at the temperature of

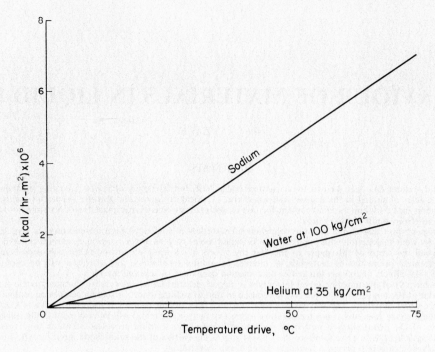

Fig. 1.—*Typical heat fluxes attainable, reactor coolants (Ref. 1)*

interest or which form complex oxides with sodium oxide of greater stability than sodium oxide. These metals generally show a number of oxides of varying valency and the precise oxide formed during corrosion in sodium may depend initially on the oxidation potential of the sodium. The oxidation behaviour of this class of material in sodium is undoubtedly the most complex, although the studies carried out at the Reactor Materials Laboratory at Culcheth, and under Professor Addison at Nottingham University, have undoubtedly gone some of the way to providing an understanding of these phenomena particularly in the case of niobium corrosion which will be discussed in more detail subsequently. Other metals in this category are probably chromium, vanadium and tantalum.

These ideas on the three basic types of corrosion behaviour in sodium, which have been arrived at as a result of years of work observing the behaviour of a range of materials exposed in sodium environments, receive valuable support from a series of quite independent observations on the wetting behaviour of transition metals in sodium carried out by Professor Addison and his collaborators, where they concluded that in the absence of any oxide film pure sodium would always spread to give a zero contact angle θ on a pure solid metal, and secondly that the observed changes in the receding contact angle θ with time and temperature were direct manifestations of the rate and the nature of the chemical reaction between liquid sodium and the oxide film. Essentially again three types of behaviour have been observed although so far only the work on iron, cobalt and nickel has been reported.[2] In these experiments it was found that above a critical wetting temperature the receding contact angle for liquid sodium on these metals decreased with time to zero contact angle, corresponding to the reduction of oxides formed on surfaces previously abraided to a mirror finish in air. These findings are in line with corrosion experiments in dynamic liquid sodium carried out at R.M.L. Culcheth with iron and nickel specimens where, after a short initial period for the reduction of the room temperature oxide, a steady linear metal loss rate is observed, presumably corresponding to a solution process

as no oxide corrosion products are found. This may be characterized as Type I behaviour, and will be discussed in greater detail in the next section. We look forward to the publication of the remainder of Professor Addison's findings on the other transition metals in order that further correlations in wetting and oxidation behaviour can be made.

A tentative assignment of the transition metals into the three categories has been attempted in Table I.

TABLE I.—*Classification of Transition Metals According to Behaviour in Oxygen Containing Sodium*

Group	Long period						
	4	5	6	7	8		
1st	Ti	V	Cr	Mn	Fe	Co	Ni
	II	III	(III)	?	I	(I)	I
2nd	Zr	Nb	Mo	Tc	Ru	Rn	Pd
	II	III	I	(I)	(I)	(I)	(I)
3rd	Hf	Ta	W	Re	Os	Ir	Pt
	(II)	(III)	(III)	(I)	(I)	(I)	(I)
Transuranic			U				
			II				

Figures in brackets indicate that there is no experimental information and the classification has been made from standard free energy of formation of oxide considerations.

I Loss of metal section by solution.

II Loss of metal section by simple oxide formation.

III Loss of metal section by formation of complex oxides with sodium.

Type I Behaviour—Solution Processes

Epstein[3] has dealt in some detail with the mechanisms of solution processes in liquid metals. The dissolution process can be pictured as occurring in two stages: first the transfer of a metal atom across the solid–liquid metal interface by breaking metallic bonds with the solid metal and reformation of metallic bonds between the solute and solvent atoms; secondly diffusion of the solute across the boundary layer into the bulk of the liquid. Two mechanisms can be distinguished: in the first of these it is postulated that the diffusion step is fast compared with the initial rate of solution and so the liquid boundary layer is not saturated, while in the second the liquid boundary layer next to the solid is saturated and the slow step is the diffusion of the solute into the bulk of the fluid. These are known respectively as solution and diffusion controlled mechanisms. Where the diffusion gradient is the rate controlling step we would expect Fick's law to apply, where the rate of dissolution J is given by the expression:

$$J = \frac{D(C_0 - C)}{x} \qquad . \qquad . \qquad (1)$$

where D is the diffusion coefficient of the solute species in the liquid metal, C_0 is the equilibrium solubility of solute at the temperature concerned, C is the solute concentration in the bulk solvent and x the thickness of the boundary layer.

If we expose a text specimen of a metal to sodium in a vessel made of the same material under isothermal conditions then solution of the metal into sodium takes place until the solubility limit for that particular temperature is reached and then ceases. The kinetics of the process are described by an expression of the type:

$$C = C_0 \left[1 - \exp\left(-\alpha \frac{A}{V} t \right) \right] \qquad . \qquad (2)$$

where C is the concentration of solute at time t, A the surface area dissolving, V the volume of liquid metal and α the specific rate constant for the dissolution process. The equation is derived by integration of an expression of Type I.

The sodium systems of interest in nuclear technology are, however, non-isothermal dynamic systems, and Epstein has used a heat transfer analogy to derive equations for mass transfer rates by liquid metals flowing through a closed tube under a temperature differential. In a diffusion controlled system the equation derived for the rate of mass transfer is

$$R = 0.023(D/d)(vd/v)^{0.8}(v/D)^{0.4}(dS^0/dt)\,\Delta T \qquad . \qquad (3)$$

where D is the diffusion coefficient of the solute in the liquid metal, d is the diameter of the tube, v is the flow velocity, v is the kinematic viscosity, S^0 is the solubility and T is the temperature differential in the circuit.

If on the other hand the process is solution controlled the relation derived is

$$R = (\alpha/2)(dS^0/dt)\,\Delta T(1 + (2\alpha L/\pi dv)^2)^{-\frac{1}{2}} \qquad . \qquad (4)$$

where L is the total length of loop and α is the specific solution rate constant.

Epstein's solubility and mass transfer data led him to the conclusion that the solution of iron in sodium was solution controlled at the metal–liquid interface according to equation (4) rather than diffusion controlled. Weeks and Klamut,[4] however, have pointed out that if one takes the iron solubility results of Baus et al.[5] then the results suggest that diffusion control may be operative. The most significant difference between the two models is that for solution rate limited corrosion the rate should be independent of liquid metal velocity, while in the case of diffusion control the rate should vary with velocity (i.e. $v^{0.8}$).

We now have evidence from recent work done at R.M.L. that the corrosion rate of a $2\frac{1}{4}\%$ chromium 1% molybdenum steel is velocity dependent from experiments carried out under dynamic nonisothermal conditions at 500°C and 600°C (ΔT in the circuit is 150°C and 250°C respectively) at velocities

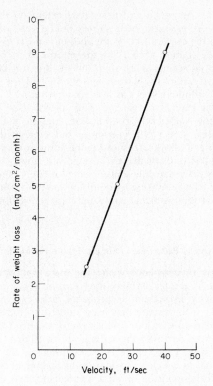

Fig. 2.—Corrosion rate of nimonic 80A in dynamic sodium at 650°C oxygen content 25·30 ppm, rate of weight loss as a function of liquid metal velocity

of 0·5 and 30 ft/sec. The results are summarized in Table II. Further experiments are necessary to determine the nature of the dependence, but the results to date throw doubt on the validity of Epstein's conclusion. Substitution of our data in Epstein's diffusion controlled corrosion equation produces quite good agreement with experimental results obtained at R.M.L. on the $2\frac{1}{4}\%$ chromium 1% molybdenum steels at 600°C if we take Epstein's value for the diffusion coefficient of iron in sodium, 2×10^{-5} cm²/sec, and Baus's figures for the solubility of iron in sodium. Calculated values of 1·3 and 34 mg/cm²/year were obtained in tests at 6·5 and 30 ft/sec liquid metal flow compared with experimental observed values of 1·2 and 22 mg/cm²/year.

Evidence of a diffusion controlled solution mechanism has been recently obtained on nickel based alloys at R.M.L. The corrosion of Nimonic 80A has been studied in sodium at 650°C under dynamic nonisothermal ($\Delta T\,300°C$) conditions at velocities of 15, 25 and 40 ft/sec, and a linear dependence of corrosion rate on velocity in this range established. The results are summarised in Fig. 2.

The utility of what we have called Type I metals in a sodium environment will be limited not by oxidation but by its rate of solution at the temperature of interest, and this will depend on the terminal solubility of the metal in sodium at the temperature of interest, the liquid metal velocity, the temperature

TABLE II.—The Effect of Velocity on the Corrosion Rate of $2\frac{1}{4}$ Cr 1 Mo Steel in Sodium at 500°C and 600°C (Oxygen level 25–30 ppm)

Work done at Reactor Materials Laboratory

Temp. (°C)	Liquid metal velocity (ft/s)	Metal loss rate (mg²/cm²/yr)	Metal loss rate (0·001 in./yr)
500	0·5	0·8	0·04
500	30	10·0	0·5
600	0·5	1·2	0·06
600	30	22	1·1

gradients in the circuit and to a lesser extent on the system geometry. It has also been shown in the case of iron to depend on the oxygen level in the sodium, and at low oxygen levels in the sodium such as we are interested in, in nuclear technology it seems likely that this is due to effects on the terminal solubility of iron in sodium and the diffusion coefficient, although this has not been proved.

Austenitic stainless steels and other alloys based primarily on iron show sufficiently low solution rates to be useable at temperatures up to 650°C in sodium, but some of the higher nickel content alloys are showing penetration rates of the order of 0·004 to 0·006 in./year at high velocities. Molybdenum shows extremely low solution rates at 600°C and may be considered as a promising material for sodium technology in the future if the problems associated with its welding can be overcome.

Type II Behaviour—Simple Oxide Formation

This type of behaviour where the metal in contact with sodium has a greater stability than sodium oxide at unit or lower activity in sodium is probably best exemplified by zirconium. This reaction has been studied by Eichelburger[6] who found parabolic rates which were independent of the oxygen concentration in the sodium above 20 ppm. Results have also been reported recently by Mackay[7] of Atomics International in which the oxidation behaviour of zirconium and several zirconium alloys was examined in a thermal syphon sodium system incorporating a diffusion cold trap. Reaction rates were examined in the temperature range 400–635°C with sodium containing oxygen at a level of 10 ppm maintained by controlling the diffusion cold trapping temperature at 150°C. In line with Eichelburger's observations on pure zirconium it was found that Zircaloy-2 oxidized at a rate independent of the nominal oxygen concentration above 10 ppm. The results of the effect of oxygen concentration are summarized in Table III.

The pretransition oxidation of zirconium and its alloys in gaseous environments is usually characterized by the equation

$$\Delta w^n = Kt$$

where w is the weight gain, t is the time, K is the rate constant and n is a constant. The value of n for zirconium oxidation in oxygen, carbon dioxide and steam lies in the range 2 to 3

TABLE III.—*Effect of Oxygen Concentration on Oxidation of Zircaloy-2 in Liquid Sodium at 595°C (after 145 hours exposure)* (7)

Cold trap temperature (°C)	Calculated oxygen concentrations (ppm)	Δw weight gain (mg/cm^2)
160	10	0·45
160	10	0·45
340	200	0·45
340	200	0·50
418	500	0·46
418	500	0·45
340	200	0·52*
340	200	0·46*

* 5 g of Na_2O_2 were added to the system

which characterizes respectively parabolic or cubic rate law kinetics. Mackay in his investigation in oxygen contaminated sodium found values in the range $1/n = 0·4$ to $0·52$. Some typical plots of $\log \Delta w$ against $\log t$ obtained at 635°C are shown in Fig. 3 where the slope of the graph is $1/n$.

The rate constants for zirconium and a number of zirconium alloys were determined over the temperature range 408–635°C and a plot of the log of the parabolic rate constants vs $1/T°K$ is shown for the zirconium alloys in Fig. 4. The activation energies as determined from the slope of the least squares straight line are $52·9 \pm 0·5$ k cal/mole for zirconium and $4·53 \pm 1·5$ kcal/mole for Zircaloy-2. These figures lie in the range of values obtained by various workers for zirconium in oxygen and CO_2 in this sort of temperature range, *i.e.* Thomas and Chirigos[8] $\sim 48\,000$ kcal/mole in oxygen, Belle and Mallett[9] $\sim 47\,000$ kcal/mole in oxygen, O'Driscoll, Tyzack and Raine[10] $\sim 43\,000$ kcal/mole in oxygen and $\sim 46\,000$ kcal/mole in carbon dioxide.

Rough comparisons of the rates of oxidation obtained by Mackay in sodium at 500°C with those obtained by O'Driscoll *et al.*[10] at the same temperature in carbon dioxide and oxygen assuming parabolic behaviour throughout give $8·4 \times 10^{-7}$ (mg/cm^2)^2 min^{-1} in sodium compared with $31·7 \times 10^{-7}$ and 880×10^{-7} (mg/cm^2)^2 min^{-1} in carbon dioxide and oxygen respectively. Thus the values found for the parabolic rate constants at 500°C are roughly four and two orders of magnitude higher in CO_2 and oxygen respectively, compared with oxygen containing sodium, and this presumably reflects a lower oxygen activity in the sodium.

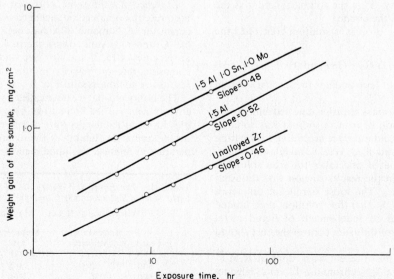

Fig. 3.—*Isothermal weight gain of zirconium and zirconium alloys exposed to liquid sodium. Sample temperature 635°C, cold trap temperature 150°C (Ref. 7)*

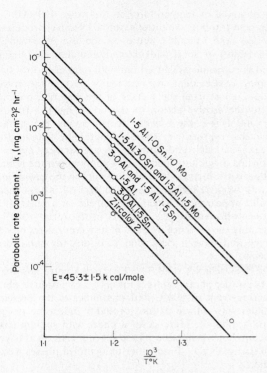

Fig. 4.—*Variation of reaction rate constant of zirconium alloys in liquid sodium with temperature (Ref. 7)*

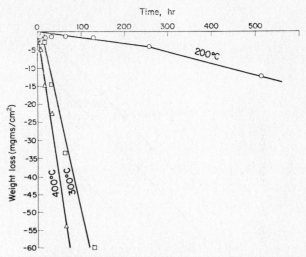

Fig. 5.—*Oxidation of uranium in dynamic sodium weight losses as a function of time of exposure oxygen level ~15 ppm temperatures 200, 300 and 400°C*

A further interesting anology between the behaviour of zirconium alloys in sodium and gas environments in Mackay's work[7] was the occurrence of a rate transition from parabolic to linear behaviour with a number of aluminium and tin zirconium-base alloys at temperatures of 500°C and below, after periods of exposure between 25 and 200 h. This transition was not observed within the time scale of the tests for the more oxidation resistant pure zirconium and Zircaloy-2.

In contrast to zirconium, the adherence of whose oxide film is excellent in sodium, it is interesting to examine briefly the oxidation behaviour of uranium in this medium. At R.M.L. specimens of uranium metal have been exposed to liquid sodium–potassium alloy containing up to 3000 ppm by weight of oxygen under static conditions in various tests at 300, 500 and 600°C. In contrast with zirconium the extent of oxidation of uranium was strongly dependent on the oxygen level. At the lowest oxygen levels weight gains on the specimens were observed while at the higher oxygen levels substantial weight losses were observed as the oxide formed was voluminous and readily spalled from the metal. The corrosion product always analysed as UO_2.

Tests were then carried out under dynamic conditions in sodium containing 15 ppm oxygen at 400°C where unalloyed

uranium lost weight linearly as a function of time from the onset of testing. Similar tests at 300 and 200°C suggested that some initial oxide film build-up occurred which at a later stage was swept away by erosive action, after which the metal loss rate increased. The results are shown graphically in Fig. 5.

In a comparison of the corrosion behaviour of a range of uranium alloys at 400°C exposed to sodium at a range of velocities, it was found that the corrosion rates decreased in the order uranium >uranium 0·5 at.% Cr >uranium 0·5 at.% Mo >uranium 10 at.% Mo. The improvements due to molybdenum are in line with findings by Antill, Peakall and Gardner[11] in CO_2 and air oxidation. As can be seen from Fig. 6 there is a tendency for the corrosion rate to increase with increasing liquid metal velocity with uranium and the 0·5 at.% alloys which is not observed with the uranium 10 at.% molybdenum alloy. This is probably due in part to the improved mechanical stability of the film in the latter case which is more resistant to erosion under dynamic conditions, so that fresh surface is not being continuously exposed to oxygenated liquid metal.

Metals showing basically similar oxidation characteristics in oxygen containing sodium as in gaseous environments of similar activity have been called Type II metals. It is believed that these are exemplified by zirconium and uranium. The excellent coherence of the pretransition oxide film on zirconium makes it a good choice for gettering oxygen from sodium in the so-called hot trapping technique. Uranium, on the other hand, shows linear kinetics in both CO_2 and oxygenated sodium at the temperatures of interest, but the

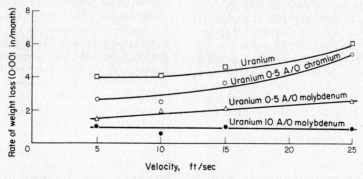

Fig. 6.—*Corrosion of uranium and uranium alloys in dynamic sodium containing ~15 ppm oxygen at 400°C (extrapolated from 120 h exposures)*

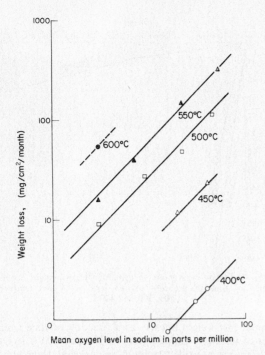

Fig. 7.—*Corrosion of niobium in sodium under dynamic conditions (25 ft/sec)*

position is complicated by the poor mechanical stability of the film in erosive conditions. It seems probable that titanium and hafnium are Type II metals.

Type III Behaviour—the Rôle of Complex Oxides in Sodium Corrosion

Niobium was originally selected as a canning material for the Dounreay fast fission reactor on the grounds of good high temperature creep strength and compatibility with uranium up to about 1400°C. At this stage work had been done on the compatibility of niobium with sodium under static low oxygen conditions and this indicated no particular problem as the available oxygen impurity in the liquid metal volume was small. When, however, pumped non-isothermal loop tests were started it rapidly became apparent that under certain conditions of temperature and oxygen content, extremely rapid loss of metal section could occur.

During the past three years Thorley at R.M.L. has made experiments on the corrosion of niobium at 400, 450, 500, 550 and 600°C under dynamic conditions at various levels of oxygen in the sodium at a fixed velocity of 25 ft/sec. Some of the results are summarized in Fig. 7. The corrosion is characterized by weight losses and as far as can be determined the corrosion rate depends linearly on the oxygen content of the sodium, the higher the oxygen level the higher the corrosion rate at any temperature. The corrosion rate of niobium is velocity dependent within the limits examined (2–35 ft/sec); the higher the velocity the higher the corrosion rate.

The observed corrosion rates at 400 and 450°C although dependent on the oxygen level are small and tolerable up to the highest oxygen content studied—40 ppm by weight in the sodium. At temperatures of 500°C and above the corrosion rate increases rapidly and depends critically on the oxygen content of the sodium. One set of experiments at 600°C with oxygen levels of 3, 7 and 12 ppm gave metal loss rates of 2·65, 8·8 and 26·5 thou.in./month, and it is quite clear that at temperatures above 450°C stringent oxygen control of the sodium must be maintained if service components made of niobium are to have a useful life in a reactor. The corrosion

rate observed at temperatures in the range 450–600°C with given cold trapping conditions can be effectively reduced to a very low and tolerable figure by the use of either liquid (magnesium) or solid deoxidants (zirconium and titanium).

In the experiments carried out with oxygen control by cold trapping it is evident that the major part of the corrosion product is lost from the surface of the material, presumably due to the erosive action of the liquid metal. In tests at 550° and 600°C the powder remaining on the surface of specimens exposed in sodium containing about 10 ppm oxygen was black and powdery in appearance, but in tests conducted in sodium containing 3 ppm oxygen the remaining product was a lustrous brittle skin, which in the case of materials with worked surfaces tended to peel off in thin sheets of metallic appearance. Chemical analysis on a range of these products showed oxygen contents in the range 10–15 at.% suggesting the presence of NbO in its lower ranges of stoichiometry and oxygen rich solid solutions (or suboxides) of niobium.

Dr. Goldschmidt of B.S.A. Research Centre has analysed X-ray powder photographs of the corrosion products obtained in various runs at 600°C and this indicates the presence of niobium with diffuse pattern probably indicating oxygen in solution, plus the presence of a phase with sodium chloride structure but which has a lattice spacing considerably greater than that of NbO. Four other unidentified phases were also found.

Professor Addison and his workers[12] who are carrying out an investigation into the reaction of the various niobium oxides with sodium, have made a compound by reacting Nb_2O_5 with sodium which they have characterized by chemical analysis as $Na_2Nb_2O_5$ which has a sodium chloride structure of a similar spacing to the one obtained as a corrosion product.

In order to obtain further evidence on possible compounds playing a rôle in the corrosion process, Nb_2O_5 contained in porous stainless steel dispensers has been immersed in dynamic sodium of low oxygen content (3 ppm) at 600°C in the R.M.L. loops in order to study the reduction processes occurring, and the reaction products have been removed after various periods of exposure and subjected to X-ray analysis by Dr. Goldschmidt. In addition to niobium metal containing oxygen, three phases designated X, Y and Z were found, the resolution of the diffraction lines improving with longer exposures at 600°C in sodium. Phase Y was identified as the rock salt structure found in the corrosion products previously, and identical with the pattern obtained by Professor Addison and his colleagues and characterized as $Na_2Nb_2O_5$. Phases X and Z have also been obtained at Nottingham during investigations into the reaction of niobium oxide with sodium and the study of the disproportionation reactions of the various ternary compounds. It seems likely that phase X is Na_3NbO_4.

The corrosion behaviour of niobium in oxygen containing sodium is undoubtedly complex and we do not yet fully understand it. The complexity is due in part to the fact that the oxides of niobium are of comparable thermodynamic stability to sodium oxide and sodium containing oxygen at less than unit activity, at temperatures of interest in reactor technology. Further, complex oxides of niobium and sodium are formed which are presumably of greater stability than the simple oxides, and which play a rôle in the corrosion process at the temperatures of interest. It is instructive to examine the thermodynamics of the sodium–niobium–oxygen system as far as it is understood.

The standard free energy of formation of sodium oxide as a function of temperature is known with a fair degree of accuracy, and the solubility of oxygen in sodium has been determined by Thorley at R.M.L. over the range 100–300°C at intervals of

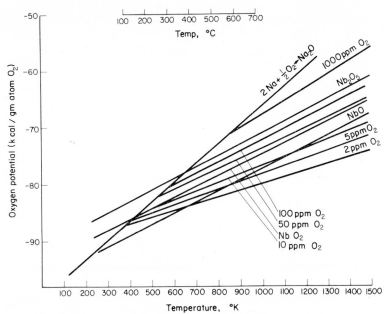

Fig. 8.—*Thermodynamics of the niobium-sodium oxygen system*

approximately 50 degrees centigrade. The results may be summarized by the equation:

$$\log_{10} \text{ solubility (ppm)} = 5 \cdot 153 - 18 \cdot 03 \times 10^2 / T,$$

where T is the absolute temperature. The heat of solution has been determined as 8,230 cal/mole. The results are summarized graphically in Fig. 8. These data have enabled a computation to be made of the free energy of oxygen dissolved in sodium at concentrations of 100, 50, 10, 5 and 2 ppm as a function of temperature, by use of the relation:

$$\Delta G_1{}^0 = \Delta G^0 + RT \ln a \, (\text{Na}_2\text{O})$$

where ΔG^0 is the standard free energy, and $\Delta G_1{}^0$ is that for $a[\text{Na}_2\text{O}] < 1$ assuming that the activity of the oxygen is proportional to its concentration. This is shown in Fig. 8.

To determine under what conditions oxygen bearing sodium is oxidizing to niobium it is necessary to know the standard free energies of formation of the various niobium oxides and any ternary compounds such as $\text{Na}_2\text{Nb}_2\text{O}_5$ or possibly Na_3NbO_4 which may be formed. Unfortunately the accuracy of the data relating to the oxides NbO_2 and NbO is much less good than that for Nb_2O_5, Na_2O and oxygen in sodium, while data on ternary compounds do not exist. However, some estimate can be made using the data compiled by Glassner and this is summarised in Fig. 8.

The data suggest that Nb_2O_5 cannot be formed in sodium containing less than 100 ppm oxygen, and can thus be ruled out for practical purposes. (Actually in static tests in sodium containing 3000 ppm oxygen, niobium pentoxide Nb_2O_5 was observed as a corrosion product on niobium.) NbO_2 cannot be formed at oxygen contents below 30 or 40 ppm oxygen at temperatures of interest, while NbO could be formed in sodium containing 10 ppm oxygen at temperatures up to around 850°C and at 5 ppm oxygen at temperatures up to 550°C. Above this temperature solid solution of oxygen in niobium is possible.

In relation to the formation of sodium–niobium–oxygen compounds at say 600°C a value of ΔH (600°C) of greater than 64 kcal for the reaction $3\text{Na}_2\text{O} + \text{Nb}_2\text{O}_5 = 3\text{Na}_2\text{O Nb}_2\text{O}_5$ would be necessary in order to make Na_3NbO_4 stable relative to NbO. Similarly the observed corrosion product $\text{Na}_2\text{Nb}_2\text{O}_5$ needs a heat of formation for the reaction

$$\text{Na}_2\text{O} + 2 \,\text{NbO}_2 = \text{Na}_2\text{Nb}_2\text{O}_5$$

of greater than 12·5 kcal to be stable relative to NbO. In the light of these considerations it can be seen that the corrosion mechanisms and the products obtained may depend critically on temperature and oxygen content of the sodium. Similar type of oxidation behaviour involving complex oxides is to be expected with vanadium, tantalum and possibly tungsten and chromium.

Conclusions

Three types of corrosion behaviour of transition metals in sodium containing sodium oxide at less than unit activity have been characterized. Depending upon whether the metal oxide has lower, comparable or greater thermodynamic stability than sodium oxide at this activity, solution, double oxide formation or simple oxide formation occurs. A number of cases where the rate of loss of metal section is dependent on (a) the oxygen level in the sodium, and (b) the velocity of the sodium have been discussed, and it has been concluded that the latter may affect metal solution rates and be responsible for erosion of oxide films. A tentative assignment of the transition metals into the three categories has been attempted in Table I.

Acknowledgments

The author is grateful to Mr. R. V. Moore, Managing Director, and Mr. F. W. Fenning, Director of Reactor Technology of the Reactor Group, United Kingdom Atomic Energy Authority, for permission to publish this papers.

Also to *J. Electrochem. Soc.* for permission to reproduce Figs. 2 and 4 from article by T. L. Mackay, *J. Electrochem. Soc.* **110**, Sept. 1963, 960–964.

References

[1] Starr, C. and Dickinson, R. "*Technological Problems with Sodium Coolant.*" Presented at European Atomic Energy Society, (France: Cannes, October, 1962).

[2] Addison, C. C., Iberson, E. and Manning, J. A. "*Liquid Metals Part V. The Role of Oxide Films in the Wetting of Iron Cobalt and Nickel by Liquid Sodium.*"

[3] Epstein, L. F. "*Static and Dynamic Corrosion and Mass Transfer in Liquid Metal Systems.*" Chemical Engineering Progress Symposium Series No. 20, **53.**

[4] Weeks, J. R. and Klamut, C. J. *Conference on the Corrosion of Reactor Materials.* I.A.E.A. CN-13/11 (Salzburg), June 1962.

[5] Baus, R. A., Bogard, A. D., Grand, J. A., Lockhart, L. B. Jr., Miller, R. R. and Williams, D. D. *Proc. Int. Conf. on the Peaceful Uses of Atomic Energy*, **9,** 356 (New York: United Nations, 1956).

[6] Eichelburger, R. L. referred to in reference 7.

[7] Mackay, T. L. Oxidation of zirconium and zirconium alloys in liquid sodium. *J. Electrochem. Soc.*, 1963, **110,** 9, 960.

[8] Thomas, D. E. and Chirigos, J. "*Oxidation of zirconium and relation to high temperature corrosion in water.*" WAPD-98 Oct. 1953.

[9] Belle, J. and Mallett, M. W. *J. Electrochem. Soc.*, 1954, **101,** 339.

[10] O'Driscoll, W. G., Tyzack, C. and Raine, T. *Proc. Conf. on the Peaceful Uses of Atomic Energy*, **5,** (Geneva: United Nations, 1958).

[11] Antill, J. E., Peakall, K. A. and Gardner, M. "*Oxidation of uranium molybdenum alloys in Co_2 and air at 500–1000°C.*" AERE M/R 2805.

[12] Addison, Professor C. C. *Private communication.*

ADVANCES IN POLYMERS

By R. N. HAWARD

Introduction

As with other materials, polymers advance in many different ways, whose respective importance differs according to the point of view of the person concerned. In this short survey an attempt will be made to avoid a specialist approach and to mention briefly the main areas of progress which are evident at the present time. As thermoplastics are the most rapidly developing part of the plastics industry, particular attention is paid to them.

From the scientific standpoint great interest attaches to the efforts which are being made to provide plastic materials with new and improved properties at the research stage. Similarly the development of many new materials from the laboratory into large-scale production during the last few years has been an outstanding event. From the economic and industrial point of view it is also necessary to mention the productive achievements of the plastics industry and the improvements which are being made in the well-established types of plastics. In this way three particular fields of interest have to be considered and these may be presented under the following headings:

High Temperature Polymers

Considerable efforts are being made to extend the high temperature performance of the organic polymers. Parallel efforts are also being directed to the preparation of polymers containing inorganic compounds with a view to extending the frontiers of polymer science to include elements which at the moment play only a minor role. Much of this work has been stimulated by the requirements of aero-space technology.

Crystalline Polymers

The discoveries of Ziegler[1] and Natta[2] have greatly increased our ability to prepare crystalline polymers from organic raw materials and have also given us a much greater understanding of their structure. During the same period an increased physical and applicational knowledge has enabled us to make even greater uses of materials such as nylon or polytetrafluorethylene which have now been known for a long time. As the crystalline polymers often have high melting points, which help to increase the temperatures at which they may be used, the number of thermoplastics which may now be exposed, with more or less impunity, at temperatures in the range 100°–200°C has notably increased. From the performance and engineering point of view many of these materials compare favourably with the older thermoplastics such as low density polyethylene, polystyrene and PVC.

Polymer for the Mass Market

In a recent discussion[3] Bernal pointed out that, in the case of the metals, a relatively small improvement in the manufacture or properties of one of the major materials might be of greater economic importance than the development of a new but highly specialized and expensive product intended for particular applications. Obviously similar considerations apply to plastics. For this reason any discussion of advances in plastics should properly pay attention to the considerable recent developments in the scale and economy of the manufacture and marketing of the major thermoplastics, which have been already available for a number of years. In a world of ever rising prices, plastics alone become cheaper and better. Thus, apart from the natural increase in the available applicational experience, new applications are continually being opened up. This development is strongly supported by engineering improvements in the technology of plastics processing, some of which are described in a later paper.

The High Temperature Polymers

An important limiting feature of most plastic materials has been the maximum temperature at which they can be used. When a plastic is heated up it will either soften or decompose at a particular temperature, generally much below the temperature at which materials such as steel or glass are still quite satisfactory. Obviously this places severe limitations on the applications of plastics wherever high temperatures are concerned and the recent development of the aero-space industries has tended to increase the interest in plastics for use under severe conditions, and particularly at high temperatures.

In order to give satisfactory service at high temperatures the first requirement is that the polymer should not decompose, oxidize or show any other form of chemical instability. Further, if it is to perform satisfactorily in most applications it is necessary that it should also maintain its rigidity up to high temperatures. For thermoplastics this is something of a contradiction of terms, since it is also necessary that above a certain temperature, generally either the glass transition temperature (T_g) or the crystalline melting point (T_m) of the polymer should be able to soften and flow according to the requirements of plastics processing techniques. As the elastic modulus will generally also drop by several decades around T_g or T_m, it is essential that these quantities should be high if a thermoplastic is to be useful at elevated temperatures. Such materials also necessarily require the use of higher processing temperatures in moulding or extrusion, if these processes are applied. For some purposes, however, film casting or sintering techniques make it possible to avoid some of these difficulties.

Inorganic Polymers

Corresponding to the requirement of improving the thermal stability and softening temperature of plastics, work has developed in two main areas. In the first place attention has been paid to the known strengths of different types of chemical bond (Table I). From these figures it is clear that a number of chemical linkages are available which are as strong or stronger than the C–C, and C–O linkages which are characteristic of so many currently successful thermoplastics. The exploitation of these high strength linkages involves the introduction of inorganic atoms into polymer chain units. This offers the hope of obtaining products of greater stability at high temperatures. A considerable amount of work has, therefore, gone into the preparation of completely new inorganic–

159

TABLE I.—*The Covalent Bond Strengths of Elements Used or Proposed for Use in Polymers*

Type of bond	Bond strength, (kcal/mole)	Reference No.
C–H	99	4
C–C	82	4
C–O (ether)	94	4
C–Si	77	4
C–S	75	4
C–B	89	4
C–N	71	4
C–P	65	4
Si–O	103	5
Si–Si	~45	6
S–S	73	4
P–N	67[a]	5
P–P	~55	6
B–O	119	5
B–N	105	5
B–B	80	5

[a] However, this is greater in $PNCl_2$—72·5 kcal/mole[5]

organic polymer and into finding new ways of linking macro-molecules together.

So far not very much has come out of this work in the form of practical results, apart from the now well established silicone rubbers with their good high temperature performance. It will be noted from Table I that the Si–O linkage has a high bond strength. An important reason for this difficulty lies in the susceptibility of many chemical bonds to forms of attack other than that of simply being dissociated by thermal energy. Thus, oxidation is an ever present threat, which, however, can often be partially countered by the use of antioxidants.[8,9,10] Other polymers, *e.g.* the rubbers which can be obtained by the polymerization of phosphonitrilic chloride ($PNCl_2$) are very easily hydrolyzed.[6] Several recent reviews of work in these fields are now available.[5,6,7,11,12] As an example of the new techniques which have been tried out, the co-ordination polymers may be mentioned. For a long time the ability of many metals to form multivalent co-ordination compounds with certain organic compounds has been well known. Whenever organic compounds can be prepared with a suitable number of active groups, then co-ordination chemistry becomes a possible means of making new polymers. An example of the type of material which has recently been examined is given above right (Ref. 7, p. 502).

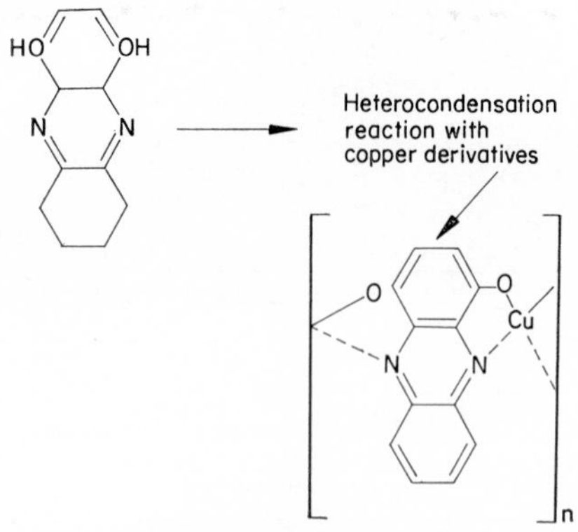

New Types of Polymer Based on Organic Chemistry

More success has attended the efforts to produce high temperature materials on more orthodox lines which still employ carbon as the most important element in the polymer. Progress seems to have been achieved on two lines. In the

An example of a " co-ordination " polymer

first place it appears that oxygen is a greater menace to the chemical stability of organic carbon compounds at high temperatures than is the thermal energy. Thus polymers where the carbon is linked up in such a way as to be resistant to oxidation are themselves much more heat stable. So the fluorocarbons are very stable and so are compounds in which all the C–H bonds are of an aromatic type. Taking advantage of this second factor it has been possible to develop several highly heat stable polymers which also have new and more rigid forms of chain structure of a type which favours high softening temperatures. This line of development is most characteristically illustrated by the new group of polymers known as the pyromellitimides.[13,14,15] The chemistry of these materials is illustrated in Fig. 1. Their great thermal and chemical stability may be illustrated by the differential thermogravimetric curves shown in Fig. 2, where it can be seen that no appreciable weight loss occurs when heating up

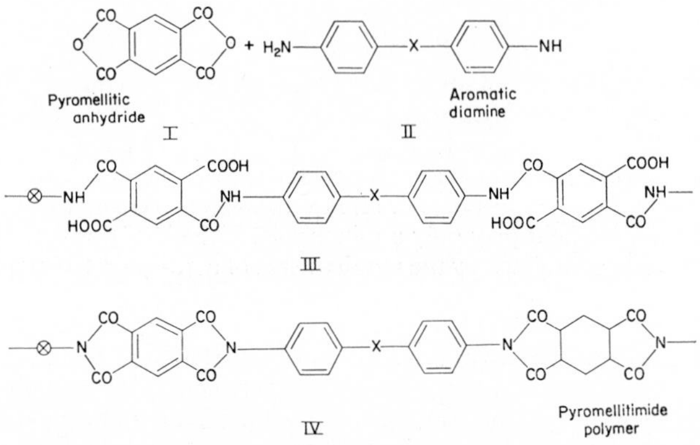

Fig. 1.—*The formation of pyromellitimide polymers*

TABLE II.—*Comparative Properties of Dielectric Film—Thickness 0·001 in.*

Property	Unit	Temperature (°C)	H-film	Polyethylene terephthalate	Polytetrafluor-ethylene
Density	g/cm³	23	1·42	1·39	2·15
Tensile strength	(lb/in²)×10³	23	25	23	3
		200	15	7	0·4
		500	5	—	—
Tensile modulus	(lb/in²)×10³	23	400	500	43
		200	250	50	2
Ultimate elongation	%	23	70	100	300
		200	90	125	
Pneumatic impact	kg–cm/mil	23	6	6	4
Melting point	°C	—	None	260	290
Moisture content	%	23	1·3 at 50% RH	0·2	0·1 at 100% RH
Zero strength temperature (will sustain 20 lb/in²)	°C	—	815	250	250
Solvent resistance	%	—	No solvent	Good	Excellent
Glass transition temperature	°C	—	>500	70	85

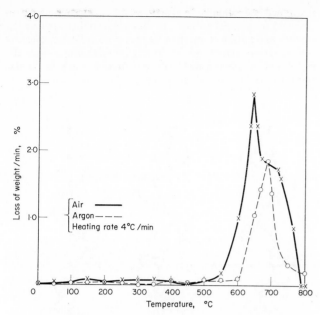

Fig. 2.—*Differential thermogravimetric curves for polymer derived from 4,4'-diamino diphenyl ether and pyromellitic anhydride*

to 600°C, and even above this temperature, up to 800°C, the amount of degradation which is observed is strictly limited. The physical properties of a film made from other polymers are given in Table II, where comparison can be made with other high temperature polymers. It will be seen that the pyromellitimide polymer also has good mechanical properties up to much higher temperatures than have previously been reached for any organic polymeric material.

In this way the discovery of the pyromellitimide polymers may be said to have opened up a new field of polymer chemistry. There is no doubt that many other aromatic cyclic polymer structures are capable of being made which may be expected also to have excellent high temperature properties, and there is every indication that a number of workers are now active in this field. For example, Marvel[16] and Wrasidlo[17] have described a series of polymers prepared for aromatic tetramines and the phenyl esters of dibasic acids which have the following structure:

The products did not soften easily and in general had a tensile strength at 300°C equivalent to that at room temperature. Thus, they were not in the ordinary sense thermoplastic though they could be dissolved in formic acid, dimethyl formamide and other solvents. From solution they were cast into films for the determination of properties.

Other new polymers based on using a series of consecutive heterocyclic chain units include the polyphenylenetriazoles.[18]

Poly(m, p phenylene) 4 phenyl triazole

This material had good properties as a film which tended to improve after heating at 290°C. Its glass transition temperature was reported as 280°C to 295°C. Another similar type of high temperature polymer which has recently been described is derived from the *p* substituted di*iso*cyanate of diphenyl methane.[18]

There seems little doubt that in the long run research will lead to several different polymers in this field, since the highest possible heat resistance will not always be required and processing properties, apart from the casting of film, are likely to become more difficult with increasingly heat resistant materials. Thus, if thermoplastic products can be obtained, a series of different compromises between processing and performance properties are to be designed.

The Crystalline Polymers

The first polymers used in the thermoplastics industry were largely amorphous. These materials included the partially hydrolyzed cellulose derivatives, polystyrene and polyvinyl chloride, all of which continue to be manufactured in large tonnages, but which have in common an essentially random molecular structure. At the present time there is no indication that any limit has been reached in the development of new and useful types of amorphous polymers, as the recently developed phenoxy plastics and the high-softening polycarbonates demonstrate. On the other hand, the characteristic factor of the present stage of development is the emergence of a number of new crystalline products with new and useful properties.

The easiest way of synthesizing crystalline high polymer is by making a completely symmetrical molecule, in which all the groups along the molecular chain are the same. Such molecules are easily packed together to give symmetrical crystalline assemblies. The most simple examples are, of course, polyethylene and polytetrafluoroethylene (Fig. 3). In

Fig. 3.—(a) *Polytetrafluorethylene—a symmetrical molecule which crystallizes as a spiral chain*

(b) *Linear polyethylene—a fully symmetrical molecule*

(c) *The introduction of methyl side chains reduces the symmetry and ease of packing of linear polyethylene*

M

molecules of this type the degree of crystallinity can be controlled by introducing a small number of random pendant groups along the chain which obstruct the packing of the chains. Such changes in polymer structure make it practicable to produce materials with a controlled degree of crystallinity. Thus, by the introduction of varying amounts of side groups it is possible to disorganize the crystalline structure and so to get material of lower melting point or even to make completely amorphous products. Thus an equimolar copolymer of ethylene and propylene is a soft, rubbery material quite unlike a straight chain polyethylene. Similarly, the polychlorotrifluorethylene is a softer non-crystalline version of the tetrafluorethylene polymer. In this way it is possible to obtain materials in which easier processing qualities may be obtained at the price of a lower softening temperature. In the case of the polyethylenes, the insertion of different structures on the side chain at varying frequency has made it possible to produce a whole series of polymers having different degrees of crystallinity from completely amorphous rubbers to rigid crystalline products. In these cases it seems that crystallinity (density) and mechanical properties change together in a quantitative way as indicated in Fig. 4.

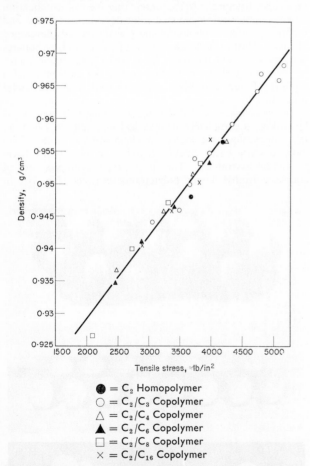

= C_2 Homopolymer
○ = C_2/C_3 Copolymer
△ = C_2/C_4 Copolymer
▲ = C_2/C_6 Copolymer
□ = C_2/C_8 Copolymer
× = C_2/C_{16} Copolymer

Fig. 4.—*Relation between density and yield tensile strength in ziegler polyethylenes*

Up to the year 1955 it was generally expected that polymers with a large number of pendant side groups would turn out to be amorphous. In that year Natta[2] discovered the regular isotactic form of polypropylene, with its regularly placed, or stereoregular, succession of methyl groups along the basic hydrocarbon chain. Such polymers could be made for the first time by using the organo-metallic catalysts discovered by Ziegler,[1] and by this single step polypropylene was changed from very poor rubber into a rigid material with good heat

resistance and valuable qualities suitable for moulding extrusion and fibre applications. In the case of polypropylene the rigidity and tensile strength of the polymer are determined by the stereo-regularity of its molecular structure and the possibility of making materials which could pack in regular spiral formations as shown in Fig. 5. Because the monomers

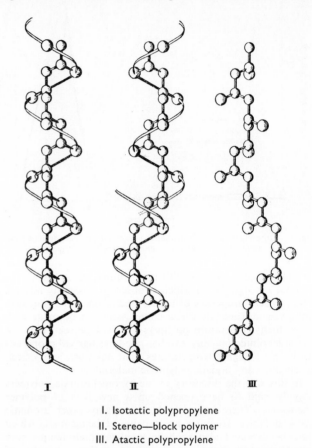

I. Isotactic polypropylene
II. Stereo—block polymer
III. Atactic polypropylene

Fig. 5.—*Steric configuration in polypropylene chains*

were readily available, this new polymer was quickly developed commercially. The first commercial polypropylenes aimed at maximum rigidity, which was achieved by obtaining the greatest possible control of their distribution of pendant methyl groups. Recently, however, it has been found that the introduction of small amounts of disorganized rubbery units can improve the impact strength of certain moulding grades, especially at low temperatures. This step is similar to the development of heterophase reinforced polymers in the styrene field.[20,21]

Once the principle and practice of controlling the intimate structure of a polymer chain had been established it became obvious to all working in the field that a whole tribe of new polymeric types had been found, so that it now became possible to envisage isotactic and crystalline polymeric materials in all kinds of polymer types, many of which were already well known in their amorphous irregular configurations. Many, if not most, of these materials have now been made and evaluated. It has turned out that in most cases the polymers have a crystalline form whose melting point can be measured. In the series of polyolefins a whole range of polymers having a different melting point can be prepared, and in some cases the polymers melt only at high temperatures (Fig. 6). Because of this property, and because in many cases the raw materials were essentially accessible, hopes were raised that a new family of commercially useful high temperature polymers would result. Unfortunately, many of these hopes

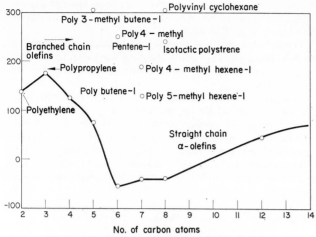

Fig. 6.—*The melting points of crystalline polyolefins*

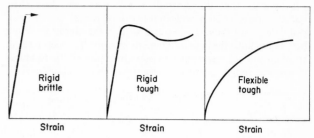

Fig. 7.—*Stress–strain curves for different types of plastic material*

have been disappointed, although the reasons for this disappointment are not as clear as one would have liked. In some cases, as with polystyrene, crystallization proceeds too slowly so that crystalline materials are not produced in normal processing operations.[22] In other cases it appears that the crystalline materials may be lacking in rigidity or impact strength.

Surprisingly, the latest polyolefin to be developed, poly-butene-1, does not have a particularly high melting point, being in this respect inferior to polypropylene. However, it shows a number of specialized applicational properties which it is claimed make it possible for a poly-butene pipe to stand pressure at 80°C for long periods.[23] Another feature of poly-butene-1 is that it shows two crystalline forms, the second one being formed from the first with increasing rapidity as the material is cooled to normal room temperatures below 60°C.[24] Although this feature, which is accompanied by a contraction of 4%, may have discouraged the early development of the polymer it does not appear, so far, to be a serious factor in its application.

Mechanical Requirements for High Performance Polymers

A very desirable feature of any polymer, indeed of almost any structural material, is the ability to combine a high level of rigidity with a high impact strength. Such materials are particularly desirable for load bearing (" engineering ") applications. Chemically, the outstanding polymer types which have useful properties of this sort include the nylons, polyformaldehyde (acetal) polymers and copolymers, poly-carbonate and the ABS terpolymers. From the mechanical point of view the desirable features may be summarized as follows:

high rigidity

high impact strength

low creep

high softening point.

It will be obvious that there is a conflict here between the requirement for rigidity and low creep (low deformation under load) and the need for a high impact strength, which requires that the material must be able to deform and take up energy.

Any impact measurement involves putting a specimen through a stress–strain process at high rates of strain. Under these conditions it is desirable to have a high energy requirement for fracture. Such energy absorption can be represented by the area under the stress–strain diagram. In order to combine toughness with rigidity it seems to be necessary that the " plastic " yield (preferably recoverable) should set in suddenly at high stresses combined with a stress–strain curve

which is approximately Hookean at low stresses (Fig. 7). This deformation must be accessible at high rates of strain.

For plastic materials this requirement can be further rationalized in the following sense. If the deformation concerned can be represented by relation of the type:

$$\text{Rate of strain} \propto S^n \text{ or } \propto e^{KS},$$

where S is the stress then the constants n or K must be as large as possible.[25] Thus the requirements for a tough rigid polymer may be summarized as follows:

(1) High modulus.

(2) High yield strength but less than fracture strength.

(3) High value of n or K (above).

In practice it is found that there are severe limitations on the structure of an organic glass which can meet these requirements. To meet this difficulty the reinforced thermoplastics have been developed (high impact polystyrene, ABS resins, *etc.*) which contain a second rubbery phase embedded in the glassy matrix. Although such inclusions inevitably have some softening action so that the overall rigidity and yield strength are reduced, this disadvantage is more than offset by the increased capacity of the polymers to deform and take up energy, especially under impact conditions.[20,21] For this purpose it is essential that the low modulus phase present should be in a rubbery condition, above its glass transition temperature.

In the crystalline polymers a situation exists which automatically provides the material with two phases since some amorphous material is always present. For this reason most crystalline polymers (like the reinforced thermoplastics) show more than one maximum when their mechanical damping coefficients are plotted against temperature. In this way it is possible to have a rigid phase together with non-crystalline regions which may be relatively soft and able to accept large deformations. Whatever the reason the observed facts are that the emergence of the crystalline nylons and of polytetra-fluorethylene as valuable plastics and the discovery of the acetals and of the crystalline polyolefins has greatly increased the availability of tough materials with relatively high rigidity.

Many crystalline polymers are also notable for having high softening points, which, however, may vary over a wide range according to the method of test. For example, the A.S.T.M. heat distortion temperature of a polymer is normally measured at one of two load levels—66 lb/in² or 264 lb/in². With homogeneous amorphous polymers it does not matter too much which load is employed, but with the crystalline polymers considerable differences are observed.

The Heat Distortion Temperature of Crystalline and Amorphous Polymers Under Different Stresses

	Amorphous		Crystalline		
Applied Stress	Poly-styrene	Polymethyl methacrylate	Poly-propylene	Nylon	Poly-acetal
66 lb/in²	87°C	90°C	103°C	200°C	158°C
264 lb/in²	83°C	80°C	62°C	75°C	110°C

It appears that the crystalline polymers, can lose their rigidity slowly over a wide temperature range, but do not completely lose their rigidity and with it the ability to retain their shape until the crystalline melting point has been passed. Another way of illustrating this point is to plot elastic modulus or tensile strength against temperature when a characteristic

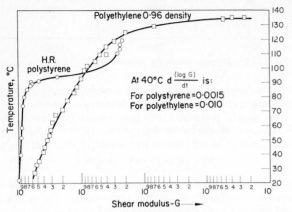

Fig. 8.—*The effect of temperature on the shear modulus of polystyrene and high density polyethylene*

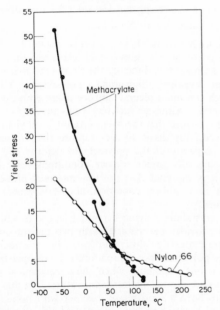

Fig. 9.—*Plots of yield stress versus temperature for nylon 66 and Polymethyl methacrylate*

difference can often be observed between amorphous and crystalline types of polymer. (Examples of this behaviour are provided in Figs. 8 and 9.*)

Further it turns out that for a crystalline polymer the melting point is always above the glass transition temperature which would determine its softening temperature if it was amorphous.

Thus, in quantitative terms it has been found that for symmetrical molecules the melting point is generally about $2 \times$ for the glass transition temperature (°C abs) and for non-symmetrical molecules it is about 50% greater.[30]   In this way crystalline polymers have an inherent advantage at high temperatures, so long as a certain amount of increasing flexibility can be tolerated up to their crystalline melting points.

Performance Comparisons Between Different Plastics

The relative performance of different types of plastic material may be usefully illustrated by graphs relating such qualities as impact strength, softening point and rigidity, three properties which enter into a wide range of applications. Although there is always some difficulty in taking precise figures from published tables because of the wide ranges which are often quoted, it is still possible to see significant results, when large differences are being considered.   The three graphs showing the relations between these properties are shown in Figs. 10, 11, and 12.   In all cases the direction of improvement is at right angles to the hyperbolic lines.   From such graphs it is possible to pick out the materials with the best mechanical performance.

Naturally many other properties have to be considered in deciding on the type of polymer for a particular duty besides simple mechanical properties.   For example many of the newer materials, and especially the crystalline types, have a useful resistance to the action of organic solvents, which will attack and dissolve polymers such as polystyrene or polymethyl methacrylate.   Another important property is that of water absorption, which may be harmful in itself, but which may also adversely affect processing and mechanical properties generally.   In this context it may be noted that many nylons and polycarbonates, which are so good from other points of view, will take up some water.   Here, however, as in other special properties there is always the possibility of improve-

---

* Although this behaviour seems fairly general, extreme cases from each group may show fairly similar behaviour.   Thus, over the normal temperature range the crystalline polyacetal shows a slightly steeper dependence of yield stress with temperature than the amorphous polycarbonate.   Above 100°C, however, the normal difference mentioned in this text seems to apply.[29]

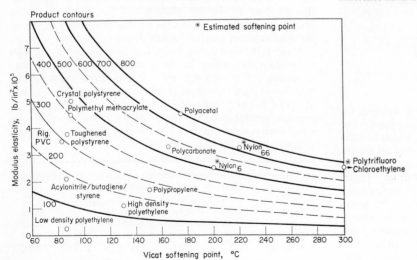

Fig. 10.—*The relation between modulus of elasticity and vicat softening point for thermoplastics*

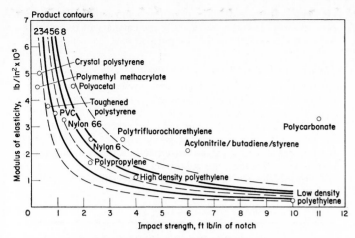

Fig. 11.—*The relation between modulus of elasticity and impact strength for different plastics*

ment based on a new element of compromize between different requirements. For example, a new type of nylon, Nylon 12, has recently been developed which has a water absorption of only 1·8% or less than 2/3 of that for Nylon 11. These compare with much higher figures for other types of Nylon.[31] Such differences are not only of interest in themselves but increase the stability of the mechanical properties, *e.g.* rigidity.

From all this it will be seen that the plastics which aim at a high performance at a medium to high price can offer an immense variety of properties and of compromizes between the differing requirements for use. In these circumstances there is little likelihood that the already large number of different types of material will be reduced. On the contrary, the trend is likely to be for more and more materials to be produced which match up evermore precisely to the requirements of engineering and product design.

The Mass Market Polymers

A major feature of the development of plastics, especially of thermoplastics, over the last ten years, has been the increase in the tonnages of material which have been made and used. Such increases, together with thousands of minor, or not so

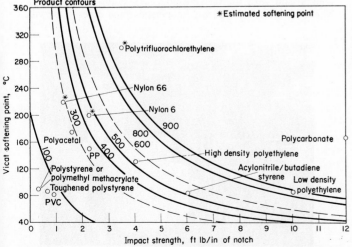

Fig. 12.—*The relation between vicat softening point and impact strength for thermoplastics*

M*

minor technical advances, have made it possible for the prices of polymeric raw materials to fall, typically by a factor of about 2 during the same period. Simultaneously there has been at least an equivalent improvement in the performance of the processing equipment which is employed in fabricating the finished or semi-finished products. These improvements have generally been accompanied by some improvement in the physical properties of the materials and certainly by no deterioration. For example, the impact polystyrenes, first introduced in 1950, have steadily improved in toughness (Fig. 13). As a result it is now possible to turn out plastic products faster, cheaper and better than ten years ago.

As the margins under consideration are substantial so the consequent changes in the employment of material are also substantial. To illustrate this point we may consider the competition between different traditional materials in their performance against different requirements. Conventional types of glass, steel, copper, brass and wood have reached generally established positions in relation to each other, although, of course, changes in their relative employment do take place, especially in response to developments in manu-

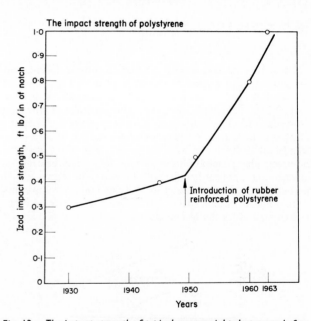

Fig. 13.—*The impact strength of typical commercial polystyrenes before and after the introduction of rubber reinforcement about the year 1950. Improvements after say, 1955 are due to the control of structure rather than to the increase in rubber content*

facturing techniques. To a certain extent, therefore, such materials may be regarded as being in equilibrium with each other against slowly changing market requirements. With plastics, however, the rate of growth has been so rapid that it is most unlikely that applicational possibilities have fully absorbed the existing improvements, quite apart from those which may be made in the future.

The changes in the relative prices per unit volume of plastics and some conventional materials are given in Fig. 14. It will be seen that the prices of the four selected thermoplastics have all dropped to a point where only wood and glass are cheaper materials on a volume basis. On the other hand, it is obvious that the actual performance of plastics in relation to other materials is affected by two other major factors apart from price, which however, tend to act in opposite directions. These are:

(1) Mechanical and other performance properties.

(2) Processability.

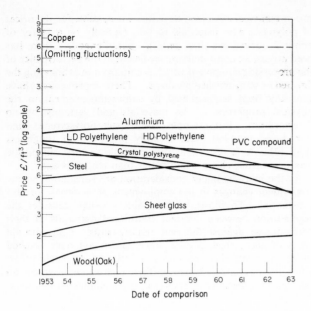

Fig. 14.—*The price per unit volume of plastics in comparison with other materials*

i.e. that of processability. In this connection the term processability includes particularly the capacity of the plastic to be formed directly into a complicated part.

The Cost of Plastic Products in Relation to Other Materials

For example the use of high density polyethylene has been compared with wood and metal wire for the manufacture of cases for milk and other beverage containers. Although the plastics articles were still somewhat more expensive than wood, the price difference, due to the processing advantages of the plastic, was not as great as those between the raw materials themselves. Further, the savings on weight and maintenance are making the plastic case the more attractive item in the long run (Table III).

TABLE III.—*The Cost of Milk Cases*

Type of case	Initial cost ($)	Annual repair ($)	Weight (lb)
Wood	0·9–2·00	0·45	9–13
Wire	3·00	0·30	9–11
High density polyethylene	2·50–2·75	—	3–3·5

The effect of taking into account a simple mechanical property such as a tensile strength is given in Fig. 15 which shows that steel is, of course, still the cheapest structural material for carrying a load. Obviously graphs of this type represent a less favourable way of looking at the performance of plastics in relation to other materials, though of course the trends are still in the same direction. For these reasons, however, the penetration of plastics into load bearing or engineering applications is still limited and there would perhaps be relatively little probability of large developments were it not for certain special advantages such as resistance to corrosion and for the second general factor mentioned above,

Another example of the mass processing of a thermoplastic to give a complicated product is given by the production of injection moulded refrigerator liners as shown in Fig. 16. It is obvious that the factor of direct processability to a complex shape plays an important part in the production of a component of this type.

Similar considerations apply to a great variety of plastics products, though it is often rather difficult to get an overall picture of the real comparative cost of plastics and metals, and in one way or another special considerations, *e.g.* temperature resistance or corrosivity, naturally also play a large part in the ultimate selection of material. An increasingly wide region of competition between plastics and other materials is that of pipes for cold water or drainage. Here the tonnages are large and the economic factors correspondingly significant. The Russians say that the cost of polyethylene pipe for cold water service is 30% less than that of steel and that less capital is tied up in making it.[34] Other figures given by Gill[35] for British conditions (Table IV) generally bear out the increasingly competitive position of plastics in this application. Field studies have been carried out at Carrington[36] on the use of filled high density polyethylene for drainage purposes in comparison with the conventional clay drains (see Fig. 17). These have shown that a 2 in. plastics pipe gives a service

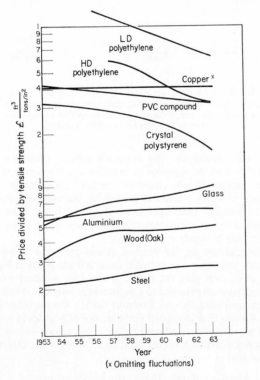

Fig. 15.—*Changes in the quantity (volume price/tensile strength) from 1953 to 1963*

Fig. 16.—*The moulding of 5 ft³ refrigerator liners (Courtesy E. K. Cole Ltd.)*

Fig. 17.—*The laying of filled high density polyethylene drainage pipe*

TABLE IV.—*The Cost of Pipes for Water Supply in Plastics and other Materials*[35]

3-inch nominal bore, Class B (200 ft working head) with joints

Material	Cost/year to buy	Cost/yard to lay
Spun cast iron	11s.	15s.–20s.
Asbestos cement	7s.6d.	15s.–20s.
Unplasticized PVC	10s.6d.	7s.–15s.

Prices vary with jointing procedures, lengths ordered and sub-soil conditions

½ inch nominal bore, Class C, (300 ft working head)

Material	Cost/yard to buy
Lead	10s.
Galvanized iron	2s.9d.
Copper	3s.3d.
Low density polythene	1s.6d.
Unplasticized PVC	1s.3d.

Average costs for digging a 10-ft long service, tapping the main, and supplying fittings—£8 (for all materials)

equivalent to that of a 3 in. clay drain. Under these conditions the cost of the clay pipes comes to 3½d per foot and that of the polyethylene (or PVC) pipe is estimated at 4½d to 5d per foot. However, because of the lightness and ease of handling of the plastics drain the ultimate cost of the installed plastics drainage is less than that of the conventional material.

In these circumstances it is not surprising to find that large developments in the uses of plastics piping are taking place in different parts of the world. This is especially the case in Austria, East Germany and Holland. Fig. 18 shows 5 in. o.d. PVC piping being made ready for installation as an undersea line to convey fresh water to an island off the Dutch coast, and illustrates the increasing scale on which plastics piping is now being used.

These examples are intended to call attention to the major possibilities of using plastics in bulk applications which arise from the present trend in price movements.

In a conference like this it is easy to focus attention exclusively on the effort of material scientists to obtain higher performance products. Naturally progress of this type is a matter of the greatest interest and importance, but the sheer economic achievements of the plastics industry are also of great significance and are continually upsetting all the cost relations between plastics and other materials. Indeed, we may be sure, that while we discuss these matters in this conference, somewhere, in some application, plastics have become for the first time the cheapest way to do the job.

Fig. 18.—*PVC pipe for under-sea water supply to an island (Holland)*
(Courtesy Wavin N.V.)

References

[1] Ziegler, K. *Agnew Chemie*, 1955, **67**, 541.

[2] Natta, G. *J.A.C.S.*, (1955), **77**, 1708.

[3] Bernal, J. D. *P.R.S.A.*, 282 (1964), 154.

[4] Mortimer, C. T. " *Reaction Rates and Bond Strengths* " (Oxford: Pergamon Press), 1962.

[5] Lappert, M. F. and Leigh, G. J. " *Developments in organic Polymer Chemistry* " (Elsevier), 1962.

[6] Hunter, D. N. " *Inorganic Polymers* " (Blackwell).

[7] Stone, F. G. A. and Graham, W. A. G. " *Inorganic Polymers* " (London: Academic Press), 1962.

[8] Scott, G. *Chem. & Ind.*, Feb. 16, 1963, p. 271.

[9] Haward, R. N. *Chem. in Ind.*, Aug. 15, 1964, 1442.

[10] Wright, B. " *Plastics* ", Sept., Nov., Dec., 1962.

[11] Brenner, W., Lunn, D. and Riley, M. W. " *High Temperature Polymers* " (Reinhold), 1962.

[12] Parvin, K. *Trans. Plast. Inst.*, **31**, (1963), 132.

[13] Amborski, L. E. A.C.S. Polymer Preprints, p. 175 (Los Angeles). April 1963.

[14] Bower, G. M. and Frost, L. W. *J. Pol. Sci.*, **A.1**, 3135, 1963.

[15] Jones, J. Idris, Ochynski, F. W., Radley, F. A. *Chem. & Ind.*, 1962, p. 1686.

[16] Marvel, C. S. A.C.S. *Polymer Preprints*, p. 1 (New York). Sept. 1963.

[17] Wrasidlo, W. and Levine, H. H. *Ibid.*, p. 15.

[18] Lilyquist, M. R. and Holsten, J. R. *Ibid.*, p. 6.

[19] Lyman, D. J. and Sadi, W. *Makromol. Chemie*, **67**, (1963), 1.

[20] Haward, R. N. and Mann, J. *P.R.S.A.*, 282 (1964), 120.

[21] Staverman, A. J. *Ibid.* p. 115.

[22] Kenyon, A. S., Gross, R. C. and Wurstner, A. L. *J. Pol. Sci.*, **40**, (1959), 159.

[23] "Chemische Werke Hüls Information Sheet ' *Isotaktisches polybutylene* '. October 1963.

24 Beer, J. and Mitchell, J. C. *J. Pol. Sci.*, **62,** S.70, (1962): 1A, (1963), 59.

25 Haward, R. N. *Trans. Farad. Soc.*, **39,** 1943, 267.

26 Nielsen, L. E. *"Mechanical Properties of Polymers"* (Reinhold), 1962, p. 170 to 200.

27 Nielsen, L. E. *Ibid*, p. 182.

28 Vincent, P. I. *"Plastics"*. Aug. 1962, Feb.-April 1963.

29 Vincent, P. I. *"Plastics"*. Dec. 1963, p. 104.

30 Beaman, R. G. *J. Pol. Sci.*, **9,** (1952), 470.

31 Anon. Rubber and Plast. *Age*, **44,** Nov. 1963, p. 1361 *Plastics Today*, No. **18,** p. 14.

32 Beck, D. L., Knox, J. R. and Price, J. A. A.C.S. *"Preprint Div. Petr. Chem."*, 31 March 1963 (Los Angeles).

33 Anon. *Mod. Plastics*, Aug. 1963, p. 78.

34 Noah, H. J. *Plastics*, April 1963, p. 389.

35 Gill, D. A. *"Inst. Publ. Health Eng."*, J., LXI, part 4, Oct. 1962.

36 Muirhead, L. A. *"The New Scientist"*. (To be published.)

RUBBER AND PLASTICS MATERIALS FOR THE AEROSPACE INDUSTRIES

By A. L. SODEN, B.Sc., A.R.I.C., F.I.R.I., F.B.I.S.*

SYNOPSIS

Present-day knowledge of high polymers, as rubbers, plastics and textiles, is reviewed and qualitative and quantitative values of some properties tabulated.
The space environment is described and the major uses of these materials, as rocket fuels, as constructional materials and as thermal ablation shields dealt with in more detail.

Introduction

In a paper of this length, it is not possible to present more than a brief review of present day knowledge of high polymers—rubbers, plastics, textiles—with particular reference to their use in one of the newest of technologies, space technology. It has been said that neither the modern motor car nor the aeroplane would have been possible without rubber. Although one will not expect it to have pneumatic tyres, probably the statement is just as true about a space ship. Of recent years many applications of rubber have been replaced by plastics, and of course plastics are now used in countless applications where metals, glass, ceramics, concrete, wood and natural fibres were previously used, not only in industry and transport, but in the home, in hospitals, in sport, on the farm. It would truly be difficult to envisage a world without polymers today. Naturally, materials development does not always keep pace with requirements, and this has been shown no more clearly than in the case of rubbers and plastics to meet the rapidly developing air and near space travel since the last war. Many of the applications are already well known, and it is a matter of selecting the material, rubber or plastics, which meets the specific requirements. In other applications, the material may be exposed to normal conditions, exceedingly high temperatures and pressures, and then very low temperatures and pressures or any combination of these, in rapid succession. There may be exposure to fuels and oxidising agents, and expected lifetimes may be from a few seconds to weeks or months.

Polymers have properties often very different from the more usual constructional materials, and it is these particular properties which make polymers indispensable in certain applications. The most important special properties are the excellent thermal and electrical properties, low densities and high physical strengths, general chemical inertness and the rubbery nature of elastomers. A unique property of elastomers which would be very important in certain applications is the large change in physical properties for a small temperature change.

The more usual applications of polymers will not be described in detail in this paper. They include seals, gaskets, O-rings, pipes, electrical and thermal insulation, tank liners, adhesives, parachutes, protective clothing, printed circuits, radomes, rocket cases, pressure vessels, guide vanes, and fins. Although these applications cover a wide field, and account for a fair proportion of the total usage, it is in the more special fields, such as the use of polymers as rocket propellants, as structural materials in space, and as thermal ablation shields, that most

interest lies. These are the aspects dealt with in most detail in this paper.

What are Polymers?

The polymers that we are interested in are rubbers and plastics, the latter including materials capable of being used as textiles. They are not of course necessarily man-made, as witness natural rubber, many natural resins, cotton and wool. What is a polymer? It is simply a material based on very large molecules, each one of which is made up of a large number of a simpler unit (the monomer) repeated end to end. Thus if the simple unit is X or it may be XY, then the polymer is $(X)n$ or $(XY)n$, where n can be a large number running up to hundreds of thousands. The possibility of polymerisation may arise out of the unsaturated nature of the monomer, which has unsatisfied valency links or double bonds as the chemist calls them. Thus, the simplest of all polymers chemically, is polythene, or polyethylene. The monomer is the gas ethylene, chemically $H_2C=CH_2$. This can be made to polymerise under the action of heat and pressure to polyethylene $(-H_2C-CH_2-)n.$, or simply $(-CH_2-)n$. The material will be predominantly long chain, with a few short side chains, but randomly kinked, so that in the mass it is deformable, but with no great tendency to recovery. In other words it is a *thermoplastic*. Note that as a polymer it is fully saturated so that by and large there is no possibility of further cross-linking several molecules together. If we start off with a monomer that has two double bonds, then one of them will be used in the long chain polymerisation process, and the other can be utilised for cross-linking. Thus, butadiene $H_2C=CH-CH=CH_2$ on polymerisation, becomes

$$(-H_2C-CH=CH-CH_2-)n \text{ polybutadiene.}$$

In this condition, it is also thermoplastic, but by various treatments it can be cross linked to some extent and becomes deformable, but with a great tendency to recover its original form. It is, in fact, a *rubber* (or elastomer) and the process of cross-linking is commonly called *vulcanisation*. Polymethyl butadiene, or polyisoprene, is natural rubber. Many of the common synthetic rubbers are substituted polybutadienes. All the above are examples of *addition polymerisation*. We may also have *condensation* polymerisation in which molecules having reactive groups can condense, eliminating a simpler substance such as water. The residual product then becomes the fundamental unit in a chain molecule of high molecular weight. Most of the *rigid plastics*, such as phenol-formaldehyde, epoxy, polyesters, are of this type. When long chains can become orientated into close parallel rows, then we can have a fibre or filament which can be treated by textile processes. These are the man-made fibres, rayon, nylon, terylene, *etc.*, but other plastics can be used as textiles,

* Rubber and Plastics Research Association of Great Britain.

169

polythene, polypropylene, polyvinylidene chloride. Now that we know what polymers are, we want to consider their properties and just how far their limitations will enable them to be used in space technology.

The Rubber-like State

Rubbers have often been considered as a fourth state of matter exhibiting many of the properties of both solids and liquids. We have seen that the property of high elasticity associated with rubbers is not a special characteristic of any particular chemical type of compound, but is the result of a particular molecular structure. The molecules must be long and flexible, attached here and there by permanent cross links, but free to move past one another. Unstretched rubber is thus a tangled mass of irregular molecules which when stretched become more or less aligned in the direction of stretching, retracting when the force is removed. This ability of rubber to undergo high deformation without permanent damage, something like 1000% elongation in the case of unfilled natural rubber, is the chief difference between rubbers and metals, or other rigid materials. For metals, deformation involves changes in interatomic distances, and very large forces are necessary—so large that before deformation has reached more than a few per cent other actions take place such as slippage between adjacent crystals. Thus, there is a yield point beyond which deformation is plastic or irreversible. In addition, the stress–strain curves for rubber in extension and compression are markedly non-linear, and for compression we have a complicated pattern of stresses and strains, which has not hitherto proved predictable. The strain for a given stress, or vice versa, depends among other things on the confining surfaces, whether there is bonding or slipping, and on the shape of the piece being compressed.

Another fundamental difference between rubbers and rigid materials is that the former have a time element in their deformation phenomena. The deformation is out of phase with the stress causing it. This has two important consequences. If we select a rubber component correctly, it can be made to damp out fluctuations of stress, and this is an important application of rubber to insulate against vibration and dynamic shock. The other consequence is that part of the energy put in the deformation is permanently absorbed and converted to heat, which may be excessive and cause " blow out ".

Yet another fundamental characteristic of the rubber like state is that its behaviour depends on temperature and frequency of deformation. Rubber becomes stiff and leathery at low temperature, and also behaves as a rigid material if an attempt is made to deform it extremely quickly. Low temperature properties of most polymers can be improved by the addition of suitable plasticisers.

The effects of low temperature on rubbers are of obvious importance in astronautics. They are of three kinds— (1) simple temperature effects, due to restricted molecular movement, giving increased " logginess ", decreased resilience, increased hardness and stiffness, with quick reversal on raising the temperature, (2) crystallisation, sometimes called first order transition, accompanied by a volume change, due to the formation of an orderly lattice of molecules by aligning of polymer chains (as occurs on stretching). This phenomenon may take hours, days or weeks, but is fastest at some definite optimum temperature for each polymer. Effects are as for (1), but reversal of the process is very slow. Not all polymers crystallise. Generally, it is the linear ones, natural rubber, thiokol, neoprene, silicones, polythene, nylon, that do so, (3) vitrification or freezing, sometimes called second order transition, or glass temperature. This is characterized by a marked discontinuity in the rate of change of a property with tem-

perature and occurs over a temperature range of a few degrees. Below this glass temperature, rubber properties cease to exist and the material behaves like a rigid solid. It is interesting to note that the glass temperature for a polymer need not necessarily be a low one, and many of the polymers that are normally considered as rigid materials are simply below their glass temperatures under normal conditions. An example is polymethyl methacrylate, familiar to everyone as Perspex. Above its glass temperature of about 60°C, it exhibits definite rubbery properties, before it begins to flow as a thermoplastic at about 100°C.

The mechanical properties of rubbers can generally be increased by incorporation of a finely divided carbon black, giving ultimate tensile strengths in the intermediate range. Thus, that for a natural tyre tread rubber is about 2 ton wt in^{-2} of original cross-section (about 4 or 5 times as much expressed on breaking section), with a breaking elongation of 400–500%. There is also increase in stiffness, tear strength and abrasion resistance. Most other fillers act as inert diluents, although some can contribute special properties.

All rubbers show to a greater or lesser extent the phenomena of creep, *i.e.* slow continuous increase of deformation beyond the relatively large initial deformation that occurs when the stress is applied. This additional deformation is not recoverable when the stress is removed and gives rise to set, either from tension or compression. Of the thermal properties of rubber, conductivity is important. Thermal conductivity is very small, so that when heat is generated in rubber as a result of deformation, this is not readily dissipated and may cause failure. On the other hand, the coefficient of expansion of rubber is large, much greater than that for metals and this has to be taken into account in the moulding and vulcanisation operations.

All commercially available rubbers are organic materials which become unserviceable at temperatures much below those at which metals operate. However, the range of temperatures is being rapidly extended upwards by the development of special polymers. Thus, we have as a rough classification, 70–130°C, natural rubber, SBR, neoprenes, acrylonitriles, polyurethanes; 130–200°C, acrylic rubbers, butyl,; above 200°C, silicones, fluorinated rubbers. When tests are carried out at room temperature after exposure at high temperatures, the fluorinated hydrocarbons and fluorinated silicones are outstanding. When the tests are carried out at the ageing temperature, a different picture emerges. Silicone rubber is outstandingly better than the fluorinated rubbers in maintaining its strength measured at high temperature. At room temperature silicone has a lower strength than the others, but when measured at 200°C it is better than the fluorinated rubbers. Rubbers undergo gradual changes with the passage of time, even at room temperature. The main cause of this is oxidation which causes molecular chain scission and also further cross-linking. This effect is accelerated by heat and light, and also by the presence of oils and some heavy metal ions. A further oxidative effect is that due to ozone in the atmosphere when the rubbers are under slight strain. Cracking occurs with the long axis of the cracks all at right angles to the direction of stress. Natural, SBR and nitriles are the worst offenders; butyl, neoprene and polyurethanes being highly resistant, while silicones, fluorinated rubbers, hypalon and acrylates are practically unaffected. Most rubbers in commercial use are affected to some extent by exposure to oils and solvents. This varies to a great extent with the rubber and with the liquid, but by and large, natural rubber and the other general purpose synthetic rubbers, SBR, and butyl, are the worst, neoprenes and nitriles being considerably better, acrylates and fluorinated rubbers being best of all. For oil and solvent resistance, silicones are not outstanding, but fluorinated silicone is in the top class in this respect. As well as aliphatic and aromatic hydrocarbons, esters, hydraulic fluids, and rocket fuels and oxidants have now to be considered.

Electrical properties of rubbers vary enormously. Mostly they are electrical insulators, but can be made antistatic or dangerously conducting. It is also possible to compound rubber so that it can be picked up by a magnet and also made permanently magnetic.

Useful properties and also some limitations of the different kinds of rubbers are given in Tables I and II.[1] Approximate quantitative values for some properties are given in Table III.

TABLE I.—*Properties of Rubbers and Limitations of Use*

Type	Useful properties	Properties that limit usefulness
Natural	High resilience, tensile strength and elongation; wide hardness range; long flex life.	Moderate - to - poor heat, oil, weather and ozone resistance.
Butadiene-styrene	Better abrasion and general ageing resistance than natural rubber.	Moderate - to - poor oil, tear, weather and ozone resistance.
Butyl	High weather, ozone and acid and alkali resistance; very low permeability to gases. Good low temperature properties.	Low tensile strength and resilience; high inflammability.
Neoprene	High heat, ageing, weather and flame resistance and flex life; moderate oil and chemical resistance.	Only moderate in several important properties.
Nitrile	Moderate-to-good heat and ageing resistance; resistant to mineral oils, petroleum solvents, dilute acids and alkalis.	Relatively poor cold resistance.
Thiokol	Maximum oil and solvent resistance.	High compression set; low tensile strength, elongation and heat resistance.
Silicone	Maximum heat and cold resistance.	Low strength properties; fairly high compression set; high cost.
Hypalon	Good ageing and ozone resistance, also resistant to many chemicals including oxidisers. Compatible with other rubbers. Used for coatings. Low gas permeability.	Poor cold resistance.
Acrylates	Good heat and oil resistance; particularly sulphur - bearing oils, also to ozone and weathering.	Poor cold resistance and moist-heat resistance.
Poly-urethanes	Very high tensile strength and resistance to abrasion, tearing and ozone. Properties highest for " cast " rubbers.	Poor moist-heat resistance. Poorer properties for sulphur - vulcanisable rubbers.
Fluori-nated	Excellent resistance to heat, fuels, oils and corrosive chemicals, including oxidising acids, also to ozone and weathering.	Relatively poor cold resistance. Very high cost.
Ethylene-propylene	Good resistance to aging, ozone, low temperature.	
Butadiene	Purity, high resilience and abrasion resistance, good low temperature properties.	Deficient in tensile properties, build-up tack and ease of processing if not blended with natural rubber.

Properties of Plastics

Functionally, plastics may be divided into rigid and flexible. From their chemistry and properties they are either thermosetting or thermo-plastic, but many rigid plastics are in fact thermo-plastic. Examples are methyl methacrylate (Perspex)

polystyrene, rigid PVC. Most of the thermosetting (and some of the thermoplastics) may be reinforced with glass fibre with marked increase in strength and rigidity. Glass fibre would appear to be to plastics, what fine particle carbon black is to rubber, although the mechanism is more akin to steel reinforcement of concrete. Unfilled thermosets are comparable with woods in rigidity (about 1×10^6 lb wt in^{-2}) whereas glass laminates are about 5×10^6 lb wt in^{-2}. Glass itself is about 10 and steel about 30×10^6 lb wt in^{-2}, but in strength the glass laminates are comparable with mild steel. The low rigidity modulus may often be compensated for by corrugating, or increased thickness of material where stresses occur, thus using one outstanding property of plastics, low density, for constructional purposes. Some plastics have outstanding resistance to fatigue, such as glass reinforced epoxy and the newer polyformaldehyde. Some have low coefficient of friction and high wear resistance such as nylon, PTFE and again polyformaldehyde. A failing of many plastics is the tendency to show creep under stress, and yet another is the tendency to lose strength and toughness and to discolour on continuous exposure to sunlight. It is well known that protection against ultraviolet light can be obtained in polythene by the incorporation of a few percent of carbon black, but this also applies to many other plastics. Quite a number of plastics materials will withstand continuous service at 100–200°C. Above this temperature the field rapidly narrows. PTFE is the only thermoplastic which can be used at 250°C, and then when there are no great stresses. A few reinforced thermosets will withstand this temperature continuously, but recently it has been found that some of them, especially phenolics, can be submitted to extremely high temperatures—2000°C and beyond—for very short times without failure. This will be mentioned again later.

Some plastics are outstanding in optical transparency, such as acrylics and polystyrene and may be used among other optical applications for " light piping ".

The electrical properties of nearly all plastics are good, many outstanding, such as the exceptionally low power factors of polythene, polystyrene and PTFE. Nearly all have high electrical resistivity and many maintain their resistivity after prolonged exposure in water.

It is, of course, not possible to deal here with properties of all individual plastics, but a few remarks on some of them, particularly those which are new or of interest to us, may not be out of place. Many of the properties are given in Table IV.[1]

The best known vinyl thermoplastic is polyvinyl chloride or PVC. It is necessary to add stabilisers for protection against degradation from heat and light and it can be plasticised to a high degree of flexibility when it shows many rubbery properties. As well as ordinary ester type plasticizers which control many of the properties of this material, one can use polymeric plasticisers, and recently one has been built in to the molecule, thus eliminating the problems involved in loss by extraction or volatilisation. In the unplasticised state, PVC has high impact strength and chemical inertness and is among the best of the thermoplastics in tensile, abrasion resistance and resistance to heat distortion. Its electrical and ageing properties are excellent, and it will not support combustion. PVF, polyvinyl fluoride, has just appeared and is now promised in bulk. It has extreme toughness and durability, resistance to weathering and chemicals and to abrasion, scuffing, staining and soiling, with high electrical properties.

Polyethylene, or polythene, is too well known to say much about, except that it is now obtainable in low, intermediate and high densities. Stiffness, strength and temperature resistance improve in that order. The high density material is now made continuously at atmospheric pressure using catalysts, resulting in more nearly linear polymers. These advances brought about the commercial use of polypropylene, pre-

TABLE II.—*Qualitative Properties of Rubbers*

	Natural	Butadiene Styrene	Butyl	Neoprene	Nitrile	Thiokol	Silicone	Hypalon	Acrylate	Polyurethane	Fluorinated
Elasticity	H	H	FL	M	M	L	FL	H	M	M	M
Resistance to compressive set	FH	FH	M	FH	M–FH	L	M	M	FH	M	M–FH
Tear strength	FH	M	M	H	M	L	L	M	M	VH	M
Abrasion resistance	H	H	M	H	M	L	L	H	M	VH	M
Resilience, cold	H	M	M	H	M	L	L	FH	L	FL	L
Resilience, hot	H	M	L	HF	M	L–M	H	H	H	FL	M
Heat resistance	FL	FL	M	FH	M–FH	L	VH	FH	H	FH	VH
Cold resistance	H	H	H	FH	L–M	FH	VH	M	FL	M	FL
Ageing resistance, general	M	M–FH	H	H	H	H	H	VH	VH	H	VH
Resistance to sunlight	L	L	H	H	M	M	H	H	H	H	H
Resistance to ozone	M	L–M	M–H	FH–H	L–M	H	H	H	VH	VH	VH
Resistance to flame	L	L	L	H	L–M	L	H	H	L	FH	VH
Resistance to fuels (aliphatic)	L	L	L	M–H	H	H	L	M	FH	FH	VH
Resistance to fuels (aromatic)	L	L	L	L	M	H	L	M	FH	M	VH
Resistance to mineral oils	L	L	L	M	M–H	H	L	M	H	FH	VH
Resistance to animal and vegetable oils	L–M	L–M	H	M–H	H	H	L–M	M	H	M	H
Resistance to water	H	M–H	FH–H	M	M	M	M	H	M	FL	H
Electrical resistivity	H	H	H	M	M	M	H	M		M	H
Electrical power loss	L	L	L	M	FH	FH	L	M		M	M
Electrical breakdown strength	H	H	H	M	M	M	H	M		FH	H
Adhesion to metals	H	H	M	H	H	L	M			FH	
Adhesion to fabrics	H	FH	FH	H	FH	L	M			FH	

VH = very high   M = medium   FL = fairly low
H = high   L = low
FH = fairly high   VL = very low.

viously known, but now in the new " stereo specific " form exhibiting a set of interesting properties. It has a higher melting point than any polythene, higher strength and toughness, a hard and good surface finish with abrasion resistance and coefficient of friction similar to that of nylon, so that it can be used for unlubricated gears and bearings. It is susceptible to oxidation by heat and ultraviolet light, as polythene, but in chemical and electrical properties it is excellent.

Nylon, familiar a few years ago only in ladies stockings, is, of course, now an engineering material of wide uses. Its excellent properties include strength and toughness, high temperature and chemical resistance, abrasion resistance and low coefficient of friction and excellent electrical properties. These, coupled with the fact that small accurate mouldings can be obtained, allow nylon to be used for unlubricated

gears, bushes, chains, cams, door closing mechanisms and also such things as miniature coil bobbins and screws.

Polytetrafluorethylene, PTFE, resembles polythene in appearance. It has a much wider working temperature range than any other plastics material (-100 to $+250°$C). It is non-inflammable and has extreme resistance to chemical attack. No solvent for it is known and only fluorine and molten alkali metals attack it. It is unaffected by any weathering and water absorption is zero. It has an extremely low coefficient of friction, that between two pieces of the material being equal to that between two pieces of wet ice. All these properties are somewhat less in PCTFE polychlorotrifluorethylene. Plastics completely new in the last few years, include polyformaldehyde and polycarbonates. The former is one of the strongest and stiffest of the thermoplastics. It has good strength retention at elevated temperatures and its

TABLE III.—*Properties of Polymers (Rubbers)*

Polymer	Density of raw polymer (g cm^{-3})	Second order transition temperature, (°C)	Brittle Point, (°C)	Ultimate tensile strength (lb wt in^{-4})	Thermal conductivity, (cal cm^{-1} s^{-1} (°C$^{-1} \times 10^{-4}$))	Maximum service temperature for long life, (°C)	Effect of high energy irradiation
Natural Rubber	0·93	−72 to −78	∼−75	4500	3·5–4·5	70	cross-link
Synthetic Polysioprene	0·92	−60	∼−60	4500		70	cross-link
SBR (23% styrene)	0·94	−62	∼−62	4000	4·5–5·5	100	cross-link*
NBR (30% nitrile)	1·00	−41	−10 to −20	3000	5·0–5·5	125	cross-link
Butyl	0·92	−75 to −80	−78	3000	∼4·5	150	degrade
Neoprene	1·23	−50	−10 to −60	4000	4·5–5·0	125	cross-link
Hypalon	1·10	−15	∼−50	2000		125	
Silicone Rubber	0·97	−118 to −128	−65 to −110	1500	3·5	200	cross-link
Fluoro-Silicone Rubber	1·4	−60	−75	1000		200	degrade
Polysulphides	1·25–1·34	−40 to −60	−15 to −50	1000		100	cross-link*
Acrylic Ester Rubber	1·09	−10	−20	1500		150	cross-link
Kel-F Elastomer or Viton	1·85	−16	−50	4000	1·5	200	degrade
Poly FBA	1·5	−10	−12	3000		200	degrade
Polyurethane Elastomer	1·25	−30 to −50	−45 to −50	6000	3–4	125	

* some resistance.

TABLE IV.—*Properties of Polymers (Plastics)*

Polymer	Density (g cm⁻³)	Second order transition temperature (°C)	Burning rate	Ultimate tensile strength (lb wt in⁻²)	Impact strength (ft lb in⁻¹)	Thermal conductivity (cal cm⁻¹ s⁻¹ °C⁻¹ ×10⁻⁴)	Maximum service temperature for long life (°C)	Effect of high energy irradiation
Polyethylene	0·91–0·96	−68	slow	1500– 5 500	2–20	7·5–8·0	90	cross-link
Polypropylene	0·9 –0·91	−35	slow	3000– 6 000	1	3·3	150	degrade
Nylon	1·09–1·14	47	very slow	7000– 20 000	2–4	~6	140	degrade
Terylene	1·38–1·40	70 to 80	slow	7000– 20 000		~5	140	degrade
Poly(methyl methacrylate)	1·17–1·20	60	slow	8000– 11 000	0·5	3·5–5·0	55	degrade
Cellulose Nitrate	1·35–1·60	66	very slow	7000– 8 000	6	3–5	55	degrade
Cellulose Acetate	1·28–1·34	69	slow	1900– 11 000	2–3	4·5–7·5	55	degrade
Cellulose Acetate-Butyrate	1·15–1·25		slow	2600– 6 900	1–4	4–8	55	degrade
Polyvinyl	1·16–1·17	+10 to −60	nil	1000– 9 000	15	3–4	60–120	degrade
Polyvinyl Acetate	1·17–1·20	28	very slow	1000– 5 000		~4		cross-link
Phenol-Formaldehyde	1·25–2·0	~75	slow	3000– 10 000	1	3–15	120*	variable
Urea-Formaldehyde	1·47–1·52		slow	6000– 13 000	0·3	~10	80	
Melamine-Formaldehyde	1·47–2·0		nil	4000– 13 000	0·5	~7·5	130	
Alkyds	1·8 –2·22	~85		3500– 7 000	0·3	5	150	
Polystryrene	1·04–1·33	81	slow	5000– 15 000	1–10	2	80	cross-link
Epoxy	1·11–1·23		slow	4000– 13 000	1–10	4	110–180	
PTFE	2·1 –2·2	−70 to −100	nil	1500– 3 000	4	6	230–300	degrade
PCTFE	2·1		nil	~5 000	3·6	6	200	degrade
Silicone	1·6 –2·0	−65 to −110	very slow	2500– 5 000		3–4	150–260	cross-link
Laminated Polyesters	1·2 –1·3	~85		8000–150 000	up to 20	5	60–100	
Ebonite	1·14–1·82	−82	slow	1000– 6 000	0·5	3·7–4·4	~60	
Polycarbonate	1·2	140	very slow	~10 000	12	4·6	135	
Acetal	1·42		very slow	10 000	1–2	6	150	

* heat-resistant, mineral-filled, 200°C.

impact strength is unaffected over the range −100°C to 100°C. It is better than other thermoplastics in resistance to creep and has a steel-like recovery with high fatigue resistance. There are no common solvents at room temperature and its abrasion resistance and coefficient of friction approach those of nylon. Polycarbonates are characterised by extreme toughness and flexibility with good impact strength at low temperatures. Even at the temperature of liquid air, they do not break with the brittleness of glass. Mechanical properties are little affected by temperatures up to about 130°C or by the small water absorption. They show excellent weather resistance and may be sterilised in steam at 120°C. Two types of resins which are of interest because of their ability to be polymerised *in situ* are the epoxies and unsaturated polyesters. These are familiar in the do-it-yourself repair kits for cars and boats, usually in conjunction with glass fibre reinforcement. The monomers are liquids and cure either by catalysts or by hardeners which react to become part of the final polymer with no residual by-products. Thus the cure can take place with or without pressure, and at room temperature, although a high temperature post-cure is necessary to develop the ultimate in properties. For adhesion between metals, plastics, glass, wood, rubber and ceramics, epoxies are unsurpassed. Both types of resins are used for coatings, laminates and casting using as reinforcing materials glass, asbestos, cotton, paper, synthetic fibres, metal foils. The casting and repairing technique has obvious uses in space, although one would have to remember the good old chemical rule that rates of reaction are approximately halved for every 10°C decrease in temperature! Again, both types of resins show excellent heat and chemical resistance and have good electrical properties.

It has already been said that textile materials are high polymers. They will, of course, be used in space, as clothing, space suits, parachutes and harness, ropes, safety equipment. A comparison of properties of some of the man-made fibres with natural ones and other materials is given in Table V.[1]

Most rubbers and plastics can be expanded or foamed with either closed or open cell structure, their normally low thermal conductivity then decreasing to a very low value. Flexible foams typified by natural rubber latex, polyurethane and PVC, are used for cushioning in upholstery and packing, toys and novelties, carpet underlay, linings for clothing and heat and sound insulators. Rigid foams, such as ebonite, polystyrene, cellulose acetate, polythene, have a number of uses, chief of which is in refrigeration or low temperature storage. Others include packings, pipe lagging and light weight sandwich laminates. There will obviously be many applications of both rigid and flexible foams in space.

TABLE V.—*Properties of Polymers (Fibres)*

	Density g cm⁻³	Moisture regain (%)	Tenacity (g/denier)	Modulus (g/den/unit strain)	Melting Point (°C)	Abrasion resistance
Steel	7·7	0	5·5	280	~1450	good
Glass	2·56	0	6–7	307	~800	poor
Manila	1·48	8	4	250	140	fair
Cotton	1·52	8·5	3	66	150	fair
Flax	1·50	12	4	200	140	fair
Rayon	1·52	13	3·5–5·5	75–175	180–200	fair
Terylene	1·38	0·4	6 –7·5	130	264	very good
Nylon	1·14	4·2	7 –8·8	45	264	excellent
HD Polythene	0·95	0	4·5–6	30	135	good
Polypropylene	0·92	0	8·5–9	70–80	165	good

Inorganic Polymers

No other element has the ability to the same extent as carbon of joining on almost endlessly in chains capable of forming cross-links. This is why we have an organic chemistry. However, other elements can be built into long chain molecules, but with one exception research has hardly passed the academic stage. The search for inorganic polymers has been caused by the requirement for extreme high temperature resistance, and nowhere has this become more urgent than in the field of missiles and rocketry. Best known amongst these materials are the silicones based on a silicon–oxygen backbone chain, not silicon–silicon, and a flourishing industry has grown up on these materials over the last 15 years or so. They range from liquids, high boiling, low vapour pressure and surface tension, very small temperature coefficient of viscosity; through greases, stable over the range $-50°C$ to over $200°C$ without melting; rubbers, flexible over the range $-70°C$ to $+250°C$; to resins, hard infusible films and coatings. General properties include outstanding thermal stability and high water repellence. Other systems referred to above have backbone structures based on phosphorus–nitrogen, phosphorus–oxygen, aluminium–oxygen, boron–phosphorus, boron–oxygen, and also with alternate silicon atoms of the silicones replaced by other metals. Difficulties encountered with these polymers include their tendency to form cyclic structures, their proneness to depolymerise when the temperature is raised, and their susceptibility to hydrolysis.

The Space Environment

Now that we know something about polymers, we must see how they fit in with the space environment.

It has already been said that great variations in temperatures and pressures are likely to be encountered. Besides temperature variation with time, there may be a differential of $200°C$ or more, between adjoining surfaces exposed to sunlight and shadow. What makes the space environment really different to any other we know, is the presence of hard vacuum, or to put it more correctly the absence of matter, at a distance of a few thousand miles from the surface of the earth, a better vacuum than can be produced in the laboratory on earth. This causes some unusual things to happen. Materials will " outgas ", or lose any adsorbed gases, with possible surface damage. Evaporation of metal surfaces far below their melting points, could be appreciable.

Sliding friction between metals may become very high, doubtless due to the absence of sufficient oxygen to renew ruptured oxide films and thus to prevent cold welding of the metal surfaces. Conventional lubricating oils would evaporate too quickly to be of use and graphite acts as a lubricant only when it has an adsorbed surface film of moisture. Dry non-volatile lubricants such as molybdenum disulphide would be alright, but plastics, particularly PTFE, nylon, polyformaldehyde, may come into their own here.

Bombardment by meteorites or micro meteorites is largely an unknown quantity. The risk does not appear to be large—the probability of impact from various size particles has been calculated and of course we already have some data from satellite detector counters—but these particles can have velocities of up to 50 mile/sec and such impacts cannot be reproduced under test conditions. It is known that at lower speed impacts, metals form cavities and then puncture as a consequence of high speed plastic flow, whereas plastics and other non-metals show a crushing and breaking up of the material, often with deep radiating cracks. Abrasion by cosmic dust may be an important factor in some instances, causing skin roughening and consequent change in emissivity, or where optical properties are important.

As well as infrared and ultraviolet there will be other energetic radiations in space, cosmic and X-rays, protons and electrons, which may have cross-linking or degrading effects on polymers. Presumably rubbers would be free from ozone attack in space, but some exaggerated form of light ageing might be found.

Polymers as Fuels

Prior to the last war and the liquid fuelled V-2, solid propellant rockets were very inefficient and it was considered at that time that they had little future compared with liquid fuels. The position is now very different, and although they do not have the punch of liquid fuels, the use of polymers as fuels in solid propellant rockets is in the U.S.A. at least, a vast industry to the tune of hundreds of millions of dollars annually. Technically it represents the greatest advance yet made in solid propellant technology. Their advantages spring from the fact that not only are they of higher energy than the older solid propellants based on, for example, asphalt, but that they can be cross-linked or polymerised *in situ*, giving good bonding to the case wall and high structural strength and integrity, with burning in a controlled and reproducible manner. They thus fulfil the dual role of fuel and binder for the oxidiser. Many polymers have been used successfully as fuels: polysulphides, polyurethanes, polybutadienes and poly*iso*butylene to mention a few. The propellants are made by mixing the finely divided oxidiser such as ammonium perchlorate or nitrate with the polymer using fairly standard techniques. The resulting dough is poured or extruded into the rocket case and cured in ovens. A limitation to the size of these units is imposed by transportation problems rather than any intrinsic difficulty in their manufacture, although a possibility exists of internal cracks or voids giving the risk of premature explosion. Such a motor would be unusable and there would also be the problem of disposing of several tons of unwanted fuel. Techniques of parallel or segmented motors are being developed to overcome these problems. An interesting example of this is the boosting of the Titan II missile, a storable liquid fuel rocket of about half a million pounds thrust by two strap-on solid rockets, each almost as big as Titan itself and each adding about a million pounds of thrust. The composite vehicle Titan III is scheduled for the military Dynasoar program (if it is not finally scrapped) and also for the later stages of the civilian Gemini program.

It is interesting to consider briefly the reason for this use of polymers. Other things being equal, the thrust developed by a fuel increases with the heat of combustion Q of the fuel and decreases with increase in molecular weight M of the gaseous products. It is actually proportional to the ratio $(Q/M)^{\frac{1}{2}}$. Thus a good fuel has a high Q/M ratio. If the values of Q for the elements are plotted against their molecular weights, they lie on a rapidly dying away curve so that Q/M is highest, but rapidly decreasing, through the elements hydrogen, helium, lithium, beryllium, boron, carbon, nitrogen, oxygen, fluorine. Since polymers consist mainly of hydrogen and carbon, they are favourably placed and should make good fuels, particularly if the ratio of hydrogen to carbon is high and there is a minimum of heavier elements such as sulphur. Approximate heats of combustion of various materials used, or usable, as fuels are given in Table VI, where it will be seen that polymers compare well with other materials. Some of the more " exotic " fuels containing beryllium and boron, are in this group and of course nitrogen compounds such as ammonia and hydrazine are used as liquid fuels. Recent work suggests that castable fluorinated polymers will make even more energetic fuels. Fluorine is in the group mentioned and can act as both fuel and oxidiser.

TABLE VI—*Heats of Combustion*

Material	Approx. heat of combustion B.t.u./lb $\times 10^3$
Hydrogen	50
Boron	25
Diborane	32
Lithium hydride	18
Natural Rubber	19
SBR	19
Polyethylene	20
Poly*iso*butylene	20
Polystyrene	18
Paraffin	18
Asphalt	17
Alcohol	11
Hydrazine	8
Sulphur	4

Polymers as Structural Materials

Other applications of polymers in space are as structural materials. One of the most recent and most interesting continues the story of large booster rockets. It is that of rocket cases made by filament winding. In this process, fibres of extreme finesness are stranded together and wound round a mandrel after passing through an epoxy resin bath. After cure the mandrel is removed. Parts made in this way are lighter and stronger than steel and cheaper to produce than their equivalents in aluminium or titanium. This process is already consuming vast quantities of glass. The second stage of the Polaris missile has some 270 000 miles of glass roving—sufficient to stretch from the earth to the moon. The latest 156 in. diameter glass fibre case made by United Technology Centre in U.S.A., the largest yet produced, has enough glass filament " to reach from the earth to the sun and back twice—over 372 million miles ". This type of construction will probably remove the size and power restrictions mentioned earlier. Pre-shaped solid propellant sections can be assembled, wound with treated glass fibres and finally encased in an epoxy glass layer and cured *in situ*.

A whole series of possible applications depend on a property which is normally considered a shortcoming of polymers, particularly rubbers. This is the temperature dependence of their physical properties and particularly the the fact that those which are not rigid normally, become so below specific temperatures, losing all their rubbery nature, as explained above. It is feasible that massive structures could be built in space using polymers that are flexible at room temperature but become rigid at the temperatures attained in space. Such structures could be folded in a small volume on the rocket and then expanded by gas pressure when in space. After a short time the structure might attain an equilibrium temperature low enough to make it rigid.

There are two important factors governing this use of polymers. The first is the physical properties of the flexible polymers below their glass temperatures. They are hard and rigid, but often brittle as well. There is little published information on this aspect of polymer properties because of the limitation of interest hitherto. Most development work in the field of improving the physical properties has been in the direction of preventing the polymer losing its elasticity at low temperatures rather than the reverse and the fact that rubbers go hard at low temperatures is usually regarded as a disadvantage. The second factor is whether sufficiently low equilibrium temperatures can be achieved in space. This will depend on the distance from the sun and on the surface finish and can be calculated, at least approximately. The result comes out that at the distance of Mars, the next planet out-

wards from the sun, there would be no doubt of the necessary low temperatures. At the distance of the earth, however, equilibrium temperatures would be above 0°C unless special shading were provided. It is possible to vary the surface colour of most polymers by the use of pigments or fillers or by metallising, thus altering the absorptive and emissive powers, without any great effect on the physical properties. In this way about 100°C variation is possible in the equilibrium temperature between say a black body and a polished silver sphere at the same point in space.

The pressurisation technique was used for the Echo I balloon satellite, launched in August 1960 and still up—a 136 lb, 100 ft diameter sphere of aluminised polyester film some 2 thou. thick. The technique could be extended to other massive structures. An orbiting space station in the form of a large wheel or doughnut so that earth gravity could be simulated in the revolving rim, has often been suggested right from the days of the early dreamers. Made initially of rubberised fabric, inflated and rigidised, it would be much easier to construct than any other form of structure. An earth mock-up of this has actually been constructed by Goodyear in America. The material consists essentially of a two-ply separated construction, held together by interconnecting threads, shapes and profiles being obtained by altering the length of threads. Rigidisation could be aided by the injection of a self-setting plastics material. Such a structure would then be comparable in many respects to a metal one. The saving in payload space would be enormous since not only would it be packed initially into a small volume, but the whole structure could be placed into orbit in a single operation. Hollow structures such as tanks could easily be expanded, whilst open structures could be constructed from polymer piping which would freeze into rigid struts and girders. Other methods to aid rigidisation include foaming *in situ*, either by conventional methods, by micro encapsulation where the reacting liquids are made in the form of thin capsules attached to the surface of the inflatable structure, or by a type of compound, inert under ordinary conditions, but foaming in a vacuum without a blowing agent, simply by the vapour pressure of the ingredients.

There will be many other uses of rubberised fabrics in space not in the rigidised condition. A large inflatable specially shaped balloon known as a Rogallo wing is to be used in place of the large parachute for the landing of the Gemini and Apollo spacecraft on dry land rather than on the sea. Although space ships will not require wheels and tyres in the accepted sense, these will be wanted on vehicles for exploration of the moon's surface, but with rather unusual requirements. Large boulders, cracks and crevasses in the surface, deep layers of dust, sloping crater walls, all must be negotiated. One answer to this and the severe N.A.S.A. weight limitation to 125 lb each, is a rubberised fabric doughnut, 16 ft in diameter and 4 ft wide, supported on a reinforced plastics hub by polyester cord spokes. Pressurised to about $\frac{1}{2}$ lb/in^2, two of these tyres will carry the 2400 earth pounds (400 moon pounds) vehicle. Again, they can be deflated for carriage from earth and for storage during the long moon night. Heavy rubber fabric was used in the Mercury capsule as a cylindrical collapsed bag between the base of the capsule and the detachable heat shield. The bag could be deployed for absorbing some of the final shock on impact with the water.

Uses for foams in space, other than as aids to rigidisation mentioned above, include the encapsulation of electronics and anti-g couches. An example of the first is Telstar, where the electronics are sealed in a 20 in. aluminium canister suspended inside the 34 in. satellite using nylon lacings. The astronaut's anti-g couch in the Mercury capsule is of reinforced plastics on an aluminium honeycomb structure, moulded to the contours of the individual, and lined with polyurethane high hysteresis-loss foam. The occupant sinks deeply into the couch during take off and re-entry, but must not revert too quickly to the undeformed shape as the acceleration ceases, as this would lead to vibration.

An application that is fundamental to space missions is the protective space suit. On earth, nearly all protective clothing is made from polymeric materials, aprons, suits, boots and gloves. All of these have to be flexible and polymers are about the only materials that can be used either in the solid form or in conjunction with fabrics. In the protective space suit the requirements are that the material be flexible, impermeable to air, and the suit not too difficult to work in or get on and off. In the extreme case it must be capable of preserving the space ship environment when the occupant ventures outside into the extremes of temperature, and almost perfect vacuum, and presence of possibly dangerous radiations. If possible it should be capable of giving him some support against the high-g forces during take-off and return to the earth. The requirement that the suit must be capable of being worked in, is perhaps the most difficult of all, since it would be all too easy to wrap the occupant up so that he could do nothing but stay put. The answer to all these problems is a multipiece suit, an outer protective layer, over a gas retaining layer and inside an undergarment with built-in small bore tubes through which can be supplied conditioned air to the correct areas of the body. Even the relatively simple suits that the astronauts are now wearing are masterpieces of tailoring and engineering skills. A fair size book could be written entirely about space suits. The four basic components, body, helmet, boots and gloves have each been modified hundreds of times and natural and synthetic fibres, natural and synthetic rubbers, thermoplasts and thermosets are all used in their manufacture. Much more sophisticated space armour may be necessary for some missions on alien bodies and these will offer immense scope for the use of man-made polymers.

Polymers as Ablation Materials

Of all the problems of space flight, probably the most serious is that of bringing back a vehicle and its occupant from orbit round the earth without the heat generated by the enormous speed of re-entry into the upper layers of the atmosphere, raising the temperature of the body to incandescence. One way of dealing with this heat is to provide a shield of a sufficient mass of material to absorb it—a heat sink. Metals take large quantities of heat to raise them to their melting points, but they are also good thermal conductors and would not shield the interior of the vessel from the high temperatures reached on the surface. Graphite would be useless for the same reason. The heat must be used up in large quantities at or near the exterior surface. The quartz like refractories are very good but difficult to fashion into shields. Organic polymers are poor conductors of heat, and fortunately, at least in this context, thermally degrade at very high temperatures and can absorb very large quantities of heat in doing so. This is the thermal ablation process, involving the transformation of the solid into a gaseous phase, preferably through a liquid or melt stage, so that the exposed surface of the shield erodes away slowly, getting rid of the heat as it does so. Glass or silica reinforced phenolformaldehyde or melamine plastics

seem to be one of the best systems. This ablation process takes place by the melting of the glass laminate on the surface and the pyrolysis of the polymer. Gaseous decomposition products are blown through the melting surface and a solid residue in the form of a heterogeneous carbonaceous structure is the final result.

That this kind of system is effective, is witnessed by the safe return to date of 20 astronauts, 9 American and 11 Russian, from space, not to mention a number of dogs, monkeys, and a mechanical crewman simulator, who incidentally was probably largely polymeric in nature. It may be recalled that during Col. John Glenn's historic return, a ground received signal suggested that his heat shield might have slipped and he was told not to jetison his retropack in the hope that this might help. The signal was a false one however and everything went off as planned. A painting, vetted for scientific accuracy by N.A.S.A. scientists and by Glenn himself, as to what the re-entry must have looked like from space, was published by the National Geographic Society.[2] It shows flaming pieces of the retropack streaming past Glenn's window and the heat shield boiling away as planned. Converging gases form a golden ball at the rear—" a real fireball outside " as Glenn calmly records. Less than a foot ahead of the capsule, the shock wave glows at a temperature of many thousands of degrees centigrade, far hotter than the temperature of the sun's surface. In our present knowledge, this and similar flights could not have been made without polymers.

Conclusion—The Future

What can we say of the future as far as the use of polymers is concerned. The practice of astronautics, if not the theory, is younger than either the rubber or plastics industries and has therefore used these materials right from the start, absorbing new ones as they come along. Among many schemes and designs for interplanetary trips, is one over 12 years old and still right up to date, of passenger and cargo ships for a 50 man expedition to the moon, a serious worked-out-to-the-last-detail study of how it might be done, taking off from an earth orbiting space station. Even at that time, before the new technique of filament winding and many new materials since, it was thought that much of the structure would be in plastics —they do not have to stand up to the high g-values and temperatures on starting from and returning to the earth. It was suggested then that such a trip would be possible in 25 years, certainly by the end of the century. There seems no reason for any less optimistic estimate now. The biggest problem then was finance. It still is, but apart from some unforeseen circumstance, man is now committed to space travel, and just as it is almost impossible to conceive of our earthly domain of land, sea, air without man-made polymers, so it will be in his newest dimension, space.

References

[1] "Materials in Space Technology." Ch. 8, (Iliffe).
[2] National Geographic, 1962, **121**, 6, 814.

CELLULAR RUBBERS AS ENGINEERING MATERIALS

By E. E. GUNN*

SYNOPSIS

The precise use of cellular elastic materials has been studied for engineering applications involving support and maintenance of compressive stresses in constrained conditions, and as differential thermal expansion mattresses where the nominal constraint may be increased or decreased, depending on the ambient thermal condition.

Empirical relationships have been obtained relating the applied stress and deformation in compression to the volume fraction of rubber in the cellular matrix and the Young's modulus of the base rubber for a wide range of densities.

The effects of cell size and ratio of " open " and " closed " cells in the cellular structure are also discussed as important factors for design consideration, in relation to stress-strain behaviour and long-term properties, such as stress-relaxation, creep, and rate of recovery.

THE use of cellular rubber cushions in engineering and packaging applications involving the support and maintenance of compressive stresses or the ability to take up differential strains requires a detailed knowledge of the behaviour of cellular elastic materials. Obviously, it would be desirable, from the design point of view, to be able to calculate and predict from known changes in strain or the maximum or minimum stress levels the necessary material parameters so that rational usage of the cushioning material is possible, with particular regard to its efficiency and the damage threshold of the packaged components. Unfortunately, this is not possible at the moment, except for some simple cases, because of the complicated behaviour of cellular materials with respect to time and temperature.

Generally, cellular structures of the type considered cover a wide spectrum of complex heterogeneous systems from a disperse gaseous phase in a continuous polymer matrix, that is, " closed cell " structures, to a dual phase system in which both the gas and the polymer are continuous phases. These latter are termed " open cell " structures. Obviously, the system in which all or the majority of the gas voids are discrete would be expected to behave quite differently, with respect to time and temperature, to that system in which the gas phase is essentially continuous. For the purpose of definition, the continuous polymer phase is considered as a homogeneous phase, although in practice this may not necessarily be the case.

In defining the cellular system it becomes clear that a number of parameters will be expected to influence the ultimate properties and behaviour of the system. Among the more important of these parameters can be listed the following:

(1) Constitution of the continuous polymer matrix.

(2) The volume fraction of cells in the polymer matrix and the physical distribution.

(3) Cell size and cell size distribution.

(4) Cell shape.

(5) Degree of orientation.

(6) Relative proportions of discrete and continuous gas phase in the whole system.

It is not proposed, in this paper, to deal with the constitution of the polymer phase, since the choice of polymer will be determined to some extent by the technology of manufacture

and, more especially, by the general conditions of the service environment, such as extremes of temperature, long-term behaviour, and resistance to ageing, chemicals, oils, and general compatibility, etc. However, it is proposed to deal with various aspects of the geometry of the gaseous phase which are liable to affect all polymers in much the same way, more particularly the marked dependence of the load/deflection characteristics on the density or volume fraction of cells, the effect of cell size, and the way in which the relative proportion of discrete cells in the gas phase affects the visco-elastic behaviour of the cellular material and its responses to time and temperature changes.

Load-deformation Characteristics

Despite the widespread application of cellular rubbers, little or no data have been reported on the relationship between the load/deformation characteristics and density, apart from the work of Talalay[1] (1954) and Gent and Thomas[2] (1959) on latex foam structures. Theoretical equations have been derived by Gent and Thomas to describe the mechanics of deformation, based on a simple model consisting of a lattice of thin struts which buckle and collapse under compression. The equations are given in terms of the Young's modulus of the matrix, the density, and an unknown function of the compressive strain. A comparison of experimental data with the theory was shown to give satisfactory agreement over a range of densities. The model described by Gent and Thomas approximates very closely to the structure produced by low-density polyurethane foams as shown in Fig. 1 and although the structure of latex foams is not so regular or well defined, the agreement between experiment and theory indicates that the mode of deformation and the basic concept of the special structure is correct.

The present simple and somewhat empirical contribution has arisen from accumulated experimental data on a variety of non-latex cellular rubbers, prepared by the expansion of the polymer phase by the following methods:

(1) Thermal decomposition of chemical blowing agents.

(2) Gas generation by reactive end-groups during the formation of the rubbery phase from low molecular weight liquids.

(3) Incorporation and subsequent removal of temporary fillers.

* Atomic Weapons Research Establishment, U.K.A.E.A., Aldermaston, Berks.

177

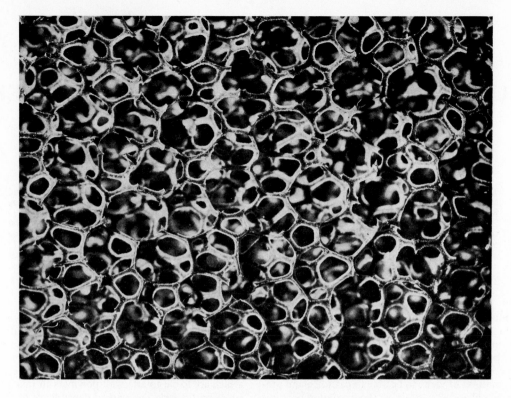

Fig. I.—*Low density polyurethane foam showing well defined fibrilar structure*

Fig. 2.—*Cellular rubber with spherical cell shape*

Fig. 3.—*Cellular rubber with irregular cell shape*

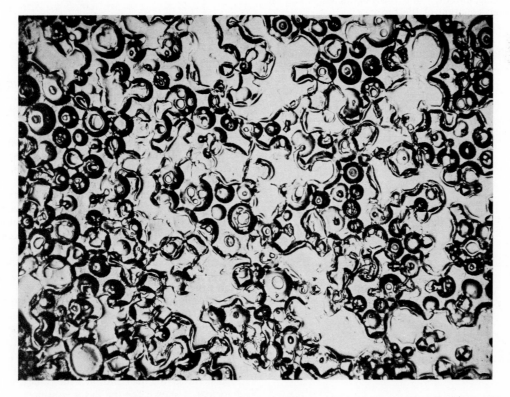

Fig. 4.—*Low density foam (0·2 g cm⁻³) showing transition from spherical to polyhedron cells*

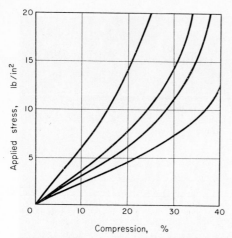

Fig. 5.—*Typical load/deflection curves for cellular rubber structures*

The range of density covered by the cellular rubbers was 0.2–0.7 g cm^{-3} and their structures were those in which the fibrilar structure as identified above in Fig. 1 was largely absent and in which the cells had a more spherical or irregular shape as shown in Figs 2 and 3. It is of interest to note that the formation of the fibrilar, polyhedral structure shown in Fig. 1 does not occur to any great extent until the polymer has been expanded to densities of 0.2 g cm^{-3} or less. Fig. 4 shows photographs of the change in shape of the cells as the density is reduced.

It has been found that the load/deformation curves of cellular rubbers, as typified by Fig. 5, can be reduced to approximately linear form over almost the whole range of compressive strains identifiable with the collapse of the cellular structure, by plotting the applied stress, S, against a function of the deformation equal to $(d^{-2}-d)$, in which d is the relative height of the deformed matrix. Typical plots are shown in Fig. 6, and the whole form of the curve can be represented by an equation of the form:

$$S = A(d^{-2}-d) \quad . \quad . \quad . \quad (1)$$

in which A is the slope of the linear curve and represents the apparent modulus of compression of the cellular structure.

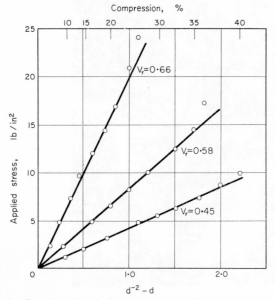

Fig. 6.—*Experimental relation between the applied stress, S, and the strain function* $(d^{-2}-d)$

Further, the apparent modulus A of the cellular matrix is related to the density, D, in g cm^{-3}, by the simple power relationship:

$$A = GD^n \quad . \quad . \quad . \quad (2)$$

where G is the shear modulus of the bulk polymer from which cellular structure has been formed, and n is a constant.

A more general form of equation (2) which has been found to be applicable to a range of base polymers of different density is given by:

$$A = GV_r^n \quad . \quad . \quad . \quad (3)$$

in which V_r is the volume fraction of polymer in the cellular structure:

$$V_r = D/\rho$$

where D and ρ are the densities of the foam and the base polymer respectively.

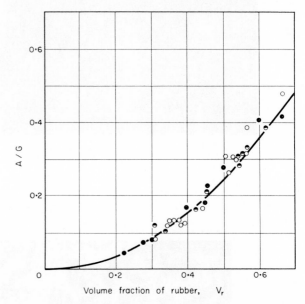

Fig. 7.—*Relationship between the reduced modulus, A/G and the volume fraction of rubber, V_r. Full line given by equation 3, putting n = 2.0*

Equation (3) is of the same form as that derived by Gent and Thomas for latex foams in small tensile strain, and also similar to those proposed by Madge (1961)[3] and Talalay also for latex foams.

Fig. 7 shows the reduced modulus A/G plotted against the volume fraction of rubber for a number of cellular rubbers produced from different base rubbers. The full line is represented by equation (3) in which n has been given the value 2. Some spread of the data for the higher volume fractions of rubber is observed and is probably due to the difficulty of controlling the relative proportion of open and closed cells in the structures.

By combining equations (1) and (3) it is now possible to calculate density, modulus, or load/deflection requirements for simple shapes. Fig. 8 shows experimental relationships for several cellular rubbers of different density: the full curves having been calculated from equations (1) and (3), inserting known values for the density and shear modulus of the bulk rubbers, and giving the constant n the value 2.0. Satisfactory agreement is shown for the cases considered, indicating the usefulness of the simple treatment for general design purposes.

Effect of Cell Size on Compression Modulus

In order to be able to study the effect of cell size on the load/deflection behaviour it was necessary, firstly, to be able to produce structures in which cell size and cell size distribution could be controlled within close limits. This can be conveniently done by the use of a temporary filler in which the filler is mixed into the polymer phase, the polymer set or vulcanized and the filler subsequently removed, Fig. 9 shows the apparent modulus of compression of a series of cellular rubbers prepared by this technique, plotted against the reciprocal of the mean cell diameter for structures of different density. The lowest density material was produced from a self-foaming silicone polymer in which the mean cell size was controlled by varying the conditions of foaming. It can be seen that the effect of increasing the average cell size is to lower the apparent compressive modulus. Clearly, the effect is more pronounced for low-volume fractions of cells (*i.e.* higher density materials) than it is for the high-volume fractions. This must presumably be due to the ease with which buckling of the cell walls occurs. However, for the same geometrical shape, decreasing cell size increases the total

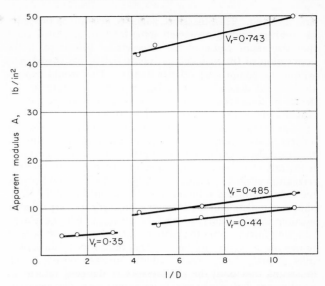

Fig. 9.—*Relationship between the apparent modulus A, and the reciprocal of the mean cell diameter, D (mm) for foams of different density*

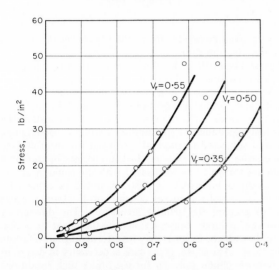

Fig. 8.—*Compression stress–strain curves for cellular rubbers. Full lines calculated from equations (1) and (3)*

number of cells if the volume fraction of cells is kept constant. Therefore, the differences in compressive modulus must be due to the differences in the distribution of cells in the matrix and the resultant differences in the distribution of cell wall thicknesses.

From statistical considerations for a random distribution of cells, it would be expected that the number of cell partitioning membranes approaching zero thickness would increase as the cell size is reduced, that is, there would be a greater likelihood of producing open cell structures which would, in turn, tend to produce softer materials. This was, in fact, found to be so for a number of the cellular structures investigated, particularly in the lower density materials and therefore, in order to take this into account it was necessary to adjust the open cell fraction in some cases by deliberately breaking down the closed cell structure by deformation of the cellular rubber. This was repeated until the open cell fractions agreed, within experimental error, in any one series. The fraction of non-intercommunicating cells within the cellular matrix was measured in an apparatus similar to that described by Doherty, Hurd and Lester[4] (1962), based on an air displacement method.

N*

Visco-elastic Effects

The effect of time and temperature on the short-term behaviour of stressed cellular cushions is extremely important in engineering applications as outlined at the beginning of this paper. The ability of the cellular structure to maintain support and to respond readily to temperature and reversible strain changes without causing discontinuity in an assembly is obviously a necessary function of the cushion.

The results of stress relaxation and creep measurements on cellular rubbers show that the magnitude of stress decay and increasing compressive strain can be considerable even at low temperatures. Factors which might be expected to contribute to normal relaxation processes, such as physical and chemical rearrangement of the molecular structure of the rubber, and possible slip between the rubber cushions and the constraining surfaces, have been shown to be negligible over the periods of

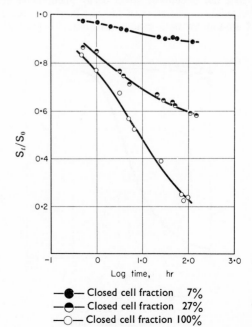

—●— Closed cell fraction 7%
—◑— Closed cell fraction 27%
—○— Closed cell fraction 100%

Fig. 10.—*Stress relaxation of cellular rubber at 21°C. (compressive strain 50%)*

time involved. This, therefore, suggests, because all the cellular rubbers studied contained some fraction of closed cells, that the major cause of the visco-elastic behaviour is the permeation of the included gas phase out of the closed cells within the compressed cellular matrix. This would explain the marked dependence of relaxation or creep rate on the degree of compression, applied stress, density and fraction of closed cells within the system. Fig. 10 shows typical stress relaxation curves at room temperature for cellular rubbers of different closed cell fractions and indicates the magnitude of the stress decay occurring. Of equal interest and importance is the rate of recovery of the same cellular materials after the relaxation period. This data is shown in Fig. 11 and because the cellular rubbers with closed cell fractions below 0·3 show almost complete and instantaneous recovery to their original uncompressed heights, it must be assumed that the elastic restoring forces within the rubber matrix must be sufficient to return the structures to their original dimensions; the closed cells possibly being under reduced internal pressure, and indicating that until the gas pressure in the cells returns to equilibrium with the surrounding atmosphere, the materials will exhibit lower compressive moduli. The fully closed cell material shows only gradual but complete recovery over a period of time similar to that of the relaxation period.

It immediately becomes obvious that the distribution of closed cells within the cellular matrix will have considerable bearing on the visco-elastic behaviour; individual closed cells behaving differently to clusters of closed cells because of the lower number of partitioning membranes through which the pressurized gas would have to permeate. It follows, therefore, that component size and shape will have some effect on the visco-elastic processes and evidence has been accumulated which shows this to be the case.

The full form of the stress–relaxation curves illustrated in Fig. 10 are similar to exponential decay curves of the Maxwellian type (Tobolsky,[5] 1960) in which the stress decay can be described in terms of a characteristic relaxation time r, and which for the pneumatic relaxation considered must be some function of the gas permeability characteristics of the polymer matrix. However, relaxation–time curves obtained at elevated temperatures and superposed along the logarithmic time axis do not fit a generalized relaxation–time curve indicating that the pneumatic stress decay phenomena are not ideal behaviour. Therefore, it has not been possible on the limited amount of data available to date, to predict stress

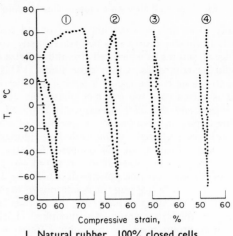

1. Natural rubber   100% closed cells
2. Natural rubber   27% closed cells
3. Polychloroprene   12% closed cells
4. Polyurethane   10% closed cells

Fig. 12.—*Temperature-strain curves for cellular rubbers at constant compressive stress*

decay or creep behaviour from suitably designed experiments of reasonable duration.

The ability of the cellular matrix to support stress during thermal excursions is shown in Fig. 12. The data show the behaviour of several different cellular rubbers of similar density and varying proportions of closed cells in the total volume of voids. The materials were held at constant stress, sufficient to produce 50% compressive strain at room temperature and subjected to thermal cycling at a rate of change of temperature of 0·5°C/min. Marked changes in compressive strain are shown to be associated with the fraction of closed cells in the cellular matrix. Also, as would be expected, the detailed shape of the curves depends on the type of polymer used to prepare the cellular structure. The differences in strain can, if large, cause serious misalignment in packaged assemblies which, in turn, may lead to damage and failure of equipment. Therefore, great care is necessary in determining the type of cellular polymer for use under such conditions.

Conclusions

It is clear from this brief account of work being undertaken on the behaviour of cellular rubbers, that the general geometry of the gas phase within the cellular matrix has considerable bearing on the mechanical behaviour of the system. Thus, it is important to ensure that the conditions of service to which they are subjected and the precise nature of the materials themselves must be fully understood if they are to be successfully applied to engineering problems. To this end, further work is being undertaken to investigate the effects of cell size and density distribution, cell shape, and directional properties imparted by deliberate orientation of shaped cells, on matrix properties.

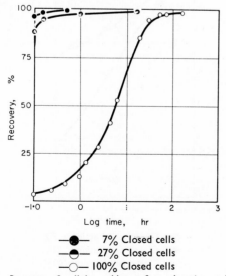

—●—   7% Closed cells
—◐—   27% Closed cells
—○—   100% Closed cells

Fig. 11.—*Recovery of cellular rubbers after relaxation at 50% compression*

References

[1] Talalay, J. A. *Ind. Eng. Chem.*, 1954. **46,** 1530.
[2] Gent, A. M., and Thomas, A. G. *J. Appl. Polymer Sci.*, 1959, **1,** 107.
[3] Madge, E. W. " *The Applied Science of Rubber* ". (London: Edward Arnold).
[4] Doherty, D. J. *et al.*, 1962, *Chem. Ind.* **30,** 1340.
[5] Tobolsky, A. V. " *The Properties and Structure of Polymers* ". 1960. (Wiley.)

IMPROVED RIGID POLYURETHANE FOAMS

By C. R. THOMAS*

Introduction

RIGID polyurethane foams are materials which may combine low density with sufficiently good mechanical properties to make them of interest for structural applications in situations where weight is required to be minimized.

The many commercial rigid polyurethane foams which are at present available are not designed for high strength applications but are intended principally for very low density filling of cavities to provide thermal insulation, and as filling material for sandwich or honeycomb composite structures where the skin material is designed to be stressed.

In order to be suitable for structural members in an unsupported condition, strengths, particularly compressive strengths, are required which are in excess of those normally associated with conventional rigid foams.

Because the compressive strength of a rigid foam is closely related to its density, it is of interest to prepare foams with the highest possible strengths in order that a desired stress may be supported with the minimum of weight. Conversely, where weight is not critical, a higher stress may be supported by a foam if the density is increased. Assuming, however, that the density is to remain constant the strength of a foam may be altered by variation of the chemical structure of the basic polymer materials.

Present Work

Difficulties Involved in Assessing Foams

Initial attempts to study the effect of changes in chemical composition on the mechanical properties of foams were complicated by variations in the foam specimens. These variations arise from the fact that when a foam is moulded it is entirely covered by a skin which has a higher density than the bulk of the material, and the density gradually decreases to a uniform value as the centre of the foam is approached. This effect operates from side to side and from top to bottom (see Fig. 1).

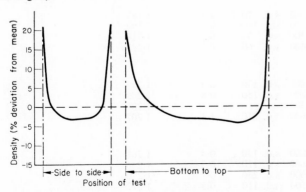

Fig. 1.—*Density distribution in a moulded polyurethane foam*

* Chemical Technology Division, U.K.A.E.A., A.W.R.E., Aldermaston.

In development work, where only limited quantities of materials may be available for evaluation it is not always practicable to remove sufficient skin to ensure complete absence of high density material. Consequently it is sometimes necessary to compare the strengths of foams at slightly different densities.

The density–strength relationship is not linear but approximates to a parabolic form (Fig. 2) such that the strength to weight ratio of high density foams is greater than that of lower densities. It is therefore necessary when comparing foams with different chemical structures to investigate a range of densities in order to construct the appropriate strength–density curves.

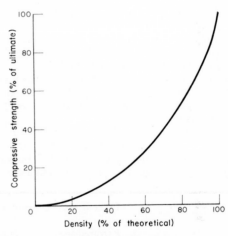

Fig. 2.—*Relationship of compressive strength to density in rigid polyurethane foams*

There is also a source of error arising from density variations within test specimens which causes a specimen to exhibit a lower compressive strength than if it were of uniform density. Other sources of error in the testing of foams are attributable to mechanical defects such as ruptured cells and to differences in the open to closed cell ratio between specimens.

Because of these accumulated errors, the scatter of results obtained in the testing of foams is large and coefficients of variance (standard deviation expressed as a percentage of the mean value) of 5% are normally obtained. Such variation may well be of the same order of magnitude as the effect under investigation, making comparisons difficult.

Elimination of the Density Variable

We have investigated the possibility of avoiding these errors by the preparation of absolute density, non-foamed polyurethanes in which density variations within specimens are eliminated, and mechanical imperfections may be visually observed. The use of such materials could permit the investigation of the relationship of chemical constitution to mechanical properties with greater precision than has hitherto been possible using foams.

TABLE I.—*Composition and Properties of Polyesters*

Polyester	Molar ratios of reactants			Hydroxyl value		Viscosity (poise at 25°C)
	trihydric alcohol	Linear dibasic acid	Cyclic dibasic acid	Theoretical	Found	
A	1·00	0·80	—	295	291	2,180
B	1·00	0·65	—	394	386	716
C	1·00	0·55	—	474	476	386
D	1·00	0·42	—	593	585	220
E	1·00	—	0·55	480	480	19,500
F	1·00	—	0·43	592	570	7,900
G	1·00	—	0·35	679	679	2,260
H	1·00	—	0·25	806	794	1,250

Much has been written about the chemistry and technology of polyurethane formation but basically the reaction involved in the preparation of absolute density polyurethanes is that between an *iso*cyanate and a hydroxyl group to form a urethane. $R'NCO + R–OH \rightarrow R'NHCOOR$. The hydroxyl groups in the present work were present in the form of hydroxyl terminated branched polyesters which were prepared in two series having respectively linear and cyclic structures. Two *iso*cyanates, hexamethylene di*iso*cyanate and tolylene di*iso*cyanate, also having linear and cyclic structures respectively were used to form, with the polyesters, four series of polyurethanes.

Experimental

The polyesters were prepared from a trihydric alcohol and either a linear dibasic acid or a cyclic dibasic acid. Each type of polyester was prepared by the direct fusion method at a series of hydroxyl values, as shown in Table I.

In order to avoid the formation of foam, which arises by the reaction of the *iso*cyanate with water or with carboxylic acids, producing carbon dioxide, the polyesters were prepared with low water and acid contents.

The polyurethanes were prepared by mixing the dry polyesters (all of which had acid values below 2 mg KOH/g) with the correct stoichiometric quantity of *iso*cyanate to react with the hydroxyl groups. In some cases a pre-polymer technique was used to dissipate part of the heat of reaction. The mixtures were degassed in vacuum (which was released before gelation occurred) and were post cured at 100–120°C for 6 hours. In this manner bubble-free clear castings were obtained which were examined by polarized light and shown to be free from mechanical strains.

Test specimens were machined as cubes of side 0·50 in. and were tested in compression at a strain rate of 0·25 in./min. All the materials (with one exception*) showed an initial high modulus followed by a sharp yield point at approximately 6% compression. The yield stress values are given in Table II.

It will be noted from Table II that the scatter of results is much smaller than that usually obtained with foams, coefficients of variance being generally below 1%.

The results given in Table II are also shown graphically in Fig. 3.

Discussion of Results

In the first series of polyurethanes based on linear polyesters and hexamethylene di*iso*cyanate relatively low values for the yield strengths were obtained, increasing linearly with hydroxyl value (Series 1, Fig. 3). As the hydroxyl value was raised, greater quantities of *iso*cyanate were required to maintain stoichiometry and the composition of the polyurethane changed. Increasing hydroxyl values brought about an increase in the content of urethane groups whilst the

TABLE II.—*Compressive Yield Strengths of Absolute Density Polyurethanes*

Polyurethane	Number of specimens	Compressive yield strength (lb/in²)		Coefficient of variance (%)	Density (g/cm³)
Series 1 (Linear Polyesters/HMDI)					
A/HMDI	10	4,100*	s.d. 200	4·9*	1·135
B/HMDI	10	9,250	s.d. 40	0·5	1·142
C/HMDI	14	11,450	s.d. 115	1·0	1·149
D/HMDI	11	12,600	s.d. 60	0·5	1·158
Series 2 (Linear Polyesters/TDI)					
A/TDI	10	13,700	s.d. 70	0·5	1·189
B/TDI	10	16,100	s.d. 110	0·7	1·199
C/TDI	10	19,300	s.d. 95	0·5	1·218
D/TDI	10	22,400	s.d. 60	0·3	1·227
Series 3 (Cyclic Polyesters/TDI)					
E/HMDI	10	19,800	s.d. 170	0·9	1·213
F/HMDI	10	19,800	s.d. 150	0·8	1·209
G/HMDI	2	19,300			1·205
H/HMDI	12	19,600	s.d. 210	1·1	1·207
Series 4 (Cyclic Polyesters/TDI)					
E/TDI	10	29,000	s.d. 130	0·4	1·261
F/TDI	6	29,600	s.d. 110	0·3	1·256
G/TDI	28	31,600	s.d. 230	0·7	1·270
H/TDI	11	32,500	s.d. 110	0·3	1·272

* This material was in the rubbery state at room temperature and did not exhibit the same stress–strain behaviour as the other polyurethanes. The stress at 10% strain is quoted in place of the compressive yield strength.

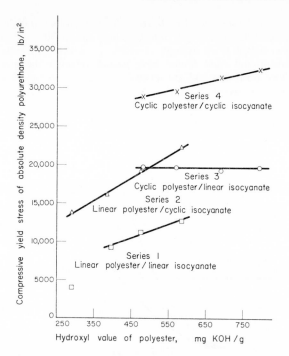

Fig. 3.—*Relationship of compressive yield stress of polyurethanes to chemical structure*

polar groups such as ester and urethane groups, and van der Waal's forces arising out of the dipole attractions of polar groups and the London dispersion forces existing in all neutral molecules.

It is probable that the secondary bonding properties of the carbon chains from the HMDI and those from the dibasic linear acid will be similar, and it is also probable that the London forces (governed by the number of protons and electrons present in the groups) will be similar for the $-CH_2COO$ (ester) and $-NH-COO$ (urethane) units. The improvement in compressive stress is therefore to be associated with the superior hydrogen bonding and dipole attraction of the urethane group compared with the less polar ester group.

In the second series of polyurethanes the linear polyesters were co-polymerized with an aromatic *iso*cyanate (TDI). The strengths of the resulting polyurethanes were higher and rose more steeply (Series 2, Fig. 3) than those in the first series, the slope of Series 2 being almost exactly twice that of Series 1.

The proportions of ester and urethane groups in the second series were virtually the same as in the first series and assuming they make the same contribution as previously, the higher strengths are thus directly attributable to the introduction of the aromatic nucleus in the *iso*cyanate. The rigid nature of the aromatic ring with its strong field of force is extremely effective in promoting inter-chain secondary bonding of the London type. In view of the relative slopes of the lines for Series 1 and 2 it appears that the magnitude of the improvement due to the urethane hydrogen bonding and dipole moment (urethane effect) is approximately equal to that arising from the introduction of cyclic structures (cyclic effect).

Confirmation of this has been obtained in the third series of polyurethanes in which cyclic polyesters were co-polymerized with a linear *iso*cyanate. As the hydroxyl value was increased the urethane content again increased but the proportion of cyclic structures decreased, being replaced by linear units (see Table III). The urethane effect and the cyclic effect were thus in opposition and the compressive strength of these polyurethanes did not change with hydroxyl value (Series 3, Fig. 3). Such a result shows that a mere increase in the hydroxyl value of a polyester is not necessarily accompanied

proportion of ester groups decreased, also the proportion of linear fragments from the *iso*cyanate increased whilst that of the linear fragments from the acid decreased. The density of crosslinking, as defined by the number of triple branching points arising from the trihydric alcohol remained virtually constant throughout the series. Values for these structural factors are given in Table III.

Because the density of crosslinking (and hence of primary chemical bonds) is constant, changes in properties of the materials are attributed to changes in the nature of the secondary bonding forces arising from the changes in the polymer structure.

Such forces may be of two types, hydrogen bonds formed between hydrogen atoms and oxygen or nitrogen atoms in

TABLE III.—*Structural Factors for Polyurethanes in Series* 1–4 (*Moles/kg of Polymer*)

Polyurethane	Crosslink density	Ester groups	Urethane groups	Linear units	Cyclic Units	
					*iso*cyanate	polyester
Series 1 (Linear Polyester/HMDI)						
A/HMDI	2·60	4·18	3·60	3·69		
B/HMDI	2·60	3·38	4·41	3·75		
C/HMDI	2·59	2·84	4·96	3·78		
D/HMDI	2·58	2·15	5·63	3·82		
Series 2 (Linear Polyester/TDI)						
A/TDI	2·58	4·14	3·57	1·87	1·78	
B/TDI	2·57	3·33	4·36	1·52	2·18	
C/TDI	2·56	2·79	4·88	1·29	2·44	
D/TDI	2·55	2·12	5·54	0·99	2·77	
Series 3 (Cyclic Polyester/HMDI)						
E/HMDI	2·51	2·76	4·98	2·49		1·38
F/HMDI	2·52	2·16	5·61	2·80		1·08
G/HMDI	2·53	1·77	5·98	2·99		0·88
H/HMDI	2·54	1·31	6·33	3·16		0·65
Series 4 (Cyclic Polyester/TDI)						
E/TDI	2·58	2·84	4·90		2·45	1·42
F/TDI	2·57	2·22	5·48		2·74	1·11
G/TDI	2·56	1·79	5·89		2·94	0·89
H/TDI	2·55	1·32	6·34		3·17	0·66

by an improvement in the mechanical properties of the polyurethane unless the chemical structure of the polymer is
correctly chosen.

The fourth series of polyurethanes, in which the cyclic
polyesters were co-polymerized with a cyclic *iso*cyanate,
represents the combination of the optimum conditions for the
formation of high strength polyurethanes.   The proportion
of urethane groups is high compared to ester groups and there
is a high proportion of cyclic structures.

The criteria for the formation of high strength polyurethanes
thus appear to be in the use of high hydroxyl value resins
which have a large proportion of cyclic structures and the use
of *iso*cyanates with cyclic structures.

The compressive yield strengths obtained by the use of such
materials in Series 4 (29,000–32,500 lb/in^2) are appreciably
higher than those normally associated with conventional
unfilled cast resins (e.g. 18,000 lb/in^2 for a typical expoxide resin)
and offered good prospects for the preparation of high strength
rigid foams.

Moreover, high deflection temperatures were obtained from
the cast urethanes in Series 4, indicating the possibility of
foams for high temperature environments.

Such foams have been prepared over a density range from
2 to 50 lb/ft^3 by the normal urethane foam technique of expansion with carbon dioxide, generated by the *iso*cyanate–water
reaction, and by expansion with chlorofluorocarbon blowing
agent. Graphs of the compressive strength of the foams from
polyester H and TDI at varying densities and temperatures are
shown in Fig. 4.   The high deflection temperatures of the

foams indicate that they have high glass–rubber transition
temperatures and so are able to retain almost 50% of their
room temperature strength at 150°C, at which temperature
conventional rigid foams have passed through the glass–
rubber transition and are incapable of acting as rigid load-
bearing materials.

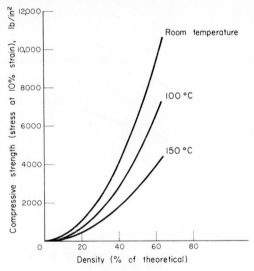

Fig. 4.—*Compressive strength–density–temperature relationships for
rigid foams from polyester H and TDI*

DISCUSSION OF PAPERS PRESENTED AT THE FOURTH SESSION

Dr. E. R. PETTY said that Professor Owen* had spoken about research on thermo-mechanical methods. How far had industry gone in a practical application of them?

Professor OWEN said that in a great many laboratories, in the chief metallurgist's office, on the floor by his desk there was a big hunk of something that he would tell you was about to go into some machine or other. The possible applications were very wide, for example, for leading edges of steam turbine blades, and all kinds of gas turbine applications, and rocketry applications, etc. But in all cases the difficulty was that it could only be done with materials in which one could put a lot of deformation, 80% or 90%. This was the limiting factor. The use came down to the fabrication problem. There were welding problems as well, and how these things were joined. All these problems were being actively looked at, but as far as he knew, there was no single application that was using a big tonnage of this stuff. It seemed, however, that all kinds of things would be made of aust-formed steel. He thought that the Ford car of America had one tiny part. It was the only mass-produced thing of which he knew.

A SPEAKER said that in his paper Professor Owen had mentioned a new marageing austenitic steel. He supposed that it was 8% cobalt, 18% nickel. He asked Professor Owen to comment on the effect of hardening; did the chemical resistance to corrosion go down? There was an austenitic stainless steel produced recently which, when it was hardened, was found to have reduced corrosion resistance.

His second comment was that the Russians claimed that by the addition of precious metals to the marageing austenitic stainless steels, they very much improved the properties of the new type of precipitation hardening of stainless steels.

Professor OWEN said that the 18% nickel, 8% chromium-molybdenum was ferritic; it was not produced as a corrosion resistant stainless steel at all. Even in the solution treated case, the corrosion resistance was poor, and when it was hardened it became even worse. This was certainly the situation, so if anyone had in mind using marageing steels for circumstances where corrosion resistance was an important factor, then it would be necessary to develop a corrosion resistant marageing steel. There were a number of steels of this kind in the experimental stage. He thought he was right in saying that the English Steel Coporation had one. Certainly the United Steel Corporation had one, and there were a number of others that had been developed on the basis of replacing the last proportion of the nickel by chromium, so that one had iron, nickel, chromium, cobalt and molybdenum alloy in order to give corrosion resistance, but these steels were at the present time only at the experimental stage. The corrosion resistance ones were not used in any quantity.

With regard to the Russians and their precious metals, he thought the speaker might be referring to austenitic stainless steels when he spoke about adding precious metals.

* Paper not available for publication.

A SPEAKER said that it was the addition of precious metals to the marageing austenitic stainless steel. They maintained that the corrosion resistance was low but he did not know that it was as bad as they made it out to be, because the need for a hardenable austenitic stainless steel was great in the chemical industry. He wondered how much the claim of the Russians was true with regard to the addition of gold and platinum and other precious metals to increase corrosion resistance, not only to austenitic stainless steel generally but also to the marageing type.

Professor OWEN said that with the marageing steels one had to be careful to distinguish between ferritic and austenitic. The 25% nickel which was the earlier marageing steel would be largely austenitic, a mixture of ferritic and austenitic. The 25% nickel was the only austenitic marageing steel to become extensively used commercially. The difficulty with this was not so much corrosion resistance which was certainly better than that of the 25% and better than the 18% nickel; the problem was primarily one of low ductility. A grain boundary type of fracture was obtained. The only information he had about precious metals was that when he was in Russia nine months ago the Russians told him that they were still working largely on this 25% nickel base, and trying to make it somewhat more ductile. They were adding precious metals for reasons that they could not explain to him, and claiming that it was more ductile. He did not think they claimed that the corrosion resistance was appreciably better. In this country and in America the 25% nickel steel had tended to fall out of favour because the austenitic stainless steel, of course, did everything that was wanted in an austenitic steel, and the marageing steel, here and in America, had been confined to the ferritic ones mostly. Almost all the work now was done on 18% ferritic, with the idea of getting strength, considering corrosion resistance as a secondary effect. They were two different classes of steel.

Dr. R. N. HAWARD asked Mr. Smith about Fig. 1 in the paper he had given. In it, Mr. Smith plotted melting-point against Young's modulus for a list of metals and obtained an array of points fanning out from the origin. He had seen them plotted differently, for example as melting-point against velocity of sound, and had seen it suggested that C_v should be multiplied by the melting-point and plotted against Young's modulus.[1] Recently, Anderson[2] had summarized some results of that nature, not only for metals but also for a number of crystals of an inorganic nature, and glass. He would be glad to have the comments of metallurgists on those treatments. Was there any agreed way of presenting data of that type which had the best theoretical backing among metallurgists?

Professor BALL said that he had looked up the figure. He thought that it was probably wrong to think of plotting a curve through it at all. It had only been presented just to show that there was a general trend, that as one went higher up in temperature, one tended to get higher up in Young's modulus, but of course, the scatter was so great that it could only be treated as a broad trend. There were methods of classification, such as plotting against temperature, or what you will, which claimed to have some validity, but he would have thought that, to put it crudely, in a lot of ways this was playing games with the properties. He thought it would be quite wrong to draw a curve through 0°C, which obviously had no meaning, and 0 Young's modulus. He thought that it was interpreting the data given in the paper much too precisely. Mr. Smith had just attempted to show that if the melting point was high, presumably there did not have to be a higher binding energy, but other factors came in rendering it impossible to get a simple curve.

Dr. PETTY said that Young's modulus was measured at room temperature and the curve should go through room temperature, not 0 degrees.

Fig. 1 was intended to show in a general way the variation in elastic modulus found with the common metals. It was not meant to imply any rigorous physical relationship between elastic modulus and melting point. An accurate analysis reveals that the elastic modulus depends on the curvature at the normal atomic spacing, of the energy-displacement curve for the particular atoms concerned. The binding energy is only related to this indirectly, so that irregularities will inevitably appear on a plot such as Fig. 1.

The CHAIRMAN said that the higher-melting-point metals had the advantage generally of higher moduli, but the disadvantage of higher density. All sorts of combinations of quantities might be plotted to support that general point.

Dr. PETTY said that Russian workers[3] usually plotted Young's modulus at the same fraction of melting-point, which usually turned out for a particular crystal structure as a straight line.[4]

Professor BALL said that the Russian approach was not a very good basis for planning research or interpretation because one had not the fundamental mechanism or model by which to assess the result when one obtained it.

The CHAIRMAN said that there were, however, marked deviations from the general rule in such metals as titanium and beryllium when modulus was plotted against melting-point. There were, therefore, always some anomalies.

Dr. J. K. HIGGINS referred to Dr. Tyzack's parabolic rate of flow in liquid sodium. In Table III, he mentioned that the rate of reaction was not dependent on the oxygen concentration above about 10 ppm. He went on to quote Mackay's work, which indicated that the kinetics were parabolic. Parabolic kinetics implied a semi-conducting oxide film on the surface of the metal. If it was accepted that there was a semi-conducting film on the surface of the metal, it should be possible to deduce from that on the basis of Wagner's treatment that the reaction rate should depend on the pressure of oxygen in the sodium to something like the sixth or eighth power. It seemed to him to be a contradiction in terms to say that there were parabolic kinetics and a protective reaction-rate and yet that it was not possible to deduce that Wagner dependence, and also that there was no dependence of oxygen rate on pressure up to 10 ppm.

Dr. TYZACK said that Mackay's work was based on rather limited observations in a thermal syphon loop probably without very good control of oxygen levels in the sodium. What Mr. Higgins said was true in relation to the Wagner theory, but he had yet to hear anyone suggest that the Wagner theory applied to zirconium. In fact, it was somewhat doubtful whether the Wagner ideas did apply to zirconium and to alloys based on zirconium. He would not imagine that experiments had been conducted critically enough to determine whether there was a solution pressure dependence of the type Mr. Higgins was suggesting. He did not believe that this had been found, anyway, in a gaseous environment.

Dr. HIGGINS said that P. Kofstad had a few years ago examined the oxidation of zirconium in oxygen and was able to get parabolic kinetics of zirconium and cubic kinetics and a transformation from parabolic to cubic depending on the solution of oxygen in the zirconium. Did Dr. Tyzack think it possible that Mackay's parabolic kinetics might change to cubic kinetics if the reaction was continued long enough? If that occurred, would Dr. Tyzack think that the process which had to be explained could possibly occur in the case of sodium, by solution of the oxygen in the zirconium giving cubic kinetics?

Dr. TYZACK said that there was no reason to doubt that dissolution of oxygen into metal could be obtained. He imagined that the kinetics of the dissolution of oxygen into the metal would be just the same as in a gaseous environment, almost irrespective of the pressure. He agreed that the variation between cubic and parabolic kinetics might reflect the relative rate of dissolution into the metal. He thought that part of it was strictly comparable with what happened in a gaseous environment.

Mr. F. ROBERTS referred to the paper by Mr. Smith, presented by Professor Ball. The paper discussed at some length the possibility of protecting metals from environment by coating techniques, and it indicated several practical problems in doing so. It was quite clear that the coating techniques required special equipment. It was difficult to reconcile that with the fact that in the final part of the paper great stress was put on the increasing use of welding techniques. It was difficult to see how the excellent properties conveyed by the coating technique could continue to be maintained if the coating surface were to be destroyed by a welding or other fabrication technique. It was not going to be easy to keep welding-technique developments in step with coating processes.

Professor BALL said that welding was a vital problem, although there would be occasions when welding was not required. Small parts could be coated after manufacture without joining, but for larger structures it would be necessary to weld the units together first and then coat them afterwards. Mr. Nichols had made the point in his introduction, and it was a point that had not been considered for fibrous reinforced materials.

Mr. D. W. C. BAKER said that the problem could presumably be solved by welding before coating, rather than by coating before welding. He believed that that was practised on tubes. However, there were processes available which permitted the welding of pre-coated materials, the damage caused being rectified subsequently by local recoating. In some cases, he understood that the coating was often beneficial in a sense that it assisted fluxing during welding.

A SPEAKER said that that was easy to rectify on the outside, but if the environment was internal, it might not be so easy to cope with after welding.

Dr. EDELEANU asked whether Professor Owen could indicate to what extent the very-high-tensile steels were resistant to hydrogen cracking, since it was normally impossible to avoid corrosion on large items, and steels susceptible to that type of failure were impractical.

The CHAIRMAN referred to the polystyrene rubber reinforcement and asked if it had a fine particle dispersion of rubber.

Mr. HOLLIDAY replied that it had a fine particle dispersion and the particles were 2 to 5 microns.

A SPEAKER asked if the problem of light stability had yet been solved with polypropylene and polythene.

Dr. HAWARD said that substantial improvements had been made in stabilising these polyolefins against light. However, the best stabiliser was still carbon black.

The SPEAKER asked if that meant that polypropylene in a film could be used in the open air with useful expectation of life.

Dr. HAWARD said that polypropylene was, of course, one of the materials which was most difficult and film the most demanding of applications. He would not recommend polypropylene film for outdoor use unless black.

Mr. D. READ asked if Dr. Haward would give his reference for the prices quoted in Table IV of his paper, and asked if the cost unit should be per yard to buy, and not per year.

Dr. HAWARD said that the figures quoted came from the Water Research Association (and cost should be per yard).

Dr. P. HANCOCK referred to the moduli measurements in Figs. 8, 10, 11, and 12 of the paper. He presumed that creep occurred in those materials at room temperature and asked whether the moduli values quoted were dynamic or static measurements.

Dr. HAWARD said that the moduli in Fig. 9 for HR polystyrene and polyethylene were made by a dynamic torsion pendulum technique, for measuring rigidity. The others had simply been taken from conventional literature on plastics, where static methods were normally quoted. The object was simply to demonstrate significant differences across a very broad range in different types of plastics material. These moduli could vary by $\pm 30\%$ according to the method of measurement and the amount of creep could vary to a similar extent.

Mr. R. P. AYERST said that his question concerned thermal expansion, which had not been mentioned. He wondered whether those who were thinking of using plastics in place of metals realised sufficiently the big difference in thermal expansion. For polyvinylchloride it was something like ten times the expansion of steel, which led to some difficulties in design of equipment. The metallurgists had solved the problem of reducing thermal expansion many years ago with Invar, and the glass technologists had succeeded in solving it more recently. Was there any possibility of the same thing happening with, say, polyethylene or any of those plastics which could be used in the chemical industry?

Dr. HAWARD said that the rather large thermal expansion was generally called shrinkage in the plastics industry because the problem arose when an attempt was made to manufacture an accurate moulding. The mould generally had to be a bit bigger than the article you ended up with, although the problem could be minimised by good moulding practice. Thus, the problem of expansion undoubtedly existed and did restrict a number of applications. One way of reducing expansion which had been looked into at Carrington was to find a combination of a filler and a polymer which had good properties, and when this could be done thermal expansion could be reduced. However, thermal expansion was still a serious problem for many applications.

Mr. A. H. COLLINS asked about the temperature resistance of polypyromellitimide. He had heard that this film would last several hundred hours at 400°C. Dr. Haward had suggested that that was due to the absence of aliphatic hydrocarbon links. It was not clear to him why the aromatics did not oxidise. Could it be regarded as a general rule that future polymers with structures of that kind would have high temperature-resistance?

Dr. HAWARD said that this was an area of complicated chemistry where he would not set himself up as an expert; but he thought it would be accepted that oxidation of a polymer proceeded from a peroxide mechanism when there was a carbon–hydrogen bond which could react to give hydroperoxide groups. These would first accumulate and then decompose, giving rise to a free radical oxidation chain reaction. This chain reaction did not happen so readily on an aromatic nucleus, which was therefore more stable. There were a large number of relatively stable aromatic structures which could be used and many people were investigating them as a means of preparing heat-stable materials for the future. The stability of this type of polymer was illustrated in Fig. 2.

Mr. J. S. ROBINSON said that plastics as a prospect for encapsulating high-quality electronic components had a lot to offer. They had been used and unfortunately failed on many occasions in the past. He asked if anyone would care to venture a date when two remaining problems would be solved: the hermetic seal to metal for leads, and good resistance to moisture transmission.

Dr. THOMAS said he thought the speaker had hit on a vital problem in encapsulation techniques. Although many plastics had satisfactory electrical properties, the business of sealing against ingress of moisture along the contact line between the plastics and the electrical connections was really serious.

Dr. HAWARD said that firstly there was ingress along the line of sealing which was different from ingress through the polymer.

Dr. THOMAS said that that was true, but they both needed to be solved to produce an encapsulate.

Dr. HAWARD said that the fluorocarbons were fairly good from the water transmission angle.

Dr. J. K. HIGGINS asked how the thermal resistance of the polymers compared with the inorganic polymers based on phosphorous nitrilic chlorides. Did the aromatic carbon rings break down?

Dr. HAWARD said that so far as he knew phosphorous nitrilic chlorides were reported to be rather poorly resistant to water. He was not aware that they were extensively used commercially or that this particular difficulty had been overcome.

Mr. COLLINS said that encapsulation might be answered by inorganic polymers such as low-melting glasses. They had been tried.

A SPEAKER said that the problem was one in which injection-moulding processes had so much to offer.

Mr. J. A. WILLIAMS said that the fluorocarbons had very good water resistance but they were almost impossible to seal, because that was one of their properties; they did not stick to anything unless they were etched by spraying them with liquid alkali metal. Then things could be made to stick together by etching the surface, and by spraying it with liquid sodium. He thought that that was actually being done by the electrical industries to attach things to PTFE, by spraying it with liquid sodium which etched the surface. Then rubber could be attached, and then a metal bond was required, so the metal was attached to the rubber. There was, therefore, PTFE, rubber, metal.

He had two questions for Mr. Soden. He had been very interested in the rocket case, because there was the possibility of the plastic chemical reactor vessel. It was a pressure vessel. It might be made of resistant dressing or possibly lined with a plastic. He asked for information about it; for example, the method of winding. Was it helical winding or layer winding? That had already been looked into by one of the plastic firms in Britain. The problem was the end. Mr. Soden had shown that there was a method of making ends by means of hemispherical ends. How were they made?

The second point was that with the filament-wound rocket cases, were they not coming back to the question of Young's modulus? Were they not rather prone to show lack of stiffness, which was reflected in the combustion of the rocket? Were they not prone to chugging, which was low-frequency and high-frequency vibrations within the combustion chamber of the rocket as it burnt backwards through the rocket composition? Were there not waves taking place inside the combustion?

Finally, with regard to the moon vehicle shown with its rubber wheels, he believed that it was thought one could use that only during the lunar night, because the surface of the moon in sunlight would approach the radiation temperature, and unless you used one of the new high-temperature plastics for making that, you might burn; or clay could be used during the day.

Mr. SODEN said that in connection with the moon vehicle there was only a problem with the blown-up wheels; in the lunar day they could be deflated and stored away when not in use, but the vehicle was not only for use during the night. With regard to filament winding, the plain fact was that nothing like this had in fact been done in this country at all. It was all being done in America.

Mr. WILLIAMS said that he disagreed.

Mr. SODEN said that he would qualify that. For large rockets or missiles nothing like that was being done in this country. Therefore much of the know-how was classified information.

With regard to the actual winding, through looking at the pictures he had seen, it appeared that it was a helical winding. As to how they made the ends, he had not thought about that. He presumed that this would be a very difficult job.

On the question of rigidity, this was difficult anyway because the metallic skin used in these large rockets like Atlas would hardly support their own weight unless they were pressurised. They had to be pressurised anyway to make them sufficiently rigid. This glass–epoxy system would not be rigid enough, he understood, for such liquid-fuelled rocket casings.

Mr. WILLIAMS said that the Atlas scheme which was rigidised by pressurising was more rigid than the non-pressurised vehicle.

The CHAIRMAN said that it was a double helix at 55° to the axis that was the optimum angle for hoop and tensile strength. The reason they were not very suitable for large-power rocket-thrust motors was because of acoustic energy absorption. One got rapid heating together with acoustic fatigue (say $\sim$ 140 dB) at launch.

Mr. WILLIAMS said that that would not occur, presumably, in a chemical reactor.

The CHAIRMAN said he thought there would be good stiffness, far better than unpressurized metal vessels.

Dr. EDELEANU said that one problem in using fibreglass to its full mechanical properties was due to the large difference in modulus between fibreglass and metals. Only when one had to make a joint, for instance a flange, the difference in modulus caused local very high stresses and led to fracture much below the breaking value of a vessel. Presumably, with time, we would establish ways of making such joints, but it would be interesting to know whether the author could give some guidance.

The CHAIRMAN said that he knew of, and had seen reports on, some considerable achievements in manufacturing metal inserts and fasteners to non-metallic structures of that type, in which metallic connections had been made, the whole being moulded and built up as an integral unit. He did not appreciate all the difficulties.

Dr. EDELEANU said that one could not use them anywhere near the limit.

Mr. WILLIAMS said that they were getting back to the previous speaker's problem of the differential expansion between metal and plastic inserts. They always gave trouble if one started to raised the temperature.

Dr. THOMAS said, on the question of chemical plant, that there was a design problem at the base of it, and if one tried to design a plastics plant in the same way as metal plant one would be troubled by flanges. They had to be designed out in some way by making the plant in one piece without flanges and moulding in any valve seats, feed holes, etc., in one piece as far as possible.

Dr. EDELEANU said that new designers were needed, not new materials.

Mr. E. C. GREEN asked Dr. Haward whether he thought it was possible to make an inorganic/organic crystalline polymer and whether such a thing would have better heat resistance than either an inorganic/organic polymer or a crystalline polymer.

Dr. HAWARD said that if one set out to do so, it would almost certainly be possible to make an inorganic/organic crystalline polymer. However, he did not know of any case where it had so far been employed, unless, of course, one talked about silicones, which were successful inorganic/organic polymers. Most of them were non-crystalline.

(Since Dr. Haward gave this reply Du Pont have, of course, announced their new ionomers which seem to fall within this field.)

Mr. L. S. EVANS said that Dr. Haward had mentioned polypropylene and HD polythene. If one was thinking of making pipes and tanks from such materials for chemical plant, on paper it looked as though polypropylene was the better material to use. Could Dr. Haward say whether one should forget about HD polythene for such applications and concentrate on using polypropylene?

Dr. HAWARD said he thought there was a case for first considering polypropylene. It had greater rigidity. It was easier, perhaps, to mould by injection moulding. The solvent resistance of the two materials was about the same, but there might be marginal differences which would be improved one way or another in certain cases. On the other hand, there might be an advantage with HD polythene against polypropylene when light stability at low temperature brittleness was important. He would also like to call attention to BS 1973, " Polyethylene Tube for General Purposes including Chemical and Food Industry Uses ".

Mr. S. A. GREGORY said that a symposium had been held by the Midland Branch of the Institution of Chemical Engineers on 25 March, 1964, which had covered most of the details and was absolutely up to date.

Mr. J. G. APPLETON said he wished to raise a point which had been touched on once or twice. He was afraid that it brought Dr. Haward under fire again on the stability of some of the polyolefines and polymers in general. Before going on with the experiment of extruding a one-piece chemical plant, he would like to know how long it would last. His organisation had done a little work themselves in trying to simulate long-term stability in the laboratory by accelerated ultra-violet exposure, but unfortunately they had not had the polymers long enough to be able to correlate short-term results with long-term life. He wondered if Dr. Haward had any comments to make with regard to work he had done on such polymers.

Dr. HAWARD said that on high density and low density polyethylene and polypropylene, a great deal of information was being collected in different laboratories in this country, and elsewhere, at the present time. With regard to correlation between accelerated tests and non-accelerated tests, this was not very good especially with light stability. However, if one used a Xenon test lamp (as compared with carbon arc) one got somewhat better correlation with daylight exposure. In talking about failure it was important to distinguish between the different types of condition which could lead to failure during ageing. Having exclusively light stability in mind, the polyethylenes would be expected to perform advantageously compared with polypropylene, especially when used with carbon black. With polyethylene and polypropylene stabilised materials could be obtained which offered a very appreciable improvement over the non-light stabilised material. At the present time, light stabilised HD polyethylene was being tried out in a number of applications where black material was not acceptable, and should give a three- to ten-year life in Britain, as far as mechanical strength was concerned. Work on polypropylene and other polyolefins was still going on, and substantial improvements were being made, and this would probably continue in future.

With regard to heat stability, this was evaluated differently, but two things might be borne in mind: first of all, the resistance of materials such as polyolefins to mechanical distortion during a short-term exposure test at high and moderate temperatures; here polypropylene was better than any polyethylene. In the absence of an imposed stress it could be exposed to 150°C without curling up. If long-term performance at, say, 50–100°C was required, then special grades either of polypropylene or polyethylene could generally be obtained with a rather large amount of anti-oxidant, and they might contain carbon black as well. In the polyethylene field, pioneering work had been done by the Bell Telephone Company on combinations of anti-oxidant and polyethylene.[6] With a phenolic anti-oxidant and a sulphur anti-oxidant in low density polyethylene the life at a temperature of 120°C and below could be enormously prolonged. Thus, the type of stabilisation which would be used was not the same for light stability and heat stability.[7] Although they were perhaps to a certain extent interchangeable, in that the light stabilised material would also be reasonably stable to heat. To obtain the best performance in each field, however, special grades had to be selected and employed.

References

[1] Zwikker, C. " *Physical Properties of Solid Material* ", 1955 (Oxford: Pergamon Press).

[2] Anderson, O. L. *J. phys. Chem.*, 1959, **12**, 41.

[3] Lozinski, M. G., and Fedotov, S. G. *Izv. Akad. Nauk. S.S.S.R. (Techn.)*, 1956, **3**, 59.

[4] Petty, E. R. *Metallurgia, Manchr*, 1961, **63**, 25.

[5] Kofstad, P. *Svensk kem. Tidskr.*, 1960, **72**, No. 2, p. 69.

[6] Hawkins *et al.*, *J. App. Pol. Sci.*, 1959, **1**, 37; Divn. of Polymer Chem. A.C.S. Reprints, Los Angeles, 1963.

[7] For a short summary and introduction to the literature see R. N. Haward, *Chem. and Ind. Anj.*, 15, 1964, p. 1442.

FIFTH SESSION

NEW CERAMICS AND REFRACTORIES

Conventional uses of ceramic materials are such as to utilise hardness, compressive strength, corrosion resistance and heat resistance to maximum advantage, while discounting to a considerable extent their brittleness, low thermal shock and unreliability under tensile stress. Any major extension in the engineering uses of ceramics will depend on the degree to which these latter weaknesses can be eliminated. In recent years a considerable research effort has been expended with this end in view and it is intended to discuss the progress that has been made both towards achieving a better understanding of the failure mechanisms involved and towards the development of new or improved ceramics. Under the latter heading developments in the fields of oxide and non-oxide ceramics, cermets and refractories will be described.

ACCORDING to a current classification, the basic constructional materials fall into three major divisions, metals, non-metallic inorganic materials and organic materials. On this basis it is probably legitimate to consider ceramics as artefacts made from inorganic materials by processes that involve comminution, shaping and firing in that order. This limitation is necessary to exclude inorganic materials such as building stones and marble statues, which are cut to shape, and glass, which is heated before shaping and is not, in this country at least, regarded as a ceramic, although a glassy phase is an important constituent of many ceramics. This definition is not, however, a rigorous one, since many refractories are used in the unfired state, some are fused and cast and some are used in the form of blocks cut from the native rock. Refractories, in the present context, are ceramics which are used in high temperature applications.

The range of potential ceramic materials, according to this definition is extremely wide since it includes all inorganic solids which might be fabricated into useful artefacts by ceramic manufacturing processes. The materials that have actually been used up to the present are mainly oxides and compounds of oxides, carbides, nitrides, borides, silicides, carbon and certain sulphides and halides. Oxides and their compounds are, of course, the traditional ceramic materials. Carbon, both in so-called amorphous forms and as graphite, and silicon carbide have been used in the manufacture of refractories for many years.

It is also relevant to point out that the chemical bonding in the materials listed varies from almost entirely ionic in some of the oxides to entirely covalent in carbon and that, while the oxides are essentially electrical insulators, the list also includes materials which are essentially metallic conductors. This need not worry us unduly. What ceramic materials have in common apparently is a lack of ductility, which precludes their being fabricated by hot or cold-working processes like metals. On the other hand they cannot normally be prepared by polymerization processes, although there are exceptions to this.

Traditional uses of ceramics are such as to utilize such properties as hardness, compressive strength, chemical inertness, impermeability, high electrical resistance and temperature

resistance while discounting their brittleness and unreliability under tensile stresses. The operation of this principle is illustrated by their use as building bricks, floor and roofing tiles, domestic and chemical ware, drain tiles, electrical insulators, laboratory ware, crucibles and furnace refractories. Interest in the wider application of ceramics as engineering materials is of relatively recent origin. It has arisen firstly perhaps because of the rapid rate of progress in various fields of engineering design (notably in the electronic, aeronautical, combustion and nuclear fields) which has led to a situation where conventional materials are, in an increasing number of applications, imposing a limit on design and performance, and, secondly, because of the emergence, largely as the result of the work of solid state physicists, of the conception of a unified science of materials. This latter development has followed the realization that the atomic and electronic processes which determine the properties of solids are frequently similar in character in different kinds of material, though they may differ in the energies involved and the frequency with which they occur.

This has led to the hope that, once materials science has learned to control these processes, it should be possible to produce materials having combinations of properties at present unknown.

Magnetic Ceramics

Probably the most unequivocal successes in this direction have been in the fields of magnetic and electrical ceramics. Before the last war, essentially all the magnetic materials used were metals.

During the ten years following the war, however, an entirely new class of oxide magnetic material based on the spinel structure of magnetite was introduced. As in the case of iron, the magnetic properties of magnetite depend on the unbalanced spins of the unpaired electrons in the iron atoms, but the situation is more complex in that the latter occur in two valence stages, Fe^{2+} and Fe^{3+} having 4 and 5 unpaired electrons, and consequently magnetic moments of 4 and 5 Bohr magnetons respectively. In the crystal these iron ions occupy two kinds of site, usually referred to as A and B sites, and the electron spins of the ions on the two kinds of site are anti-parallel, i.e. they are oriented in opposite directions. There

* Department of Refractories Technology, St. George's Square, Sheffield 1.

are, however, twice as many B sites as A sites so that these oppositely oriented magnetic moments do not annul each other. Actually, in magnetite, which is a spinel of the type known as inverse, half of the Fe^{3+} ions occur on the A sites while the B sites are occupied by the remaining Fe^{3+} ions and the Fe^{2+} ions. The molecular formula is thus properly written $(Fe^{3+})_A (Fe^{2+}Fe^{3+})_B O_4$, the net magnetic moment per molecule being 4 Bohr magnetons.

The saturation magnetization corresponding to this value per molecule is only about one third that of iron, but it can be increased appreciably by replacing a proportion of the Fe^{2+} ions by Zn^{2+} ions.[1,2] These enter the A sites, forcing an equal number of Fe^{3+} ions into B sites, and have themselves zero magnetic moment, so that the magnetic moment per molecule is increased. The maximum value obtainable in this way is between 5 and 6 Bohr magnetons per molecule, when approximately half of the Fe^{2+} ions have been replaced by Zn^{2+} ions. The value then falls again since the introduction of the non-magnetic Zn^{2+} ions weakens the strong AB interaction which is responsible for the antiparallelism between the A and B sites and the much weaker AA and BB interactions then cause antiparallelism within the A and B sites.

The usefulness of the magnetic ferrites, however, depends less on the saturation magnetizations that can be achieved than on their high electrical resistivities, which are of the order of 10^8 times higher than those of metals. This property, since it eliminates the possibility of eddy currents, enables them to respond extremely rapidly to reversals in the direction of imposed magnetic fields and with low energy loss. They can thus be used at much higher frequencies than metals and have found extensive use in transformer cores for radio and television equipment and transmitting and receiving devices operating in the microwave region, i.e. at frequencies of the order of 10^{10} cycles/s. Other applications are, as permanent magnets, in filters and other devices required to work at low field strengths and in memory units of digital computers, where a square hysteresis loop is required.

The number of different cations that can occur in the spinel lattice is very large, including univalent and tetravalent ions as well as di- and trivalent ions, and this has enabled compositions to be developed having properties specially suited to particular applications. For example, nickel–zinc ferrite is widely used in microwave devices where a low variation of energy loss with frequency is required and manganese-magnesia–ferrite where a square hysteresis loop is required.

Several magnetic ferrites which are not spinels have also been developed, e.g. $BaO.6Fe_2O_3$, whose high remanence and coercivity make it particularly suitable for permanent magnets, the compound $3BaO.2CoO.12Fe_2O_3$ which is suitable for microwave applications and an yttrium–iron garnet, $3Y_2O_3.5Fe_2O_3$, which has a selective response at an even higher frequency.

Typical properties of ferrites are shown in Table I.

TABLE I.—*Typical Magnetic Properties of Ferrites*

Material	Saturation magnetization (Gauss)	Coercivity (Oersted)	Initial permeability	Resistivity (ohm cm)
Iron	21 500	0·2	500	10×10^{-6}
Mn–Zn ferrite	4 000	0·5	1 500	50
Ni–Zn ferrite	3 000	1·0	500	10^5

The manufacture of ferrites as high-permeability, low loss magnetic materials requires close control over ceramic fabrication techniques. Thus while the saturation magnetization is determined primarily by the chemical composition, the initial permeability depends on the ease with which boundaries separating domains, i.e. regions within the crystal having different directions of spontaneous magnetic polarization, can move in the applied magnetic field to permit the growth of favourably oriented domains. Hence for materials to be used at low field intensities large grain size and freedom from intra-granular pores and inclusions are desirable to permit unimpeded movement of the domain boundaries. In strong fields, once the domain walls have moved into stable positions, further magnetization involves rotation of the direction of magnetization in the domains and a fine grain size is required, combined with high density and low porosity, to minimize boundary stresses resulting from magnetic strain anistropy which would lead to energy losses. To meet these requirements close control over the process is required.

In addition, during firing, control of the atmosphere is necessary to ensure that iron and other variable valency elements occur in the fired product in the state of oxidation required by the stoichiometric composition of the ferrite. The importance of such control is illustrated in Fig. 1, which shows equilibrium phase relationships in the ternary system $MgO–FeO–Fe_2O_3$ at an oxygen pressure of 0·2 atm.[3,4] In the ternary diagram, the compositions of fully-oxidized mixtures, which are stable at low temperatures and consist of Fe_2O_3 and $MgFe_2O_4$ or $MgFe_2O_4$ and MgO (depending on the $MgO–Fe_2O_3$ ratio) lie along the $MgO–Fe_2O_3$ edge. The dashed straight lines sloping from left to right show the paths along which various mixtures would change during heating as they lost oxygen and the compositions reached on these at various temperatures are indicated by their intersections with the isotherms (continuous lines with temperatures alongside).

The remaining heavier lines, (some of which are shown broken where their position is regarded as tentative) divide the area of the triangle into fields in which the various phases exist at equilibrium. Compositions falling to the left of AB consist of Fe_2O_3 and a spinel solid solution having a composition lying on AB, while compositions between BA and FE (produced in both cases to the edge of the diagram) consist of spinel only. Similarly compositions lying in the area defined by the phase boundaries FE produced, ED and DC will consist of spinel and magnesio-wustite (MgO with part of the Mg^{2+} sites occupied by Fe^{2+} and Fe^{3+} ions and having one cation vacancy for every two Fe^{3+} ions). Compositions lying to the right of CD will consist of the magnesio-wustite phase only. On crossing the lines DEF a liquid phase will be formed. This will occur between 1591°C when no MgO is present (point F on the Fe_2O_3 edge) and 1713°C in compositions whose dissociation paths intersect ED.

The smaller diagram shows the temperature ranges over which these phase combinations exist plotted against the compositions of the fully oxidized mixtures, area AB FE being the area in which a single spinel phase will exist.

Less complete data are also available on the system $MgO–FeO–Fe_2O_3$ at other oxygen pressures[5] and on a number of other systems containing oxides that occur in commercial ferrites.[6] Fig. 1, however, will probably be sufficient to give a general indication of the nature of the changes that may occur during firing. In practice control of the composition during firing is usually based on a trial-and-error approach, $CO–CO_2$ or other gas mixtures being usually introduced at certain temperatures in an attempt to obtain a stoichiometric spinel as the final product. Firing schedules can also affect the magnetic properties in another way, due to the fact that in certain spinels the distribution of the cations between the A and B sites changes towards a random one as the temperature increases. Because of this effect the spontaneous magnetization of magnesium ferrite after quenching from the firing temperature increases as the latter increases.

Electrical Ceramics

The use of ceramic materials other than magnets by the electrical and electronic industries covers a wide range of applications including insulators, dielectric materials and such semi-conductor devices as rectifiers, transistors and thermistors. Since many of the semi-conductor applications are rather borderline, being more in the field of applied physics than ceramics, I do not propose to deal with these specifically, although the development of semi-conducting glazes for the insulators of high tension power transmission lines is primarily a ceramic development.

Ceramics have, of course, long been used as insulators at moderate frequencies, *e.g.* in telephone systems, power transmission lines and domestic appliances. The general requirements for this use are high electrical resistance, impermeability to moisture, resistance to atmospheric corrosion, a smooth surface and adequate mechanical strength and these requirements have generally been met by the use of porcelains made from mixtures of clay, flint and feldspar maturing at 1200–1400°C to give a product of almost zero porosity.

While porcelains are well-suited for use at low frequencies, their use at high frequencies is restricted by the fact that dielectric loss occurs leading to inefficient operation and heating. This behaviour is due mainly to charge displacement within the glass phase, involving the jumping of certain network modifying cations, and in particular Na^+ ions, between equivalent positions in the structure under the influence of the applied alternating field. The relaxation time associated with this process is such that at low frequencies it occurs essentially in phase with the applied field so that the loss is small, but at high frequencies it results in a phase retardation of the charging current so that loss occurs. At room temperatures this loss usually passes through a maximum within the frequency range 10^3 to 10^6 cycles which is of particular importance in many dielectric applications. At higher temperatures, as the jump frequency of the ions increases, the maximum is displaced to higher frequencies.

Since the jump frequency is directly related to the mobility of the ions in the structure, mobile ions such as Li^+ and Na^+ give higher losses than less mobile ions such as K^+ or Rb^+, or divalent Group II cations. In making low-loss ceramics it is, therefore, necessary to avoid the use of fluxes containing soda, replacing these by compounds of potash or preferably of magnesium, lime or barium.

One of the earliest low-loss ceramics to be used, following the advent of radio, was the so-called clinoenstatite body made by firing mixtures of talc ($3MgO . 4SiO_2 . H_2O$), and potash feldspar, the latter component being now often replaced by additions of Mg, Ca and Ba carbonates to obtain a lower power factor.[7] After firing, these bodies consist mainly of clinoenstatite ($MgSiO_3$) in a glassy matrix. Another modification is to add sufficient $MgCO_3$ or MgO powder to produce forsterite (Mg_2SiO_4) after firing. Still another type of low-loss body is made from zircon ($ZrSiO_4$) and ball clay with additions of Mg, Ca or Ba zirconium silicates.

Recent developments in microwave technology have, however, created a demand for materials capable of operating efficiently and without breakdown at frequencies up to 10,000 Mc/s and over, at temperatures up to 500°C and in some cases against steady potentials in the kilovolt range. Two important applications of ceramics in this field are as valve envelopes, where the use of a ceramic makes larger power outputs possible and permits higher outgassing temperatures than glass–metal construction and as micro-wave windows for klystrons. Another example is the use of ceramic–metal construction in miniaturized circuits where the operating temperatures are high owing to the high component densities achieved. The electrical, thermal and mechanical requirements for such applications are extremely exacting.[8,9] Thus for valve envelopes and microwave windows respectively

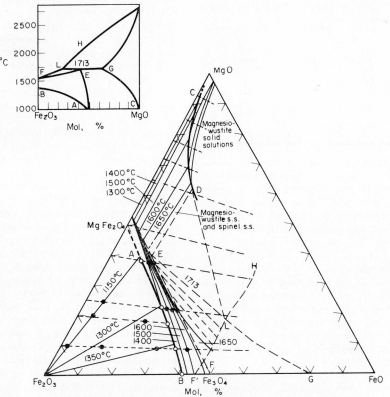

Fig. 1.—*Phase equilibrium relationships in the system MgO–FeO–Fe₂O₃ in air (see text).*

O*

minimum volume resistivities at 400°C of 10^9 and 10^{10} ohm cm are required with a room temperature resistivity not less than 10^{14} ohm cm. Similarly, for microwave windows, the power factor (tan δ, where δ is the angle of retardation of the charging current) at 1, 100 and 10,000 Mc/s should be less than 0·001, 0·0008 and 0·0005 at room temperature and less than 0·0008 and 0·001 at 10,000 Mc/s at 200°C and 400°C, while for valve envelopes it should be less than 0·001 at all three frequencies at room temperature. Other requirements are that the electric breakdown strength should be high and that the thermal conductivity should be adequate to dissipate heat developed due to dielectric losses. The thermal expansion should be large to avoid excessive stresses at metal–ceramic junctions after brazing, and the material should be fine grained, and impermeable and free from large pores or inclusions which may lead to failure by local heating either as a result of gas discharge within the pores or excessive electrical losses at the inclusions.

These requirements are leading designers to turn to pure oxide ceramics, and a considerable research effort is now being expended on the fabrication and testing of the more promising materials of this type. Of these, alumina is at present the most widely used, though many commercial aluminas fail to meet the specifications imposed either because of their impurity content or because they are insufficiently dense and homogeneous. Attention has, therefore, been directed towards the aluminas of higher purity and towards material of the pore-free " Lucalox " type, which is described in a later section. Other attractive materials are beryllia, on account of its low power factor up to 500°C and exceptionally high thermal conductivity.

Typical properties of ceramic insulating materials are shown in Table II.

TABLE II.—*Electrical Properties of Ceramic Insulators*
(After A. J. Moulson and P. Popper[8])

Material	Permittivity (10^6 c/s)	Tan δ × 10^4 (10^8 c/s) 20°C	Tan δ × 10^4 (10^8 c/s) 500°C	Thermal Expansion (°C^{-1} × 10^6)
Electrical Porcelain	5·3	115	—	4–7
Steatite	6·4	11	150	8–9
Forsterite	6·2	3·0	—	10–11
BeO	6·7	1·9	35	7
99% Al_2O_3	9·3	0·6	25*	7·4
94% Al_2O_3	8·9	5·2	40*	7·2
Fused SiO_2	3·8	—	—	0·5

*At 10^7 c/s.

The requirements of materials for use as dielectric media in condensers are similar to those for insulators except that a high dielectric constant is required, implying a high degree of polarization in electric fields, and that its temperature coefficient should be low. During the past 20 years a considerable number of high permittivity ceramics have been developed many of them based on TiO_2 and its compounds. These include the spinel, Mg_2TiO_4, and various compounds having the perovskite structure ($CaTiO_3$, $BaTiO_3$, $PbTiO_3$, etc.). A feature of these compounds is the occurrence of oxygen ion octahedra in the structure forming the coordination shells of the Ti^{4+} cations and the high dielectric constant, which in most cases is too high to be accounted for in terms of the electronic polarization of the O^{2-} ions alone, is considered to be associated with displacement and distortion of the oxygen octahedra relative to the central Ti^{4+} ions.

In this respect $BaTiO_3$ and the other perovskites occupy a special place in that they are ferro-electrics, *i.e.* they undergo spontaneous electric polarization on cooling through a Curie point in much the same way as ferromagnetic materials undergo magnetic polarization. This polarization is associated with a change in the symmetry of the crystal from cubic to tetragonal and also with the formation of domains of different polarization direction within the crystal. The dielectric constant also passes through a sharp maximum at the Curie point.

This rapid increase in dielectric constant as the Curie point is approached, which is also accompanied by an increase in tan δ in high frequency fields limits the maximum temperature of use of $BaTiO_3$ to 70°C. A feature of the perovskite structure, as with the spinels, however, is the number of cations that can replace Ba^{2+} and Ti^{4+} ions (Ca^{2+}, Sr^{2+}, Pb^{2+}, Cd^{2+}, for Ba^{2+} and Zr^{4+}, Sn^{4+}, Hf^{4+} for Ti^{4+}) and this makes it possible to vary the temperature characteristics by varying the composition. This effect has been utilized to produce perovskites having a wider temperature range of use, one such material being a solid solution of $PbTiO_3$ in $TaTiO_3$ which can be used at temperatures up to 100°C.[10]

In addition to its use as ferro-electric material $BaTiO_3$ is also strongly piezo-electric and has found applications as a transducer in various ultrasonic applications and in microphones, strain gauges, etc. After fabrication it is necessary to polarize the material by cooling it through the Curie point in a strong electric field.

Nuclear Ceramics

The nuclear field is at present one of the most promising fields of application of ceramics. Since, however, nuclear ceramics are the subject of another paper, they will be mentioned only briefly here.

The ceramic materials of interest in reactor technology are primarily the refractory compounds of the fissionable elements, for use as fuels, and alumina, beryllia and impermeable graphite, for the construction of cans. For the former purpose UO_2 is attractive in that it can fairly readily be sintered to high density when slightly oxygen-rich, because fission gas release, which is diffusion controlled, is slow and predictable up to 1600°C.[11] Other advantages are its high resistance to irradiation damage and its compatibility with metallic canning alloys. Recent work has shown that these properties are not materially affected when a small percentage of PuO_2 is present in solution.[12]

Disadvantages of UO_2 are that it is incompatible with liquid sodium and that its low thermal conductivity, which is about one fifth that of uranium metal, leads to steep thermal gradients during irradiation, and high centre temperatures. This can cause rapid fission gas release and may cause melting in highly-rated fuel elements.[11] As an alternative to single phase UO_2 fuel elements, the use of dispersions of UO_2–ThO_2 solid solutions in BeO is now receiving attention.

Advantages of UC are its higher thermal conductivity and its compatibility with liquid sodium, these being offset to some extent by its high chemical reactivity and the difficulty of sintering it to high densities. Largely because of the latter difficulty, work on carbide fuel elements in the past has been directed mainly towards the use of dispersions of the dicarbide in graphite. A disadvantage of this type of fuel element is its high rate of fission gas release, and to overcome this drawback methods have been devised for coating the particles of the dicarbide with pyrolytic graphite before incorporating them in the graphite matrix. Recently, however, it has been found that UC can be sintered successfully if stringent precautions are taken to prevent oxygen pick-up[13] and this discovery may lead to the development of dense, single-phase UC fuel elements.

A possible disadvantage of UC arises from the fact that it is incompatible with a wide range of Fe–Cr–Ni alloys which

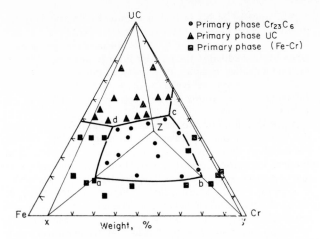

Fig. 2.—*Section Fe–Cr–UC through quaternary system U–Fe–Cr–C showing fields of primary crystallization.*

react with it at high temperatures to form UNi_5, UFe_2 and $Cr_{23}C_6$. The nature of this incompatibility is illustrated in Fig. 2 which shows the fields of primary crystallization in the section Fe–Cr–UC of the quarternary system Fe–Cr–U–C.[14]

In the field of canning materials a particularly notable development has been the discovery of methods for producing impermeable graphite.[15,16] In one of these the graphite after pressing is impregnated with furfuryl alcohol containing a suitable catalyst and then heated to 1000°C to carbonize the alcohol. In another, carbon is deposited in the pores of the graphite by pyrolysis of benzene vapour in nitrogen at 750°C. In the experimental high temperature helium-cooled reactor now being built under the Dragon project of the O.E.E.C., use of fuel elements consisting of enriched uranium and thorium carbides dispersed in graphite and having impermeable graphite cans will it is anticipated permit can-surface temperatures of 800–1000°C to be achieved.

Pure Oxide Ceramics

Most traditional ceramics contain fluxes, either as impurities in the raw materials used, or as deliberate additions, and these play an important part in the firing process since they melt to form a liquid phase which is drawn by capillarity into the interparticle voids causing shrinkage, and, if enough liquid is formed, a completely dense, vitrified body may be produced. There are, however, many applications, in particular those where maximum refractoriness and creep resistance are required, where the presence of low melting phases is undesirable. Recognition of this limit on high temperature performance led to the development of sintered alumina ware in Germany before the last war. At the present time impervious ware is probably available commercially in alumina, magnesia, beryllia, thoria, stabilized zirconia and spinel ($MgAl_2O_4$).

Although some 24 oxides with melting points above 1750°C are known to exist, many of these are unsuitable for general use as ceramics because of undesirable physical or chemical characteristics or because they are too expensive, and current interest in this field appears to be concerned mainly with improving the quality of established materials by achieving lower impurity contents and lower residual porosities.

Since the early work of Kuczynski and others,[17,18] which established that densification during sintering takes place by volume diffusion of vacancies from the surfaces of pores, and that grain boundaries promote densification by acting as sinks

for vacancies, the most important advance has been the elucidation of the role of grain growth during sintering.[19]

In the early stages of sintering, grain growth is inhibited by the pores but, when closure of the latter has reached a certain stage, they cease to be effective and a critical stage is reached where it is possible for grain boundaries to escape from the restraint of the remaining pores allowing grain growth to occur. This follows from the condition, first derived by Zener[20] for the case of inclusions in metals, that grain growth will stop when R the radius of curvature of the grain boundaries is such that

$$\frac{r}{R} \doteqdot \frac{4}{3f}.$$

Here r is the average radius of the inclusions and f their volume fraction in the material R, for a grain having a given number of faces, increases as the grain size increases and its limiting value is of the same order as the limiting grain size. When this condition is fulfilled for a system of grains of more or less uniform size, however, a larger grain having a larger number of sides will still be able to grow at the expense of smaller grains whose growth has been stopped. Under such conditions the larger grains can continue to grow giving rise to discontinuous grain growth. The significance of this behaviour in sintering is that, as densification proceeds, a critical porosity is reached at which certain preferred grains start to grow rapidly so that residual pores are engulfed in the growing grains. They are then very difficult to close since they have no grain boundaries adjacent to them to act as sinks.

A few years ago, these principles were applied to the sintering of alumina, additions of finely divided MgO being made to the material to inhibit grain growth, and this led to the production of a dense, pore-free, translucent alumina which has been named " Lucalox ". Fig. 3 shows the structure of " Lucalox " as compared with that of a normal recrystallized alumina.

Recent work suggests[21] that the added MgO controls grain growth, not by forming obstructing inclusions, but rather by being adsorbed in solution at grain boundaries. It has also now been found possible to produce translucent magnesia, by hot pressing.

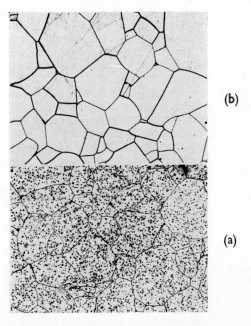

(b)

(a)

Fig. 3.—*Micrographs by reflected light of (a) normal sintered Al_2O_3 showing pores within grains and (b) " Lucalox ".*

Non-oxide Ceramics

Non-oxide ceramics of interest at present include carbides, nitrides, borides and carbon. As a group they represent a wide spectrum of properties, ranging from insulators to electronic conductors, and including the most refractory materials known, HfC, TaC and carbon. Carbon, both in so-called amorphous forms and as graphite, and SiC, the former usually bonded with tar and pitch and the latter with clay have been used for many years as furnace refractories. Recent interest in this field also stems largely from their potential usefulness as high temperature structural materials, including such applications as rocket nozzles, ablation heat shields, radiant heating tubes, heating elements, crucibles and gas turbine blades.

During the past few years a considerable number of compounds new to the ceramics field have been prepared and investigated from this point of view. Generally, such investigations have covered methods of preparation and their influence on the properties of the product, which can be considerable, making assessment of their ultimate usefulness difficult in many cases. A difficulty with most of the materials that have been examined so far is that they cannot in general be sintered to high densities. It has, therefore, been necessary to resort to hot pressing of the pre-made material, or to formation of the compound *in situ* by heating artefacts prepared by pressing one of the components in the gas or vapour of the other.

Examples of the latter process are the production of components of Si_3N_4 by heating compacts of powdered silicon in nitrogen or ammonia,[22] and the production of self-bonded SiC by heating mixtures of SiC grain and colloidal carbon in silicon vapour.[23] For this method to be successful, it is necessary that reaction should take place without appreciable change in the dimensions of the specimen, which usually implies that the product should " grow " into the interparticle voids as it forms, and calls for close control over particle size and grading and cold-pressed density. TiN having a porosity of only 13% has been successfully prepared by this method.[24] In reaction-sintered Si_3N_4 the porosities are usually higher than this, being of the order of 20% or over. Of the two methods, hot pressing generally gives the higher densities and better mechanical properties, but is expensive.

A third method of preparation is by pyrolysis of the appropriate vapours, the product being deposited on a substrate. This method is at present mainly used for applying coatings but pyrolytic graphite compounds are now being manufactured in the U.S., using a process originally developed in this country.

Important recent advances in the field of non-oxide ceramics include the development of self-bonded SiC and of silicon nitride-bonded SiC, the former prepared as already indicated by heating mixtures of SiC and carbon in Si vapour and the latter by heating mixtures of SiC and Si in nitrogen. In terms of high temperature strength and oxidation resistance these represent a considerable advance over earlier forms of bonded SiC. Another recently introduced grade contains unreacted graphite particles in a dense matrix of SiC to confer high thermal shock resistance.

Of the " newer " materials reaction-sintered Si_3N_4 has attracted particular attention because of its high strength, resistance to oxidation and chemical attack, and low coefficient of expansion ($2·5 \times 10^{-6}$ °C^{-1}) which confers on it a high degree of resistance to thermal shock. Blades made of this material have successfully withstood 250 hr of operation in a stationary gas turbine at 750°C without apparent deterioration, and a number of other successful applications, including rocket nozzles, have been reported.

A feature of Si_3N_4 is that it cannot be densified by hot pressing when pure, a feature it shares with BN.[25] It has, however, been found that it can be successfully hot pressed when MgO is added to the powder prior to pressing.[26] By this method densities up to 3×10 g/cm^3 and porosities as low as 0·1% have been achieved with a flexural strength of 100 000 lb/in^2 at room temperature and 70 000 lb/in^2 at 1200°C.

A possible limitation to the wider use of non-oxide ceramics lies in the fact that for resistance to oxidation in oxidizing atmospheres they rely on the formation of an oxide skin. Present indications are that oxidation rates through such layers become appreciable at temperatures over 1500–1600°C even in the most promising cases. Figures quoted, however, show wide variations in behaviour depending on the nature of the film formed as well as on the substrate, *e.g.* borides appear to be generally superior to carbides at temperatures up to 1600°C while compounds of Ti are usually better than compounds of Zr below 1840°C, the melting point of TiO_2, but inferior above this temperature. These variations suggest that the possibilities of " alloying ", where this is possible, would be worth exploring.

Furnace Refractories

In the field of furnace refractories, recent developments have been dominated by the trend towards higher operating temperatures in the metallurgical and other user industries. One effect of this trend has been a decline in the use of silica, which in spite of its excellent refractory properties, is limited as regards high temperature operation by its relatively low melting point of 1725°C, and an increase in the use of basic refractories and high alumina refractories. Current developments in combustion engineering, including the increasing use of oxygen, suggest, however, that this trend towards higher operating temperatures is likely to be limited only by the refractories available.

To meet this situation, since it now seems unlikely that non-oxide refractories will have sufficient durability over long periods under oxidizing conditions at extreme temperatures, current research is being directed towards the possibility of improving conventional refractories.

A particularly important development in this direction has been the discovery that the distribution of the low melting phases may be capable of being controlled and their harmful effects minimized by suitable heat-treatment or by adjustment to the composition. This possibility was first demonstrated by the observations that when chrome-magnesite refractories are fired at temperatures in excess of 1600°C, the silicates normally responsible for bonding tended to coalesce within the interstices between the refractory grains, permitting the development of a direct bond between the latter. Later it was demonstrated that the development of this type of bond was accompanied by a marked increase in the high temperature tensile strength of the bricks.[27] Subsequently the nature of the factors which govern the distribution of the silicate phase in basic refractories was investigated by Jackson *et al.*,[28] who studied the effect of Cr_2O_3 and Fe_2O_3 on the size of the dihedral angle formed in the silicate phase at points of contact between periclase (magnesia) grains. Ideally the condition that a liquid phase should penetrate completely between two solid grains which it wets, is that the surface energy of the solid–solid interface should be greater than twice that of the solid–liquid interface, *i.e.* $\gamma_{ss} > 2\gamma_{sl}$. When $\gamma_{ss} < \gamma_{sl}$ penetration will not occur but a balance of forces will be reached when

$$\gamma_{ss} = 2\gamma_{sl} \cos \frac{\phi}{2},$$

where ϕ is the dihedral angle measured in the liquid phase. Further, as γ_{ss} decreases and γ_{sl} increases ϕ will increase and the penetration tendency will decrease. The importance of these considerations in cermets has been shown by the work of Parikh and Humenik.[29] In practice the size of the angles observed in a microsection will appear to vary so that it is necessary to measure a large number of angles and plot a histogram. The most frequently occurring angle is then the true angle.[30,20]

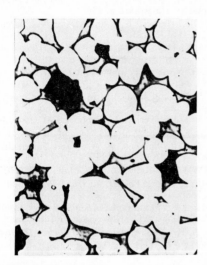

Fig. 4.—*Micrograph by reflected light (×630) of mixture of 85% MgO : 15% CaMgSiO₄ after firing at 1550°C. Silicate grey. Pores black.*

Fig. 4 shows the structure obtained by Jackson *et al.* in a body consisting of 85% MgO and 15% monticellite by weight, which illustrates these points, the dihedral angles being the re-entrant angles between the periclase grains. The estimated true angle was 25°. Fig. 5 shows the effects of additions of Cr_2O_3 and Fe_2O_3, singly and together, on the angle up to the limit of solubility of the additions, which is indicated by the dashed line ab. It will be evident that Cr_2O_3 increases the dihedral angle and should thus promote direct bonding, whereas Fe_2O_3 has the opposite effect. These conclusions were confirmed by determining the ratio of the grain boundary area to the phase boundary area in the structure which did in fact increase with Cr_2O_3 addition and decrease with Fe_2O_3 addition.

In another investigation[31] the effect of Cr_2O_3 on melting relationships in the region of the 6-component-system $CaO-MgO-Al_2O_3-Fe_2O_3-Cr_2O_3-SiO_2$ to which basic refractories belong, is being investigated. This work is showing that the temperatures of initial melt formation in basic refractory compositions are raised appreciably by addition of Cr_2O_3, while the amount of melt formed at a given temperature is considerably reduced.

The Problem of Brittleness

The low resistance of ceramic materials to mechanical and thermal shock is still the the major obstacle to their widespread use and in spite of intensive investigation of the mechanisms of failure no solution to this problem is yet in sight. Briefly the situation seems to be as follows.

So far as single crystals are concerned two kinds of behaviour appear to be encountered in ceramic materials, *viz.* that exhibited by structurally simple substances like MgO, NaCl and LiF, which can deform plastically by glide of

dislocations on simple slip systems, and that exhibited by more complex substances like SiO_2 and possibly Al_2O_3, where deformation involves complicated slip systems which only operate with difficulty, if at all, at low temperatures.

The latter can possibly be regarded as true brittle solids. In the former, on the other hand, slip usually occurs in a relatively small number of glide bands and is initiated by surface cracks which tend to propagate, as slip proceeds, by the release of elastic energy from dislocations converging on them. This process continues until a crack reaches the critical Griffiths size when spontaneous failure occurs.[31] As usually prepared, therefore, such crystals appear brittle.

When the surface is carefully prepared to remove flaws, crystals of this type do exhibit ductility to a degree in that they can be bent, but ultimately cracks are nucleated within the crystal by mechanisms that involve the impingement of dislocations on intersecting slip bands. Propagation and fracture then occur as before.

When polycrystals are considered, a further condition for ductility is introduced, this being that the grains should be able to undergo an arbitrary change of shape and the condition that a crystal should be capable of doing this is that it should slip on five independent slip systems.[32] (This is known as the von Mises criterion). In MgO, however, only two slip systems that are independent in the von Mises sense operate, and brittleness is inevitable. (It has been shown that over 350°C, in LiF, slip on (100) planes becomes possible in addition to that on (110) planes and a marked increase in plasticity occurs.[33])

Various suggestions have been made as to how these difficulties can be overcome. One recent suggestion is that by introducing other ions into the structure, slip on easy slip systems may be inhibited until a stress is reached at which more difficult systems become operative and general slip occurs.

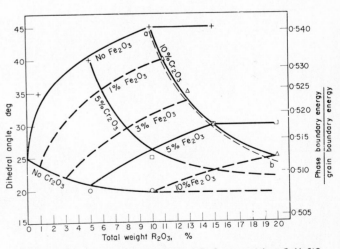

Fig. 5.—*Effect of additions of Cr₂O₃ and Fe₂O₃ to periclase-CaMgSiO₄ mixtures on dihedral angle formed at contacts between periclase grains.*

Another suggestion recently made by Gilman[34] is that by utilizing to the full the intrinsic strength of the stronger ceramics, which might involve the use of components made from single crystals, such high strengths might be achieved that ductility could be dispensed with. Cottrell,[35] however, has pointed out that the elastic energy stored at high stress levels in high strength ceramics would cause them to fracture explosively if they suffered even minute surface damage.

References

1   Gorter, E. W. *Nature*, 1950, **165,** 798.

2   Volger, J. *Research*, 1954, **7,** 196 and 230.

3   Woodhouse, D. and White, J. *Trans. Brit. Ceram. Soc.*, 1955, **54,** 333.

4   Phillips, B., Somiya Sh. and Muan, A. *J. Amer. Ceram. Soc.*, 1961, **44,** 167.

5   Paladine, A. E. "*Tech. Rep. No.* 46," 1999 (Raytheon Manuf. Co. Waltham, U.S.A.).

6   Paladino, A. E. "*Tech. Rep. No.* 32," 1958 (Raytheon Manuf. Co., Waltham, U.S.A.).

7   Bloor, E. C. "*Ceramics, A Symposium*", 1953 (Stoke: British Ceramic Soc.), p. 227.

8   Moulson, A. J. and Popper, P. "*Special Ceramics 1962*" (London: Academic Press), 1963, p. 355.

9   Kreuchen, K. H. *Ibid.*, p. 387.

10   Kingery, W. D. "*Introduction to Ceramics*", 1961 (New York: Wiley).

11   Murray, P. *Trans. Brit. Ceram. Soc.*, 1963, **62,** 71.

12   Sayers, J. B. *Ibid.*, p. 39.

13   Russell L. E. and Harrison, J. D. L. "*Paper CN*-16/22, *IAEA Conference*", 1963, Prague.

14   Briggs, G., Dutta S. K. and J. White, "*Paper A*16, *Harwell Conference on Uranium Carbide*", Nov. 1963.

15   Watt, W., *et al.* "*Nuclear Power*", February, 1959.

16   Carley-Macaulay, K. W. and McKenzie, M. "*Special Ceramics 1962*", 1963 (London: Academic Press), p. 151.

17   Kuczynski, G. C. *J. of Metals*, 1949, **1,** 169,

18   Kingery, W. D. and Berg, M. *J. Appl. Physics*, 1955, **26,** 1205.

19   Coble, R. L. *Ibid.*, 1961, **32,** 787 and 793.

20   Quoted by Smith, C. S. *Trans. A.I.M.M.E.*, 1948, **175,** 15.

21   Jorgensen, P. J. and Westbrook, J. H. "*General Research Lab., Report No.* 63—*RL*–3255*M*", 1963.

22   Parr, N. L., Martin G. F. and May, E. R. W. "*Special Ceramics*", 1960 (London: Heywood), p. 102.

23   Popper, P. *Ibid.*, p. 209.

24   Gooding, R. W. and Parratt, N. J. *Powder Metallurgy*, 1963, **11,** 42.

25   Ingles, T. A. and Popper, P. "*Special Ceramics*", 1960 (London: Heywood), p. 144.

26   Seeley, G. G., Herbert, J. M. and Moore, N. C. *Powder Metallurgy*, 1961, **8,** 145.

27   Ford, W. F., Hayhurst, A. and White, J. *Trans. Brit. Ceram. Soc.*

28   Jackson, B., Ford, W. F. and White, J. *Trans. Brit. Ceram. Soc.*, 1963, **62,** 577.

29   Parikh, N. M. and Humenik, M. *J. Amer. Ceram. Soc.*, 1957, **40,** 315.

30   Harker, B. and Parker, E. R. *Trans. A.S.M.*, 1945, **34,** 156.

31   El-Shahat, R. M. and White, J. *Ibid.*, in the press.

32   Clarke, F. J. P., Sambell, R. A. J. and Tattersall, H. *Phil. Mag.*, 1962, **7,** 393 and 1977.

33   Groves, W. G. and Kelly, A. *Phil. Mag.*, 1963, **8,** 877.

34   Budworth, D. W. and Pask, J. A. *Trans. Brit. Ceram. Soc.*, 1963, **62,** 763.

35   Gilman, J. J. "*Physics and Chemistry of Ceramics*", 1963, Ed. Klingsberg, C. (New York: Gordon and Breach).

36   Cottrell, A. H. "*Paper read at Royal Society Discussion on New Materials*", 1962.

STRENGTHENED GLASS

By B. SUGARMAN, M.Sc., D.I.C., F.Inst.P.*

SYNOPSIS

The term " glass " is defined and the various theories of glass structure are discussed briefly. Many factors contribute to make glass very much weaker than its theoretical strength but the most important is considered to be the surface condition. The problem is not necessarily one of strengthening glass; it is primarily one of producing a flaw-free surface, protecting the surface against subsequent damage and making it resistant to abrasion. Many possible techniques for achieving strengthening have been postulated in the literature. Because glass breaks in tension, many strengthening processes aim at producing a compressive skin on the surface of the glass which will then withstand a greater stress before fracture. Recently, methods of chemical toughening, including ion-diffusion techniques, have been developed to a promising stage. Processes available commercially at the present time are basically thermal toughening (using air as the quenching medium) and chemical toughening. For containers various coatings have been used with some success. Although great advances have been made in the field of chemical toughening, attention must be paid to the physico-chemical reactions at the surface if further progress is to be made.

Introduction

Definition of the term " glass " and some consideration of the various theories of glass structure are prerequisites of any discussion of possible ways of strengthening the material. The published literature contains many definitions of the term, differing in emphasis and points of detail, but sufficiently similar to make random selection possible for most practical purposes. When a liquid cools to the point at which it is solid, i.e. possesses a viscosity greater than $10^{14.5}$ poises (according to Condon[1]), it becomes, if no crystallization occurs, a glass and has no long-range order or three-dimensional periodicity. In general, glasses are considered as forming by solidification of a liquid but in some specific cases they can be formed direct from the vapour phase. This description will suffice as a glass technologist's working definition of a " glass ".

Zachariasen,[2] and Warren and co-workers[3] made valuable contributions to the study of the structure of glass and laid the foundation for the " continuous random network " theory which provided the impetus for much of the following work. Earlier Randall et al.[4] published results of X-ray examinations on vitreous materials and concluded that glasses were aggregates of extremely small crystals or crystallites. The " crystallite " theory was postulated in 1921 by Lebedev,[5] who was engaged in work on the annealing of glass. Later workers (e.g. Valenkov and Porai-Koshits[6]) have criticized both theories. These workers believed that within the main body of the glass were regions of molecules, ions or atoms in large groups, and in these groups the degree of order was large relative to the mean order of the glass. These groups can be regarded as small, distorted crystals separated by zones of low order. Eckstein,[7] Peyches,[8] Zarzycki,[9] Garino-Canina,[10] Stevels,[11] etc. have all made contributions to the knowledge of glass structure and the models postulated generally include some degree of order in islands or groups within a matrix of low order. The location of the various ions in the structure profoundly affects the physical properties and, under some circumstances, the strength of the glass, but detailed discussion of glass structure is beyond the scope of this brief review.

Although the structure of glass is still being explored, it should be stressed that, for all practical purposes, glass may be considered as a rigid, fully-elastic material, with no crystalline structure immediately apparent. Further, for most

applications, the determining factors for its full utilization are its strength, chemical durability, hardness, and transparency; in some cases heat resistance may be of special significance. Chemical durability is determined to some extent by the glass composition,[12] and there is evidence to show that micro-hardness is a function of composition.[13] The strength of glass is a much more difficult phenomenon to discuss in simple terms and, as will be commented upon later, if one requires ultra-high strength it may be a necessary prerequisite that complete transparency is unattainable. In general, transparent solids are either glasses or single crystals and, in some cases, although conversion from a glass to a partially-crystallized material gives a great increase in strength, transparency suffers.

Strength of Glass

In this paper " strength " is considered as tensile strength, which is by far the most important aspect in engineering applications of glass. From theoretical considerations it can be shown that a silicate glass should have a strength of between 10^6 and 3×10^6 lb/in^2 and which will be of the order of $0.2E$ where E is the Young's modulus of the glass. For silicate glass E is approximately 10^7 lb/in^2. In an homogeneous glass there seems to be little correlation between strength and composition, although it is now possible to produce glasses with higher Young's moduli. If glass is theoretically so strong a major question to be answered is why in practice is it so weak? That it is relatively weak in practice because of mechanical damage to the surface on a microscopic or sub-microscopic scale is well known. Users of glass often take, for design purposes, ultimate strengths of 1000–5000 lb/in^2, dependent upon the application. Unfortunately, early recorded work on strength was not very well documented and Griffith[14] was, it is believed, the first person to explore the correlation between strength and size. Many workers investigating this problem have not been fully cognisant of all the factors which can affect the strength of glass. These include surface conditions, atmospheric environment, durability, effect of heating and the effect of sustained loading. The size effect, at first thought to be of major importance, has been shown by recent work not to be so and fibres and rods can now be made with strengths of 5×10^5 lb/in^2 and above.[15, 16] Tests on vitreous silica fibres have

* The British Glass Industry Research Association, Sheffield, 10.

shown strengths as high as 2×10^7 lb/in^2.[17] The effect of water and the atmosphere of test can have a pronounced effect on glass strength and some of the mechanisms associated with these effects are still unexplained, as are some of the effects of heating to relatively low temperatures, *i.e.* below the strain point, which is defined as that temperature from which a piece of glass can be quickly cooled without introducing permanent strain.

Griffith suggested the presence of minute cracks or flaws in glass which, whilst being much smaller than a visible crack or flaw, acted as stress raisers and reduced the effective strength of the glass. Unfortunately, these " Griffith cracks " have never been revealed but sophisticated experimental techniques recently applied[18] have resulted in a greater appreciation of the possible shape and magnitude of such flaws. However, whereas Griffith has suggested flaws throughout the glass, it is now generally thought that such serious strength-reducing flaws as exist do so only at the surface. Within the mass of the glass there may well be defects which could be bubbles, *etc.*, and these in themselves could act as stress raisers of low power. This may explain why maximum strengths only approximately 0·4 of the theoretical strength are the highest yet attained even when the glass surface is " defect free ".

We thus see that a main problem is that of the removal of surface defects or flaws, and Holloway[19] has demonstrated that rods and fibres broken in bending do so at low stresses when a defect is at, or near to, the surface. Associated with this flaw removal there must, however, be the possibility of the maintenance of the defect-free surface. The problem of strengthening glass, and by this we mean the utilization of a greater proportion of the inherent strength of the material, must therefore be considered in the light of preventing defects forming on the surface.

Two basic approaches are possible: producing a flaw-free surface and protecting it against defects or abrasion; or healing surface defects and at the same time making the surface resistant to abrasion.

Possible Ways of Strengthening Glass

Various authors (*e.g.* Brekhovskikh[20]) have postulated techniques, additional to the established ones of flame polishing and flaw removal by treatment in hydrofluoric acid, by which strengthening of glass can be achieved and, whilst some of these may be very practical yet uneconomic, some are perhaps neither practical nor economic. It is the search for techniques which are both practical and economic that occupy the thoughts of the many active participants in this fascinating field.

The following techniques which are all dependent upon the alteration of the physico-chemical glass structure have been propounded:—

(1) Action of nuclear radiation (neutrons, protons, gamma rays).

(2) Introduction of additional ions or ionic groups into the structure of the glass (electro-diffusion).

(3) Replacing the ions having large radii by ones having smaller radii (or vice versa).

(4) Introduction into the glass of neutral inorganic molecules and/or metals in the atomic state.

(5) Action of high pressure.

(6) Orientation of the structure by external actions.

(7) Introduction of organic molecules into inorganic glasses.

(8) Creation of inorganic polymers.

Not all of these techniques have been investigated although some are the subject of patents. Of those most likely to be practical and economic perhaps the ion-substitution techniques must be considered the most promising, although there seems to be every reason to believe that special, *i.e.* non soda-lime-silica, glasses may be required to effect the greatest increases by this technique.

Nuclear-radiation techniques according to Brekhovskikh result in transformations, *i.e.* $Na^{23} \rightarrow Na^{24} \rightarrow Mg^{24}$, $Ca^{40} \rightarrow Ca^{41} \rightarrow K^{41}$, $Ca^{44} \rightarrow Ca^{47\beta} \rightarrow Sc^{47} \rightarrow Ti^{47}$ and the dimensions of the nucleus of the newly formed atoms are smaller than the bombarded nucleus. This author states that densification of the structure and strengthening of the glass will occur. French patents[21, 22] claim strengthening of alkali borosilicate glasses, with or without lead and alkali earth oxides, by neutron bombardment. It has also been postulated that by the controlled cooling of glasses containing metals in the atomic state it may be possible to obtain aggregation of crystallites and thus promotion of crystallized glass, *i.e.* glass ceramics. The field of glass ceramics is most certainly one of great potential and interest and is closely linked to new processes recently announced by the Corning Glass Company, which include ion-diffusion processes.

The basic requirement for glass is that it should be able to withstand adequately and safely the shocks to which it will be subject in use. Over and above the possibilities of strengthening already mentioned, the thermal toughening process currently exists and will be considered later, together with other possible practical techniques, in more detail. Protection of the surface has also been mentioned and the way in which such protections operate is still the subject of much research.

Practicability of High-strength Glass

We have already discussed the possible ways of modifying the surface to make it more resistant but it is not perhaps obvious that many of the suggested procedures aim at producing on the surface of the glass a compressive skin. Glass, a brittle material, breaks in tension and if the surface stress is compressive then the component will withstand a much greater stress before fracture. Many of the processes may be applicable to a pristine surface and as such these surfaces will not be so " defective " as surfaces that have been contaminated or abraded. Some processes will operate, in all probability, on damaged surfaces and presumably partially heal defects, perhaps as a result of the heat treatment which is often part of the process.

It is now well established that by the treatment of a glass in a bath of hydrofluoric acid, surface flaws can be removed and initial defects, visible under a high-power microscope as bruises or abrasions, become saucer-shape depressions whose dimensions in the plane of the glass are large in comparison with their depth. The stress concentration factors introduced by these modified defects are thus quite low and strengths approaching 5×10^5 lb/in^2 have been obtained for soda–lime–silica glass treated in this way. Unfortunately, attaining high strength without maintaining it is of little use, and therefore workers have been active in exploring various coatings to protect either an HF treated surface or a pristine surface as obtained from a glass-forming machine. Until recently, surface coatings have been applied to glass articles after they have been annealed in a lehr and whilst such treatments have been beneficial in reducing scuffing (a word traditionally used to describe bruising and abrasion primarily as a result of glass-to-glass contact) the benefits are often not permanent. The treatment of glass surfaces by silicones has been explored in some detail but only in limited cases have commercial organizations in the United Kingdom undertaken the treatment as a normal commercial process.

A very active interest is taken in the United States in

coatings, and recently new coatings, which are applied to the hot article before annealing, have been introduced.[23] These will be discussed later. In the United Kingdom a sulphuring treatment has been used to afford protection against abrasion and weathering. This process, adequately described in the literature, has been shown to be an ion-substitution process whereby the sodium in the skin of a conventional soda–lime–silica glass is replaced by hydrogen in the ionic form.[24] Electro neutrality is maintained and the glass surface becomes compacted relative to the base glass. According to Sendt,[25] the effect of sulphuring depends upon the presence of water and the compressive stress desired as a result of the process may not necessarily be obtained. It would seem that the complex diffusion processes which take place are not yet fully explained but cation substitution at the surface of the glass is all important.

In the field of containers the use of SO_2 in the lehr is an established process, as is also the use of pellets of ammonium sulphate.[26] In these cases the process is applied primarily to improve the durability rather than to specifically strengthen the article. Kurz[27] has claimed advantages in the use of aluminium-sulphate pellets but the mechanism of this process is again subject to some speculation. Commercial annealing of containers in lehrs is usually carried out to leave a slight residual compressive stress on the outside skin for, as has been previously stated, glass breaks in tension. Tensile stresses on exposed surfaces are highly dangerous and, whilst they may conceivably occur due to inhomogeneous glass, great attention must be directed to the annealing treatment. Recently developments in metal-organic compounds have indicated that the hot treatment of glass containers by spraying metal-organic compounds of titanium (e.g. isopropyl titanate) can result in a durable and hard coating of TiO_2.[28] The appearance of such containers after treatment is somewhat akin to that of a bloomed lens but, from some tests reported to the author, it would appear that the treatment does not result in a discrete coating. Diffusion of the titania may take place and this causes, in the glass, an increase in refractive index and perhaps a change in hardness and linear thermal-expansion coefficient. If the titania does effectively diffuse to become a network former, then the process may be one of great commercial promise. If a hot treatment results in the skin of the glass having a lower linear thermal-expansion coefficient than the body of the glass when the glass is cold, then the skin compressive stress can result in a greatly strengthened glass component.

So far no mention has been made in detail of the only process universally operated for strengthening glass—thermal toughening. The technique of thermal toughening is that discovered by Prince Rupert who quenched, in water, small drops of molten glass. It was found that the body of the glass was very resistant to impact but if the tail of the drop was broken, the mass of glass disintegrated explosively. The glass at a temperature near its softening point is cooled rapidly on the outside whilst the inside of the glass remains hot. As the complete mass cools down, the solidification of the inside, after the solidification of the outside, causes a compressive stress on the outer skin. The inner portion of the glass is in tension to balance the outer skin stress. This toughening process has been put to good use in windscreens, tumblers, and simple pressed or blown articles; but nowadays most articles are quenched by jets of cold air rather than by water immersion. During this century many hundreds of patents have been applied for, and granted, on the toughening of glass by heat treatment. Many other cooling media have been proposed including grease, tar, and waste gases.[29] Alkali salt baths have also been used and this process could perhaps be contrasted with ion-diffusion processes to be discussed later. Metals have also been adopted but, without

doubt, air chilling is the most universally used and, with the recent introduction of zonal toughening, the disadvantage of loss of vision when a conventionally-toughened windscreen fracture has been overcome.

Sil'vestrovich and Boguslavskii[30] claimed in 1959 that the toughening of plate and sheet glass by quenching in baths of chlorosilanes could greatly increase strengths as a result of the silane reaction with the Si–O bonds on the surface of the glass. They claimed that strengths as high as 55 kg/mm^2 (78 500 lb/in^2) could be obtained, contrasting with strengths by normal air toughening of 21 kg/mm^2 (30 000 lb/in^2). It is of interest to record that in a subsequent paper by Vitman et al.[31] the explanation of the higher strength given was that the increased heat transfer by quenching in a silane bath resulted in a greater quenching and hence a greater toughening.

Another method which, it is believed, has received some attention is the technique of casing a glass article by a second glassy material of lower linear thermal-expansion coefficient than the main body of the glass. This technique, although in principle very sound, may be difficult to apply because of the need to ensure that the composition of the body of the glass is such that it has a softening point above that at which the casing can be applied without distortion taking place. By producing a skin modification in the compositional sense, it is possible to obtain substantial compressive stresses and hence strengthen the glass. The depth of the compressive skin or layer, and it may be a casing or it may be a compositional alteration in the glass, is obviously of great importance in determining the resistance of the article to abrasion, and there must be a minimum skin depth which will provide adequate abrasion resistance. With casings the properties of the article will be dependent upon the characteristics of both the body glass and the casing glass and, in so far as some interdiffusion may occur, the glasses must be chemically compatible. Because special glasses will probably be needed it is not thought that the process will find very general application but it may be a practical technique for wide-mouth containers or domestic utensils.

Recently-developed Techniques for Strengthening Glass

Over the last few years the Corning Glass Company[32] has released information on some strengthening processes, the general name for which is Chemcor. Not all of the methods have been described but from the published literature there is no doubt that they include ion-diffusion techniques. It is well established that cation substitution, i.e. lithium for sodium, sodium for potassium, sodium for lithium, or potassium for sodium, etc., can result in surface compressions or tensions dependent upon whether or not the ion diffusing in is larger than the ion diffusing out, provided that the diffusion takes place at temperatures below the strain point. At temperatures above the strain point different results are obtained and the Corning Glass Company, in a patent,[33] has described ways in which lithium diffusion into a sodium-alkali glass can effect a great strengthening of the glass. After strengthening by immersion in a bath of molten lithium salt, increases in strength of up to 1150% have been claimed. The abraded strength after treatment is 75,000 lb/in^2 as against the abraded strength of 5000–6000 lb/in^2 for untreated annealed material. In all the work reported by the company the samples have been subjected to a controlled abrasion by rolling in a ball mill in 30-grit silicon carbide. To satisfactorily withstand this abrasion the strengthened layer was required to be about 0·003 in. deep. It would appear that the highest strengths are obtained from special glass compositions containing TiO_2, which acts as a nucleator for the formation of β-spodumene. The great strengthening is attributed to the formation of β-spodumene which has a negative linear thermal expansion coefficient. Without TiO_2 present in sufficient quantity, strength increases of the order of only 300% are obtainable but, in this case, the material after strengthening remains transparent or translucent. With high concentrations of TiO_2, in addition to the formation of β-spodumene, precipitation of the TiO_2 occurs and the whole body of the glass becomes opaque. From the foregoing it will be seen that the key to the problem of strengthening by this process is the formation of β-spodumene, although substitution of lithium ions for sodium ions above the strain point also yields some strengthening.

A second novel way of obtaining strengthening has also been patented by the Corning Glass Company.[34] In this process by controlled heat treatment of specially formulated lithia–alumina–silicate glasses with little or no other alkali ion content, microscopic and sub-microscopic crystals of β-eucryptite are formed. Unlike the lithium salt bath process, no change in composition is claimed between the body of the glass and the skin but only a crystallization which takes place at or near the glass surface. Again, β-eucryptite has a lower linear thermal expansion coefficient than the base glass and therefore after heat treatment the material has a compressive skin stress and is thus strengthened. A further claim in this particular patent is that the untreated glass can be strengthened by an HF treatment prior to the heat treatment. Glasses subjected to this preferential crystallization treatment retain their inherent transparency due, it is claimed, to the fineness of the crystals formed and the fact that the difference in refractive index of the glass and of the β-eucryptite crystals is only slight. Strengthening by this process is of the order of 300% (measured on abraded specimens).

In an original paper by Kistler,[35] evidence is quoted of the strengthening which can be obtained by substituting potassium ions for sodium ions in a soda–lime–silica glass of commercial manufacture at temperatures below the strain point. In his paper and patent[36] reference is made to unabraded strengths of approximately 69 000 lb/in^2 for glass which, unstrengthened by a diffusion process, has a strength of 20 000–26 000 lb/in^2. Substantial strength increases are thus possible. Acloque[37] has also reported strengthening by a similar process in thin microscope cover slides of a somewhat different composition. BGIRA[38] has also investigated the strengthening potential and practicability of potassium-ion diffusion in a commercial soda–lime–silica glass of composition close to that of a conventional bottle glass. At temperatures below the strain point the diffusion of cations larger than those in the " as-produced " glass results in a substantial skin stress which is compressive in nature. These techniques are therefore in contrast to the Corning processes which, as far as have been revealed, operate above the strain point. Such low-temperature diffusion processes do not produce crystalline material but so far, a significant potassium-ion diffusion has been achieved only to a depth of about 0·001 in., and this is clearly not enough to withstand adequately the kind of abrasion encountered in commercial practice. The magnitude of the compressive stress appears to be satisfactory but in order to ensure adequate abrasion resistance, greater skin depths will have to be obtained and it may well be that this will make the process uneconomic.

Commercial Achievements to Date

It has been impossible in this paper to present, other than in a somewhat sketchy outline, processes proposed or existing for strengthening glass, but it is perhaps worth while concluding with what may be regarded as the achievements to date and the possibilities for the future.

In the field of flat glassware the only available forms of strengthening are:

(1) Thermal toughening.

(2) Chemcor.

(1) With thermal toughening, standard soda–lime–silica glass in a wide range of thicknesses and sizes can be toughened adequately to give an operational strength (unabraded) of 20,000–25,000 lb/in^2. Many processors operate the toughening technique, which can be zonal for specific requirements. Difficulties in obtaining a high degree of toughening exist in glass of a thickness less than about 0·187 in.

(2) With Chemcor, using specially formulated glasses, very high strengths up to 10^5 lb/in^2 flexural strength can be obtained in thin glasses, perhaps as thin as 0·08 in., but the size limitation is not known. It is likely that the strengthening process, together with the glass cost, will prevent the material's being competitive with thermally toughened glass but the flexibility of the strengthened glass is a distinct advantage. According to the manufacturers, glass 0·1 in. thick can be flexed a thousand times over a form with a radius of 30 in. without damage.

It is believed that one flat-glass manufacturer is currently in a position to strengthen conventional soda–lime–silica glass by an ion substitution process of the Kistler form but no details are available.

In the container field currently available forms of strengthened ware are of three types:

(1) Thermally toughened.

(2) Chemcor processed.

(3) Coated.

(1) Thermally-toughened containers are available only in a very limited range of designs—mainly tumblers, cups, and similar widemouth containers. These have found great use in canteens and the like.

(2) A Chemcor process has been disclosed for the production of extremely high-strength tableware. These articles, marketed under the trade name " Centura ", are three times stronger than ordinary tableware. The process could obviously be applied to other containers but the articles are not transparent and may well be uneconomic for mass container production in both production rate and price.

(3) The field of coating containers is much more difficult to define but, in so far as sulphuring and, to some extent, treatment with aluminium and ammonium salts are carried out, these may possibly be regarded as coatings or surface skin modifiers. Various other coatings, e.g. mono stearates, silicones, etc., are also in vogue but the coatings are, in the main, soluble in water and act primarily as anti-scuffing coatings or treatments to improve durability and not primarily as strengthening coatings.

Recent processes with metal-organic compounds, producing coatings of high reflectivity and good anti-scuffing properties, may also be regarded as a valuable contribution.

Future Possibilities

Up till now the greatest advances in stronger glass have been made by chemical or thermal treatments on specially formulated glasses. These advances stem in many respects from the work of Kistler in the field of ion substitution and the work by the Corning Glass Company on glass ceramics. Whilst the phenomena involved in these techniques are becoming better understood, attention to the physico-chemical surface reactions which take place is still of the utmost importance if further progress is to be made. The hardness of glass and its relation to a stressed skin are worthy of more attention, as is much more study of the way in which strengthening really occurs.

No substantial breakthrough has been made in the field of containers as yet, but there can be no doubt that with increased knowledge about the surface of glass and its reaction with other materials, be they gases, inorganic salts, metal-organic compounds, or liquids, further advances will be made towards providing stronger glass. When this time comes not only will architects, engineers, technologists, and housewives have a better material to use but the increased potentialities of this theoretically very strong material will be realized.

Acknowledgments

The author wishes to acknowledge the assistance of his colleagues at BGIRA in the preparation of this paper. Permission to publish has been granted by the Council of BGIRA and the opinions expressed are those of the author and not necessarily representative of the Research Association.

References

1. Condon, E. V. *Amer. J. Phys.*, 1954, **22**, 43.
2. Zachariasen, W. M. *J. Amer. chem. Soc.*, 1932, **58**, 3841.
3. Warren, B. E., Krutter, H., and Morningstar, O. *J. Amer. ceram. Soc.*, 1936, **19**, 202.
4. Randall, J. T., Rooksby, H. P., and Cooper, B. S. *Z. Kristallogr.*, 1930, **75**, 196.
5. Lebedev, A. A. *Trans. opt. Inst., Leningr.*, 1921, **2**, 51.
6. Valenkov, N., and Porai-Koshits, E. A. *Z. Kristallogr.*, 1936, **95**, 195.
7. Eckstein, B. *Glastech. Ber.*, 1963, **36**, 371.
8. Peyches, I. *Silicates Industr.*, 1963, **28**, 223.
9. Zarzychki, J., and Mezard, R. *Physics and Chemistry of Glasses*, 1962, **3**, 1963.
10. Garino-Canina, V. *C.R. Acad. Sci.,, Paris*, 1961, **252**, 1807.
11. Stevels, J. M. *J. Soc. Glass Tech.*, 1951, **35**, 284.
12. Morey, G. W. "*Properties of Glass*", 1954 (New York: Reinhold).
13. Ainsworth, L. *J. Soc. Glass Tech.*, 1954, **38**, 479.
14. Griffith, A. A. *Phil. Trans.*, 1920, **A221**, 163.
15. Thomas, W. F. *Physics and Chemistry of Glasses*, 1960, **1**, 4.
16. Proctor, B. *Physics and Chemistry of Glasses*, 1962, **3**, 7.
17. Hillig, W. B. "*Symp. res. mech. du verre*", 1962 (Paris: Union Scientifique Cortinentale du Verre).
18. Ernsberger, F. M. "*Advances in Glass Technology*", 1962 (New York: Plenum Press Inc.)
19. Holloway, D. G. *Phil. Mag.*, 1959, **4**, 1101.
20. Brekhovskikh, S. M. *Glass and Ceramics, Moscow*, 1960, **17**, No. 7, p. 24.
21. Companie de Saint-Gobain S.A. *French Patent* 1.253.955.
22. Companie de Saint-Gobain S.A. *French Patent* 1.253.956.
23. E. I. du Pont de Nemours & Co. *U.S. Patent* 2,831,780.
24. Douglas, R. W., and Isard, J. O. *J. Soc. Glass Tech.*, 1949, **33**, 289.
25. Sendt, A. "*Advances in Glass Technology*", 1962 (New York: Plenum Press Inc.)
26. The United Bottle Glass Manufacturers Ltd. and Seddon, E. *British Patent* 556,602.
27. Kurz, F. W. A. *British Patent* 835,820.
28. Haslam, J. H. in *Metal-Organic Compounds*, "*Advances in Chemistry*", No. 23, 1959 (New York: American Chemical Society).
29. Frikell, G. *Glas-Email-Keramo-Technik*, 1958, **9**, 201, 250, 288.
30. Sil'vestrovich, S. M., and Boguslavskii, I. A. *C. R. Acad. Sci. U.R.S.S.*, 1959, **129**, 1362.
31. Vitman, F. F., Boguslavskii, I. A. and Pukh, V. P. *C.R. Acad. Sci. U.R.S.S.*, 1962, **145**, 85.
32. Stookey, S. D., Olcott, J. S., Garfinkel, H. M. and Rothermal, D. L. "*Advances in Glass Technology*", 1962 (New York: Plenum Press Inc.)
33. Corning Glass Works, Inc. *U.S. Patent* 2,779,136.
34. Corning Glass Works, Inc. *U.S. Patent* 2,998,675.
35. Kistler, S. S. *J. Amer. ceram. Soc.*, 1962, **45**, 59.
36. Research Corporation, Inc. *British Patent* 917,388.
37. Acloque, P. "*Symp. res. mech. du verre*", 1962 (Paris: Union Scientifique Continentale du Verre).
38. British Glass Industry Research Association. To be published.

The manuscript of this paper was received on 20 December 1963.

ADVANCES IN NUCLEAR CERAMICS

By F. J. P. CLARKE and P. MURRAY*

SYNOPSIS

The development of nuclear ceramic fuels offers economic advantages compared with metallic systems. These arise not only from the increased lifetime in power reactors but also from their ability to operate at higher temperatures, thus enabling higher thermal efficiency and lower generating costs to be obtained. To achieve these objectives relatively small improvements over established technology are required. Nevertheless, appreciable research and development effort has been necessary and several examples are given of the way in which investigations on sintering and microstructure have led to these developments.

Finally, reference is made to the importance of the long-term research proceeding on the fundamental properties such as brittleness and thermal shock of ceramic materials in general. If these disadvantages could be overcome then dramatic advances would be possible leading to the wider application of these materials.

Introduction

Advances in nuclear ceramics mean cheaper electricity from nuclear power stations and hence a valid criterion by which to judge an advance as significant is the effect it has on the cost of generating electricity. An improvement in the properties of materials that reduces the cost by $0 \cdot 01$ d/kWh can lead to considerable annual savings and to achieve this we do not necessarily have to seek *radical* improvements in properties such as a change from brittle to ductile behaviour. Relatively small changes, such as a decrease in porosity from 15% to 5%, or an increase in mechanical strength from 10,000 to 20,000 lb/in^2 can have a significant influence on the cost of electricity produced from nuclear power stations. But to produce even small improvements of this type involves considerable research and development effort often developing and using techniques which are novel to the traditional ceramist. An essential step in obtaining improved properties and behaviour frequently lies in understanding the phenomena involved at a detailed atomic level; background knowledge at this level is often meagre and has to be built up as the central research project progresses. For this reason, the economic criteria suggested above are not the sole ones to be used in judging an advance as significant. Advances in our background knowledge of the behaviour of ceramics, especially in their single crystal form has increased rapidly over the last decade and must rank as a significant contribution not only to nuclear science but to our understanding of the solid state. In this paper specific advances are discussed to illustrate these points.

Replacing Metal Fuels by Ceramics—the Advantages

The first advance concerns the replacing of uranium metal by the ceramic uranium dioxide in the development of the fuel element for the Advanced Gas Cooled Reactor (which is the successor to the Magnox/Uranium system); the A.G.R. prototype is now operating at 35 MW(E) at Windscale and contains approximately 13 tons of uranium canned in stainless steel in the fuel elements. The performance of a gas-cooled reactor depends on the temperature of the gas from the core and the higher this is the greater is the thermal efficiency of the

* Metallurgy Division, Atomic Energy Research Establishment, Harwell.

plant. The gas temperature depends especially on that of the can containing the fuel and with uranium metal canned in magnox (a magnesium alloy) the maximum practical can temperature is in the range 450–500°C; the cheapest cost of electricity with this type of system has recently been given at $0 \cdot 66$ d/kWh for the Wylfa power station.[1] To decrease this cost means raising the can temperature and thus changing both the fuel and the can, and this has been done in the Windscale A.G.R. It is estimated[2] that a 2×500 MW(E) A.G.R. power station similar to this could produce electricity for under $0 \cdot 5$ d/kWh and that a figure of $0 \cdot 4$ d/kWh might be attainable. Clearly this advance has important economic implications and one important feature that made this possible was the development of methods by which low porosity ($<5\%$) uranium bodies could be produced. The low porosity was necessary to obtain a high density of uranium atoms and to minimize the fission gas release that occurs on irradiation in a reactor.

In the normal ceramic practice prevalent in 1950–1955 the raw materials were calcined at high temperatures followed by crushing, grinding and grading treatments prior to pressing, drying and firing, and the porosities of the conventional products were usually in the region of 15–20%. In special applications, such as in nuclear ceramics, there was initially the premium on high bulk-density mentioned above; the importance of the effects of porosity on the mechanical and thermal properties of ceramics such as uranium was also appreciated at an early stage, and much attention was paid to fabrication processes and in particular to the sintering and hot pressing of pure materials. It was inevitable, therefore, with these synthetic ceramics, for consideration to be given to the preparation of fine powders by lower-temperature processes such as the thermal decomposition of compounds, since " dead burning ", or the use of high-temperature processes, was known to have a deleterious effect on the reactivity and, by analogy, the sintering behaviour of oxides such as magnesia. Detailed investigations were therefore made on the properties of uranium dioxide (prepared by reduction of higher oxides) and their correlation with sintering behaviour.

Uranium dioxide is the first example of a fine or reactive oxide powder to be used on a large scale, the main reason being that heat-transfer conditions necessitate the application of UO_2 as small diameter pellets in nuclear reactors. No difficulties arise, therefore, due to the high volume shrinkage

209

P

on sintering. In the chemical extraction route, uranium dioxide powder is prepared by the reduction of a higher oxide such as UO_3 with hydrogen in the temperature range 500–800°C and the powder particles obtained in this way are agglomerates of crystallites. The particle size and crystallite size of the uranium dioxide are functions of the characteristics of the higher oxide and of the reduction temperatures: the higher the reduction temperature, the greater the particle size and crystallite size of the powder produced. As reduced, the composition is $UO_{2.0}$ but uranium dioxide powders will oxidize in air at low temperatures (18–100°C) and powders with particle sizes in the region of 1μ will generally oxidize to compositions of about $UO_{2.02}$ after an exposure of one month at room temperature. Preparations of smaller particle size in the range 0.1μ oxidize more rapidly and may heat up so violently that partial conversion to U_3O_8 occurs.

The main technique for preparing solid UO_2 from powder is the usual one of cold compacting followed by sintering in a controlled atmosphere, and studies of the sintering behaviour of non-stoichiometric oxides have uncovered some interesting aspects of the sintering process. Typical results on two types of powder from two different sources are shown in Fig. 1.

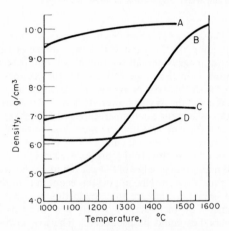

Fig. 1.—*Density versus sintering temperature for two types of uranium oxide and two sintering atmospheres*

The compacts were all prepared by cold pressing in metal dies at 10 ton/in², followed by sintering at the various temperatures shown for 2 hr in atmospheres of both argon and hydrogen. There is a major difference in the behaviour between the two types of oxide and, in addition, sintering atmosphere plays a significant part in determining the bulk density obtained under a given set of conditions. As indicated, the two oxides differed in oxygen content, and as hydrogen is known to reduce the oxygen in excess of stoichiometric at temperatures of 500°C and above, it is plausible to attribute the enhanced sintering behaviour of the higher oxygen content in argon solely to a large departure from stoichiometry. However, as is well known, particle size also plays an important part in determining sintering behaviour, the smaller the particle size the more readily sintering occurs. When the surface areas of the two powders were determined, the one of lower oxygen content had a value of 0.2 m²/g and the other oxide approximately 8 m²/g, as determined by the nitrogen-absorption method. The possible effects of particle size and excess oxygen are therefore inter-related, and as the particle size of one of the oxides was approximately 40 times smaller than that of the other, its enhanced sintering behaviour could possibly be attributed entirely to this feature without involving explanations based on departure from stoichiometry.

To separate the effects of these two variables, uranium dioxide powder of high surface area was prepared in an inert atmosphere to stoichiometric composition and then allowed to slowly oxidize at room temperature in air. Samples of different oxygen content were then cold compacted and given a standard sintering treatment of 2 hr at 1450°C in argon. In this way the relationship between oxygen content and sintered bulk density shown in Fig. 2 was obtained, the particle size

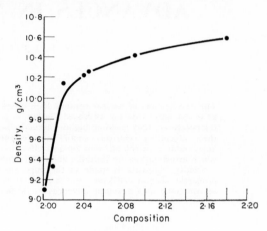

Fig. 2.—*Density versus oxygen content for uranium oxides sintered at 1450°C for 2 h in argon*

remaining sensibly constant during the oxidation process. These results indicate that departure from stoichiometry plays a definite part in the sintering of the oxide, although the mechanism by which the extra oxygen operates to aid sintering cannot be stated definitely. If a diffusion mechanism is responsible for sintering, the rate of change of density will be determined by the slower of the two ionic diffusion rates. The diffusion rate of the oxygen in excess of the stoichiometric amount is known to be extremely rapid and so the cation diffusion rate will probably be rate-determining and must therefore be affected by the departure from stoichiometry to explain the observed sintering results. The effect of surface area can be obtained directly by comparing the hydrogen sintering curves in Fig. 1, and the use of the higher-surface-area oxide results in a lowering of the temperature required for sintering to high bulk density by about 150°C in this case. More recent results with powders of higher surface area indicate that the sintering temperature in hydrogen can be reduced to as low as 1200°C.

By the use of these methods, high bulk density (greater than 95 % theoretical) UO_2 can be readily produced and in addition many of the general principles established have been applied to other pure oxides such as magnesia and beryllia.[3] In the latter case, by paying attention to the characteristics of the powders obtained by decomposition of the hydroxide and sulphate, and to the effects of impurities on the processes occurring in the early stages of sintering, bulk densities in the region of 99 % theoretical can be obtained;[4] these bodies have the low permeability necessary if beryllia is to be used as a matrix in dispersed fuels based on UO_2.

In the above example of UO_2, the advantages arising from its development and application can be defined rather precisely; it may be relevant, however, to refer to the possibilities with other nuclear fuels where advantages certainly exist although their worth cannot be stated explicitly at present.

Since the heat rating and power output from UO_2 fuel elements are limited by the low thermal conductivity, research is being carried out on interstitial compounds such as carbides and nitrides because of their higher thermal conductivity (which is approximately three times that of oxide at room temperature and increases still further at higher temperatures, since the conductivity is invariant with temperature and does not show the sharp decrease exhibited by the oxide). All the work reported here has been concerned with the uranium and plutonium compounds, although we believe that the results are applicable to the more commonly known carbides and nitrides (which are being mainly considered for their improved thermal properties and in certain cases, such as silicon nitride, for their low thermal expansion characteristics).

Studies on these materials have been mainly centred in the area dealing with fabrication routes and properties, since it must be demonstrated that practical routes exist from which satisfactory material can be obtained for physical property determinations. In our studies on carbides, the two routes investigated have been arc melting and casting and, alternatively, direct sintering of carbide powder. Two of the major previous difficulties associated with the arc fusion and casting process for carbide have been the control of composition and the production of crack-free castings. These difficulties have now been largely overcome by the development of a caesium-doped graphite electrode to give a stable arc so that reproducible conditions can be obtained from melt to melt, with negligible pick-up of carbon from the

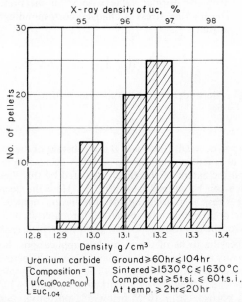

Fig. 3.—Density distribution of sintered uranium carbide pellets

electrode. A drastic reduction in the time at maximum power in the melting cycle is also a significant feature in the control of carbon content. In addition, the use of a special type of mould has greatly reduced the incidence of cracking, and satisfactory rods of uranium monocarbide can now be cast with controlled carbon content (4·80% ±0·03%).[5]

A major advance has also been made in the second technique, namely that of direct sintering of the carbide powder.[6] Prior to this work, temperatures greater than 1800°C were necessary to obtain products of 90% theoretical density. It has now been shown that, both for uranium monocarbide and solid solutions of plutonium carbide in uranium monocarbide, densities in excess of 95% theoretical can be achieved at 1500–1600°C in argon, provided that fine powders are used and protected from oxidation at all stages of the fabrication process. Typical results on the bulk-density distribution in batches of sintered pellets of uranium monocarbide are shown in Fig. 3. The detrimental effect of oxygen contamination on the sintering characteristics of carbide powders has also been demonstrated (Fig. 4) and it is essential to maintain the oxygen

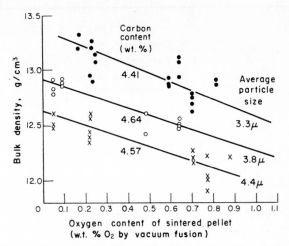

Fig. 4.—The effect of oxygen on the sintering of uranium carbide

and water vapour contents of the sintering atmosphere at a low level.

While the above work on monocarbides has been mainly concerned with the behaviour of the compounds themselves, our main interest and, we suggest, the main interest in the wider field mainly arises from the generic nature of the carbides and the other interstitial compounds of this type which possess metallic type properties (such as nitrides, sulphides and aluminides). There are possibilities in developing a wide range of materials with different properties, since not only do carbides of the refractory metals such as zirconium, niobium and tantalum form solid solutions with the monocarbides, but in addition eutectic systems exist between the monocarbides and the mononitrides and transition metals such as iron and chromium. There is also interaction between these carbides and the refractory metals.

As yet, the possibilities in these fields are relatively unexplored but it may be relevant to draw attention to two recent results. Firstly, it has been found that the addition of zirconium carbide to form solid solutions with uranium monocarbide results in an improvement in the oxidation resistance by about a factor of 10, much higher strengths are obtained, and there is an improvement by at least a factor of 5 in the thermal shock resistance.[7] Secondly, results on the properties of uranium monocarbide–iron cermets containing up to 10 wt.% iron, in which the structure consists of primary carbide grains in a eutectic network of carbide and iron, show considerable improvements so far as the strength and thermal conductivity are concerned.[8] Some of the preliminary results of these compositions are shown in Table I. It should be

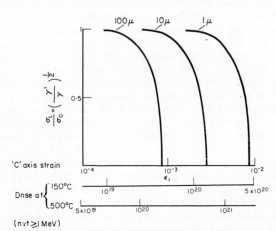

Fig. 5.—Plot of decrease in fracture stress against irradiation induced strain and neutron dose for different grain sizes.

TABLE I.—*Some Properties of Skull-Cast UC-Iron Cermets*

Compression stress (ton/in²)	UC, 16–36		UC–2½ wt.% Fe, 47–67
Transverse rupture stress (ton/in²)	UC, 3–6		UC–10 wt.% Fe, 10–30
Thermal conductivity (cal/cm² cm s °C)	UC–10 wt.% Fe	0·0735	
	U metal	0·064	
	UD skull cast	0·051	
	UO_2	0·02	

		Gain in weight (mg/cm² h)	
		500°C	700°C
Oxidation in CO_2	UC–10% Fe	0·1–0·2	1·0–2·0
	U metal	0·3	6·0
	UC, plunge sintered	2·5	14·0
	UC, skull cast	rapid oxidation samples disintegrate	

Uranium density (g/cm³)	UC	13·0
	UC–2½ wt.% Fe	12·4
	UC–5 wt.% Fe	11·9
	UC–10 wt.% Fe	10·9
	UO_2	9·7

emphasized that these cermets are of the chemically bonded type as opposed to mechanically bonded oxide cermets; the matrix, to begin with, has a high thermal conductivity and we are thus concerned with materials where considerable improvements in thermal shock resistance can be obtained.

Unlike the oxides, therefore, the " alloying behaviour " of carbides and other interstitial and intermetallic compounds affords real possibilities of obtaining materials with improved thermal and mechanical properties.

Some idea of the economic advantages to be obtained in the nuclear field by improvements in the properties of ceramics can be derived with respect to the A.G.R. Further long-term developments are dependent on replacement of the stainless steel can (with its temperature limitation of about 700°C) by a ceramic can leading to an all-ceramic fuel element. The limiting feature now becomes thermal stress and the heat output (H) is proportional to the thermal stress resistance of the material (*i.e.* $H \propto \sigma K/E\alpha$). Thus if the strength were to be doubled by developments in fabrication (higher bulk density and smaller grain size in high purity sintered material), the heat output would be doubled leading to a saving in generating costs of about 2%.[9]

Effect of Microstructure on Irradiation Behaviour

One of the problems involved in the use of ceramics in reactors lies in the effects of irradiation on their properties. For example at an early stage in the studies on beryllium oxide it was found that sintered specimens when irradiated for a year at ~150°C in the Harwell Dido reactor would fragment. The basic cause lay in a phenomenon well known to ceramists, *viz.* anisotropic expansion of the individual grains in a polycrystalline body. In beryllium oxide, anisotropic expansion is produced by reactor irradiation, since atoms are displaced from their normal lattice sites and agglomerate on certain crystallographic planes. This preferential agglomeration can be detected and observed by a variety of techniques including X-ray diffraction and electron microscopy. As a result there is a build-up of strain between grains in maximum misorientation, and it is the release of the strain energy that results in fragmentation. Normally when a crack grows the work required to separate the atoms ahead of the crack tip comes from the relaxation of the crystal around the sides of the crack and the Griffith equation is based on equating this relaxation energy to the work required to form the new sur-

faces. When, in addition, residual strain is present it is available to assist crack propagation at the grain boundaries, and the effective surface energy at the grain boundary is changed from its normal value γ to γ' in the presence of strain. The fracture stress is changed correspondingly from σ_0 to σ_i so that

$$\frac{\sigma_i}{\sigma_0} = \left(\frac{\gamma'}{\gamma}\right)^{\frac{1}{2}}$$

Now, γ' is dependent on the grain size, l, of the material and we may write

$$\gamma' = \gamma - A\epsilon_i^2 l$$

where ϵ_i is the misfit strain and A is a constant of the material. Hence the fracture stress can be raised by decreasing the grain size, and the extent of the effect predicted by this theoretical approach can be gauged from Fig. 5. Here the decrease in fracture stress is plotted against irradiation induced strain and reactor dose at two temperatures for materials of different grain size; the advantage of small grain size is clearly shown.

For beryllia to be of use in nuclear applications, however, the porosity must also be lower than 5% since the permeability to gases is of prime importance. (The permeability coefficient for viscous gas flow shows a marked drop from ~10^{-11} cm² at 10% porosity to <10^{-18} below 5% porosity). Since the simultaneous achievement of small grain size and low porosity in sintered material is difficult, severe problems arose in fabrication; as in the case of uranium dioxide the answer lay in a detailed characterization of the starting powders and a correlation of these characteristics with those of the sintered material.   As a result of this research, nuclear grade beryllium oxide was produced with a porosity of <3% and a grain size <5μ. This material has withstood reactor doses four to five times as great as the original large grain size material without fragmentation and makes the use of beryllium oxide worthy of consideration as a matrix for a dispersed fuel.

Basic Research Aspects

The basic problem about the use of ceramic materials in reactors and other high temperature environments lies in their poor resistance to mechanical and thermal shock. As discussed earlier these undesirable characteristics can be overcome to some extent by alteration of properties such as strength, thermal conductivity, Young's modulus and coefficient of expansion. Alternatively, if limited ductility could be introduced into the material then it would not have to accommodate the shape changes determined by the environment in a completely elastic manner. Considerable research effort has been devoted in the past decade to both of these approaches. In the former case most of the work has been concentrated on improvements in strength, whereas in the second case there have been general studies on the principles involved in the brittle/ductile behaviour of ceramics.

It has been found that the ultimate strengths of many common ceramic materials such as magnesia and alumina in single crystal form are around the theoretical strength, i.e. $\sim 10^6$ lb/in^2 and at these stresses elastic strains of several percent can be obtained. However, the very high elastic energy that is stored in these materials under such high stresses renders these materials extremely sensitive to the smallest defects which are introduced in practice. Thus, in alumina, magnesium oxide or silica, the critical Griffith crack size is about 500 atomic spacings at 10^6 lb/in^2. Although these materials, therefore, are potentially of very high strength, in practice it has only been possible so far to obtain such strengths in single crystals. In addition, it is much more difficult to obtain flaw-free polycrystals owing to the presence of pores and even taking into account recent advances in fabrication methods, it appears doubtful whether it is practicable to aim at strengths much in excess of 10^5 lb/in^2 for sintered polycrystalline oxides. An important problem in this respect lies in explaining why carbides can be obtained by standard manufacturing techniques with strengths in excess of 10^5 lb/in^2 (for example the rupture modulus of sintered titanium carbide of 5% porosity is quoted as 160 000 lb/in).[10] To be able to make a firm statement about the extent to which the potential strength of ceramics can be achieved we must have more basic information about the influence of pore size and shape, and the factors that determine these particularly in interstitial compounds such as carbides.

The possibility of making ductile ceramics has received a great deal of attention in recent years. However, it should be pointed out that in many applications we do not want ductile ceramics since, in fact, one of the basic limitations in the use of metals lies in the fact that at high temperatures they become too ductile to be useful. Clearly there is little to be gained in replacing a ductile metal by an equally ductile ceramic as far as this limitation is concerned. What is needed is a *tough* ceramic with the ability to absorb a limited amount of strain in a plastic manner and possible ways in which this might be done without reducing the creep strength have recently been suggested.[11] If we accept for the time being the view that we must learn to live with ceramics containing cracks, then the only way of overcoming brittleness is to allow sufficient plastic flow to occur to blunt the cracks and prevent their propagation. In materials such as alumina and beryllia, dislocations are immobile below about 1000°C because their movement is related to atomic diffusion processes. Thus in these materials we cannot hope for toughness by crack blunting below this temperature. In magnesia, however, plastic flow can occur at room temperature and one might hope for plastic blunting of cracks; yet, as is well known, magnesia is not a very good ceramic material from the point of view of these considerations. The reason for this is that due to the presence of dislocations in the material, crack propagation can be assisted. The strain field of a dislocation configuration can supplement the elastic strain field due to the applied load and cause failure by growth of a crack that is orders of magnitude below the critical Griffith size. These recent findings show that by treating the surface, ductility can be induced in single crystals at room temperature; the processes responsible for the ductility in a flaw-free single

P*

crystal have, however, been found to cause enhanced crack propagation when cracks are present initially. Now the reason for this in basic terms is that the number of effective slip systems on which the dislocations are operating is generally insufficient to allow crack blunting. The solution to this problem is to study ways of changing the effective number of slip systems and this in turn reduces to the problem not of creating new slip systems but of changing the efficiency of operation of those that already exist. It is clear from plastic deformation experiments, that broadening of the slip bands occurs in magnesia due to the fact that dislocations jump or slip across to other planes. Now slip on these other planes, or secondary systems occurs at much higher stresses than on the primary slip planes. If we could decrease this stress or alternatively increase the stress in the primary slip systems, then the two stresses would be matched and there would be sufficient slip systems operating for crack blunting. One possibility here is to alloy the material in the true physical metallurgy sense. We know, for example, from experiments on single crystals of MgO that the yield stress is raised by the presence of impurities and hence there is the possibility that by the addition of impurities the primary slip system could be made operative only at the higher stresses comparable to those of the secondary cross slip systems.

In polycrystalline materials, even if cracks are absent, the grain boundaries present a further hazard since slip can produce cracks at these points.[11] The reason for this behaviour is that the elastic strain caused in one grain by slip in an adjacent grain cannot be relieved without the operation of a certain number (5) of slip systems (von Mises).[12] Thus the general requirements for polycrystalline accommodation in metals turn out to be the criteria for crack blunting and prevention of cracking at grain boundaries in ceramics. In magnesia some toughness must be expected above 600°C since the secondary slip systems operate with reasonable efficiency. The surface sensitivity can be suppressed by strain hardening and it has been shown that in magnesia flow stresses above 10^5 lb/in^2 can be obtained in this way. The outcome is that from this basic research approach we are now in a position to define the principles involved in obtaining tougher ceramics and the aims of future research directed to this end have been narrowed; we now understand the basic mechanisms of plastic flow in some of these materials, we now know the basic conditions for crack initiation and propagation and we have indications as to how to prevent the latter; furthermore, we are moving into the position of using well-established physical metallurgy approaches and procedures for dealing with these problems.

Conclusions

In nuclear ceramic applications small property changes can often produce important economic advantages in the cost of generating electricity from nuclear power stations. However, even small property changes have proved very difficult to obtain because existing materials have been so intelligently exploited by traditional ceramists and the knowledge of fundamental mechanisms that would have guided further advances was not extensive. Hence the further advances involved both applied and basic research effort, often using techniques quite unknown to the traditional ceramist. This approach has resulted in advances that are significant not only in the nuclear power field but by analogy in the ceramic area in general. The last decade has resulted in a foundation being laid in our knowledge of basic mechanisms operating in especially oxide and carbide ceramics—it is vital to further progress that the next decade should see the gap between basic knowledge and applied processes narrowed still further.

References

1 *Nuclear Engineering* (1964), **9,** 7.

2 Kronberger, H. " *Nuclear Materials* (*Special Issue* 1964) *International Conference on BeO* ", Sydney, Australia, October, 1963. *J. Nuclear Materials* (1964), **14,** 41.

3 Murray, P. *J. Brit. Ceram. Soc.*, (1963) **1,** 113.

4 Livey, D. T. and Hey, A. W. " *U.K.A.E.A. Report A.E.R.E. R*.4447 " (1963). *J. Nuclear Materials* (1964), **14,** 285.

5 North, J. M., quoted by Frost, B. R. T., Mardon, P. G. and Russell, L. E., Proc. " *Plutonium as a Power Reactor Fuel* " Conference, Hanfor, U.S.A., Report HW 75007 (1962).

6 Russell, L. E. and Harrison, J. D. L. " *New Nuclear Materials Including Non-Metallic fuels* " (Vienna, I.A.E.A.) (1963), **1,** 543.

7 Hill, R. J. " *U.K.A.E.A. Harwell Report A.E.R.E. M*.1129 " (1962).

8 North, J. M. U.K.A.E.A., A.E.R.E., Harwell (*private communication*) (1964).

9 Iliffe, C. E. U.K.A.E.A. Risley, *Private communication* (1964).

10 Kingery, W. D. " *Introduction to Ceramics* " (Wiley, 1960), p. 610.

11 Clarke, F. J. P. and Kelly, A. *Trans. Brit. Ceram. Soc.*, (1963)**62,** 785.

12 von Mises, R. *Z. Angen. Math., Mech.* (1928), **8,** 161.

CHEMICAL ASPECTS OF NUCLEAR CERAMIC DEVELOPMENT

By L. E. J. ROBERTS, M.A., D.Phil.*

SYNOPSIS

The part played by chemical research in the development of high-melting compounds as nuclear fuels is reviewed. Major effort is required on:

(i) The determination of phase diagrams.

(ii) The provision of thermodynamic data; it is particularly necessary to determine equilibria at high temperatures in systems, such as the actinide oxides, which exhibit wide ranges of non-stoichiometry.

(iii) Surface reactions, as affecting the release of gases at high temperatures and the level of impurities in powder preparations.

(iv) Preparative routes, both to establish convenient and cheap methods and to optimize the microstructure of materials for particular applications. The control of composition is often crucial and needs analytical effort, as does the determination of impurity levels.

Examples are drawn from the work carried out on oxides and carbides; the current status of other interstitial-type compounds with the sodium chloride structure is reviewed briefly.

Introduction

The pace of development in the field of nuclear engineering is largely dictated by the advances in the science and technology of materials. The designer may have a good idea of the specification he would like, but he is usually constrained to use available materials until his demands can be met. These demands cover a wide range; ceramic compounds are needed both as fuels and moderators, capable of withstanding temperature-cycling and temperature gradients; new metals and alloys are being developed for service as fuel containers and in reactor cores; materials resistant to liquid metals and fused salts are required in some applications. Complex problems of preparation, analysis, phase stability, compatibility, and reprocessing exist for almost every material used, and hence the scope for chemical research is almost limitless. This paper concentrates on the development of high-melting compounds for nuclear fuels and stresses some aspects of chemical research, since research on physical properties of these materials is dealt with in another paper to this symposium.† It is the author's belief that some general points are of interest quite outside the nuclear field.

Oxide Fuels

The dioxides of uranium and plutonium are most important nuclear fuel materials; major parts of the industry will be based on their use for many years to come. They are members of complex oxide systems; there are some sixteen distinct oxides of uranium and at least five of plutonium. Many of the complications that arise during the use of the dioxides stem from this fact, and the variable valency of uranium and of plutonium; similar problems will occur in most applications of oxide phases containing transition metal cations.

Phase-diagram Work

Much of the chemistry of the uranium oxides became understandable when the phase diagram was established. The phase

boundaries change markedly with temperature and the mobility of oxygen in these structures is such that it is very difficult to quench-in the structures which are perfectly stable at high temperatures. X-ray work in a high-temperature camera established the main features between UO_2 and U_3O_8 up to about 900°C.[1] At higher temperatures, measurements of the oxygen pressures in equilibrium with the solid have been employed.[2] The phase diagram between UO_2 and U_3O_8 is sketched in Fig. 1. The main feature of importance is the very wide range of composition of the non-stoichiometric phase UO_{2+x} at high temperatures.

UO_2, UO_{2+x}, U_4O_9 and the oxides $\gamma_1(UO_{2\cdot33})$ and $\gamma_2(UO_{2\cdot30})$ are closely related and are all based on the fluorite structure of UO_2. X-ray density and measurements prove conclusively that the additional oxygen is entering interstitial positions in the lattice: the density increases, and the unit cell volume decreases regularly as the oxygen content increases. The overall symmetry of the UO_{2+x} and U_4O_9 phases remains cubic; the γ_1 and γ_2 phases are tetragonal but can be regarded as slightly distorted cubic structures with $c/a = 1\cdot030$ and $1\cdot016$. The crystallographic positions of the excess oxygen in UO_{2+x} and in U_4O_9 have recently been determined by neutron diffraction.[3] The local atomic arrangements around an interstitial oxygen atom are the same in each case, and it is clear that the U_4O_9 structure is an ordered arrangement of

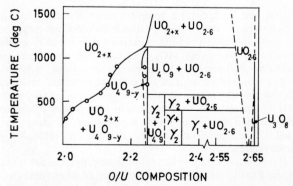

Fig. 1.—*Portion of phase diagram of U–O system.* [*Reproduced by permission from Quarterly Reviews*, **15**, 442 (1961)]

* Chemistry Division, AERE Harwell, Didcot, Berks.
† " Advances in Nuclear Ceramics " by F. J. P. Clark.

215

units of UO_{2+x}; different types of ordering probably lead to the γ_1 and γ_2 structures. Further oxidation leads to the U_3O_8 type of structure; this is orthorhombic, with a much lower density and completely different types of atomic co-ordination.

Oxides of plutonium higher than PuO_2 do not exist, or, if they do, they are very unstable. However, PuO_2 can be readily reduced, unlike UO_2, which loses oxygen only if heated under very reducing conditions to temperatures above 1800°C.[4] Again, the main difficulty in establishing the phase diagram of the $Pu-O_2$ system arises from the extremely labile nature of the compounds and the virtual impossibility of quenching the phases which exist at high temperatures. The main features have recently been established by X-ray crystallography at temperatures from 20° to 900°C.[5] A cubic phase exists over a range of composition from PuO_2 to $PuO_{1·61}$ at temperatures above 650°C. This is another grossly non-stoichiometric phase with a structure based on the fluorite structure; the cation sub-lattice is intact, but the anion sub-lattice is oxygen deficient.

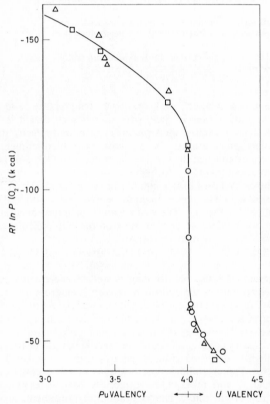

Fig. 2.—*Chemical potential of oxygen in non-stoichiometric uranium and uranium-plutonium oxides at 1000°C*

UO_2 and PuO_2 form a complete range of solid solutions, which show, to some extent, the oxidation-reduction behaviour of both substances. Solid solutions rich in UO_2 oxidise initially to give cubic MO_{2+x} phases, but, under strongly oxidizing conditions, U_3O_8-like phases are formed, sometimes with division into two phases of different metal composition.[6] Plutonium-rich phases oxidize to give only single, cubic MO_{2+x} phases, but can divide into two phases if strongly reduced and cooled to room temperature, as does PuO_2 itself.[5-7] Oxygen-deficient MO_{2-x} phases are stable at high temperatures.

It is worth noting that several of these properties are typical of the fluorite structure. A wide range of solid solutions is possible between oxides of IV-4, IV-3, IV-2 and even IV-1-valent cations, all with oxygen-deficient anion sub-lattices.

This property has been exploited, for example, in the stabilization of the high-temperature form of zirconia and the use of doped ZrO_2 and ThO_2 as resistors in high-temperature furnaces which can operate in air. Oxygen-deficient solid solutions based on ZrO_2 and ThO_2 are pure anionic conductors and have been used as such in galvanic cells reversible to oxygen ions.[8] The electrical conductivity of ThO_2 containing 8% La_2O_3 or Y_2O_3 is the same in air as it is in rigorously dried hydrogen,[9] and the specific conductivity reaches $\sim 0·1\,\Omega^{-1}$ at 1400°C.

Extensive studies have been made of solid solutions of UO_2 with ThO_2, ZrO_2, rare earth and alkaline earth oxides. In the presence of any excess oxygen, oxygen-deficient phases readily oxidise back to the MO_2 composition even at room temperature, the U being oxidised from the IV- to the V- or VI-valent state. Even oxides such as MgO that do not dissolve freely in UO_2 itself will form extensive solid solutions if the MO_2 composition can be retained. All solid solutions of the fluorite structure which contain uranium can be oxidized beyond the MO_2 composition, in the same way as UO_2 itself, so long as the average U valency does not exceed $\sim 5·5$. The presence of a sufficient proportion of a non-oxidizable cation stabilizes the cubic form—*e.g.* solid solutions containing ~ 40 mol % of ThO_2 oxidize to give cubic MO_{2+x} oxides only, as do those containing PuO_2. This method of avoiding oxidation to U_3O_8 can be used to provide ceramic bodies which should be more stable in oxidizing environments, the comparatively small density increase on oxidizing to a MO_{2+x} phase being less disruptive than the large density decrease caused by the formation of U_3O_8.[10]

The fluorite structure is thus quite flexible. Extensive ionic substitution is possible and the structive is stable over wide composition ranges at high temperature. Oxygen is freely mobile at temperatures of 200°C and above. Further research will almost certainly lead to new applications of this family of materials.

Thermodynamic Measurements

The use of oxygen-equilibrium pressures in determining phase boundaries has already been mentioned. Such data can also be used to predict compositions attainable under various conditions of preparation and in compatability calculations. The precise control of composition is important: excess oxygen in UO_2 leads to lower thermal conductivity and the separation of U_4O_9 at grain boundaries on cooling, but also to higher plasticity at high temperatures.

Markin and Bones have used high temperature emf cells, with oxide electrolytes, to investigate in detail the oxygen potentials of the UO_{2+x}[11] and $(U, Pu)O_{2+x}$[12] phases as a function of temperature and of composition. The measurements illustrate the great change in oxidation potential that occurs very close to the stoichiometric composition. To a first approximation, the oxygen pressure in equilibrium depends only on the oxidation number of the cation of variable valence, *i.e.* plutonium below $MO_{2·00}$ and uranium above $MO_{2·00}$, and the composition is therefore expressed in this way in the figure. (Fig. 2).

A more directly useful plot is one of oxygen potential ($RT \ln P(O_2)$) against temperature (Fig. 3). Included in this figure are similar plots for H_2/H_2O and CO/CO_2 mixtures. Some consequences can be seen immediately—(*a*) Because of the small numerical values of the partial molal entropy as $x \to 0$, the oxygen potential of a stoichiometric oxide is virtually independent of temperature. It is thus in equilibrium with a fairly wet hydrogen stream ($\sim 1\%$ H_2O) at all temperatures up to 1500°C and can be reduced and cooled in such a gas mixture; (*b*) similarly, equilibration with a 10/1 mixture of CO and CO_2 will not lead to any appreciable departure from stoichiometry; (*c*) dry H_2 ($\sim 10^{-2}\%$ H_2O) will reduce a

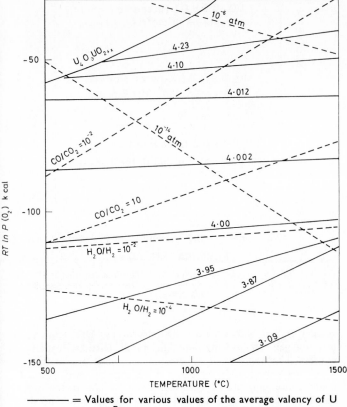

= Values for various values of the average valency of U or Pu

— — — = Chemical potentials of CO/CO_2 or of H_2O/H_2 mixtures

. . . . = Lines of constant oxygen pressure

Fig. 3.—*The chemical potential of oxygen in* $(U, Pu)O_{2\pm x}$ *solid solutions*

$(U, Pu)O_2$ oxide well below stoichiometry at high but not at low temperatures; and (d) CO_2 containing 1% of CO becomes oxidizing towards UO_2 at temperatures above 800°C.

Facts such as these can be immediately exploited in different stages of the preparation of powder and of pellets. Further, the behaviour in use can be predicted to some extent. For example, no reaction with iron or nickel containers is likely to occur unless the oxide fuel contains a considerable excess of oxygen, though beryllium and zirconium may always reduce UO_2. The concentration gradient of oxygen through a fuel bar which is subjected to a steep temperature gradient will depend on the composition of the surrounding gas, assuming that the gas will have access to all parts of the fuel through cracks and pores; if the gas contains H_2O or CO_2, the composition will tend to follow one of the lines of constant gas composition shown in Fig. 3.

Oxidation Behaviour

It is obvious from the results already presented that UO_2 can be handled only under fairly reducing conditions at temperatures above 500°C if no oxidation is to occur. The oxidation potential of a normal " vacuum " (10^{-4} mmHg) or of " pure " argon (10 ppm oxygen) is high on this scale, though the extent of oxidation will be limited by the supply of oxygen.

The oxidation of UO_2 and of solid solutions such as $(U, Th)O_2$ at lower temperatures has been extensively studied and a review has been published.[13] All preparations of UO_2 oxidize at room temperature, an energetic chemisorption being followed by a process involving some penetration of the lattice, perhaps to a depth of ~ 50 Å; the extent of

oxidation at this stage is thus dependent on the surface area of the preparation; a preparation of 3 m^2/g will reach a composition of $UO_{2 \cdot 05}$. Very small particles ($< 0 \cdot 1 \mu$) oxidize pyrophorically if exposed suddenly to air at room temperature, sometimes as far as U_3O_8; this oxidation can be controlled by long exposure to oxygen at -80°C, or to low pressures of oxygen, before exposure to 1 atm at room temperature.

Further oxidation of large particle-size preparations occurs at temperatures above 100°C; the oxygen can penetrate the entire crystal at such temperatures but the isothermal oxidation ceases at $UO_{2 \cdot 33}$. Oxidation to U_3O_8 occurs at a distinct second stage in the reaction at temperatures above 200°C.

The importance of surface processes is well illustrated by the case of PuO_2. Early reports indicated that PuO_2 could be prepared in a non-stoichiometric form, with compositions approaching $PuO_{2 \cdot 1}$. Detailed work by Rand and Jackson[14] has shown that this excess oxygen is on the surface only; PuO_2 will chemisorb oxygen by an activated process at temperatures above 200°C. The extent of O_2 absorption depends on the surface area and the density falls as absorption proceeds, due to the formation of a layer of light atoms. It is worth noting that the condition of the surface ions may be very different from those in the bulk solid and this too may have an effect on surface processes such as sintering.

Gas Adsorption

The nature of the surface of preparations of UO_2 made in different ways has been investigated. UO_2 will chemisorb hydrogen at temperatures above 500°C, and preparations cooled in hydrogen may be expected to carry about 0·3 cm^3 H_2/m^2. The hydrogen will be desorbed at quite low temperatures as water if the oxide is exposed to air, or as hydrogen at high temperatures if no excess oxygen is allowed to be present. Ways of removing the hydrogen must be found if the UO_2 is to be incorporated into cermets and not sintered at high temperatures.

UO_2 that has been prepared by reduction in carbon monoxide may be contaminated with carbon, which appears to be present as a type of " surface carbide " and not as bulk carbon[15]. The reaction involving the deposition of carbon was inhibited by the addition of a few per cent of carbon dioxide to the monoxide. We note again the care which must be exercised in order to obtain clean or reproducible oxide surfaces.

Microstructure of Particles

In addition to controlling the composition and surface state of an oxide preparation, it is necessary for most purposes to control the microstructure of the particles themselves— the particle size and texture.

The choice of the optimum oxide particles for the conventional cold pressing and sintering method of fabricating ceramic bars depends on the details of the sintering cycle adopted. For most routes, it has been found best to have preparations of surface areas $\sim 2 \, m^2/g$ and particles of high density. Smaller particles cannot be handled in air without taking precautions to avoid excessive oxidation and tend to sinter partially at too low temperatures, forming closed pores full of gas and desorption products which hinder densification.

A large literature exists on the preparation of UO_2[16] and I shall cite only a few examples to illustrate general points. The surface areas of preparations from higher oxides has varied from 0·1 to 40 m^2/g depending on the surface area of the starting material and on the temperature of reduction and subsequent heat treatment. A study of the microstructure of UO_2 prepared from UO_3, U_3O_8 and " ammonium diuranate "[17] showed that the surface area (as measured by gas adsorption methods) of preparations reduced at a given temperature was very dependent on the surface area of the parent material, but that the crystallite size of the UO_2 depended more on the heat treatment; large particle-size U_3O_8 reduced at low temperatures thus yielded particles consisting of a mass of small crystallites, whereas particles produced from small particle-size material tended to approximate to single crystals. The low densities of some preparations of UO_2 (Table I) can be explained in this way, as due to the imperfect packing of crystals in a particle, forming closed pores; it was noted that, in preparations from U_3O_8, low-density UO_2 resulted only from low-density U_3O_8. Further, this particle structure was very tough; UO_2 of density 10·15 g/cm³ (92·5% if theoretical density) could be oxidized completely at 800° to U_3O_8 and reduced again at 600° to yield UO_2 of density 10·40 g/cm³; a considerable amount of closed porosity survived two chemical reactions with associated changes of crystal structure and molar volume.

TABLE I.—*Helium Densities of UO_2 Powders*

Preparative Route	Density (g/cm²)	Mean Particle size (microns)	Mean Crystallite size (microns)
Crystal Density, from X-ray data	10·97		
$UO_3 \rightarrow UO_3 \rightarrow UO_2$	10·81	0·066	0·05
A.D.U.→UO_2	10·71	0·60	0·5
A.D.U.→U_3O_8→UO_2	10·90	0·41	0·4
A.D.U.→U_3O_8→UO_2	10·87	0·38	0·03
$UO_2 (NO_3)_2 6 H_2 O \rightarrow U_3 O_8 \rightarrow UO_2$	10·32	0·81	0·12
$UO_2 (NO_3)_2 6 H_2 O \rightarrow UO_3 \rightarrow UO_2$	10·15	1·00	0·17
Steam oxidation of uranium	10·85	—	—
$UO_3 2 H_2 O \rightarrow (UO_3) \rightarrow UO_2$	10·25	—	—
$UO_3 H_2 O \rightarrow (UO_3) \rightarrow UO_2$	10·34	—	—

Further evidence of the importance of intermediates in determining the microstructure of the final product is provided from a detailed study of the hydration, dehydration, and final reduction of UO_3.[18] The UO_3 can be hydrated in liquid water or in water vapour to yield hydrates of two classes, of approximate composition $UO_3 2 H_2O$ and $UO_3 0.8H_2O$, with considerable expansion of the particles. The course of the dehydration was followed by thermogravimetric and DTA analysis, together with measurements of X-ray diffraction patterns and particle volume. Some of the DTA results are shown in Fig. 4. The first endotherm is due to the loss of water from material composing the outer shells of the particular type of UO_3 used, which had been prepared by denitration of uranyl in a fluidized bed; the second endotherm is at the characteristic temperature for the loss of all water from the hydrates, and the endotherm at 700°C is due to loss of oxygen and the formation of U_3O_8. The exotherm at 490°C is significant; there is no change of weight or of X-ray pattern, but a colour change, increase in surface area, and decrease of chemical reactivity indicates that this exotherm is due to the final crystallization of some amorphous UO_3. The hydration–dehydration cycle resulted in a large increase in surface area and the formation of an expanded, porous particle. The interest in this series of researches was to obtain UO_3 that was chemically reactive towards H_2 and HF; optimum conditions were found to be a mild hydration treatment to give the dihydrate but under conditions where crystal growth was not easy, followed by dehydration and reduction to UO_2 at temperatures below the crystallization temperature for UO_3; the crystallite size and porosity of the large particles were major factors.

Lastly, mention should be made of methods of obtaining large single crystals of UO_2, which are necessary for some compaction processes such as vibro compaction.[11] Pulverized

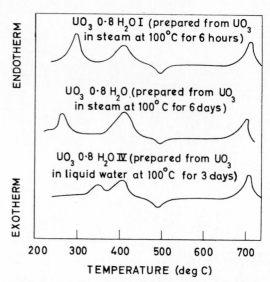

Fig. 4.—*Differential thermal analysis plots for decomposition of UO_3 0·8 H_2O in air. [Reproduced by permission from Trans. Far. Soc. **59**, 493 (1963)]*

fused UO_2 has been used for this purpose but UO_2 tends to lose oxygen on melting and the fused particles usually contain a precipitate of U metal. A convenient method which could be readily scaled-up is the electrolysis of halide melts containing uranyl chloride, UO_2Cl_2; the conditions can be varied to obtain deposits of UO_2 on the anode up to 1 cm in size.[19]

Carbide Fuels

Oxides suffer from two major disadvantages as nuclear fuels: the thermal conductivity is low, and the vapour pressure at the melting-point is high. Considerable attention is therefore being given to the development of high-melting compounds with high conductivities, approaching those of metals. The most advanced of these are the carbides.

Some parts of the U–C phase diagram have yet to be established with certainty, but the main features are beyond doubt. There are three carbides, UC, U_2C_3 and " UC_2 ". UC has the NaCl structure and exists at low temperatures only over a narrow composition range, from about $UC_{0.96}$ to $UC_{1.00}$; this is in surprising contrast to ThC and PuC, which both show wide composition ranges on the carbon-deficient side. U_2C_3 has a very narrow composition range and decomposes peritectically at ~1800°C. " UC_2 " and UC are said to be mutually soluble above 1800°C, and the " UC_2 " phase itself is deficient in carbon, though the range of composition is unknown. The thermodynamic data available has been reviewed recently;[20] the data are accurate enough for a number of calculations of equilibria but nothing is known of the variation in activity over non-stoichiometric ranges and the data are not accurate enough for calculation of the phase diagram.

On grounds of conductivity and density, the monocarbide is the favoured fuel except as a dispersion in graphite. UC can be prepared by reaction of U metal with carbon or hydrocarbon gases, but preparation directly from the oxide might have economic advantages, since the oxide is easily and cheaply produced. The overall reaction is $UO_2+3C \rightarrow UC+2CO$ and the pressure of carbon monoxide must be kept below the equilibrium value for the forward reaction to proceed. The reaction can be carried to completion in 2 hr at 1400° under continuous pumping.[21]

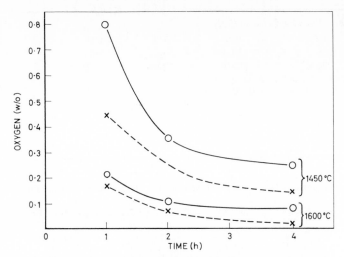

Fig. 5.—*Oxygen retained in carbide as a function of reaction time, during UO_2-C reaction*

The reaction kinetics observed suggested a diffusion-controlled process, but the rate of reaction was essentially independent of the particle size of UO_2 over the range 2–20 μ and of carbon over the range 0·1 to 5 μ. The reaction was much slower if coarser grades of UO_2 were used and the rate was very dependent on the pressure of CO, being reduced by a factor of 10 if the residual pressure of carbon monoxide was allowed to build up to a value of one-half of the equilibrium pressure at the reaction temperature. Many features remain to be explained but it is clear that carbide containing only small amounts of oxygen can be prepared in this way; Fig. 5 is a plot of the retained oxygen as a function of reaction time and reaction temperature. The reaction can also be carried out in a stream of flowing argon at temperatures of 1500–1650°C to give products containing only 0·2 wt % of oxygen.[22]

Carbide produced directly from the oxides can be sintered to high densities at 1550°C after grinding, provided that the grinding and handling is carried out in a pure argon atmosphere. Surface oxidation and hydrolysis which result when carbide powders are exposed to oxygen and water vapour lead to poor sintering characteristics.[23] It seems likely that the residual oxygen is substituted for carbon in a U(C, O) solid solution and that sintering can proceed smoothly so long as carbon monoxide gas is not released at a late stage in the process. Oxygen and nitrogen can certainly substitute for C in the UC lattice, and alter profoundly the properties of the phase—*e.g.* a U(C, N) phase is stable with regard to the formation of U_2C_3. Further elucidation of the effects of oxygen and nitrogen substitution on the physical and chemical properties is an important field of work.

Some illustrative results have been obtained during studies of the reaction of the higher carbides with hydrogen. This work was directed towards controlling the composition of the carbide at a late stage in the preparative process. The C/U ratio is not easily controlled with precision in any preparative route, and the presence of free U or a higher carbide can lead to awkward compatibility problems. The equilibrium methane-hydrogen ratios for the reaction:

$$UC_2 + 2\,H_2 \rightleftharpoons UC + CH_4$$

suggest that carbon can be removed from higher carbides by hydrogen at temperatures below 1200°C. Sowden *et al.*[24] have shown that this reaction proceeds readily at 1000°C, using UC_2 prepared directly from the oxide; the course of the reaction is illustrated in Fig. 6. The ultimate level of

carbon content is considerably lower than the value for stoichiometric UC, but oxygen analysis indicated that the mol ratio metal/(carbon+oxygen) was unity. This was so within narrow limits for preparations of various oxygen contents and the results indicated that an upper limit of oxygen solubility in the UC lattice under the conditions used may be represented by the formula $UC_{0.86}O_{0.14}$.

Nitrides, Sulphides, and Phosphides

The monocarbides are members of a large class of phases, all crystallizing with the NaCl structure, which have semi-metallic properties and high melting-points. They are formed by a variety of rare-earth, actinide, and transition metals. Comparative studies have started on UN, US, and UP. To some extent, the desirable properties of these phases may be combined by making suitable solid solutions; UC and UN form a complete series of solid solutions and UC is soluble in US to the extent of about 40 mol %.[25]

The literature has recently been reviewed[26] and only a few features will be mentioned here. The higher nitride, U_2N_3, may be prepared from the metal, from the oxide, or from UCl_4, and decomposed to yield UN at 1200°C. The product is not easily fabricated into bars by cold pressing and sintering, but can be compacted by hot pressing at 1500° or by arc-melting under 10–20 atm of nitrogen; UN decomposes above 1800°C *in vacuo*, losing nitrogen, and the dissociation pressure is 1 atm at 2800°C. UN itself has a narrow range of composition, like UC, and does not appear to dissolve oxygen to any considerable extent. UN is much more resistant to hydrolysis than UC and does not react appreciably even with boiling water, nor with steam below 250°C; UN can be handled safely in moist air at 20°C even when powdered, in striking contrast to UC.

The monosulphide, US, has long been known as a useful ceramic, in common with ThS and the monosulphides of some rare earth metals. Crucibles of CeS, ThS, and US have been used as containers for molten metals and halides.[27] Methods of preparing US_2 from U, UH_3, UO_2 and UCl_4 are known, but the final stage in the preparation of US involves homogenizing with uranium metal at 1400°C or degradation of higher sulphides at temperatures approaching 2000°C. There may be considerable incentive to develop methods of preparing US at lower temperatures; for example, the higher sulphides can be reduced electrolytically in fused salt baths.[28]

US is quite a stable sulphide and addition of US to UC is said to reduce the reaction of UC with many metals.[25] Experience in fabricating ceramic rods of US has already

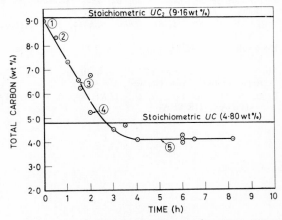

Fig. 6.—*Conversion of UC_2 in flowing hydrogen at 1000°C, (UC_2 composition—9·03 w/o total C; 0·69 w/o O; 0·79 w/o free C. Surface area of UC_2-0·04 m^2/g)*

TABLE II.—*A comparison of the Properties of Possible Ceramic Fuels*

Property	UO_2	UC	UN	US	UP
Crystal Density (g/cm³)	10·97	13·63	14·32	10·9	10·3
Melting Point (°C)	2750	2400	2850	2460	>2400
Thermal Conductivity (cal cm⁻¹ s⁻¹ °C⁻¹)	0·018 at 100°C 0·008 at 700°C	0·05 at 1000°C 0·05 at 700°C	0·04 at 300°C 0·05 at 800°C	—	—
Coefficient of Expansion °C ($\times 10^6$)	10·8	11·5	9·2	11·8	—
Free Energy of Formation at 1000°C (Kcal/mole)	207	19·1	43·9	79·7	~30
Vapour Pressure at 2000°C (mm)	10^{-2}	$<2 \cdot 5 \cdot 10^{-3}$	$3 \cdot 10^{-2}$	$3 \cdot 10^{-3}$	—

shown the importance of controlling the oxygen impurity, which is present in US as the stable oxysulphide UOS. This forms a eutectic with US and facilitates sintering to high densities, though the properties of the compact at high temperatures would be adversely affected by the ultimate decomposition of UOS. The range of composition of US has been given by Cater *et al.*, who studied the vaporization of US in detail,[29] as $US_{0 \cdot 96}$ to $US_{1 \cdot 01}$.

The phosphide, UP, is made in a similar way: reaction of phosphorus or phosphine with uranium metal giving a higher phosphide, which is degraded to UP in vacuum or in an argon stream at 1100–1300°C. Recent results at Harwell suggest that UP may be phosphorus deficient, the degree of substoichiometry increasing with temperature. UP decomposes at high temperature, like UN, losing phosphorus preferentially. UP is far more resistant to ignition on heating in oxygen than is UC, UN, or US.

Some properties of these compounds are collected in Table II, for comparison. There is little doubt that this family of compounds will furnish further valuable new materials as our knowledge of them improves.

Acknowledgments

The author wishes to thank the editor of *Quarterly Reviews* for permission to reproduce Fig. 1; and also the editor of *Transactions of the Faraday Society* for permission to reproduce Fig. 5.

References

[1] Gronwold, F. *Journal of Inorganic Nuclear Chemistry*, 1955, **1**, 357.

[2] Roberts, L. E. J., and Walter, A. J. *Journal of Inorganic Nuclear Chemistry*, 1961, **22**, 213. See also Blackburn, P.E., *J. phys. Chem.*, 1958, **62**, 897; Aronson, S., and Belle, J. *J. chem. Phys.*, 1958, **29**, 151.

[3] Willis, B. T. M. *AERE Report R.4414*, 1963 (Harwell: UKAEA).

[4] Rothwell, E. *AERE Report R.3897*, 1961 (Harwell: UKAEA).

[5] Markin, T. L., Gardner, E. R., and Bones, R. J. *AERE Report R.4602*, 1964 (Harwell: UKAEA).

[6] Brett, N. H., and Fox, A. C. *AERE Report R.3937*, 1963 (Harwell: UKAEA).

[7] Brett, N. H., and Russell, L. E. *Trans. Brit. Ceram. Soc.* 1963, **62**, 97.

[8] Kiukkola, K., and Wagner, C. *Trans. electrochem. Soc.*, 1957, **104**, 379.

[9] Bridger, N. J., Denne, W. A., Markin, T. L., and Rand, M. H. *AERE Report R.4329*, 1963 (Harwell: UKAEA).

[10] Hoenig, C. L., Handwerk, J. H., Kittel, J. H., and Breden, C. R. *J. Amer. ceram. Soc.*, 1958, **41**, 117.

[11] Markin, T. L., and Bones, R. J. *AERE Report R.4178*, 1963 (Harwell: UKAEA).

[12] Markin, T. L., and Bones, R. J. Unpublished work.

[13] Roberts, L. E. J. *Quart. Rev. chem. Soc., Lond.*, 1961, **15**, 442.

[14] Rand, M. H., and Jackson, E. E. *AERE Report R.3636*, 1963 (Harwell: UKAEA).

[15] Roberts, L. E. J., Walter, A. J., and Wheeler, V. J. *J. chem. Soc.*, 1958, p. 2472.

[16] Belle, J. (Ed.). " *Uranium Dioxide* ", 1964, Chapters II and III. (Washington: U.S. Government Printing Office).

[17] Anderson, J. S., Harper, E. A., Moorbeth, S., and Roberts, L. E. J. *AERE Report C/R.886*, 1955 (Harwell: UKAEA).

[18] Dell, R. M., and Wheeler, V. J. *Trans. Faraday Soc.*, 1963, **59**, 485.

[19] Robins, R. G. *Journal of Nuclear Materials*, 1961, **3**, 294. See also Scott, F. A., and Mudge, L. K. *Journal of Nuclear Materials*, 1963, **9**, 245.

[20] *IAEA Technical Reports Series, No. 14*, 1963 (Vienna: IAEA).

[21] Ainsley, R., Harder, B. R., Hodge, N., Sowden, R. G., White, D. B., and Wood, D. C. *AERE Report R.4327*, 1963 (Harwell: UKAEA).

[22] Harrison, J. D. L., and Isaacs, J. W. In " *Symposium on Carbides in Nuclear Energy* ", Paper B6 (Harwell: UKAEA).

[23] Russell, L. E., and Harrison, J. D. L. " *AERE Report R. 4328* ", 1963 (Harwell: UKAEA).

[24] Sowden, R. G., Hodge, N., Moreton-Smith, M. J., and White, D. B. In " *Symposium on Carbides in Nuclear Energy* ", Paper C4 (Harwell: UKAEA).

[25] Shalek, P. W., and White, G. D. In " *Symposium on Carbides in Nuclear Energy* ", Paper A19 (Harwell: UKAEA).

[26] Dell, R. M., and Allbutt, M. *AERE Report R.4253*, 1963 (Harwell: UKAEA).

[27] Eastman, E. D., Brewer, L., Bromley, L. A., Gilles, P. W., and Lofgren, N. L. *J. Amer. ceram. Soc.*, 1951, **34**, 128.

[28] Didchenko, R., and Litz, L. M. *Trans. electrochem. Soc.*, 1962, **109**, 247.

[29] Cater, E. D., Gilles, P. W., and Thorn, R. J. *J. chem. Phys.*, 1961, **35**, 608.

The manuscript of this paper was received on 6 January, 1964.

IMPROVED GRAPHITE FOR NUCLEAR REACTORS

By J. M. HUTCHEON*

SYNOPSIS

In nuclear reactors moderated with graphite and cooled with carbon dioxide the graphite suffers displacement of atoms from the lattice by fast neutrons and chemical attack by highly aggressive species resulting from irradiation of the carbon dioxide.

The neutron damage leads, *inter alia*, to non-uniform dimensional changes and hence to internal stresses in the core bricks; the chemical attack reduces the amount of moderator and weakens the structure.

Extensive in-pile and out-pile studies performed in the Authority's laboratories have identified particular structural features of the graphite which can be quantitatively associated with its irradiation behaviour. From this starting point a specification has been prepared for a graphite more suited to reactor applications than previously available materials, and development work, in the laboratory and in industry, has made considerable progress towards meeting this specification on the tonnage scale.

Technological Background

In graphite moderated gas-cooled reactors, as used in the nuclear power stations pioneered in this country, the graphite has two prime functions. It is both moderator and structural material: for the latter reason it has to satisfy criteria of integrity. These are more stringent than for materials in non-nuclear plant since the high radiation levels within the core of the reactor preclude any maintenance work on graphite during its life, except at very considerable expense. Moreover, since power stations are expected to have a life of about 30 years, such guarantees demand accelerated tests and extensive extrapolations, and these must have a correspondingly firm base. The Atomic Energy Authority's experimental work on graphite has been concerned primarily with two new types of stress introduced by the reactor environment. The first of these is a corrosion process resulting from the radiolytic breakdown of the carbon dioxide coolant. Although the normal thermal reaction between graphite and carbon dioxide at the relevant temperatures and pressures is too slow to be of any consequence, carbon dioxide breaks down under irradiation[1] to give active species. These attack the moderator at a rate which would gasify a significant fraction of the moderator in 30 years, with a consequent loss in structural strength. The other characteristic damage mechanism arises directly from the basic role of the graphite, which is to provide atoms which will slow down neutrons by collision without absorbing them. Since the fission energies of the neutrons are very much greater than the bond energies in the carbon crystal displacements of atoms from the lattice are to be expected. These are manifested as an increase in the internal energy of the graphite, gross dimensional changes (which are the main topic considered in this paper), marked decreases in thermal and electrical conductivity, and increases in strength and modulus. All these changes in properties are sensitive to the graphite temperature, many of them being less at higher temperatures. This provides a method of control by design, so that in modern reactors of this type the moderator is kept during normal operation at temperatures not lower than about 230°C. For life-time neutron exposures now being considered, however, it may well be cheaper to develop an improved material, and with further development of the reactor type this will become even more desirable.

* Reactor Materials Laboratory, U.K.A.E.A., Culcheth, Warrington, Lancs.

At first sight both these phenomena are of such a fundamental nature that modification to the material might not seem to promise much success. This is particularly the case since the nuclear limitations placed on choice of moderator imply that for this general family of reactor, the moderator has to be virtually pure carbon. The degree of freedom conferred, in more conventional systems, by the possibility of alloying is therefore absent here. Carbon, however, is unusual in the wide variety of its physical forms, which the carbon technologist tries to describe in terms of crystal size, crystal perfection (normally closely connected to crystal size), crystal orientation, and pore structure. It is among these parameters that a solution must be sought.

Nature of Artificial Graphite

As a starting point it will be appropriate to describe briefly the grade of graphite, known as PGA (*i.e.* " pile graphite, Grade A "), which has been developed over the years for use in British nuclear reactors. The first aim was to eliminate impurities which would capture, and thus waste, thermal neutrons. The manufacturing method for this grade of graphite closely follows that used for electrodes but makes use of specially selected raw materials; a calcined petroleum coke is mixed with a medium soft coal tar pitch, and the mix extruded as blocks which, typically, are 8 in. square by 30 in. long with a 5 in. diameter axial hole. These blocks are then fired on a very slow schedule over a period of 2–3 months at temperatures up to a maximum of about 1000°C to give hard, abrasive amorphous carbon bodies. They are subsequently impregnated with another pitch and re-fired in order to increase the density, and finally fired at a temperature of about 2700°C. All operations are conducted with scrupulous care to avoid contamination. The last process, termed " graphitisation ", has the function, in conventional applications of graphite electrodes, of reducing the resistivity. In the nuclear application its main function is to drive off many of the impurities present in the original raw materials, and also, as a result of crystallite growth, to convert the abrasive carbon to a softer, easily machined, material. The resulting product has well-developed graphite crystals ($Lc = 150$ Å, $La = 600$ Å), is fairly highly oriented (thermal expansion parallel to extrusion direction at 20–120°C = 0.8×10^{-6} °C^{-1}, perpendicular to extrusion direction = 2.8×10^{-6} °C^{-1}) and has density about 1·70 g/cm³. This density taken in conjunction with the crystal density of about 2·26 g/cm³ corresponds to a volume porosity of about 25%. The predominant pore size is around 7 μ.[17]

The Corrosion Problem

Methods of reducing the corrosion by modifying the coolant, although important, are not relevant to this contribution and are discussed elsewhere. The present paper deals only with the work done with the object of modifying the graphite.

The source of the corrosion is that active species, possibly oxygen atoms, are formed by a reaction such as

$$\text{Gamma energy} + CO_2 \rightarrow CO + O \qquad . \quad (1)$$

and may recombine by a reaction which may be simplified as

$$O + CO \rightarrow CO_2 \qquad . \qquad . \qquad . \quad (2)$$

The introduction of graphite into this system provides a competitor for the active species by reactions such as

$$C + O \rightarrow CO \qquad . \qquad . \qquad . \quad (3)$$

Since CO is demonstrably formed from CO_2 and graphite at temperatures where the thermal reaction is not detectable, the active species cannot all recombine in the gas phase and some must reach the graphite surface to give reactions such as (3).

A series of experiments was made[18] in which specimens were irradiated in sealed capsules in a carbon dioxide atmosphere, the annulus between the specimen and the capsule being one variable and the gas pressure another. These showed that at reactor pressures the efficiency of utilisation of the radiation in gasifying the carbon was independent of free volume of gas. In another set of experiments in which composite graphite specimens, made up of closely-fitting demountable shells, were exposed directly to flowing carbon dioxide under irradiation it was found[2] that each individual shell lost weight at the same rate. These observations were consistent with the view that for the gas within the graphite pores, the predominant fate of the active species produced in reaction (1) was to attack the graphite, as in reaction (3) while for the gas outside the graphite, except for a thin film, recombination (*e.g.* reaction (2)) was predominant.

These experiments concentrated attention on the pore structure of the graphite. Although they gave a reasonable basis for speculation about the particular pore parameter which was important, further experiments seemed desirable in order to isolate this directly.

Experiments with Graphites of Different Pore Structure

Graphite specimens were prepared with wide variations in pore structure, with the intention that whatever might turn out to be the important pore parameter there would be a sufficient range of variation of this parameter that it could be identified by analysis of the measured reaction rates.

This range of graphites was obtained by using a variety of base materials and impregnants, and graphites more porous than the standard PGA were made by pre-oxidising this material thermally up to weight losses of 5%.

The experimental results indicated no correlation of reaction rate with either surface area or permeability, but good linear correlation (for constant CO_2 pressure and dose-rate) with open pore volume, as shown in Fig. 1. It will be seen from the figure that this correlation holds over nearly a ten-fold range of open porosity.

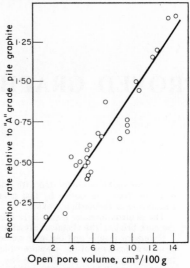

Fig. 1.—*Effect of open pore volume on reaction rate*

The independence of internal surface area shown by the results is to be expected if reaction (2) is very efficient since this implies that the active species can only make one collision. Increase in the available area therefore will not increase the probability of reaction.

The absence of any correlation with permeability confirms that for the range of graphites examined, transport limitations do not control reaction rate.

The direct dependence upon open porosity implies that, for the range of graphites examined, a constant proportion of the species produced according to equation (1) reach the pore walls and react by equation (2), so that the specific reaction rate is directly dependent upon the mass of CO_2 associated with (*i.e.* in the open pores of) unit mass of graphite. It is therefore consistent with the direct relation between reaction rate and gas pressure which was demonstrated separately.

The lack of any effect of closed porosity, not accessible to helium, which is present in PGA to the extent of about 4% by volume, but was significantly varied in these specimens, is also consistent with the general picture of the reaction which emerged.

Long-term Effects

As corrosion proceeds the open porosity will of course increase, and Fig. 1 in fact implies an exponential increase of weight loss with time. In modifying the structure of the graphite, therefore, to produce a lower open porosity one must also take account of any changes in the rate at which this porosity will increase during corrosion. The results of some studies on these lines are shown in Fig. 2. Curves of Type A

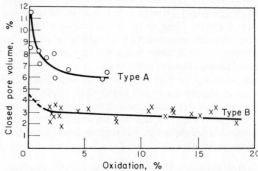

Fig. 2.—*Variation of closed pore volume with in-pile oxidation*

are obtained from graphites impregnated with synthetic resins. Such materials, which polymerise to solid forms before appreciable thermal degradation to carbon takes place, characteristically give products of lower density[2] but with most of the porosity in the form of closed pores. Hence the initial open porosity and in-pile carbon dioxide reactivity are low. Large reductions in permeability are also obtained in this way. When exposed to oxidising conditions, however, the closed porosity opens up very rapidly, as is shown by the curve in Fig. 2, and in fact the rapid opening of closed porosity ceases at a point on the burn-off scale close to that corresponding to the removal of all the carbon residue derived from the resin. Hence, in order to ensure continued satisfactory performance of the graphite in the reactor from this point of view, it is necessary also to specify the change of reactivity with burn-off at least over the first few per cent. The necessary low change (Type B curve) is obtained in practice by using impregnants such as tars or coumarone resins which give[5] thick cell wall structures to the coke deposited in the pores.

Industrial Development of Graphites with Improved Corrosion Resistance

This work therefore provided the manufacturer with a firm basis for development of suitable materials on the production scale. Open porosity can be controlled by impregnation, with comparatively minor changes to the standard manufacturing process. The work on pore-opening gave a pointer to the types of impregnant with most probability of success. Further assistance was provided by the conclusion that reduction in pore diameter (by comparison with PGA), with resultant decrease in permeability and increase in surface area, was not particularly significant in this context. These considerations taken together indicated that a target of about 5 cm³/100 g open porosity (compared with 12 cm³/100 g from PGA) was a reasonable one at which to aim, having regard to an economic balance.

Dimensional Changes

The power ratings now being proposed for gas-cooled graphite moderated reactors imply that, on a statistical basis, every carbon atom in the graphite structure will be displaced from its lattice position every few months, although a large proportion, dependent on temperature, will rapidly return to their original, or equivalent, positions. Considerable changes in physical properties will therefore occur, including dimensional changes in the graphite bricks. The preference for moderator temperatures between 300 and 450°C in current designs reduces the number of permanent displacements, but there is still a significant reduction in design complexity to be achieved[6] by minimizing dimensional changes in the graphite.

The changes in dimensions occur because permanent displacements of carbon atoms from the lattice lead to a growth

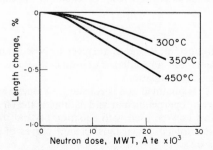

Fig. 3.—(a) *Dimensional changes in PGA graphite perpendicular to extrusion with neutron dose 300–450°C*

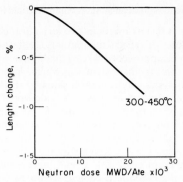

Fig. 3.—(b) *Dimensional changes in PGA graphite parallel to extrusion with neutron dose 300–450°C*

of the crystal in the c-direction (perpendicular to the layer planes) and shrinkage in the a-direction (parallel to the layer planes). Although at low doses and temperatures the main effect is to cause growth of the graphite in the direction perpendicular to extrusion, as shown by the early work[7] in this field, at temperatures now of interest the gross effect is of shrinkage in both directions, as shown in Fig. 3, which displays experimental results covering a dose equivalent to most of the life of current C.E.G.B. reactors.

Accommodation Factors

It is clear that there must be some accommodation in the graphite structure for the c-axis expansion of the crystals, as was indicated by the early experiments which showed[7] that the c-axis lattice parameter of the crystals, measured by X-ray methods, increased proportionally much more than the gross dimensions. There is an obvious analogy with thermal expansion since it has long been known that the volume thermal expansions of normal commercial graphite (ca. 5×10^{-6} °C^{-1}) are much lower than the volume thermal expansion coefficient of the crystal (ca. 25×10^{-6} °C^{-1}) measured by Nelson and Riley.[8]

For a range of graphites, the rates of irradiation-induced growth perpendicular to the extrusion direction, measured in these early experiments, showed a good linear correlation with the thermal expansion coefficients measured in the same direction.

Under these conditions, the changes in the a-direction of the crystal are negligible and this correlation is a particular case of the general model which can be represented by the equation

$$\frac{1}{l_x}\frac{dl_x}{d\gamma} = A_x \frac{1}{X_c}\frac{dX_c}{d\gamma} + (1-A_x)\frac{1}{X_a}\frac{dX_a}{d\gamma} \qquad . \quad (4)$$

where A_x represents an accommodation factor in the direction x and the other terms are generalised strain coefficients representing the fractional strain per unit of stress γ. The term in l_x refers to strain of the polycrystalline aggregate in a direction x and those in X_c and X_a to the strains in the typical graphite crystal referred to directions respectively perpendicular to and parallel to the basal plane. The equation, which is derived by conventional thermodynamic reasoning,[10] applies quite generally whatever the mechanism of straining the crystal. In particular it can be applied to thermal expansion, to irradiation-induced crystal changes, or to the swelling produced by intercalation of bromine atoms within the layer planes. The quantity γ is for these three cases, represented by temperature, neutron dose or percentage bromine uptake respectively.

Physical Significance of Accommodation Factor

The factor A has its origin in two structural characteristics of the graphite. It reflects the mutual orientation of crystallites, and can be approached at least qualitatively by structural techniques, that is the extent to which large c-direction growths in a crystal can be compensated by shrinkages in the a-direction in adjacent crystals. An additional effect arises from the highly anisotropic nature of the graphite crystal which, at room temperature, has thermal expansion coefficients of $27 \times 10^{-6}\ °C^{-1}$ and $-1·5 \times 10^{-6}\ °C^{-1}$ in the c-direction and a-directions respectively. Taken with the fact that graphite is made at temperatures of $2700°C$ and higher, this anisotropy produces, as the graphite is cooled, strains in the c-direction of the crystal which are greater than the material can tolerate. Mrozowski[11] therefore postulated that artificial graphites should contain micro-cracks in directions parallel to the basal planes of crystals. Sutton and Howard,[12] from a study of the thermal expansion of graphites from $-200°C$ to $+700°C$, were able to show that the accommodation could not be accounted for entirely by orientation effects but was in part

Fig. 4.

due to the presence of these micro-cracks, the presence of which they were able to demonstrate directly by electromicroscopy, as shown in Fig. 4. Measurements of crack dimensions and crack frequency permitted a calculation of the integrated volume of these cracks which was found to agree well with the " closed porosity " determined by a comparison of the X-ray crystal density of graphite with the density of an artefact determined by immersion in helium. Subsequently, it was shown[13] that irradiation of graphite caused these microcracks to close, as the crystals expanded in the c-direction.

It would therefore be expected that an artificial graphite with a well-developed, but not perfect, long-range crystal structure, consisting essentially of parallel chains of nearly oriented crystallites, would be highly anisotropic and would show marked changes in accommodation factor as the oriented microporosity was filled. This structure is found in cokes derived from highly aromatic hydrocarbons, such as are used in the manufacture of PGA, and this material shows the

expected behaviour when irradiated at lower temperatures.[14] A material in which the crystallites are more random, however, will show a higher degree of internal compensation between c- and a-direction changes in the crystal. Its bulk dimensional stability, for all forms of crystal dimensional change, will therefore be greater, oriented microporosity is less likely to be present and the graphite will be more isotropic.

Condition for Stability

The above reasoning gives some hope that dimensional stability is, in principle, capable of control by changes in the material and gives broad indications of the parameters to be manipulated. For a quantitative evaluation of the required value of A, however, equation (1) must be further examined.

The condition for complete stability is clearly that the left-hand side of this equation should always be zero, i.e. that

$$\frac{A_x}{1-A_x} = -\frac{1}{X_a}\frac{dX_a}{d\gamma}\bigg/\frac{1}{X_c}\frac{dX_c}{d\gamma} = \delta \text{ (say)} . (5)$$

where γ now refers to the neutron dose.

Since the terms on the right-hand side of the equation are properties of the crystals only, the value of A_x must be independent of direction and the graphite must be isotropic.

Hence, to determine the actual value of δ (or A) at any dose it is necessary first to determine the crystal coefficients at that dose, i.e. the terms $\frac{1}{X_a}\frac{dX_a}{d\gamma}$ and $\frac{1}{X_c}\frac{dX_c}{d\gamma}$ in equation (5).

Determination of Critical Value of δ

It might be thought that the crystal coefficients could be measured directly by X-ray methods, as already mentioned.[7] It was found, however, that for higher doses, changes in the interlayer spacing did not correlate at all with microscopic dimensional changes in the graphite, and this held up progress for a considerable time. The explanation seems to be that displaced carbon atoms can ultimately form new layers, or portions of layers, within the crystal so that the crystal dimension changes are not reflected in c-spacing changes.

Equation (4) is of course in differential form and for a complete mathematical solution to the problem it is necessary to know how each of the terms on the right-hand side varies with both dose and temperature. The failure of the X-ray method makes it very difficult to devise any way of separating the accommodation factor and crystal coefficient terms which is completely free of ambiguity but considerable progress has been made on the following lines:[15]

Under the irradiation conditions defined in Fig. 3 the thermal expansion coefficient of the graphite remains constant with increasing dose.

The thermal expansion form of equation (4) can then be written

$$\alpha_x = A_x\,\alpha_c + (1-A_x)\,\alpha_a   .   (6)$$

where α_x is constant, α_c and α_a are given by Nelson and Riley's measurements on unirradiated graphite and are assumed unchanged with irradiation.

Hence, A_x is obtained and is constant. Values appropriate to the directions perpendicular and parallel to the block extrusion axis can now be used with equation (4) and the experimentally determined dimensional change curves of Fig. 3 to obtain $\frac{1}{X_c}\frac{dX_c}{d\gamma}$ and $\frac{1}{X_a}\frac{dX_a}{d\gamma}$ for any appropriate value of the dose γ.

Substitution of these into equation (5) gives the appropriate value of δ.

The result of the analysis is shown in Fig. 5 from which it is seen that after an initial rapid change, where dimensional changes are in any case small, the required value of δ is almost constant for temperatures of practical interest.

Critical Thermal Expansion

The value of δ thus obtained, for the required temperature, leads to the value of α, the macroscopic thermal expansion coefficient of an isotropic graphite which should be stable. These values are tabulated below, and it will be seen that in some cases they approach the maximum possible value for the crystal (*ca.* 8×10^{-6}).

TABLE I.—*Critical Thermal Expansion Coefficients for Dimensional Stability*

Irradiation temperature (°C)	Approx. thermal exp. coeff. (°C^{-1}) at 20°–120°C
300	$4 \cdot 6 \times 10^{-6}$
350	$5 \cdot 6 \times 10^{-6}$
450	$7 \cdot 8 \times 10^{-6}$

It is desirable to know whether stability will be retained at doses beyond those shown in Fig. 5. Stability will be lost if δ no longer remains constant, or if A begins to change, as a result of closure of the oriented microporosity. The continued constancy of δ will require further experimental demonstration but the latter condition can be examined in terms of the physical significance of A. Graphites with the high thermal expansion quoted in Table I must necessarily have little oriented microporosity. There should therefore be small scope for change due to closure of such porosity with increasing crystallite strain, *i.e.* with increasing dose. This has been confirmed by experiments in which crystal strain has been induced in such graphites by bromination.[16]

Crystal Size Variation

It is an implicit assumption in the above treatment that the crystal growth coefficients are the same for all graphites considered and that the only parameter varying between different graphites is therefore the accommodation factor A. In fact, empirical studies indicate that the rate of dimensional change with dose increases as the crystal size becomes smaller. At least at the present stage, therefore, graphites are specified to be made from cokes which give well-developed crystals on graphitisation.

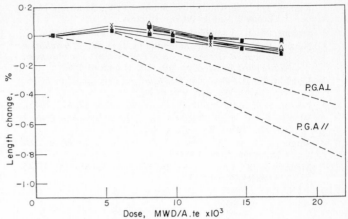

Fig. 6.—*Comparison of experimental graphite with PGA graphite at 350°C*

Consequences for Fabrication

The problem put to the graphite maker therefore is to produce a graphite which is isotropic, has large crystal size, and has the highest available thermal expansion coefficient. His line of attack is influenced by his empirical experience, by the known facts that both irradiation growth and thermal expansion are controlled primarily by the structure of the initial coke, rather than by subsequent processes, and by certain general considerations concerning the physical significance of the accommodation factor, A.

On this basis, graphites have been obtained with isotropy ratios as low as $1 \cdot 1$ and with thermal expansion coefficients close to $5 \cdot 0 \times 10^{-6}$. Irradiation experiments with such materials give a significant improvement in dimensional stability, over the standard PGA, as indicated in Fig. 6.

Large-scale Development

It has thus been found possible to specify a graphite meeting the requirements for radiolytic corrosion resistance and dimensional stability, which are important for moderator applications. In making such material the manufacturer almost inevitably improves density and strength at the same time, both of which help the nuclear reactor designer to obtain more economic designs, but do not of themselves justify much increase in cost.

Full-size blocks of graphite are now being manufactured in large-scale pre-production trials in order to check how clearly this specification can be met and current indications are that it will prove to be quite practicable.

Acknowledgment

The author wishes to acknowledge his help to many colleagues in the Reactor Materials Laboratory, in particular to Dr. P. T. Nettley, in the preparation of this paper.

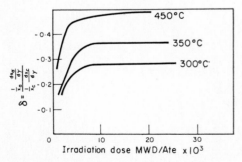

Fig. 5.—*Variation of δ with dose and temperature*

References

1 Anderson, A. R. *et al. Proc. 2nd Int. Conf. on Peaceful Uses of At. En.*, 1958, **7**, 335, P/303.

2 Lind, R. and Wright, J. " *Gas Reactions with Graphite in the A.G.R. B.N.E.S. Symp. The Advanced Gas-cooled Reactor* ", pp. 203–211 (London) 1962.

3 Hutcheon, J. M., Cowen, H. C., Godwin, N. F. *Proc. 5th Conf. on Carbon*, **2**, 379 (Pergamon Press) (1963).

4 Kipling, J. J., Sherwood, J. N., Shooter, P. V., Thomson, N. R. " Carbon ", Vol. I (1963). In press.

5 Jenkins, M. J. Unpublished work at R.M.L. Culcheth.

6 Nettley, P. T., Bridge, H. and Simmons, J. H. W. " Irradiation Behaviour of Graphite." B.N.E.S. Symp. The Advanced Gas-cooled Reactor, pp. 191–201 (London) 1962.

7 Kinchin, G. H. Proc. 1st Int. Conf. no Peaceful Uses of At. En. (1956), Vol. I, p. 475, P/442.

8 Nelson, J. P. and Riley, D. P. Proc. Phys. Soc., 57, 477 (1945).

9 Woods, W. K. et al. Proc. 1st Int. Conf. on Peaceful Uses of At. En. (1956), Vol. VII, p. 462, P/476.

10 Simmons, J. H. W. Proc. 3rd Conf. on Carbon, p. 559 (Pergamon Press) (1959).

11 Mrozowski, S. Proc. 1st and 2nd Conf. on Carbon, pp. 31–45 (Waverley Press) (1956).

12 Sutton, A. L. and Howard V. C. J. Nucl. Mats., 7, 58 (1962).

13 Thrower, P. A. and Reynolds, W. N. Ibid., 8, 221 (1963).

14 Simmons, J. H. W. and Reynolds, W. N. Inst. of Metals Monograph No. 27, p. 75 (1962).

15 Kelly, B. T. R.M.L. " Internal document ".

16 Brocklehurst, J. E. and Bishop, R. A. To be published in Carbon.

17 Bond, R. L. and Spencer, D. H. T. " The pore structure of Pile Graphite Grade 'A'—US/UK Symposium on Gas Coolant Compatability ", Harwell, 1962—GCM/UK/27.

18 Copestake, T. B. and Corney, N. S. " Radiation Induced Reactions in the System, Carbon Dioxide, Carbon Monoxide, Graphite—US/UK Symposium on Gas Coolant Compatibility ", Harwell, 1962—GCM/UK/25.

THE COUNTER DIFFUSION OF GASES IN NUCLEAR GRAPHITE

By T. R. JENKINS, B.Sc., A.M.I.Chem.E.,* J. B. MORRIS, B.Sc., Ph.D., D.I.C., A.R.I.C., A.M.I.Chem.E.,* and F. ROBERTS, B.Sc., F.R.I.C., M.I.Chem.E.*

SYNOPSIS

Graphite is a well known refractory with excellent machining properties, good thermal and electrical conductivity, and moderately high strength at elevated temperatures. The present paper is concerned with the use of graphite as both moderator and fuel cladding material in high-temperature nuclear reactors at temperatures of 1000°C or more. The function of the cladding material is to contain the radioactive fission products, notably the gases, and thus prevent contamination of the surrounding coolant gas. However, the conventional process for manufacturing graphite always produces a porous material. The pore properties of a graphite suitable for cladding fuel in the high temperature reactor must be such as to allow efficient back-sweeping of the radioactive fission product gases by a small overpressure of coolant gas, thus preventing the escape of radioactive fission gases into the main coolant stream.

In order to study this problem the counter-diffusion of gases through the pores of various graphites has been examined using the system helium/nitrogen, and the results have been analysed by an equation based on normal gas-in-gas diffusion in a capillary model with frequently-linked pores. An attempt has been made to correlate the diffusion coefficients with more easily measured pore parameters, namely the permeability coefficients and pore size data.

Introduction

Graphite is a well-known refractory with excellent machining properties, good thermal and electrical conductivity, and moderately high strength at elevated temperatures.[1] It is widely used in the construction of electrodes for the chemical and metallurgical industries. In recent years, it has been used as a material of construction in heat exchangers[2] and as the moderator in gas-cooled nuclear-power reactors of the Calder Hall type. The present paper is concerned with the use of graphite as both moderator and fuel-cladding material in high-temperature nuclear reactors of the DRAGON and PEACH BOTTOM (U.S.A.) types, at temperatures of 1000°C or more. The function of the cladding material is to contain the radioactive fission products, notably the gases, and thus prevent contamination of the surrounding coolant gas.[3] However, the conventional process for manufacturing graphite always produces a porous material. Some of the pores are inaccessible to fluids, but the major part of the porosity forms a network which is open to the atmosphere. Despite the development of processes by means of which the pores can be partially blocked, it has not yet been possible to produce totally impermeable graphite. It was therefore decided in the case of the DRAGON reactor to operate the inside of the fuel elements, which are clad in graphite, at a lower pressure than that of the surrounding coolant gas. A small inward flow of coolant gas would thus sweep back any radioactive gases which might otherwise escape through the pores of the graphite, and by connecting the interior of the fuel elements to a clean-up plant external to the reactor core, the fission products could be safely collected. However, the permeability of the graphite must be low enough to prevent overloading of the clean-up plant, and its pore structure must be such as to confer satisfactory diffusion characteristics with regard to the back-sweeping of fission gases. Graphites suitable for this duty are being developed in the Chemical Engineering Division, AERE, on behalf of the OECD high-temperature gas-cooled (DRAGON) reactor project at Winfrith.[4, 18] The permeability constants, open

voidage and pore-size distribution of experimental graphites have been studied.[4, 5] This paper mainly deals with a study of the diffusion of gases through various graphites and the effects of superimposed pressure gradients; it also considers the relationship between the diffusion coefficient and other pore properties such as permeability and pore-size distribution.

The results of the present work can be shown to support a model for the pore structure of graphite based upon a concept of fine capillaries, of varying sizes, and with a high degree of interconnection with each other.

Theoretical

Brief review of previous work

Since Hewitt and Sharratt[6] have recently reviewed the literature on gaseous diffusion in porous media, only a brief account need be given here. In general, authors have adopted models for porous solids based on systems of capillaries, but recently Evans, Watson, and Mason[7] have proposed a different approach, the so-called " Dusty Gas " model. They consider that the porous material can be represented by a cloud of particles which is analogous to a third gaseous component, with the restriction that the molecules are fixed in space (*i.e.* " dust " particles). However, it would appear that the application of this model is at present limited to media of uniformly-sized pores since only uniformly-sized " dust " molecules have been considered.

Capillary model of porous media

In order to provide a theoretical basis for the present work on diffusion, it is useful to discuss the capillary model in some detail, because it will be shown that the diffusion kinetics depend on the type of capillary structure and on the distribution of pore diameters. The analysis considers the relationship between the gas fluxes and compositions of a binary gas mixture in a porous body. No restriction is placed on pressure gradient, and no attempt is made to consider the separate problem of relating the pressure drop to the gas fluxes and compositions. It is assumed that the diffusion of

* Chemical Engineering Division, AERE, Harwell, Didcot, Berks.

a binary gas mixture through a porous body takes place solely via the gas phase within the open porosity.

Several authors have considered that the porosity of a solid such as graphite can be represented as a system of capillaries.[11,12] One approach is to assume that all the pores are separate and have no communication with each other throughout the solid. This is called, for convenience, the Isolated Capillary Model (IC). This model is not very appropriate for a material such as graphite, and a new one is therefore considered, namely the Connected Capillary Model (CC). In the latter case it is assumed that all the pores meet each other at frequent intervals within the porous medium, forming a linked three-dimensional network, with the important consequence that the gas phases in neighbouring pores are continuously equilibrated with each other. One property of the IC model is that only about one-third of the total open porosity should be accessible from a given pair of opposite faces of an isotropic block of graphite. However, the whole of the open porosity should be accessible with the CC model.

The general diffusion regime

The diffusion of gases through graphite can be described if the diffusion in a single capillary is set down and then integrated over the whole of the pore structure of the graphite. Consider the steady-state flow of a binary gas mixture at a mean linear velocity v along a straight cylindrical tube of diameter d.† Let the composition of the gas vary with distance z along the capillary, hence leading to a counter diffusion of the two component gas species 1 and 2. When the pore diameter d is much greater than the molecular mean free path λ, the total molecular current g of either of the species across a fixed plane will be given by the sum of a diffusion term and a convective term:

$$g_1 = -\frac{\pi}{4} d^2 D_{12} \frac{dc_1}{dz} + \frac{\pi}{4} d^2 v c_1 \qquad . \qquad (1)$$

where D_{12} is the normal gas-in-gas diffusion coefficient, and c_1 is the concentration of species 1 molecules at position z. The equation assumes that there is no radial variation of gas velocity or composition.

Assuming that the gas mixture is ideal, equation (1) can be rewritten thus:

$$g_1 = -\frac{\pi d^2 D_{12} P}{4RT} \cdot \frac{dx_1}{dz} + Gx_1 \qquad . \qquad (2)$$

where x_1 is the mol fraction of species 1, $G = g_1 + g_2$ is the total gas flow, P is the total pressure, T is the temperature, and R is the gas constant.

If the pore diameter d is considerably smaller than λ, equation (2) does not hold, since in this case transport is by Knudsen or molecular flow:

$$g_1 = -\frac{\pi d^3 v_{01} P}{12RT} \cdot \frac{dx_1}{dz} \qquad . \qquad . \qquad (3)$$

where v_{01} is the molecular velocity of species 1, equal to $\sqrt{(8RT/\pi M_1)}$ where M_1 is the molecular weight. It is assumed that the reflection of molecules from the tube walls is completely diffuse. Thus transport in this regime may be characterised by a diffusion coefficient D_{K1} given by:

$$D_{K1} = \tfrac{1}{3} v_{01} d \qquad . \qquad . \qquad (4)$$

No convective term is present in equation (3) because the gas molecules make collisions only with the pore walls, which are at rest.

† *Symbols have the meanings given them on page 235.*

It is desirable, however, to express the gas transport g_1 by a single general equation which covers both the normal and Knudsen transport regimes. This can be done, for example, by adapting an expression put forward by Evans, Watson, and Mason.[7] The current of species 1 along a capillary is given by:

$$g_1 = -\frac{\pi P d^2}{4qRT} \cdot \left(\frac{1}{D_{12}} + \frac{3}{v_{01} d}\right)^{-1} \cdot \frac{dx_1}{dz} + Gx_1 \bigg/ \left(\frac{3D_{12}}{v_{01} d} + 1\right)$$

$$(5)$$

It will be noted that a tortuosity term, q, has been introduced $(q > 1)$ because in graphite the pores may not be straight. A comparable expression applies for species 2 molecules. Although no rigid proof can be given that equation (5) is valid for a cylindrical capillary in the general case, it has the merit that both flow regimes can be derived from it as limiting cases. For ideal gases D_{12} is equal to $\tfrac{1}{3} \bar{v}_0 \bar{\lambda}$ where $\bar{v}_0$ and $\bar{\lambda}$ are the mean molecular velocity and mean free path of the gas mixture. Thus it can be seen that when d is much greater than $\bar{\lambda}$ equation (5) simplifies to (2), and when d is much smaller than $\bar{\lambda}$, the equation simplifies to (3).

If there is a spectrum of pore sizes in graphite, where n_i is the number of capillaries of diameter d_i per unit area normal to the mean direction of transport, the average flux of species 1 through the material is:

$$j_1 = \sum_i n_i g_{1i} \qquad . \qquad . \qquad (6)$$

It is shown in Appendix I that in the general regime the two capillary models lead to different gas-transport equations.

Another important conclusion is that with neither model is it correct to use an equation for a porous body which is based on the single capillary equation (5), modified by the insertion of two constants D_1 and δ_1 as follows:

$$j_1 = -\frac{PD_1}{RT} \cdot \frac{dx_1}{dz} + \delta_1 J x_1 \qquad . \qquad . \qquad (7)$$

where $J = j_1 + j_2$. The treatment of Evans *et al.*[7] of the general flow regime is in fact based on equation (7), and thus their Dusty Gas Model would seem to have limited applicability where a range of pore sizes exists in the material, as mentioned previously.

Normal gas-in-gas diffusion

Consider now the difference between the two structure models when transport is wholly by normal gas-in-gas diffusion, *i.e.* when the capillary diameters are all much greater than $\bar{\lambda}$. Equations (6) and (2) for the IC model yield on integration the following expression for the average flux of one component through a porous body of thickness L when gas concentrations of this species of $x_{(0)}$ and $x_{(L)}$ are maintained on each side. (It is assumed that pressure P does not vary significantly through the medium.)

$$j = \sum_i n_i G_i \cdot \frac{x_{(0)} - x_{(L)} \cdot \exp\left[-4qRTLG_i/(\pi D_{12} P d_i^2)\right]}{1 - \exp\left[-4qRTLG_i/(\pi D_{12} P d_i^2)\right]} \cdot$$

$$(8)$$

Again it is not possible to write the differential equation corresponding to (8) in the form of equation (7). However, equations (6) and (2) applied to the CC model yield a fairly simple expression:

$$j = J \cdot \frac{x_{(0)} - x_{(L)} \exp\{[-RTLJ/P(D_{12})_e]\}}{1 - \exp\{[-RTLJ/P(D_{12})_e]\}} \qquad . \qquad (9)$$

where $J = j_1 + j_2 = \sum_i n_i G_i$ is the total flux of gas, and $(D_{12})_e$ is an effective normal diffusion coefficient defined by:

$$(D_{12})_e = \frac{\pi}{4q} . D_{12} . \sum_i n_i d_i^2 . \qquad . \qquad (10)$$

As a first approximation the term $\sum_i n_i d_i^2$ may be related to the open porosity ϵ and tortuosity q thus:

$$\epsilon = \frac{\pi}{4} . q . \sum_i n_i d_i^2. \qquad . \qquad (11)$$

Hence equation (10) becomes:

$$(D_{12})_e = \frac{\epsilon}{q^2} . D_{12} \qquad . \qquad (12)$$

Thus for normal gas-in-gas diffusion the two models still give different transport relationships, although the CC model yields a fairly simple expression, namely equation (9). Moreover, in this case the differential form of equation (9) is of the same type as the single capillary expression; in equation (7) $D_1 = (D_{12})_e$ and $\delta_1 = 1$. Under these conditions a single parameter $(D_{12})_e$ characterises the diffusion properties of the material, and it is not necessary separately to know the pore-size distribution. This is not so for the IC model.

General diffusion in media containing uniformly sized capillaries

Consider next the special case where the porous body contains capillaries of only one diameter d. Application of equations (6) and (5) gives the same expression for both models, namely:

$$j = J \left(\frac{3D_{12}}{v_0 d} + 1 \right)^{-1} . \frac{x_{(0)} - x_{(L)} \exp\{[-RTLJ/P(D_{12})_e]\}}{1 - \exp\{[-RTLJ/P(D_{12})_e]\}} .$$

$$(13)$$

The differential form of equation (13) corresponds to equation (7), and so in this particular case it is possible to characterise the graphite by the latter equation where:

$$D_1 = \left(\frac{1}{(D_{12})_e} + \frac{3q^2}{\epsilon v_{01} d} \right)^{-1} . \qquad . \qquad (14)$$

and

$$\delta_1 = \left(\frac{3D_{12}}{v_{01} d} + 1 \right)^{-1}$$

$$= \left(\frac{3(D_{12})_e q^2}{\epsilon v_{01} d} + 1 \right)^{-1} \qquad . \qquad (15)$$

Thus, where the pores are all the same size the transport of gases through graphite can be represented by equation (7) involving the two material constants D_1 and δ_1, which are defined above. Alternatively the characteristics of the porous body may be defined in terms of two other parameters $(D_{12})_e$ and $(D_K)_e$, the latter being given by:

$$(D_K)_e = \frac{1}{3} . \frac{\epsilon}{q^2} v_0 d \qquad . \qquad (16)$$

Equation (16) is merely the expression for a single capillary, equation 4, modified by the factor ϵ/q^2. Hence equations (14) and (15) can be re-written:

$$D_1 = \left(\frac{1}{(D_{12})_e} + \frac{1}{(D_{K1})_e} \right)^{-1} \qquad . \qquad (17)$$

$$\delta_1 = \left(\frac{(D_{12})_e}{(D_{K1})_e} + 1 \right)^{-1} \qquad . \qquad (18)$$

When the capillaries are of uniform diameter d, the permeability coefficient K_0 becomes (see Appendix III):

$$K_0 = \frac{3\pi}{64} . \frac{\epsilon}{q^2} . d \qquad . \qquad (19)$$

Thus equation (16) can be modified to:

$$(D_K)_e = \frac{64}{9\pi} K_0 v_0. \qquad . \qquad (20)$$

It is sometimes suggested[12] that the general regime of gaseous diffusion through a porous medium can be described by relationships containing the coefficient D_1 as defined by equation (17), where $(D_{12})_e$ and $(D_{K1})_e$ are given by equations (12) and (20) respectively. (The constant $64/9\pi$ in equation (20) is frequently replaced by $4/3$). However, the analysis above shows that this proposition is correct for only the particular case of a material possessing pores of uniform diameter. When there is a spectrum of pore sizes it is not possible to characterise the material by a term such as D_1. The concept of the parameter $(D_{K1})_e$ becomes worthless and the relationship, equation (20) would have no meaning (except for the special case where all the pores are much smaller than $\bar{\lambda}$).

Experiments to differentiate between the two models

The analysis above has shown that the two structure models are indistinguishable in all flow regimes for bodies containing a single size of pore. In practice graphites generally possess a distribution of capillary diameters. In principle a distinction between the two structure models can be made when transport is in either the general or normal regime. (The models give the same transport-rate equation if diffusion is exclusively Knudsen.) However, it is only feasible to test one case, namely normal gas-in-gas diffusion in the CC model, equation (9), because verification of the other transport equations requires the measurement of the flow G_i along each size of capillary. In spite of this limitation it was considered sufficiently important to test the validity of equation (9), rewritten thus:

$$(D_{12})_e = \frac{RTLJ/P}{\log_e[(j_1 - Jx_{1(L)})/(j_1 - Jx_{1(0)})]} . \qquad (9A)$$

The experiments were accordingly designed so that both transport fluxes and terminal gas concentrations could be measured. For each set of conditions $(D_{12})_e$ was computed using equation (9A).

Experimental

The diffusion coefficients quoted in this paper have been determined using helium and nitrogen in a steady-state diffusion apparatus. The general circuit layout is shown in Fig. 1. Essentially, the method consists of admitting pure helium and nitrogen, at various pressures, to either side of a graphite septum. Countercurrent diffusion takes place and, under equilibrium conditions, the two exit gas streams are analysed and the flow rates measured.

Reasonably pure helium and nitrogen are used without further purification except drying. Pressure-reducing valves are used to bring gas pressures down to about 20 lb/in² g. The gases pass through tubes filled with anhydrone to remove

Q*

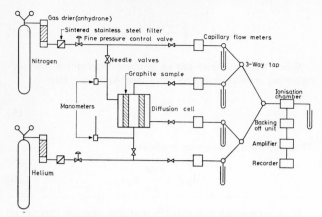

Fig. 1.—*Diffusion apparatus-circuit layout*

traces of water vapour, and then through sintered stainless-steel filters. The graphite sample, clamped between rubber gaskets inside the diffusion cell, is in the form of a 4-in.-long cylinder of wall thickness about 0·4 in. with outside diameter, depending on the extrusion diameter of the graphite, in the range 1·5 to 2·5 in. In the diffusion cell, helium is fed to the inside and nitrogen to the outside of the graphite wall at pressures of between one and two atmospheres, governed by the fine-pressure-control valves.

During a run, helium diffuses through the porous graphite wall into the nitrogen stream and, similarly, nitrogen diffuses into the helium. The two exit gas streams from the diffusion cell are throttled down to atmospheric pressure by means of needle valves and their flow rates are maintained in the region of 2 ml/s, measured by capillary flowmeters having dibutyl phthalate manometers. Each individual capillary was calibrated by means of a soap-bubble flow meter using pure

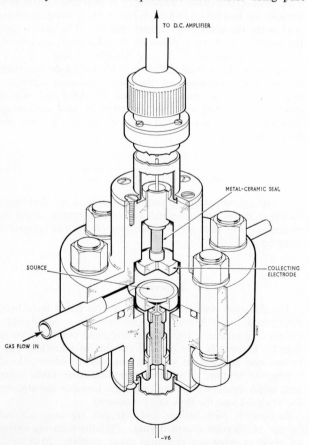

Fig. 2.—*β-Ray ionisation chamber*

gases. Graphs of pressure drop *versus* flow rate give straight-line plots through the origin with the gradient of the line inversely proportional to the gas viscosity. Hence, when metering gas mixtures, the viscosity is first computed and then the indicated flow rate corrected to this viscosity. The gas streams bubble to atmosphere against a head of 2 in. of dibutyl phthalate. By means of a system of three-way taps, the gas streams can be selected in turn and passed through a β-ray ionisation chamber for analysis.

The use of β-ray ionisation chambers in gas analysis is well-known and many designs and techniques have been described.[13, 14] The main features of the ionisation chamber used[15] are made clear by reference to Fig. 2. The chamber consists of two flanged halves, joined together with an " O "-ring seal. A sealed radioactive source supplies the β-rays for the ionisation and also acts as one of the electrodes. The other electrode is a 0·7-in.-diameter brass disc situated so that the electrodes are 0·4 in. apart. A potential difference of 165 V is applied. Electrical connections are made through metal–ceramic seals. The chamber walls, made from brass, are at least a half an inch thick to provide adequate shielding both for radiation and to exclude extraneous currents. For satisfactory operation, sufficient radiation is required to give an ionisation current of about 10^{-9} A. The radioactive source chosen was Strontium 90 with a half-life of 28 years; 40 millicuries was found to be sufficient. The response of the instrument was linear, the current ranging from 7×10^{-10} A for pure helium to $3 \cdot 7 \times 10^{-9}$ A for pure nitrogen. The composition of mixtures could be measured to less than 10^{-3} mol fraction. The apparatus and the technique described is not restricted to helium and nitrogen: any pair of gases can be studied in this way provided that their ionisation cross-sections are significantly different.

The permeability coefficients, B_0 and K_0 were also measured for all the graphites tested, using a vacuum decay method.[5] In addition, the pore size distribution in the base stock graphites (*i.e.* unimpregnated) was measured by a mercury porosimeter. Details of the graphites are given in Tables II and III.

Results

All the graphites examined in this work had diffusion characteristics which could be well correlated by equation (9):

$$j = J \frac{x_{(0)} - x_{(L)} \exp\{- RTLJ/[P(D_{12})_e]\}}{1 - \exp\{- RTLJ/[P(D_{12})_e]\}} \quad . \quad (9)$$

Table I shows the full results obtained from a typical diffusion experiment, based on one graphite, and it can be seen that over the wide range of fluxes and gas compositions the value of $(D_{12})_e$ as calculated by equation (9A) at s.t.p. is reasonably constant. This is also illustrated by Fig. 3 where $(D_{12})_e$ is plotted against the pressure drop ΔP applied across the specimen, measured in the direction of the transport of nitrogen. (Pressure drop conveniently represents in a single variable the range of fluxes and compositions used.) In fact there is seen to be a slight rise in $(D_{12})_e$ as ΔP departs from zero. In all probability this is due to the fact that equation (9) is strictly only valid when ΔP is very small compared to P. Mean values of $(D_{12})_e$ for each of the graphites studied are recorded in Table II, along with the standard deviations.

Fig. 3 also shows the quantity D' plotted against ΔP. D' is an apparent diffusion coefficient for the particular experimental conditions, and is defined by:

$$D' = \frac{jL}{c_{(0)} - c_{(L)}} = \frac{jLRT}{x_{(0)} P_{(0)} - x_{(L)} P_{(L)}} \quad . \quad (21)$$

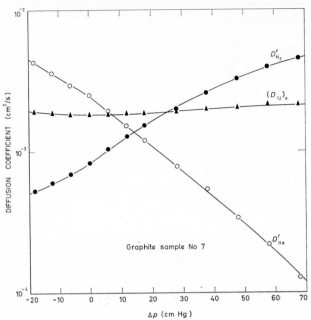

Fig. 3.—*Plots of various diffusion coefficients against pressure difference*

Fig. 3 illustrates how the transport flux of each species is assisted or retarded by a pressure drop acting with or against the direction of transport.

Discussion

Diffusion mechanism

Since all the graphites appeared to behave as suggested by equation (9), it seems that (*a*) the transport of gases is by normal gas-in-gas diffusion with no noticeable contribution by Knudsen flow, and (*b*) the pore structure of the graphites studied consists of a system of frequently linked capillaries (CC model) rather than discrete pores (IC model). It is true that equation (9) would also apply to the latter model if the pores were of uniform size, but this cannot be the situation for each of the 40 or so materials studied. The pore structure of some of the graphites was examined by a mercury penetration method, and in no case were all the pores found to be of a single diameter. Fig. 8 shows the size distribution in the graphite whose diffusion results are given in Table I.

Hewitt *et al.*[9, 10] reported diffusion experiments with oxygen and nitrogen in graphites of B_0 ranging from 7×10^{-10} to 8×10^{-13} cm.[2] Their experiments were so designed, that $x_{(0)}$ was virtually zero, and only one of the transport fluxes was directly measured. However, they were able to derive the flux of the other gas species by applying the standard permeability equation to the measured pressure drop. These workers also found that their results could be correlated fairly satisfactorily by equation (9) in agreement with the conclusions of the present study.

At the point where D_1' and D_2' intersect in Fig. 3, $j_1 \sim -j_2$, *i.e.* $J \sim 0$. Hence according to equation (9), $D' = (D_{12})_e$ at this condition. The intersection occurs at $D' = 1 \cdot 37 \times 10^{-3}$ cm²/s, which when corrected to a pressure of 1 atm gives a value of $1 \cdot 84 \times 10^{-3}$ cm²/s. This agrees well with $(D_{12})_e$, $(1 \cdot 85 \times 10^{-3}$ cm²/s). An interesting feature in Fig. 3 is that at zero pressure gradient the ratio of the transport fluxes (equal to the ratio of D_1'/D_2' at this point) is not unity as might be expected for normal diffusion, but is in fact 3·0. Various authors[8, 16] have argued that in porous bodies at zero pressure gradient the flux ratio should equal $\sqrt{(M_2/M_1)}$

not only for the Knudsen regime but also for normal diffusion. For the nitrogen/helium system the value is 2·64, fairly close to the presently observed ratio.

It cannot necessarily be assumed that all graphites would behave as CC models with normal gas-in-gas diffusion characteristics, but it would nevertheless appear from the present work that graphites with a permeability coefficient B_0 of as low as 1×10^{-13} cm² would perform similarly under similar conditions. It seems reasonable to suppose that other gas pairs would behave in the same way provided no significant physical or chemical interaction between the gases and the graphite took place.

Relation between diffusion and other pore properties

Pore parameters of graphite such as the permeability constants B_0 and K_0 are far easier to measure than the effective diffusion coefficient $(D_{12})_e$ and so it would be useful to establish a relationship between $(D_{12})_e$ and other pore properties. Let d^* and A^* be a characteristic pore diameter and pore area respectively as defined by:

$$d^* = \frac{\sum n_i d_i^3}{\sum n_i d_i^2} = \frac{\pi}{4} \cdot \frac{q}{\epsilon} \sum n_i d_i^3 \qquad . \quad (22)$$

and

$$A^* = \frac{\sum n_i d_i^4}{\sum n_i d_i^2} = \frac{\pi}{4} \cdot \frac{q}{\epsilon} \sum n_i d_i^4 \qquad . \quad (23)$$

then it follows from Appendix II that:

$$B_0 = \frac{\epsilon A^*}{32 q^2} \qquad . \qquad . \quad (24)$$

and

$$K_0 = \frac{\epsilon d^*}{4 q^2} \qquad . \qquad . \quad (25)$$

Making use of equation (12), these two equations become respectively:

$$\frac{B_0}{A^*} = \frac{1}{32} \cdot \frac{(D_{12})_e}{D_{12}} \qquad . \qquad . \quad (26)$$

$$\frac{K_0}{d^*} = \frac{1}{4} \cdot \frac{(D_{12})_e}{D_{12}} \qquad . \qquad . \quad (27)$$

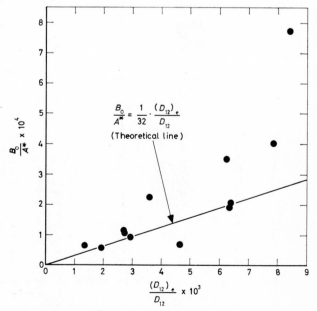

Fig. 4.—*Plot of B_0/A^* versus $(D_{12})_e/D_{12}$*

TABLE I.—*Results of a Typical Diffusion Experiment*

Graphite sample number 7.

Sample dimensions: Internal diameter = 2·53 cm
External diameter = 4·44 cm
Length = 10·16 cm

Permeability constants $B_0 = 8·23 \times 10^{-13}$ cm²
$K_0 = 6·21 \times 10^{-8}$ cm

Diffusion data:

Temperature (°C)	22·3	22·5	22·5	22·3	22·3	22·4
Atmospheric pressure (cmHg)	75·02	74·97	74·87	74·83	74·76	74·81
Nitrogen pressure (cmHg)	94·98	88·86	82·79	76·74	100·74	106·81
Helium pressure (cmHg)	94·98	94·93	94·83	94·79	94·72	94·77
% helium in nitrogen	16·88	18·48	23·49	28·79	13·17	10·10
% nitrogen in helium	4·626	3·605	2·773	2·134	6·458	8·456
Helium diffusion rate* (ml/s)	0·2829	0·3356	0·3975	0·4638	0·2217	0·1777
Nitrogen diffusion rate* (ml/s)	0·09326	0·07260	0·05579	0·04289	0·1305	0·1712
$(D_{12})_e \times 10^3$ (cm²/s)	1·82	1·82	1·87	1·92	1·83	1·85

Temperature (°C)	22·4	22·4	22·4	22·6	22·8	22·5
Atmospheric pressure (cmHg)	74·77	74·78	75·08	75·12	75·11	75·13
Nitrogen pressure (cmHg)	112·68	122·92	133·05	143·14	153·09	162·99
Helium pressure (cmHg)	94·75	94·74	95·04	95·08	95·07	95·09
% helium in nitrogen	7·898	5·071	3·163	1·795	1·080	0·6026
% nitrogen in helium	10·70	15·40	21·17	27·56	34·94	39·36
Helium diffusion rate* (ml/s)	0·1386	0·08900	0·05864	0·03414	0·02022	0·01112
Nitrogen diffusion rate* (ml/s)	0·2173	0·3114	0·4266	0·5595	0·7152	0·8533
$(D_{12})_e \times 10^3$ (cm²/s)	1·85	1·89	1·99	2·02	2·12	2·10

* Measured at the given atmospheric pressure.

TABLE II.—*Permeability and Diffusion Data for all the Graphites.*

Sample No.	Graphite composition*			Permeability constants		Diffusion coefficient $(D_{12})_e$ (cm²/s)	Standard deviation of $(D_{12})_e$ (%)
	Grist	Binder	Impregnant	B_0 (cm²)	K_0 (cm)		
1	G and B	P	—	$4·74 \times 10^{-12}$	$1·02 \times 10^{-7}$	$2·56 \times 10^{-3}$	10·9
2	G and B	P	H	$2·55 \times 10^{-13}$	$8·99 \times 10^{-9}$	$1·85 \times 10^{-4}$	19·7
3	C	P	P	$2·33 \times 10^{-11}$	$5·84 \times 10^{-7}$	$6·41 \times 10^{-3}$	12·5
4	C	P	H	$1·95 \times 10^{-12}$	$4·28 \times 10^{-8}$	$8·89 \times 10^{-4}$	10·6
5	G and B	P	—	$9·53 \times 10^{-13}$	$9·72 \times 10^{-8}$	$4·54 \times 10^{-3}$	8·2
6	G	P	P	$7·75 \times 10^{-12}$	$1·24 \times 10^{-7}$	$1·12 \times 10^{-3}$	3·9
7	G	P	—	$8·23 \times 10^{-13}$	$6·21 \times 10^{-8}$	$1·95 \times 10^{-3}$	5·4
8	G and B	R	—	$5·04 \times 10^{-13}$	$2·46 \times 10^{-8}$	$9·67 \times 10^{-4}$	3·8
9	G	P	R	$2·79 \times 10^{-11}$	$1·74 \times 10^{-7}$	$1·95 \times 10^{-3}$	7·6
10	C	P	P	$3·18 \times 10^{-12}$	$1·42 \times 10^{-7}$	$2·19 \times 10^{-3}$	3·5
11	G and B	P	H	$6·26 \times 10^{-13}$	$1·88 \times 10^{-8}$	$2·39 \times 10^{-4}$	12·1
12	C	P	P	$3·37 \times 10^{-12}$	$1·38 \times 10^{-7}$	$2·03 \times 10^{-3}$	20·9
13	C	P	H	$1·92 \times 10^{-12}$	$4·45 \times 10^{-8}$	$9·71 \times 10^{-4}$	8·4
14	G	P	H	$1·87 \times 10^{-12}$	$4·51 \times 10^{-8}$	$9·09 \times 10^{-4}$	9·6
15	C	P	P and R	$3·83 \times 10^{-12}$	$1·35 \times 10^{-7}$	$2·07 \times 10^{-3}$	9·5
16	C	P	R	$4·86 \times 10^{-12}$	$1·63 \times 10^{-7}$	$3·50 \times 10^{-3}$	14·6
17	G and B	P	—	$2·00 \times 10^{-12}$	$1·33 \times 10^{-7}$	$5·59 \times 10^{-3}$	5·5
18	G	P	—	$3·59 \times 10^{-12}$	$1·58 \times 10^{-7}$	$4·45 \times 10^{-3}$	6·1
19	G	P	R	$1·09 \times 10^{-12}$	$5·48 \times 10^{-8}$	$8·75 \times 10^{-4}$	5·5
20	G	P	R	$5·46 \times 10^{-12}$	$4·82 \times 10^{-7}$	$3·11 \times 10^{-3}$	2·4
21	G	P	R	$4·60 \times 10^{-12}$	$1·70 \times 10^{-7}$	$2·87 \times 10^{-3}$	3·9
22	G	P	R	$2·00 \times 10^{-11}$	$4·66 \times 10^{-7}$	$4·33 \times 10^{-3}$	7·3
23	G	P	R	$1·02 \times 10^{-13}$	$9·35 \times 10^{-9}$	$2·45 \times 10^{-4}$	3·4
24	G	P	R	$4·00 \times 10^{-12}$	$1·18 \times 10^{-7}$	$6·02 \times 10^{-4}$	6·0
25	G	P	—	$2·19 \times 10^{-11}$	$5·25 \times 10^{-7}$	$5·99 \times 10^{-3}$	9·1
26	G	P	—	$1·58 \times 10^{-11}$	$5·24 \times 10^{-7}$	$4·51 \times 10^{-3}$	4·2
27	G	P	—	$2·16 \times 10^{-11}$	$4·82 \times 10^{-7}$	$3·31 \times 10^{-3}$	14·7
28	G	P	—	$3·62 \times 10^{-12}$	$5·26 \times 10^{-8}$	$1·38 \times 10^{-3}$	9·2
29	G	P	—	$2·28 \times 10^{-11}$	$2·15 \times 10^{-7}$	$4·13 \times 10^{-3}$	6·9
30	G	P	—	$1·20 \times 10^{-11}$	$1·78 \times 10^{-7}$	$2·10 \times 10^{-3}$	3·7
31	G	P	—	$3·33 \times 10^{-12}$	$9·70 \times 10^{-8}$	$1·93 \times 10^{-3}$	5·3
32	G	P	H	$4·87 \times 10^{-13}$	$2·10 \times 10^{-8}$	$7·19 \times 10^{-4}$	7·2
33	C	P	P	$7·30 \times 10^{-12}$	$3·08 \times 10^{-7}$	$2·55 \times 10^{-3}$	4·3
34	C	P	P	$2·35 \times 10^{-12}$	$6·26 \times 10^{-8}$	$1·06 \times 10^{-3}$	6·0
35	C	P	P	$4·24 \times 10^{-12}$	$1·09 \times 10^{-7}$	$1·73 \times 10^{-3}$	7·8
36	C	P	H	$2·14 \times 10^{-13}$	$8·38 \times 10^{-9}$	$2·88 \times 10^{-4}$	11·2
37	C	P	H	$9·45 \times 10^{-13}$	$1·95 \times 10^{-8}$	$6·88 \times 10^{-4}$	6·0
38	C	P	P	$1·89 \times 10^{-11}$	$5·62 \times 10^{-7}$	$6·37 \times 10^{-3}$	7·3

* Key to symbols: G = scrap graphite P = pitch
C = coke R = resin
B = carbon black H = hydrocarbon gas

TABLE III.—*Pore Size Parameters*

Sample number	d^* (cm)	A^* (cm²)
1	$1 \cdot 11 \times 10^{-4}$	$2 \cdot 12 \times 10^{-8}$
5	$4 \cdot 98 \times 10^{-5}$	$4 \cdot 64 \times 10^{-9}$
7	$6 \cdot 06 \times 10^{-5}$	$7 \cdot 72 \times 10^{-9}$
8	$6 \cdot 60 \times 10^{-5}$	$7 \cdot 80 \times 10^{-9}$
17	$5 \cdot 98 \times 10^{-5}$	$4 \cdot 96 \times 10^{-9}$
18	$9 \cdot 10 \times 10^{-5}$	$1 \cdot 03 \times 10^{-8}$
25	$1 \cdot 32 \times 10^{-4}$	$2 \cdot 83 \times 10^{-8}$
26	$2 \cdot 64 \times 10^{-4}$	$8 \cdot 36 \times 10^{-8}$
27	$3 \cdot 66 \times 10^{-4}$	$3 \cdot 23 \times 10^{-7}$
28	$1 \cdot 95 \times 10^{-4}$	$6 \cdot 64 \times 10^{-8}$
30	$3 \cdot 20 \times 10^{-4}$	$1 \cdot 30 \times 10^{-7}$
31	$1 \cdot 10 \times 10^{-4}$	$2 \cdot 96 \times 10^{-8}$

The parameters d^* and A^* can be computed from measurements of pore-size distribution. B_0/A^* and K_0/d^* are plotted against $(D_{12})_e/D_{12}$ in Figs. 4 and 5 respectively for those graphites for which the pore-size spectrum was measured. The value taken for D_{12} at s.t.p. is $0 \cdot 71$ cm²/s.[17] The straight lines corresponding to equations (26) and (27) are also shown in the figures. The results scatter to some extent about these lines.

Equations (26) and (27) can be combined to give:

$$\frac{K_0^2}{B_0} = 2 \cdot \frac{(d^*)^2}{A^*} \cdot \frac{(D_{12})_e}{D_{12}} \qquad . \qquad . \quad (28)$$

K_0^2/B_0 is shown in Fig. 6 plotted against $(D_{12})_e/D_{12}$ for all the materials studied in this work. The ratio $(d^*)^2/A^*$ is, of course, not necessarily constant for all the graphites, and this factor may account for the fairly wide scatter in Fig. 6. The line corresponding to equation (28) with $(d^*)^2/A^* = 1$ is shown in Fig. 6 for comparison. This is the line for uniformly sized capillaries.

Values of the ratio $(d^*)^2/A^*$ were obtained directly for those graphites whose pore-size distribution had been measured. These were found to vary from $0 \cdot 4$ to $0 \cdot 8$ with a mean of $0 \cdot 6$, as illustrated by the plot of $(d^*)^2$ against A^*

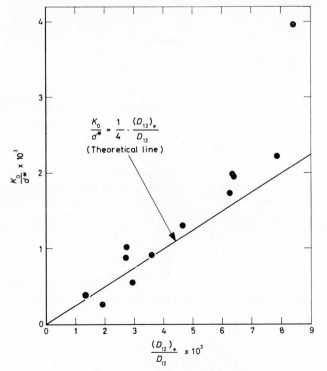

Fig. 5.—*Plot of K_0/d^* versus $(D_{12})_e/D_{12}$*

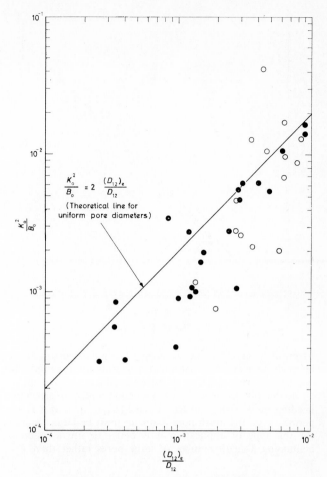

Fig. 6.—*Plot of K_0^2/B_0 versus $(D_{12})_e/D_{12}$*

in Fig. 7. Since there was no reason to suppose that these selected samples were systematically different from the total number of graphites examined, confirmed by comparing the two sets of points plotted in Fig. 6, it may be surprising to find that the range of values of $(d^*)^2/A^*$ implied by this figure is much greater, extending from $0 \cdot 2$ to 2.

Experimental errors and inadequacies in the theoretical treatment probably contribute to the scatter of results in Figs. 4 and 5, and to the discrepancy between Figs. 6 and 7. In addition, pore-size spectra as measured by means of a mercury porosimeter suffer from the following limitation: the porosimeter does not differentiate between blind pores and transport pores but merely measures the entrance "diameter" of all accessible pores. Hence a relationship between pore sizes as measured by the mercury porosimeter and other pore properties is necessarily empirical.

There is therefore an approximate relationship between the diffusion parameter $(D_{12})_e/D_{12}$ and the permeability parameter K_0^2/B_0, the best correlation being given by equation (28), with $(d^*)^2/A^*$ equal to $0 \cdot 6$. Fig. 6 shows considerable scatter, however, and no great improvement is obtained by inserting the actual value of $(d^*)^2/A^*$ for each individual graphite, as determined by the porosimeter, into equation (28).

The use of graphite as a reactor-fuel tube

The results of the present work can be used as a guide to the selection of graphites for service where counter diffusion of gases is an important factor. For instance, the design of some of the fuel tubes in the DRAGON high-temperature gas-cooled reactor allows the purging gas to enter the tubes

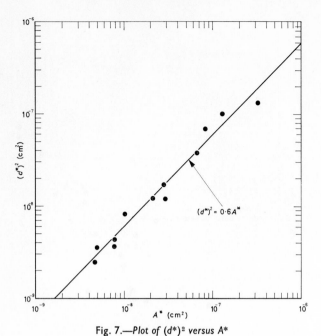

Fig. 7.—Plot of $(d*)^2$ versus $A*$

by means of pores in the graphite. The pore structure must be such that for the particular permeability required the counter- or back-diffusion of fission-product gases is kept to an acceptably low level. The discussion under the previous heading shows that in order to make $(D_{12})_e$ small at a given permeability, the mean pore diameter must be large. Hence for this type of application it is better to use a graphite containing a small number of large pores rather than *vice versa*.

Conclusions

The transport of diffusing gas mixtures through about 40 graphites covering a range of permeability coefficient B_0 from 1×10^{-13} to 3×10^{-11} cm^2 has been shown to follow the normal gas-in-gas mechanism under s.t.p. conditions. The results indicate that these graphites behave as systems of frequently cross-linked capillaries. The diffusion coefficients correlate approximately with permeability data.

The results can be used as a guide to specify the properties of a graphite suitable for use as the fuel tube in a high-temperature gas-cooled reactor.

Acknowledgments

This work was carried out in the Chemical Engineering Division of AERE, Harwell, and was supported by the OECD Dragon Project at Winfrith, Dorset.

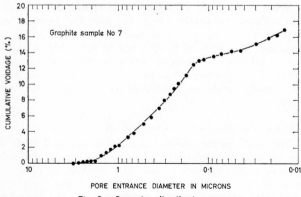

Fig. 8.—Pore size distribution curve

Appendix I

Gas transport in the general regime: Comparison of the two structure models

The basic differential equation assumed for a single capillary is:

$$g_{1i} = -\frac{\pi P d_i^2}{4qRT} \cdot \left(\frac{1}{D_{12}} + \frac{1}{v_{01} d_i}\right)^{-1} \cdot \frac{dx_{1i}}{dz}$$

$$+ \left[G_i x_{1i} \middle/ \left(\frac{3D_{12}}{v_{01} d_i} + 1\right)\right] \quad (1)$$

The average flux through the porous medium is:

$$j_1 = \sum_i n_i g_{1i}$$

$$= -\frac{\pi P}{4qRT}\sum_i \left[n_i d_i^2 \middle/ \left(\frac{1}{D_{12}} + \frac{3}{v_{01} d_i}\right)\right]\frac{dx_{1i}}{dz}$$

$$+ \sum_i \left[n_i G_i x_{1i} \middle/ \left(\frac{3D_{12}}{v_{01} d_i} + 1\right)\right] \quad (2)$$

Equation (2) can be integrated for the IC model, since the individual gas currents, and hence the sum G_i, are independent of z. The result, with the boundary conditions (a) $z = 0$, $x_{1i} = x_{1(0)}$, (b) $z = L$, $x_{1i} = x_{1(L)}$, leads to:

$$j_1 = \sum_i \left[n_i G_i \middle/ \left(\frac{3D_{12}}{v_{01} d_i} + 1\right)\right]$$

$$\times \frac{x_{1(0)} - x_{1(L)} \exp[-4qRTLG_i/(\pi D_{12} P d_i^2)]}{1 - \exp[-4qRTLG_i/(\pi D_{12} P d_i^2)]} \quad (3)$$

However, equation (2) cannot be integrated analytically for the CC model. Although the gas concentration x_1 in this model is now independent of capillary diameter d_i, the current term G_i is a function of position z. It is therefore clear that the transport relationships in the general regime are not the same for both models.

Appendix II

Permeability relationships

(a) PERMEABILITY OF IC MODEL

The flow G_i due to viscous and slip mechanisms of a gas of viscosity μ along a single capillary of tortuosity q is:

$$G_i = -\frac{1}{RT}\left(\frac{b}{q} \cdot \frac{P_i}{\mu} \cdot d_i^4 + \frac{k}{q} v_0 d_i^3\right)\frac{dP_i}{dz} \quad (1)$$

where $b = \pi/128$ and $k = \pi^2/64$.

Since the capillaries are isolated, G_i is independent of z. Integration, with the boundary conditions (a) $z = 0$, $P_i = P_{(0)}$ (b) $z = L$, $P_i = P_{(L)}$, gives:

$$G_i = \frac{\Delta p}{RTL}\left(\frac{b}{q} \cdot \frac{\overline{P}}{\mu} \cdot d_i^4 + \frac{k}{q} \cdot v_0 d_i^3\right) \quad (2)$$

where $\Delta P = P_{(0)} - P_{(L)}$ and $\overline{P} = \frac{1}{2}\{P_{(0)} + P_{(L)}\}$.

The total gas flux through the porous body is therefore:

$$J = \sum_i n_i G_i$$

$$= \frac{\Delta p}{RTL}\left(\frac{b}{q} \cdot \frac{\overline{P}}{\mu}\sum_i n_i d_i^4 + \frac{k}{q} \cdot v_0 \sum_i n_i d_i^3\right) \quad (3)$$

(b) PERMEABILITY OF CC MODEL

$$G_i = -\frac{1}{RT}\left(\frac{b}{q}\frac{P_i}{\mu}d_i^4 + \frac{k}{q}v_0 d_i^3\right)\frac{dP_i}{dz} \quad . \quad (1)$$

Since the pores make frequent connections with each other, pressure equalisation occurs in the limit throughout the medium. Thus P_i is independent of capillary diameter d. The gas current G_i is in general not independent of position z, due to the remixing process. However, the total gas flux through the material must be independent of z. The total flux is:

$$J = \sum_i n_i G_i$$

$$= \frac{1}{RT}\left(\frac{b}{q}\frac{P}{\mu}\sum_i n_i d_i^4 + \frac{k}{q}v_0\sum_i n_i d_i^3\right)\frac{dP}{dz} \quad . \quad (2)$$

Integration with the same boundary conditions as in (a) yields:

$$J = \frac{\Delta p}{RTL}\left(\frac{b}{q}\cdot\frac{\overline{P}}{\mu}\sum_i n_i d_i^4 + \frac{k}{q}\cdot v_0\sum_i n_i d_i^3\right). \quad (3)$$

(c) DISCUSSION OF PERMEABILITY EQUATIONS

Both models lead to the same expression for the permeability of a porous medium. It is not therefore possible to distinguish one model from the other by permeability tests.

Comparison with the normal empirical permeability equation, viz,

$$K = \frac{JRTL}{\Delta p} = B_0\cdot\frac{\overline{P}}{\mu} + \tfrac{4}{3}\cdot K_0 v_0 \quad . \quad (1)$$

shows that the two permeability constants of a porous body are given by:

$$B_0 = \frac{b}{q}\sum_i n_i d_i^4 \quad . \quad . \quad (2)$$

$$K_0 = \tfrac{3}{4}\cdot\frac{k}{q}\sum_i n_i d_i^3. \quad . \quad . \quad (3)$$

The open porosity of the material is:

$$\epsilon = \frac{\pi}{4}q\sum n_i d_i^2. \quad . \quad . \quad (4)$$

If the body contains pores of only one diameter d, equations (2) and (3) reduce to:

$$B_0 = \frac{4b}{\pi}\cdot\frac{\epsilon}{q^2}d^2 = \tfrac{1}{32}\frac{\epsilon}{q^2}d^2 \quad . \quad . \quad (5)$$

$$K_0 = \frac{3k}{\pi}\cdot\frac{\epsilon}{q^2}d = \frac{3\pi}{64}\cdot\frac{\epsilon}{q^2}d. \quad . \quad . \quad (6)$$

Symbols Used

A^* = characteristic pore cross-section (equation 23) (cm^2).

b = numerical constant = $\pi/128$.

B_0 = viscous permeability coefficient (cm^2).

c = concentration (mol/cm^3).

d = pore diameter (cm).

d^* = characteristic pore diameter (equation 22) (cm).

D = diffusion coefficient (cm^2/s).

D_{12} = normal binary diffusion coefficient (cm^2/s).

g = transport current of single species (mol/s).

G = total transport current = Σg (mol/s).

j = transport flux of single species. (mol/cm^2 s)

J = total transport flux = Σj (mol/cm^2 s).

k = numerical constant = $\pi^2/64$.

K_0 = slip permeability coefficient (cm).

L = thickness of porous medium (cm).

M = molecular weight (g/mol).

n = number of pores per unit area (cm^{-2}).

P = pressure (dyn/cm^2).

ΔP = pressure drop across medium (dyn/cm^2).

q = tortuosity.

R = gas constant (erg/mol degC).

T = temperature (degK).

v = linear gas velocity (cm/s).

v_0 = molecular gas velocity (cm/s).

x = mol fraction.

z = distance co-ordinate (cm).

ϵ = fractional open porosity.

δ_1 = constant in equation (7).

λ = mean molecular free path (cm).

μ = viscosity (P).

Subscripts

$_{1,2}$ = gas species.

$_K$ = Knudsen.

$_e$ = effective.

$_{(0)}$ = $z = 0$.

$_{(L)}$ = $z = L$.

References

[1] Roberts, F., Mason, I. B., Price, M. S. T., and Bromley, J. "*Progress in Nuclear Energy*", Series IV, 1961, **4**, 105 (Oxford: Pergamon Press Ltd.).

[2] Hilliard, A. *Industr. Chem. Mfr.*, 1963, **39**, 525.

[3] De Bruijn, H. *Trans. Instn chem. Engrs*, 1963, **41**, 96.

[4] Roberts, F., Longstaff, B., and Jenkins, T. R. "*AERE Report R.3943*", 1963 (London: HMSO).

[5] Jenkins, T. R., and Roberts, F. "*Proceedings of the Fifth Carbon Conference*", 1963, **2**, 335 (Oxford: Pergamon Press Ltd.).

[6] Hewitt, G. F. and Sharratt, E. W. *Nature, Lond.*, 1963, **198**, 952.

[7] Evans, R. B., Watson, G. M., and Mason, E. A. *J. Chem. Phys.*, 1962, **36**, 1894.

[8] Hoogschagen, J. *Industr. Engng Chem.*, 1955, **47**, 906.

[9] Hewitt, G. F., and Morgan, J. R. "*AERE Report R.3814*", 1961 (London: HMSO).

[10] Hewitt, G. F., and Sharratt, E. W. "*AERE Report M.1081*", 1963 (London: HMSO).

[11] Adzumi, H. *Bull. chem. Soc. Japan*, 1937, **12**, 304.

[12] Carman, P. C. "*Flow of Gases through Porous Media*", 1956 (London: Butterworth & Co. (Publishers) Ltd.).

[13] Otvos, J. W., Deal, C. H., Smith, V. M., and Zucco, T. F. *Analyt. Chem.*, 1956, **28**, 1958.

[14] Lovelock, J. E. *Journal of Chromatography*, 1958, **1**, 35.

[15] Bishop, G. B. Private communication.

[16] Scott, D. S., and Dullien, F. A. L. *A.I.Ch.E. Journal*, 1962, **8**, 113.

[17] Walker, R. E., and Westenberg, A. A. *J. Chem. Phys.*, 1958, **29**, 1139.

[18] Roberts, F. *Chem.-Ing.-Tech.*, to be published.

The manuscript of this paper was received on 31 January, 1964.

DISCUSSION OF PAPERS PRESENTED AT THE FIFTH SESSION

The CHAIRMAN said that his introductory remarks concerned general topics which had been raised earlier on the subject of materials science. He wanted to emphasise a different aspect, which seemed to him at least as important as the aspects which had already been emphasised during the meeting.

On Monday, they seemed to be along the lines of the engineer telephoning his materials man, and that phrase had been used—" to fix him a material to do a specified job "—a perfectly valid activity. He wondered whether he dared whisper it in the present audience, but there might be some phenomena that the engineer had not heard of. They were the phenomena from which the new technologies emerged, and the materials scientist had to take part in creating the technologies, as well as in the other functions that had been discussed.

To quote an example, practically all the physics underlying masers and lasers was known in 1912 following Einstein's discussion of the absorption and emission of radiation. Laser technology had come about in the past few years, and the people concerned with developing the materials had had to combine their knowledge of physics and chemistry.

The materials were developed on the basis of an understanding of the atomic and electronic processes involved. It seemed to him that there was nothing new in that. For example, a polymer scientist in the development of new material utilised detailed knowledge of organic molecular structure; his work was closely related to his knowledge of the microscopic structure; and the same was true of the materials research which was leading to new technologies—semiconductors, lasers, and so forth.

It seemed to him that the important thing was that, in this activity, chemistry and physics should be recognised as inseparable disciplines; also metals and non-metals; and, in his view, crystalline solids on the one hand and amorphous solids and liquids on the other.

Among other things that had to be faced in the long term was that " quantum mechanics " was an industrial technique; and it had to be recognised that the materials scientist was involved in a two-way process—originating technologies and improving materials in existing technologies.

He wished to say that after the discussion which had taken place on the Monday, in which it seemed to him that the above points had not been sufficiently emphasised.

Dr. J. K. BEDDOW said that the curve of strength versus time at temperature was similar to an ageing curve, and he asked Mr. Sugarman if there was any sign of precipitation at all.

Mr. SUGARMAN said that there was no sign of precipitation, as far as could be seen. In fact, he thought that this was a stress relaxation phenomenon that occurred more rapidly at temperatures approaching the softening point or transformation point.

Professor P. HOSEMANN drew attention to an observation made by his department on single quartz crystals, in which the dynamic interference theory enabled one to see the single dislocation.[1] The observation was that, just touching the surface of the quartz a little with one's finger one could see finger-prints in the reflection pattern (right side of Fig. 1).

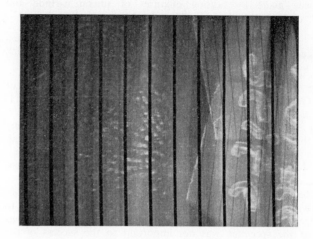

Fig. 1.

On the left-hand side of Fig. 1 some letters were written in ink, which could be seen clearly, too. The higher reflection power of the the traces proves that a higher amount of lattice distortion is introduced there. From dynamical interference theories one knows that the lattice must be distorted to a depth of at least 50 Å. The effect could be connected with the Griffith cracks.

Mr. SUGARMAN said that it was down to at least 100 Å.

Mr. B. A. PROCTOR referred to the remark by White and Sugarman that no one had ever seen Griffith cracks. This, Proctor felt, was hardly surprising because there were no such things as Griffith cracks.

If a piece of fused silica, or glass, were freshly drawn from the molten state a smooth surface resulted, and provided the surface was not touched in any way the glass would be strong. In other words, it contained no Griffith cracks.

Immediately such a piece of glass were touched or abraded in any way it would be weakened, and it was to explain the common experience of weak glass that Griffith introduced his concept of micro-cracks. That had been an extremely useful concept and in fact there were *actual cracks* in the surface of *abraded* or *mechanically damaged glass*, introduced by the abrasion, which were responsible for its weakness.[2] Another way to weaken glass was to heat it, which again introduced surface stress raisers and tied in with the defects shown in the present paper.

Unfortunately the concept of " Griffith cracks " had become part of the mythology referred to by Professor Owen the previous day in the sense that they were often accepted as an integral and inherent part of the glass. That was not correct: it was mechanical damage which introduced the cracks to the glass surface.

Professor Hosemann's comments were an illustration that in another material, surface damage was of tremendous importance and similar results were available with alumina.[3]

Mr. SUGARMAN said that although there was room for discussion on terminology, this was by no means a controversial point; he was in agreement with the speaker, but so many people made reference to Griffith cracks, that one felt that common usage of the expression was probably justified. Certainly, glass was only weak when the surface became damaged. It was an inherently strong material.

Mr. C. R. SHAKESPEARE commented on Professor White's paper. On page 200, Professor White mentioned the formation of silicon nitride-bonded silicon carbide—and stated that it was made by heating mixtures of silicon carbide and " carbon " in nitrogen. That should read " silicon ".

Professor WHITE said that this was so and that there were a certain number of mistakes in the draft of the paper which would be corrected.

Mr. SHAKESPEARE referred to reference 24, the work of Gooding and Parratt, which was in *Powder Metallurgy*, **11**, and not in " *Special Ceramics* " as indicated.

He disagreed with some comments on page 200 concerning the reaction of sintered materials, where Professor White said, " For this method to be successful, it is necessary that reaction should take place without appreciable change in the dimensions of the specimen ". He would not agree with that because, although that usually occurred, all that was necessary was that porosity should remain long enough for reaction to go to completion. What happened to the external dimensions of the specimen was not important to the success of the reaction.

Professor WHITE said that in the statement quoted he was not concerned with whether the reaction would go to completion or not, but whether a sound specimen would be produced by reaction sintering. There were many examples where reaction during sintering caused expansion, *e.g.* this often occurred when mixed powders which reacted to form compounds were fired, and usually resulted in weak, porous specimens. In addition, one of the big advantages of silicon nitride was that it could be machined when it was partially nitrided and nitriding could then be completed without appreciable change in dimensions. This was a valuable characteristic although perhaps not essential.

Mr. SHAKESPEARE pointed out that Professor White said later: " This implies that the product should ' grow ' into the inter-particle voids as it forms, and calls for close control over particle size and grading and cold-pressed density." His department had made silicon nitride from all manner of particle sizes and densities.

Professor WHITE agreed that it was possible to make reasonably satisfactory silicon nitride articles without close control of these variables, as they had themselves done, but he asked Mr. Shakespeare if he would not agree that for optimum properties control was necessary.

Dr. R. H. HAWARD asked Mr. Sugarman, who had emphasised the extent to which glass suffered through damage, if he would outline how far it had been possible to make the strength of glass more permanent by protection with other materials.

Mr. SUGARMAN said that this easily could be the subject of another discourse. Looking at it in terms of the commercial side, because this was what he was primarily interested in, most of the protective coatings which had been applied, particularly on bottles, had been developed for anti-scuffing properties, easier handling, and so on; most of them were palliative treatments, not cures. Very few of them were capable of withstanding washing and/or sterilisation. It was only recently that titanium dioxide coatings applied in certain ways had been used as protective coatings for bottles. These had been available for some while in the States and had been recently introduced in this country. He was not aware in detail of the way in which these had been applied, but there had been disclosures in the press which indicated that a technique was by spraying some organic titanate. The important thing was that a refractory oxide skin was produced which had a high melting point. This was a claim made in a patent. That it stuck on was an interesting point. It did not appear to be a discrete coating as such, and it therefore looked as if there might be a measure of penetrability.

Mr. P. RADO said that Professor White had stated that he would finish on a pessimistic note; the brittleness of ceramics. He could mention one dense recrystallized ceramic which was more brittle than any other. That was calcium fluoride. It had the highest thermal expansion of all ceramics, of 25×10^{-6}. As regards alkali attack, it had a weight gain but there were some very positive properties to it as well. It was not only one of the few materials not attacked by molten uranium, but it was also a reaction product in the smelting of uranium by calcium reduction of the tetrafluoride, and it seemed to be logical to use a reaction material as a reaction vessel. Calcium fluoride had been available in very high purity, which was of very great importance for the smelting of pure uranium, especially enriched uranium and plutonium. It was made by slip-casting, which implied that there was no binder and therefore no residue of carbon. That helped the purity of the smelted uranium.

Since then, it had been found that calcium fluoride was not attacked by hydrofluoric acid. It was the only ceramic not attacked by hydrofluoric acid. Most silicates were very viciously attacked. It was very slightly attacked if the temperature of the hydrofluoric acid was raised; it had been used in fluorine atmospheres at 900°C. It had unique optical properties and could possibly be used for special electrical and electronic purposes. It should offer quite a wide range of applications for the chemical engineer, especially where a refractory which was resistant to hydrofluoric acid had not been available in the past.

Professor WHITE said that the use of calcium fluoride as crucibles illustrated a point he had tried to make in the paper, that any inorganic material became a ceramic material once it was used to fabricate ceramic articles. Its usefulness for melting pure uranium illustrated also the importance of thermochemical considerations when looking for refractories for use in contact with reactive metals, since it depended on the fact that while liquid uranium was capable of reducing even the most stable refractory oxides with solution of oxygen in the metal, the analogous reaction with calcium fluoride did not occur.

Professor R. HOSEMANN referred to the table in Mr. Roberts' paper showing helium densities of uranium dioxide varying from 10·34 to 10·81, depending on how the uranium dioxide was made. His question was whether the small density of 10·34 was produced by a higher amount of vacancies.

Mr. ROBERTS said he did not think this was so. There were details in the paper relevant to this question. The lattice parameters showed no variation with density; some variation would be expected if the low density preparation contained a large proportion of vacancies.

Also, the crystallite size calculated from the width of the diffraction lines was always much smaller than the particle size calculated from the surface area whenever the helium density was much lower than the crystal density of 10·96. This suggested that the low-density preparation consisted of particles having a complex microstructure, with a large number of crystallites packed together in an impermeable mass in one particle. Although possibilities such as Professor Hosemann put forward could not be excluded and some poorly crystalline material might be present, he thought that the low densities were mainly due to poor packing of crystallites.

Dr. J. MANN said that he was interested in Dr. Clarke's paper because what Dr. Clarke was saying was that, with the ceramics, he wanted limited increase in ductility. In the polymer field, there was a similar problem with polystyrene, which was brittle, and those in that field had learnt to live with the fact that it was brittle. They had not attempted to change the properties. They had added to the polystyrene a dispersion of rubber spheres which stopped cracks growing by elastic deformation. In Clarke's system, to do a similar thing, he presumed that some particles would have to be put in which would stop the cracks by plastic deformation of some sort. In another paper, an experiment had been quoted in which gold particles were dispersed in sodium chloride to stop cracking. He asked Dr. Clarke if he thought there was a possibility of solving his problems by that sort of technique.

Dr. CLARKE replied that it depended on the testing conditions. Under a constant stress application the most important thing was the stress to start fracture, and Dr. Mann's rubber spheres would not necessarily make the material stronger. However, in a constant strain application (such as mechanical and thermal shock) what mattered was the work of fracture. Under such a condition a finite amount of elastically stored energy had to be absorbed (i.e. that stored by the shock), and the higher the work of fracture the less cracking this energy would cause. Dr. Mann's rubber spheres cause microcracking in the body of the polystyrene near the crack tip and so increase the work of fracture which helps to absorb the stored elastic energy. This makes the material better able to withstand shock. This sort of mechanism accounts for the limited toughness of graphite. Precipitates, as in the case of gold in sodium chloride, might also help to absorb energy, perhaps in a different manner.

Dr. MANN said that his suggestion of what was happening was that though some energy might be stored much was dissipated in the form of microcracks not harmful to the material. The material still hung together. What mattered, in Clarke's example, was that there should be no catastrophic cracking.

Dr. CLARKE said that he agreed with Dr. Mann. The more the stored energy could be dissipated by subsidiary cracking, the better. In practise this meant localising the energy near the source of shock, and hence near the crack that it caused to grow. Catastrophic cracking is catastrophic usually because it is not localised in this way.

Dr. J. K. BEDDOW referred to Hutcheon's graph of open-pore content of the graphites. He wondered how the open-pore content was controlled. Was the open-pore proportion related to the closed-pore proportion? Could the closed-pore proportion be controlled, and was there any relationship between crystal size and the pore or particle size?

Mr. HUTCHEON said that in these experiments the open pore volume variations derived primarily from variation in number of impregnations, type of impregnant and heat treatment conditions. For a minority of the material differences in binder and in size distribution of the filter was also relevant. As was explained in more detail in the paper, however, the experimental materials were not prepared with the intention of representing open porosity variations alone.

Open porosity plus closed porosity was roughly constant, since the densities of the different materials did not vary widely. Otherwise there was not much systematic variation of closed porosity among these materials. In order to obtain such control, he would think it necessary to vary the binder and filler materials, for example by using special carbons, such as vitreous carbon.

In such an isotropic polycrystalline carbon of small crystal size there would be some packing voidage between the crystals and the size of these voids must be related to the crystal size. In many commercial graphites, however, this formed only a part even of the closed porosity. In such materials most of the porosity was open, in the form of pores of the order of a few microns in size, and was present because the binder impregnant had carbonised, with gas evolution, from the liquid phase.

Dr. J. K. HIGGINS said that he had a question about the accommodation coefficient. Experiments in his department on vitreous carbon showed that the crystallite size was about 20×40 Å in the A and C directions respectively and the crystallite were all randomly orientated. There was no orientated microporosity in the material. The substance had been irradiated and it was found that, contrary to the predictions of equation 3, the material with smaller crystals randomly orientated had more shrinkage than larger-grained material. It was found to have a 2 per cent shrinkage in all directions, which was greater than the PGA figures quoted in Fig. 3a.

Mr. HUTCHEON said that, for material of the crystal size Dr. Higgins quoted, significant shrinkages would be expected despite its high thermal expansion, and this was specifically stated in the paper. Comment on the numerical values for the shrinkage would, of course, require knowledge of the irradiation parameters, namely dose, dose rate, temperature and neutron energy spectrum.

Professor HOSEMANN said that experiments on single monocrystals of quartz seemed to prove that inside a crystalline lattice there existed domains where a high number of oxygen bridges were broken and abraded by water. They had almost pore-like shapes, and if such things could happen to single fine crystals, the more one had to take into account such phenomena with regard to glass.

Mr. R. H. BIDDULPH said that he wished to take issue on one of the points in Professor White's paper, the fabrication of non-oxide ceramics. He rather arbitrarily dismissed them, saying that they had to be fabricated by hot pressing. His company had made many of them by cold pressing, sintering, by slip casting, and quite a lot of work was being done on plasma spraying.

He also had a question for Mr. Sugarman. The Chemcor glass seemed to be the answer to the physical chemist's prayer in its strength, but could it be joined by normal glass-blowing techniques?

Mr. SUGARMAN said that the easiest answer was to say that the Chemcor glasses were toughened glasses in the sense that they had a skin compressive stress. They were therefore subject to exactly the same type of manufacturing difficulties as thermally toughened glass. In other words, if a piece was purchased there was no claim made that it was unbreakable; it was just more difficult to break. In the same way, there was also a statement saying that it must not be worked, drilled or cut.

Professor WHITE said that what he had said was that *certain* non-oxide ceramics could not readily be sintered or even hot-pressed to high densities. Silicon nitride, for instance, could not normally be either sintered or hot-pressed. It could, however, be hot-pressed if MgO was added to it. Uranium monocarbide also did not normally sinter satisfactorily. It had, however, been found comparatively recently that, if the oxygen and water contents of the atmosphere were kept low enough, it could be sintered.

Mr. K. M. HILL asked if plastics could be modified by putting in fillers to provide a certain compression effect in the same way as toughened glass. He was not thinking of fillers on the gross scale but on the atomic scale, that is actually attached to the polymer chain.

Dr. MANN said that he did not know the answer to the question as posed. However, it was clear that polystyrene and glass were different systems. A strong skin under compressive forces could be obtained with polystyrene by injection moulding. Unlike glass, however, this did not materially increase the tensile strength. The reason for this was that cracks were generated inside the polystyrene which propagated outwards, leading to fractures of the strong skin. The stresses for generation of these internal cracks were only slightly higher than those required to cause failure from the surface in polystyrenes not possessing a strong skin.

Dr. HAWARD: The lecturer described the growth of a brittle crack in a ceramic material and mentioned the desirability that this crack would become blunted or rounded off by deformation processes while at the same time the bulk of the material would retain its shape. This appears to be a form of the more commonly considered criterion of requiring at the same time toughness and rigidity. One way of formulating the physical requirement for meeting these conditions is to provide for a high rate of increase in the rate of strain with increasing stress. This type of behaviour allows the material to deform quickly where a high stress is present while it remains rigid at low or moderate stresses. I should be glad to have the speaker's opinion of the possible significance of this concept in relation to ceramic materials.

If he looks at the written version of my own paper on p. 163 and the illustrated graph on p. 163 he will see that I have also mentioned this concept in relation to plastics, although unfortunately in presenting this paper the point was omitted through shortage of time.

Dr. CLARK: Dr. Haward's formulation may be a physical requirement for toughness but I believe that something must also be said about the relative rates of strain increase on, and the number of, the independent slip systems that are operative. On the latter point the condition laid down by von Mises may be more stringent than is really needed if account is taken of the fact that in many ceramics the cracks themselves will not lie on an arbitrary plane (*e.g.* they may all lie on cleavable planes).

Mr. P. RADO (*The Worcester Royal Porcelain Co. Ltd., Worcester*): In his introduction Professor White also referred to halides being within the range of potential ceramic materials but he did not include them when discussing non-oxide ceramics. May I, therefore, mention calcium fluoride, which has become a vital link in the chain of the processing of

uranium for nuclear applications, particularly where very high purity is essential, *e.g.* enriched uranium and plutonium. It is eminently suitable as a reaction vessel in the reduction of uranium tetrafluoride to uranium metal by calcium, because it is not only one of the few materials not attacked by molten uranium but it is also the reaction product besides uranium. Using the material which is formed in the reaction for reaction vessels eliminates or at least reduces the risk of contaminating the reduced metal. Besides, calcium fluoride is commercially available in exceptionally high purity and this is essential for producing uranium billets of the highest purity. Extraction efficiency has been enormously increased by using *dense* calcium fluoride crucibles. Such completely impervious crucibles sufficiently large—say 4 l. capacity—for industrial application can only be made economically by the method known as slip-casting (followed by sintering) as applied to oxide ceramics. It was Murray who first conceived the idea of slip-casting since fluorides have ionic properties similar to those of oxides.

Dense calcium fluoride ceramics have a number of advantages over other uranium reduction vessels such as magnesia. They enable greater extraction yields to be obtained, produce uranium billets which are not only purer but which, showing no interaction with the vessel material, do not need dressing or re-melting; besides they ensure easy and quick manipulation.

Impervious calcium fluoride ware is remarkable in other respects. It has an extremely high thermal expansion, *viz.* 25×10^{-6}, the highest of all ceramics. This does not, however, preclude its use at elevated temperatures.

It is the only ceramic not attacked by hydrofluoric acid. It shows no loss in weight whatsoever when immersed in cold (20°C) hydrofluoric acid of 10% concentration for 100 h. Hardly perceptible losses of a few parts per million occur with concentrated hot hydrofluoric acid but with increases in temperature, concentration and time of immersion the losses are again " reduced ", finally giving way to gains in weight. This strange phenomenon is possibly due to a departure of the calcium fluoride from stoichiometry, adsorption of moisture or attack on trace impurities which may be present in the calcium fluoride. In any case these changes in weight are hardly significant since they only amount to a few parts per million.

Calcium fluoride ceramics are resistant to fluorides (*e.g.* lithium and lead fluorides) at elevated temperatures as well as to hydrofluoric acid, and have also been successfully used in fluorine atmospheres at temperatures approaching 1000°C. They thus have potential applications where lack of materials which are both refractory and resistant to fluorine and its compounds made such uses impossible so far.

They offer an ideal refractory for fluoride glasses.

Apart from their resistance to molten uranium they are not attacked by molten calcium. Other potential uses in the metallurgical field might be in the refining of noble and rare metals.

Exhibiting predominantly ionic conduction in the bulk phase at moderately high temperatures calcium fluoride is suitable as a solid electrolyte in electrochemical cells.

Furthermore, calcium fluoride is a well-known laser material.

References

[1] Barth, H. *Z. Elektrochem.*, 1959, **63**, No. 8, p. 908. Barth, H., and Hosemann, R. *Z. Naturf.*, 1958, **13a**, 9.

[2] Proctor, B. A. *Applied Materials Research*, 1964, **3**, No. 1, p. 28.

[3] Morley, J. G., and Proctor, B. A. *Nature, Lond.*, 1962, **196**, 1082.

SIXTH SESSION

R

NEW METHODS IN METAL WORKING

By H. Ll. D. PUGH, B.Sc., F.Inst.P., F.I.M., M.I.Mech.E.* and M. T. WATKINS, B.Sc., F.Inst.P.†

SYNOPSIS

Continued developments in industry generally, but more particularly in the fields of chemical engineering, nuclear energy, aviation and space exploration have created a demand for materials which can withstand ever-increasing stress and temperature or other special conditions imposed by the environment in which they are required to operate. In an effort to meet these requirements new alloys have been developed and use is now made of materials which were barely known a few years ago. Materials with the desired properties, however, are of value only if they can be formed and it is axiomatic that processing difficulties increase as the required mechanical properties are improved. It has been found necessary therefore to supplement existing forming processes by methods involving new techniques and often novel forms of energy.

Among the new processes that are being developed is the application of high hydrostatic pressures to support deforming materials. A description is given of the work that has been carried out on the use of a high pressure liquid to effect the extrusion of a range of materials varying from soft materials such as aluminium up to high strength materials. Extrusion of rounds, complex sections and tubes can be effected in this manner. The potential of this method as an alternative to wire drawing is also discussed. There is considerable current interest for many reasons in various materials all of which are brittle. A method is discussed in which the product merges into a pressurized liquid whereby successful cold extrusions of brittle materials can be effected.

During the last ten years there has been a marked increase in the application of high rate methods in the working of metals in such operations as forming, shaping, forging, extrusion, welding, compacting, etc. In such methods energy derived from chemical explosives, high voltage discharges, electro-magnetic fields or fast moving masses is released rapidly and applied over a relatively short interval of time. Each new process has its characteristic features and a particularly advantageous field of application which are briefly discussed.

The rate of technical progress is such, however, that the industrial implications of one technique are barely assessed before another is offering further possibilities. Thus the potential of laser and electron beam techniques in the working of metals have yet to be explored.

Introduction

Modern technological progress imposes ever-increasing demands on man's ingenuity in utilizing to their best advantage the materials and techniques at his disposal. Developments in industry generally, but more particularly in the fields of chemical engineering, nuclear power, aviation and space exploration have created a demand for materials, which in addition to meeting the requirements of strength, weight, temperature, corrosion resistance, ablation, *etc.*, must often operate *in vacuum*, in the presence of electromagnetic radiation high-energy particles, *etc.*

New materials, refractory alloys, more complex dispersion hardening alloys, ceramics, cermets, *etc.*, are continually being developed to meet these new requirements. It is, however, unfortunately true that the more demanding the requirement the more difficult the material is to process into the desired form. The refractory alloys have high recrystallization temperatures which necessitate forging and extrusion at temperatures above the present practical limits (*e.g.* 1370°C for molybdenum). The nickel base and cobalt base high temperature alloys become increasingly difficult to form and in some instances are available in the desired shape only in the cast or sintered conditions. In sheet form titanium has directional properties due to its hexagonal close-packed structure which necessitates special forming techniques.

There are often additional problems in that the desired shapes are large and/or particularly complex and may be required in relatively small numbers. Thus, in recent years much attention has been given to the development of new fabrication techniques often involving novel methods of producing energy.

* Head of Plasticity Division, Materials Group, National Engineering Laboratory, East Kilbride, Glasgow.

† Plasticity Division, Materials Group, National Engineering Laboratory, East Kilbride, Glasgow.

Hydrostatic Extrusion

One of the major disadvantages in the conventional cold extrusion of metals is the large extrusion pressure required, a good deal of which is not essential to effect the required change of shape but is used, for example, in overcoming frictional forces. A new process which goes some way to overcoming this disadvantage is called hydrostatic extrusion. This process, together with that of wire drawing, was first tried but not developed by Bridgman.[1] The bulk of the research and development work on the method appears to have been carried out by Vereshchagin[2] and his co-workers in Moscow and by Pugh[3-5] and his colleagues at the National Engineering Laboratory, U.K.

The process of hydrostatic (or ramless) extrusion is essentially one in which the billet is extruded through a die by pressurized liquid instead of the conventional ram. The apparatus used at the National Engineering Laboratory for hydrostatic extrusion is shown diagrammatically in Fig. 1. The die, together with a high pressure seal is located on a shoulder in the bore of the high-pressure container. The billet, nosed to fit the conical die and provided with a guide ring at the back to prevent any tendency to tilt, rests in the die. The high-pressure container is filled with liquid which is pressurised either by forcing down the top plunger by means of a press or in some other convenient manner. It may be noted that, if a ram is used to build up the pressure as in Fig. 1, it need not necessarily operate in the same bore as that containing the billet and can, if desired, be located in a transverse bore. By placing the high pressure seal at the bottom end of the die the high-pressure liquid can then be used to give lateral support to the outside of the die thereby obviating the necessity of using the large shrink rings which are essential in conventional cold extrusion dies. In this way extrusion of steels and other high-strength materials can be carried out through thin-walled dies since the support pressure is increased as the extrusion

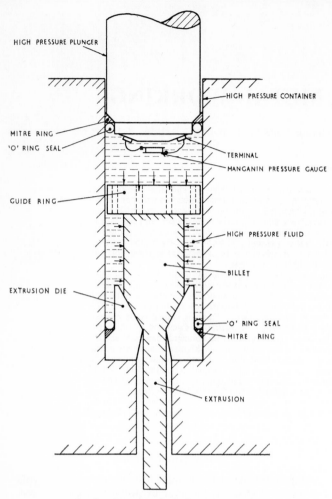

Fig. 1.—*Apparatus for hydrostatic extrusion*

HIGH PRESSURE PLUNGER

HIGH PRESSURE CONTAINER

MITRE RING

'O' RING SEAL

TERMINAL

MANGANIN PRESSURE GAUGE

GUIDE RING

HIGH PRESSURE FLUID

BILLET

EXTRUSION DIE

'O' RING SEAL

MITRE RING

EXTRUSION

pressure is increased. By nosing the billet to the same angle as the die the assembly acts as an unsupported area seal and it is not necessary to provide the billet with an artificial seal.

The method can, of course, be used for the extrusion of rods and of tubes of various sections. A selection of shapes in mild steel, aluminium, copper and lead obtained at the National Engineering Laboratory using this process are shown in Fig. 2.

Extrusion Pressure

Some of the obvious advantages of the process of hydrostatic extrusion can be readily seen by reference to Fig. 3 which gives a diagrammatic representation of conventional and hydrostatic extrusion of a billet through a conical die. The work done in extruding a product is made up of four parts. The first, to produce the change of shape by homogeneous deformation, is that required to extend the billet uniformly until its diameter is reduced to that of the product and can be obtained by integration of the stress–strain curve. The second part is the redundant work associated with the strains set up and subsequently reversed during the process as a result of the geometry of the dies. For example, fibres near the periphery of the billet are bent as they approach the die face in order to be able to move towards the die throat where they are again bent in the reverse direction in order to emerge as part of the product. Clearly this factor is dependent on the die geometry and is largest for a square-entry die. The third and fourth parts of the work done during extrusion are those required to overcome friction at the die–billet and container–billet interfaces respectively.

It is obvious from Fig. 3 that, in hydrostatic extrusion, the friction at the container–billet interface is eliminated. Further, since molybdenum disulphide is usually put into the pressure transmitting liquid a supply of high-pressure lubricant can be ensured at the right place for continuous and efficient lubrication. This lubricating liquid is dragged along the billet–die interface during extrusion as is indicated by its presence on the outside of the extruded product and in this way the friction between the billet and the die is considerably reduced. Indeed, because of this effect the process holds considerable promise as a means of providing continuous lubrication suitable for the extrusion of very long products. Finally, because small-angled dies can be used the redundant work due to the reversal of direction of flow of the work material can be reduced. Although in principle small-angled conical dies could be used in conventional extrusion it is clear that, when the punch reaches the top of the cone, extrusion is at an end and there is a large unextruded discard.

The effect on the extrusion pressure of the decrease in redundant work due to the reduction in die angle is shown in Fig. 4 for the 99·5% aluminium and the HE 30 aluminium alloy (0·7% magnesium, 1% silicon, 0·7% manganese). It will be noted that the Russian results on aluminium AD 1 (99·5%) and for copper show that the maximum extrusion pressure is a minimum at angles of around 30°. This is to be expected since, as the die angle decreases, the area of contact between the die and the billet increases and, for a given coefficient of friction the total frictional force increases, whilst the redundant work decreases. In the case of 99·5% aluminium this minimum occurred at a smaller angle in tests by Pugh and Ashcroft[4] indicating that the operative coefficient of friction was less than that in the Russian work.[2] This is confirmed by the fact that the pressures obtained by Pugh and Ashcroft for the extrusion of aluminium at a ratio of 7 were about the same as those required by the Russians for a ratio of only 4.

It also follows from the foregoing that the pressure for hydrostatic is less than that for conventional extrusion under similar circumstances by an amount depending on the efficiency of conventional lubrication. This is particularly true for long billets where lubrication tends to break down in the conventional process. The pressure to extrude some typical metals hydrostatically at various extrusion ratios are given in Fig. 5. It may be observed that there is an approximately linear relation between pressure and the logarithm of the extrusion ratio as is commonly observed in conventional extrusion. Fig. 5 also gives the relation for the calculated pressure for the homogeneous deformation of aluminium alloy HE 30

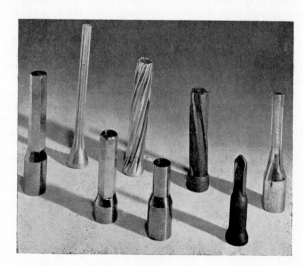

Fig. 2.—*Selection of shapes in mild steel, aluminium, copper and lead produced by hydrostatic extrusion*

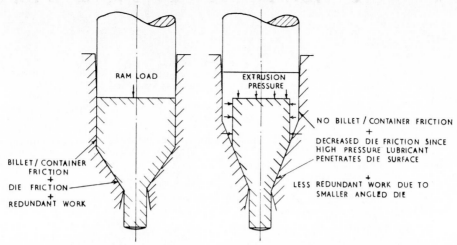

Fig. 3.—*Diagram of conventional and hydrostatic extrusion showing forces involved*

which is the minimum pressure required to effect the change of shape. It may be seen that the pressure for the hydrostatic extrusion is only about 30% greater than this minimum value. This means that the redundant work in extruding material through a die of angle of 45° together with the friction accounts for not more than 30% of the minimum extrusion pressure. Thus, this process of hydrostatic extrusion is getting very close towards eliminating the redundant factors which are almost inevitable in the extrusion and other metalworking processes.

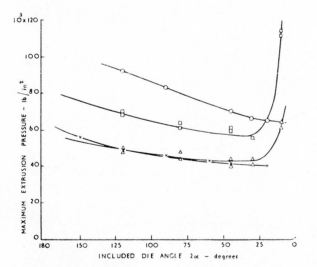

Extrusion ratio

7·1 ⊙ = Aluminium alloy HD 44 } Pugh and Ashcroft[4]
7·1 × = Aluminium (99·5% purity, }

4·1 △ = Aluminium ADI } Beresnev, Vereshchagin and Ryabinin[6]
2·1 ☐ = Copper }

Fig. 4.—*Effect of die angle on hydrostatic-extrusion pressure*

Lubrication

From experiments on the extrusion of AD 1 aluminium through a conical die of 80° angle at an extrusion ratio of 4·4, Beresnev, Vereshchagin and Ryabinin[6] found that water, together with a layer of "hypoid" lubricant on the specimen, gave the best surface finish and with one exception the lowest extrusion pressure. However, for a number of their experi-

ments they used a mixture of kerosene and transformer oil with "hypoid" lubricant on the specimen. Pugh and Ashcroft[4] after a few trial experiments used a mineral oil SAE 30 containing molybdenum disulphide dispersion. A comparison of the pressures to extrude aluminium and, of the angle at which the pressure was a minimum, given above in Fig. 4, implies that the molybdenum disulphide dispersion gives the more efficient lubrication.

The combination of molybdenum disulphide dispersion in SAE 30 oil was found to be efficient in a number of cases. Thus, for example, no difference could be detected in the pressure required for the hydrostatic extrusion of mild steel billets with or without a phosphate coating. However, it was not completely effective for the extrusion of some of the more difficult and harder metals and other types of lubricant had to be used. These included a metallic coating of copper, silver and lead, fluon, a molybdenum disulphide grease and latex rubber solution.

It sometimes happens that the pressure builds up to a higher value than that required to effect the extrusion once the billet has started to move, presumably because static friction is larger than sliding friction. In such circumstances the billet is extruded at high speed because of the excess energy in the liquid. It has been proved that, in many such cases, the products have a much better surface finish than the same materials extruded at low speeds under otherwise identical conditions. The probable explanation is that the liquid and lubricant is dragged along the conical face to build up a protective lubricating film at an even higher pressure at the die–billet interface, *i.e.* a hydrodynamic lubrication mechanism obtains.

The Use of Small-angled Dies in Hydrostatic Extrusion

The advantages in reduction in extrusion pressure obtained by using small-angled dies in hydrostatic extrusion and the elimination of the large discards which are inevitable in the conventional process have already been mentioned. In addition, conical dies eliminate the piping defect which manifests itself as a truncated hole at the back end of an extrusion thereby saving some 10–15% of material.

The use of small-angled dies combined with efficient lubrication at the die–billet interface enables the work material to slide easily over the die face and results in a reasonably uniform deformation across the product in marked contrast to the severe dragging back and shearing which is commonly observed on the surface of products which have been extruded in the conventional manner through large-angled dies. This

R*

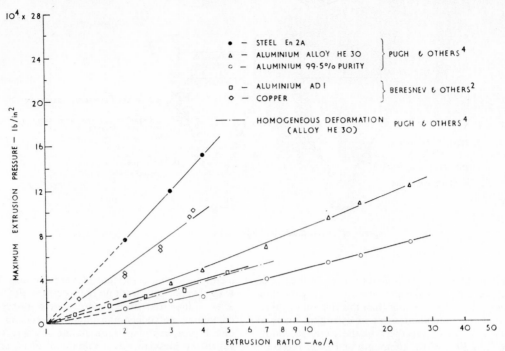

Fig. 5.—*Hydrostatic extrusion pressure for five metals through a 45° die*

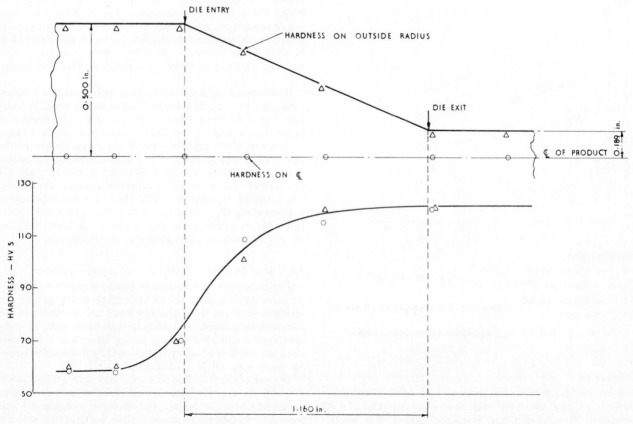

Fig. 6.—*Hardness values on periphery and axis of a copper rod hydrostatically extruded through a 30° die*

Fig. 7.—*Conventional extrusion through a 120° conical die and hydro-static extrusion through a 45° conical die of a billet of high speed steel*

however long it may be with respect to its diameter. This has been verified experimentally by carrying out the extrusion of billets in both aluminium and lead whose length to diameter ratio was 40 : 1. Since the high pressure liquid acts as an infinitely flexible container the billets do not even have to be straight. This was also verified with an aluminium billet, of length to diameter ratio of 40, wound into the form of a spiral with one end placed in the conical die. The pressure in the liquid was then increased and the spiralled billet extruded as a straight product as shown in Fig. 8. The ability to extrude billets of large length/diameter ratios in this way coupled with the continuous supply of high pressure lubricant described above makes this process ideal for the extrusion of long products. The same reasoning can be extended to the extrusion of billets in the form of a coil. To verify this prediction a perspex container was made so that the inside of the high-pressure chamber could be seen. This, of course, permitted the use of only small pressures and consequently it was not possible to extrude a metal billet. Instead, a plastic

uniformity of deformation gives rise to a uniform distribution of properties across the product, as can be seen from the hardness measurements along the centre line and along the periphery of a copper billet which had been extruded through a 30° die at an extrusion ratio of 7 (Fig. 6).

This elimination of the severe shearing at the periphery of the products by extruding in the hydrostatic manner through small-angled dies can have real practical advantages. Thus, for example, it has been found possible to cold extrude without cracking through a 45° die, a high-speed tool steel (0·8% C, 4·1% Cr, 6·4% W, 1·8% V, 5% Mo) with an initial hardness of 260 HV. The conventional extrusion of the same steel through a 120° die resulted in a severely cracked product. Both extrusions are shown in Fig. 7. The successful extrusion of the high-speed tool steel in the hydrostatic process is ascribed to the elimination of the severe shearing of the surface which would otherwise lead to surface cracking. Another potential advantage of such a process is that it may eliminate the coarse-grain banding defect which occurs in some aluminium alloys by the elimination of the large amounts of cold work done on the surface and which give rise to grain growth in such areas on subsequent heat treatment.

Hydrostatic Wire Extrusion

It is possible from a consideration of the stress system to divide the billet (Fig. 1) into two regions. In the lower region which encloses the deformation zone the stress system is complicated but is such that the principal stresses are different and enable deformation to take place. In the upper part of the billet the stress system is hydrostatic, the stresses being equal to the applied hydrostatic pressure. These two regions are divided by a boundary which defines the entry to the die. Consequently the upper part of the billet cannot be buckled

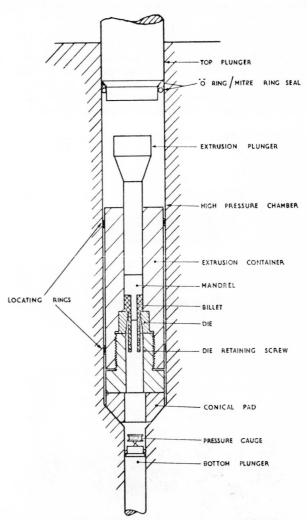

Fig. 9.—*Apparatus for extrusion into a pressurized liquid*

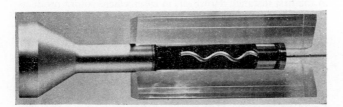

Fig. 8.—*Hydrostatic extrusion of a spiralled billet*

rod whose length to diameter was greater than 8000 was wound on a reel which was mounted on trunnions inside the perspex high-pressure vessel. One end of the plastic rod was brought out through a conical die. By pressurizing the liquid the reel could be seen to rotate as the plastic rod extruded. A coil of lead has been also extruded in the same manner. In this form the process is almost identical with that of wire drawing with the advantage that the reduction in area which can be achieved at each pass is not limited by the strength of the extruded product. Indeed, it is possible to achieve very large reductions per pass since there are no tensile stresses in the system.

Cold Extrusion of a Brittle Material

Tensile tests carried out at the National Engineering Laboratory and elsewhere has shown that the strain to fracture is considerably increased by the presence of a sufficiently high hydrostatic pressure. It is suggested that the surprisingly large reductions of area which can be achieved without fracture in the conventional extrusion process is due to the large hydrostatic components of compressive stress set up in the work material by the dies and the tooling. Indeed, the hydrostatic compressive stresses set up by the tooling are performing the same function in increasing the ductility of the materials as the liquid pressure is in the tension tests carried out under pressure. If this argument is true then it follows that, in the case of the conventional extrusion of brittle materials in which the product emerges in a cracked form, the hydrostatic compressive stresses set up by the tooling are insufficiently large. However, if these stresses could be augmented then one ought to get a satisfactory uncracked product. The hydrostatic compressive stresses set up by the tooling can be increased by placing the conventional extrusion rig in a pressurized liquid. Experiments along these lines were carried out using the apparatus shown in Fig. 9. This consists of a conventional extrusion apparatus in which there

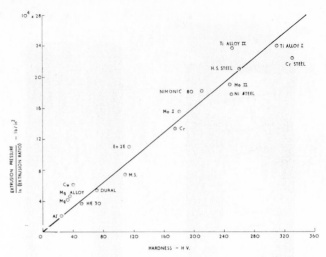

Fig. 11.—*Effect of billet hardness on pressure–ratio for hydrostatic extrusion of rod through a 45° die*

is metal-to-metal contact between the ram and the billet and the whole rig is surrounded by a liquid pressure. The validity of the above argument has been clearly demonstrated for a number of metals, two typical examples of which are shown in Fig. 10. In both cases the cold conventional extrusion with the product emerging into atmosphere results in badly cracked or completely disintegrated products. However, when the bismuth product is extruded into a pressurized liquid it is completely sound except at the low pressure end whilst the brass product, although cracked, is nevertheless a complete tube. An uncracked product would clearly require higher pressures. Further experiments were carried out which showed the existence of a critical pressure at which the cracking was inhibited. This critical pressure was a function of extrusion conditions and, of course, of the metal being extruded and showed a maximum at an extrusion ratio of about 2. This work has shown quite clearly that brittle materials can be extruded without any cracking by ensuring that the product emerges into a pressurized liquid. The actual pressure to be applied cannot at the present state of knowledge be predicted but will depend not only on the work material but also on the extrusion conditions.

Hydrostatic extrusion combined with the use of back pressure as described above gives a novel and generalized method of extruded materials using high-pressure liquids which holds considerable promise for cold extrusion for the more difficult materials which are now coming into vogue. This method is called differential pressure or fluid-to-fluid extrusion.

Cold Extrusion of Difficult Materials using High-pressure Liquids

The application of the above method to the extrusion of a whole range of materials has been carried out at the National Engineering Laboratory. Because of simplicity, the method of hydrostatic extrusion, that is, without a back pressure, is used in the first instance. However, in cases where sound products cannot be obtained by hydrostatic extrusion alone, it is necessary to use the differential pressure extrusion. Indeed, in cases where hydrostatic extrusion gives products which are marginally acceptable, improved results can invariably be obtained by using the differential pressure method.

Table I summarizes the results of all the work carried out at the National Engineering Laboratory on the use of high liquid pressures for the extrusion of a range of metals. The Table also includes the published results of Beresnev and

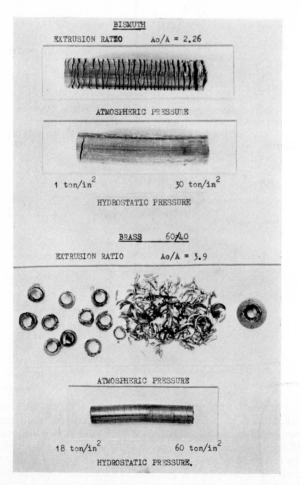

Fig. 10.—*Hydrostatic extrusion of brittle materials into a pressurized liquid*

TABLE I.—*Results for the Pressure (p) Required for the Cold Hydrostatic Extrusion of Several Metals Where $p = a \ln R + b$*

Material	Billet hardness (V.H.)	Extrusion ratio	Die angle (°)	Pressure transmitting fluid	Billet lubrication	a (10^3 lb/in²)	b (10^3 lb/in³)	Back pressure (10^3 lb/in²)	Product hardness (V.H.)
Aluminium (99·5%)	24	2–12	90	MoS₂ in mineral oil	None	22·0	3·3	0	43–50
Aluminium (99·5%)	24	2–25	45	MoS₂ in mineral oil	None	23·5	−4·0	0	—
AD 1 aluminium (99·5%)	—	1·2–20	80	Kerosene/trans-former oil (1 : 2)	Hypoid lubricant	31·7	2·0	0	—
AD 1 aluminium (99·5%)	—	1·5–5	45	Kerosene/trans-former oil (1 : 2)	Hypoid lubricant	27·8	1·5	0	—
Aluminium (type 1100) annealed	—	2–50	90	Water	Teflon (PTFE) on die and billet	34·6	0	0	—
HE 30 aluminium	51	2–12	90	MoS₂ in mineral oil	None	40·5	0	0	—
HE 30 aluminium	51	2–25	45	MoS₂ in mineral oil	None	40·5	−6	0	—
Aluminium alloy AMg (2–2·8% Mg)	—	7·7	45	Kerosene/trans-former oil (1 : 2)	Hypoid lubricant	69	0*	0	—
Aluminium alloy Ak6	—	1·61	45	Kerosene/trans-former oil (1 : 2)	Hypoid lubricant	59	0*	0	—
Duralumin I	—	1·2–5	80	Kerosene/trans-former oil (1 : 2)	Hypoid lubricant	74	9	0	—
Duralumin II	71	6·25	45	MoS₂ in mineral oil	MoS₂ in grease	54·5	0*	0	—
60/40 brass L62	—	2·15	80	Kerosene/trans-former oil (1 : 2)	Hypoid lubricant	178	0*	0	—
Copper M2 (99·7%)	—	1·2–5	80	Kerosene/trans-former oil (1 : 2)	Hypoid lubricant	69	7	0	—
Copper M2 (99·7%)	—	1·6–3·4	45	Kerosene/trans-former oil (1 : 2)	Hypoid lubricant	73·2	0	0	—
Copper (annealed)	—	2–20	90	Water	Teflon on die and billet	71·4	0*	0	—
ERHC copper	40	1·2–6	45	MoS₂ in mineral oil	MoS₂ in grease	60·3	0	0	120
Magnesium	28	7–12	45	MoS₂ in mineral oil	MoS₂ in grease	42	0*	0	—
Magnesium (1% Al)	36	12	90	MoS₂ in mineral oil	MoS₂ in grease	46	0·	0	—
Magnesium (1% Al)	—	4	45	MoS₂ in mineral oil	MoS₂ in grease	42·1	0*	0	—
Steel St–15	—	1·43	45	Kerosene/trans-former oil	Hypoid lubricant	290	0*	0	—
A1S1 1020 steel	—	4	90	Water	Teflon on die and billet	158	0*	0	—
Mild steel (0·05% C)	108	2	45	MoS₂ in mineral oil	MoS₂ in grease	74	0*	0	—
Mild steel—En 2E (0·15% C)	113	1·2–6	45	MoS₂ in mineral oil	None	91	2	0	—
Steel I	150	2	45	MoS₂ in mineral oil	MoS₂ in grease	178	0*	0	285
Steel II	330	2	45	MoS₂ in mineral oil	MoS₂ in grease	224	0*	0	370
HS tool steel	260	1·56–1·7	45	MoS₂ in mineral oil	MoS₂ in grease	210	0*	0	340
Nimonic 80	210	2	45	MoS₂ in mineral oil	MoS₂ in grease	182	0*	0	373
Titanium alloy I (2% Al, 2% Mg)	250	2	45	MoS₂ in mineral oil	MoS₂ in grease	237	0*	0	340
Titanium alloy II (5% Al, 2% Sn)	310	2	45	MoS₂ in mineral oil	MoS₂ in grease	240	0*	0	335
Molybdenum I (0·01% C) annealed	180	3	45	Glycerine and glycol (4 : 1)	Latex and MoS₂ in grease	156	0*	49	—
Molybdenum II (0·01% C) hot rolled at 1040°C	245	3	45	Glycerine and glycol	Latex and MoS₂ in grease	190	0*	0	—
Zirconium	170	1·78	30	Glycerine	Graphite and MoS₂ in grease	183	0*	0	—
Chromium	175	3	45	Glycerine and glycol	Latex and MoS₂ in grease	134	0*	34	204
Zircalloy (reactor grade 2)	265	2	90	Glycerine and glycol	Latex and MoS₂ in grease	253	0*	11	—
Beryllium (vacuum cast)	—	1·5	45	Glycerine and glycol	PTFE, Latex and MoS₂ in grease	202	0*	16	—
Beryllium	—	1·21	45	Kerosene/trans-former oil	Hypoid lubricant	507	0*	0	—
Beryllium (hot extruded)	—	1·5	90	Water	Teflon (PTFE) on die and billet	334	0*	0	—
Yttrium (annealed)	—	24	90	Water	Celvocene grease	66	0*	0	—

* Insufficient data makes it necessary to assume $b = 0$

HE 30 aluminium—0·7% Mg, 1% Si, 0·7% Mn
Aluminium alloy Ak6—2·2% Cu, 1% Si, 0·6% Mn, 0·6% Mg
Duralumin I—4% Cu, 0·7% Fe, 0·7% Si, 0·6% Mn, 0·6% Mg
Duralumin II—2% Cu, 1% Fe, 1·5% Mg, 1% Ni
Steel I—0·16% C, 4% Ni, 1·3% Cr, 0·4% Mn, 0·45% Mo
Steel II—0·15% C, 1·5% Ni, 12% Cr, 0·7% Mn, 0·7% Mo

Vereshchagin and their co-workers[2] as well as of Randell and his colleagues.[7] In the case of those metals where results of extrusion pressure p are available for a range of extrusion ratio R they are expressed by the linear relationship:

$$p = a \ln R + b$$

where a and b are constants which are tabulated in Table I. Approximately linear relations are generally obtained for all metals, as for example, in Fig. 5. However, in a number of cases only isolated results were available for various metals and these were, in general, for different extrusion ratios. Consequently, in plotting the results in Fig. 11 on a consistent basis, it has been assumed that, for all results, the value of b is zero and the plot has been of the ratio of extrusion pressure divided by the logarithm of the extrusion ratio as a function of hardness. The results of all the materials tested with the exception of beryllium lay about a straight line through the origin for a range of hardnesses varying from about 25 HV to about 330 HV. The equation which represents this line is given as:

$$p = 0.8\, H \ln R$$

where p is the extrusion pressure in 1000 lb/in² and H is the billet hardness on the HV scale. Whilst it is to be expected that the extrusion pressure is a function of some strength characteristic of the work materials and of $\ln R$, the degree of correlation is rather surprising, the maximum deviation of points from the line being 20%. The above empirical relationship will be of particular value for making estimates of the pressure to be expected for the hydrostatic extrusion of untested materials at different extrusion ratios until such time as an improved relationship is obtained. It must, of course, be remembered that this relationship applies for a 45° die and probably for the types of pressure transmitting media and lubrication described above.

It is of interest to note that, of all the materials tested and shown in Table I, only four, namely, molybdenum, chromium, zircalloy and beryllium, required the use of the differential-pressure-extrusion method and that it was possible to cold extrude such materials as the 12% chrome steel, the high-speed tool steel, Nimonic 80 and some of the titanium alloys without the use of a back pressure at all. As far as is known the results for molybdenum and beryllium using the differential-pressure method represent the first time that these metals have been cold extruded, an operation which many people had previously thought to be impossible. These two results in particular give some indication of the potential of this method for the working of the newer and more difficult materials. The results obtained with these metals and the ability to cold extrude metals having a hardness of 330 HV30, high-speed steel, titanium alloys and 12% chrome steel without cracking has exceeded expectation and throws new light on the practical potentialities of the method.

High-speed Working

In metal-working operations such as forming, shaping, forging extrusion, welding, compacting, etc., there has been a marked increase in the application of high-speed methods in which energy is derived from chemical explosives, high-voltage discharges, electro-magnetic fields or fast-moving masses. This increase in activity has been stimulated by the promise of certain advantages which were said to accrue from high speeds of metal deformation.

Whilst many of the original claims have not been wholly substantiated these methods facilitate the forming of complex shapes and reduce tooling costs since only the female die is required; often this may be made of cheap materials such as

nodular iron, Kirksite, epoxy resins, *etc.* Explosive forming[13] has the added advantage that it can be used to produce limited numbers of relatively large parts for which the cost of conventional press tools would be uneconomical or required press loads in excess of available capacity and for which the expense of a larger press would be prohibitive. The conservation of heat in the work piece by reducing the time it is in contact with the dies during deformation is a major consideration in the forming of metals by fast moving masses.

Explosive Working

Explosives commonly used for metal-working operations fall into two groups. High explosives such as dynamite, PETN, TNT and RDX, having a conversion time of microseconds, are normally fired in open systems and develop a pulse of extremely high pressure (2×10^6 to 4×10^6 lb/in²) of relatively short duration. Low explosives such as gun powder or cordite, have a conversion time of milliseconds and develop much lower pressures (4×10^4 lb/in²) which can be sustained for longer periods. They are normally used in enclosed systems which help to increase the time for which the pressure acts.[14]

Explosives may be placed in contact with the work piece or located at some distance from it, in which case the energy is transmitted through an intervening medium.

In the contact process, much of the energy of deformation is transmitted to the metal and appears in the form of a stress pulse which can be either destructive or beneficial depending on how the energy of the stress waves is utilised in the system, *i.e.* on whether the reflection and interaction of the stress wave fronts give rise to tensile fractures in the material.[14] If, as is normally the case, the velocity of detonation of the explosive is substantially greater than the velocity of sound in the metal the shock waves have high peak pressure and the probability of fracture is high. If the velocity of detonation is less than the velocity of sound in the metal, there is no shock wave, pressure is exerted ahead of the detonation front, is lower in value and there is no tendency to fracture.[15]

Explosives in sheet or bulk form have been used as contact charges in the compacting of powders, in swaging, surface hardening, welding, etc. Pearson has briefly summarized the currently available information regarding explosively activated presses and their effectiveness in the compacting of powders.[16] As yet there is insufficient evidence to indicate whether the process conferred particular advantages over the normal methods of compacting. Various types of cable

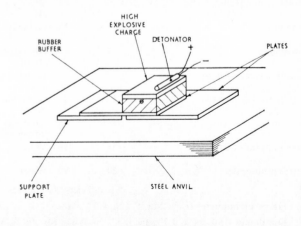

PEARSON[18]

Fig. 12.—*Arrangement of charge for welding plates*

fitments have been successfully swaged on to wire ropes[7,9] whilst the surface hardness of austenitic, manganese and other steels has been significantly increased. It is claimed that these hardening effects can be controlled to a depth of 2 in.[15] Specimens of the same metal or of two dissimilar metals, even if of widely different melting points, can be welded together by means of explosives.[15,17,18] One of the proposed methods is outlined in Fig. 12; others have been briefly summarised by Boes[19] who has also suggested a tentative mechanism for the joining process. Two specific applications have been reported in detail, namely the welding of tube[20] and the cladding of sheet.[15] A sheet of copper 6·35 mm thick has been welded to steel, a sheet of Hasteloy 1·59 mm thick to a sheet 38 × 38 cm, 12·7 mm thick of steel and a sheet of stainless 12·7 mm thick to a sheet 208 × 254 cm, 483 mm thick of chrome molybdenum steel. These sheets were heat treated and then rolled.

In the stand-off process the magnitude of the pressure pulse is not only dependent on the type, amount and shape of the explosive charge as before but also on the stand-off distance, the intervening medium and the manner of its confinement.[14] Various media such as air, water, Plasticine, rubber and PVC

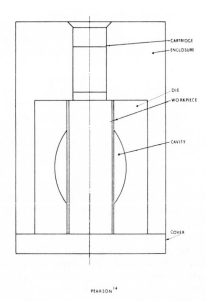

PEARSON [14]

Fig. 13.—*Bulge forming with low explosive*

have been used to transmit energy. Liquids are particularly efficient if the effects of confinement are small, whilst plasticine is effective in the deformation of localised areas of a specimen.[17]

The process is particularly useful for a range of forming, flanging and sizing operations on a variety of metals in sheet form. The shapes produced have ranged from steel helmets, pods, hemispherical dishes, communication reflectors, contoured tubes, to contoured panels of increasing complexity. The size of product ranges from inches to feet and domes, etc., in aluminium and steel of 20–50 ft diameter are now being considered.[13]

A typical bulging operation on tube using a low explosive in an enclosed system is shown in Fig. 13, the transmitting medium being air. The inner surface of the tube is usually protected by a thin layer of plastic material or a thick layer of grease. A typical flanging operation on plate using a high explosive in an open system is shown in Fig. 14, the transmitting medium being water. A blank holding ring is required to prevent wrinkling of the part.

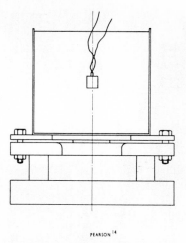

PEARSON [14]

Fig. 14.—*Flanging with high explosive*

High-voltage Discharge Forming (Electrohydraulic)

In this method the energy stored in high-voltage condensers is suddenly discharged across a small gap in water and the resulting arc produces a shock wave which can be used to deform the work piece contained in suitable dies rapidly. The basic circuit for an electrohydraulic forming unit is shown in Fig. 15. A bank of condensers is charged from a power pack, the size and performance of which determines the time of charging and consequently the rate at which the unit could be operated under repetitive conditions. The inductance of the circuit is kept as low as possible to ensure rapid discharge of energy. The rapid switching of high voltages is achieved by air gap ionisation switches, low pressure ionisation switches or ignitrons. The air gap switches are simple and cheap to construct but are noisy in operation and dissipate a considerable percentage of the available energy. The ignitron valve, however, is usually limited to peak discharges of up to 100 kA at 25 kV. The leads from the switch and condenser bank terminate in two electrodes which are immersed in water and suitably located relative to the die. The gap between the electrodes may be closed by a wire or left open but this has little effect on the deformation produced in the work piece by a given energy of discharge.[21] A wire, however, does ensure a more consistent breakdown of voltage, breakdown at lower voltages or across wider gaps and it permits the initiation of a shock wave in a non-conducting liquid. The deformation produced in a work piece by a given energy of discharge is influenced by the diameter of the wire but not significantly by its shape between the electrodes nor by the material from which it is made.[22] Provided the gap is a certain minimum distance below the free surface of the transmitting medium the deformation produced is independent of this depth. For repetitive working, however, the use of a wire is not desirable.

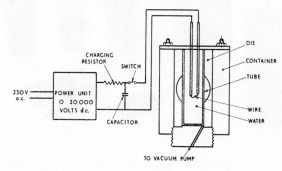

Fig. 15.—*Circuit diagram*

Fig. 16.—*N.E.L. experimental electrohydraulic forming equipment*

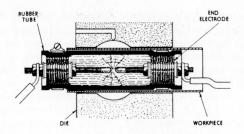

DISCOVERY 1963 24 (6) p22

Fig. 18.—*Forming of tubular shape by discharge within a rubber tube filled with water*

When it is inconvenient or impossible to fill a tubular work piece with water, the terminals and water may be contained in a rubber tube. The terminals, which form a small gap along the centre of the tube may be brought out through one end or both ends as shown in Fig. 18. The tubular work piece is deformed by the expanding rubber tube; the extent of the deformation being less than that required to rupture the tube.

Electro-magnetic Forming

The basic equipment to provide the electrical energy is the same as that used for electrohydraulic forming. This energy, however, is discharged through an air cored coil in which the work piece is usually placed and the magnetic field set up in the coil induces a voltage and current in the work piece which is opposite to that in the coil (Fig. 19). In the absence of a magnetic field within the work piece a force proportional to the square of the coil-field density is exerted on the outside surface of the work piece. As the work piece is compressed the magnetic field gives up its energy, consequently the magnetic field is generated in short pulses.[24-26]

In magnetic forming the conductivity of the metal work piece determines the extent to which it is deformed by a given stored energy. Materials which are good conductors such as aluminium and copper can be deformed much more efficiently than stainless steel. Poor or non-conducting work pieces can, however, be wrapped in thin copper foil prior to deformation.

Cylindrical coils encircling the work piece are used to produce localised contraction, or to compress a tubular shape on to a solid work piece. Cylindrical coils located within a hollow tube are used to produce localized expansion or to expand the work piece into fittings or split dies. In addition to the cylindrical coils, flat coils may be used to compress flat plates into die cavities. In many cases, metal pieces known as field shapes are often inserted within the coil in order to concentrate the field force to localized areas of the work piece.[25]

Since the coil exerts a significant force on the work piece it must have adequate strength and impact resistance. For a long life, the magnetic field must be limited so that the force it produces is less than the compressive strength of the coil material. It is possible, however, to achieve very large fields and exert very large pressures with expendable coils, the reaction force being derived from the inertia of the system.

The experimental unit at N.E.L. (Fig. 16) consists of a bank of six condensers each of capacity 8·5 MFD which can be charged at 2 mA to 20 kV and is capable of discharging by an air gap switch energies of up to 10 kJ. The industrial type unit has four condensers which can be charged at 250 mA and switched through an ignitron valve. Considerations involved in the design of larger capacitor banks up to 100 kJ have been described by Buser and Wolfert.[23]

Clearly with suitable tooling and electrode arrangements the technique can be applied as an alternative to most of the stand-off operations carried out with chemical explosives such as forming, drawing, flanging, piercing, embossing, coining, *etc.* In view of the limited energy available the process is restricted to the manufacture of small or medium-sized components in relatively thin gauge sheet material. The equipment is, however, particularly suited for the forming of complex tubular components using a die and electrode arrangement shown in Fig. 15. The various types of tube bulging and flaring, the piercing of holes with and without raised lips, the expansion of tubes on to flanges or into tube plates, the forming of coarse screw threads or corrugations, the contraction or swaging of tubes, *etc.*, clearly demonstrate the flexibility of the process in producing shapes which would otherwise involve quite difficult pressing operations with collapsible tooling (Fig. 17).

Fig. 17.—*Electrohydraulic forming of re-entrant shapes and bulging of tubes*

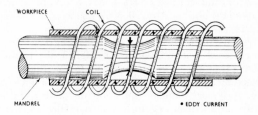

DISCOVERY 1963 24 (6) p22

Fig. 19.—*Electromagnetic forming*

Forming by Fast-moving Masses

High-rate forming, particularly the extrusion and closed die forging of solid billets, has been undertaken in more conventional type equipment in which a press ram is operated at high speeds. These speeds are generally achieved by the rapid expansion of a compressed gas which activates the ram as in the case of the Dynapak machine (General Dynamics Corporation U.S.A.)[27] and the Counterblow Press (U.S. Industries Clearing Division).[28] These machines, Fig. 20, and their mode of operation have been extensively described in the literature and it will suffice to indicate that they provide energies ranging from 8000 to 225 000 ft-lb at ram speeds of approximately 60 ft/s and are capable of cycling at 3–20 strokes/min depending on the equipment.

The equipment has been used primarily for hot extrusion[27] or closed die forging of selected products in Ni–Cr–Mo steels (e.g. flange, shaft, gear blank, rotor, spline plate) in Cr–Mo steels (e.g. canopy hook, rotor) in stainless steel (e.g. compressor vane) in nitralloy (e.g. port blank) at temperatures within the range 1100° to 1200°C, in tungsten (e.g. X-ray target) at 1660°C, in copper at 760°C and in aluminium alloy at 430°C. Little information is available on the life of tools under these conditions, although in one case it was stated that 2400 diaphragms were forged in tool steel at 1100°C before the punch was replaced. The life of the die was approximately 2–3 times that of the punch.

Whilst lubrication was said to contribute significantly to the successful forming of parts an equally important consideration was the reduced time the work material was in contact with the dies and the consequent conservation of heat in the material during working.

A detailed investigation[29] is in progress to assess the feasibility of extruding long products in a vertical Dynapak machine, in particular a T-section of 0·05 in. thickness from billets of titanium alloy (6 Al 4 V Ti), stainless steel (11·5–13% Cr) and Ni–Cr–Mo at steel elevated temperatures and with glass lubrication. Whilst no major difficulties were encountered on the mechanical aspects, the inertia forces set up by the high speed of the product emerging from the die caused necking down and separation of the product so that the desired length of section was not obtained.

Studies are also in progress with laboratory type impact machines[30] to assess the feasibility of the cold extrusion of certain materials at a wide range of ram speeds. As may be expected, similar effects due to inertia forces are observed and necking down, and separation of the product occurs depending on the extrusion ratio and the ram speed.

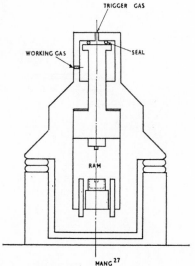

Fig. 20.—Compressed gas press

Properties of Explosively-formed Materials

Williams[31] reports the results in which hemispherical pressings produced statically were sectioned axially, checked for hardness and the work hardening compared with that obtained in similar shapes produced by explosive forming. In the explosive tests the metal diaphragms were clamped rigidly to the top of the die and the charge initiated in water at a fixed stand-off distance. In the static tests a hemispherical punch was pushed slowly on to the diaphragms mounted and clamped as before. It was found that mild steel and commercially pure soft titanium work harden more and stainless steel, Nimonic 75, Nimonic 90 and super-annealed aluminium alloy HS 15 work harden less after static pressing than after explosive forming as shown in Fig. 21. It will be noted that the last four materials possess face-centred cubic lattices whilst mild steel has a b.c.c. and titanium a closed packed hexagonal lattice at room temperature.

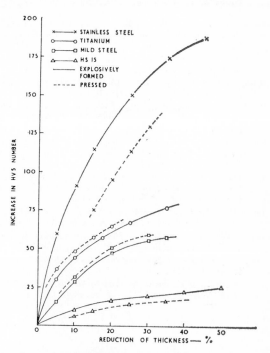

Fig. 21.—Comparison of work-hardening arising from explosive forming and from pressing (Williams[31])

Using a ring-type specimen, explosively deformed at a mean initial strain rate of approximately 10^3 s^{-1}, Johnson, Stein and Davis[32] measured the uniform elongation to fracture for several materials and compared the values with those obtained on specimens pulled to fracture in a testing machine at a mean strain rate of 10^{-3} s^{-1}. The dynamic uniform elongation to fracture was greater than the static value for materials of low ductility such as 4340 steel in both annealed and hardened conditions and a titanium 6% Al, 4% V alloy and less than the static value for materials of high ductility such as 7075 T6 Aluminium, 304 Stainless Steel, 1015 Steel and Armco Iron.

Changes occur in the microstructure of materials as a result of cold working due to explosive forming. These have been examined by Williams,[31] Verbraak[33] and workers[34] at I.R.D. Co. and the results summarised elsewhere. One effect of explosive forming is of particular significance to the chemical industry in that some materials may require a subsequent full or partial annealing treatment if stress corrosion cracking is to be avoided.

Acknowledgments

This paper is published by permission of the Director of the National Engineering Laboratory of the Department of Scientific and Industrial Research.

References

[1] Bridgman, P. W. "*Large Plastic Flow and Fracture*", 1952, (McGraw-Hill.)

[2] Beresnev, B. I., Vereshchagin, L. F., Ryabinin, Yu. N., and Livshits, L. D. "*Some Problems of Large Plastic Deformation in Metals under High Pressure*", Acad. Nauk. USSR., Inst. Fiz. Vysokikh Daolniy, Moscow 1960, English Translation Tech. Doc. Liaison Office ASTIA, USA 259251, May 1961.

[3] Pugh, H. Ll. D., "*Brit. Pat. Applications Nos.* 17603 (1958), 6626 (1959) *and* 20500", (1961).

[4] Pugh, H. Ll. D. and Ashcroft, K., "*Symposium on the Physics and Chemistry of High Pressures*", London, June 1962. Published by the Society of Chemical Industry, 1963, p. 163.

[5] Pugh, H. Ll. D., "*Proceedings of International Research in Production Engineering Conference*", Pittsburgh. Published by ASME, Aust 1963, p. 394.

[6] Beresnev, B. I., Vereshchagin, L. F. and Ryabinin, Yu., *N. Inzh-fiz Zh.* **3**, 43, 1960.

[7] Randall, R. N., Davies, D. M., Liergiej, J. M. and Lowenstein, P. "*Modern Metals*", **XVIII** (7), 68, August 1962.

[8] "*Bibliography on Explosive Metal Working. D.M.I.C. Memorandum No. 51*". 7th April, 1960, OTS PB 161201, Defence Metals Information Centre, Battelle Memorial Institute.

[9] Gibbs, K. M., "*An ASTIA Report Bibliography on Explosive Forming*", Feb. 1962, Armed Services Technical Information Agency, Arlington 12.

[10] Carr-Harris, G. G. M. "*Metal Forming using Explosive Charges, T.I.S. Report No. 74, March* 1961", Technical Information Service, N.R.C., Ottawa.

[11] Beck, D., "*Explosive Forming. A.W.R.E. Library Bibliography No.* 2, *May* 1961". U.K.A.E.A., A.W.R.E., Aldermaston.

[12] Ecker, W., Muller-Axt, F. "*Hochgeschwindigkeitsbearbeitung* 1. *Werkstatt and Betrieb*", 1963, **96**(3), pp. 163-177.

[13] Orr, J. P. "*Trends in High-energy Forming of Metals*", A.S.M.E., Reprint 62.MD.21.

[14] Pearson, J. "*The Explosive Working of Metals, NOTS TP* 2421, *NAV ORD Report* 7033", Feb., 1960, OTS PB 161828.

[15] Holtzman, A. H., Rudershausen, C. G. "*Recent Advances in Metal Working with Explosives. Sheet Metal Industries*", 1962, **39**(422), pp. 399-413.

[16] Pearson, J. "*The Explosive Compaction of Powders. A.S.T.M.E., Paper SP*60-158".

[17] Harris, J. T. *Applied Studies of Metal Forming by Explosives. Sheet Metal Industries*, 1962, **39**(422), pp. 383-413.

[18] Pearson, J. "*Explosive Welding*". A.S.T.M.E., *Paper SP*60-159".

[19] Boes, P. J. M. *Some Aspects of Explosive Welding. Annalen C.I.R.P.*, **XI**, *Sept.* 1963, Hague, pp. 137-141.

[20] Willis, J., Murdie, D. C. *Sheet Metal Industries*. 1962, **39**(427), pp. 811-814.

[21] Kirk, J. W. *Impulse Forming by Electrical Discharge Methods. Sheet Metal Industries*, 1962, **39**(424), pp. 535-540.

[22] Kegg, R. L., Kalpakcioglu, S. "*Research in Electrical Discharge Forming of Metals*, A.S.T.M.E., *Paper SP*62-78".

[23] Buser, R., Wolfert, P. "*Experimental* 100 000 *Joule Capacitor Bank for Plasma Research, Electronics*", 1960, pp. 58-61.

[24] "*Magnetic Forming. Aircraft Production*", 1962, Aug., **24** (8), pp. 264-267.

[25] "*Magnetic Forming. Metal Working Production*", 1961, June, pp. 65-70.

[26] Birdsall, D. H., Ford, F. C., Furth, H. P., Riley, R. E., "*Magnetic Forming. American Machinist*, 1961", **105**(6).

[27] Mang, W. G., "*Dynapak. A new dimension in High Energy Rate Forming. Sheet Metal Industries*, 1962", **39**(424), pp. 541-554.

[28] Anon. "*New Equipment for High-energy Rate Forming. Sheet Metal Industries*", 1962, **39**(424), pp. 573-576.

[29] Rippel, J. M. *High-energy Rate Extrusion Program. A.S.D Project No.* 7-882, *Progress Reports* 1-9. *Contract AF*33(600)41948. A.S.T.I. Agency, Arlington 12.

[30] Cole, B. N. "*High-speed Forming of Metals*". Third International Machine Tool Design & Research Conference, Birmingham, Sept. 1962.

[31] Williams, T. *Some Metallurgical Aspects of Explosive Forming. Sheet Metal Industries*, 1962, **39**(423), pp. 487-493.

[32] Johnson, P. C., Stein, B. A., and Davis, R. S., "*Basic Parameters of Metal Behaviour under High Rate Forming. Report No. WAL TR* 111.2/20-1". Watertown Arsenal Laboratories, 1962. OMS Code 5010. 11. 8430051.

[33] Verbraak, C. A. The effect of Explosive Forming on the Properties of Anisotropic Materials. *Archiv für das Eisenhüttenwesen*, 1962, **33**(11), pp. 757-760.

[34] Anon. *New Scientist*, 1963. No. 359, Oct. 3, p. 23.

LATEST METHODS IN GLASS FORMING

By Dr. L. H. A. PILKINGTON

SYNOPSIS

The requirement of flat glass is primarily to transmit light and exclude the elements. The development of glass to fulfil this function is briefly sketched from the earliest days of windows.

Two processes developed Plate glass to provide high quality distortion-free glass for mirrors, large windows, and later car windscreens, and Sheet glass for cheaper and smaller windows in houses.

The Plate process developed to a high efficiency, grinding and polishing both sides of the glass simultaneously, but has now been replaced by a new process for making high quality glass—the Float process.

Sheet glass has developed from the Crown process through the Cylinder and Mechanically Drawn Cylinder process to the present Flat Drawn Vertical process, with emphasis on high speeds and efficiencies and ever-increasing quality.

High speeds and greater output bring with them problems of greater and more sophisticated instrumentation and increasing tempo of development work requires more first-class scientists and engineers. The author expresses some views on the quality and source of these people so essential to good and rapid progress.

BEFORE I can discuss this subject I must describe briefly the historical background to the two main processes and products of the flat glass industry—Plate glass and Sheet glass.

The original requirement of a pane of glass, namely to admit light and exclude the elements, was first met by thin sheets of horn. These sheets were neither cheap nor durable. Crown glass was the first type of glass to be used for this purpose. Glass was gathered on the end of a hollow blowing iron and formed into a hollow sphere by a combination of blowing and swinging the iron. When the sphere was completed it was reheated, opened up opposite to the blowing iron, again reheated and spun rapidly by hand so that the glass was spun into a disc. This disc was then annealed and finally cut up into small sizes usually not larger than 8×8 in. These were used in windows in the form of leaded light because of their small size.

The disadvantages of this process are obvious—smallness of size and lack of flatness leading to optical distortion.

The first advance was in size, that was achieved by blowing cylinders of glass about 6×2 ft in diameter, annealing them, splitting them with a diamond cut and then reheating and flattening them in a furnace.

Uniformity of thickness was also much improved and the process lasted from 1830 to 1910 when it was replaced by the mechanically drawn cylinder which could be made up to about 30 ft high and 4 ft in diameter. This was a spectacular process, particularly when the cylinder was cut off at the bottom and the whole 30 ft cylinder was swung from the vertical to the horizontal position.

All these processes seem roundabout methods of producing a flat sheet, but until 1920 no satisfactory method of producing a flat sheet straight from a bath of molten glass had been achieved, mainly because no method of avoiding the " waisting in " of the sheet, due to surface tension, had been devised.

This was achieved first in the semi-extrusion–semi-drawing process known as the Fourcault process, and later in the Pittsburgh process which is entirely a drawing process in which the edge of the sheet is solidified rapidly above the glass by contact with metal rollers or plates, either water or air cooled. These metal objects have the effect of forming a rigid edge which prevents the " waisting in " of the ribbon. This is the process which is still in use.

A flatter glass providing better optical properties was needed and a process was developed originally in France but used extensively in this country. Glass was poured from a refractory pot onto a table where it was rolled out and then moved to a kiln where it was annealed. Subsequently it was bedded onto a circular table which was passed under first a grinding head and then a polishing head.

The glass produced was much flatter and was used mainly for mirrors and large windows, but due to the elaborate process it was very expensive.

Little improvement took place in this process until the 1920's and then in the United States the first process for manufacturing a continuous ribbon of glass was developed by C. W. Avery of the Ford Motor Company. He solved the engineering problems but was in trouble with the glass making. At the end of 1922 those problems were solved in collaboration with Pilkingtons and a successful continuous ribbon of glass was made. Simultaneously experiments were being carried out by F. B. Waldron in St. Helens to develop a machine which would grind and polish continuously. This machine consisted of a series of cast iron tables which supported plates of glass and moved under grinding heads and then under polishing heads. The glass had then to be turned over and the process was repeated on the other side.

The next step in the development of this process was obviously the simultaneous grinding and polishing of both sides of the glass. Experimental work started in 1930 and the first machine was installed at Doncaster in 1935, followed by a second machine at St. Helens in 1937. For some time these machines ground and polished the glass on both sides, but later, due partly to the higher production speeds from the furnace, and partly due to the inflexibility of the process, it was decided to grind both sides simultaneously, and then store the glass and polish it on separate machines. In this way it was possible to provide glass of the different qualities at any time, which had proved difficult when the complete process was operated. The twin grinder and polisher, as it was called, was not only made more efficient, particularly in labour utilisation, but it was also extremely good in producing glass of very high planimetry; very much superior to glass produced on the older table process. So good was it as a highly efficient product of very high quality glass, that it was licensed widely in both Europe and the United States.

Float Glass

Grinding and polishing of glass requires a great deal of elaborate and expensive machinery, and until recently there was no process which could make glass suitable for motor car windscreens, mirrors and high quality shop windows, which did not involve grinding and polishing.

However, in 1952 Alastair Pilkington got the idea that a ribbon of glass could be formed onto a bath of molten metal and could be removed from the bath at the other end, annealed and emerge from the annealing lehr ready to be examined, cut, packed and despatched.

Experiments were started and in 1958 glass was sold in substantial quantities to one customer, and in 1959 the glass had become readily available and has almost completely replaced plate glass in our factories—in fact, in St. Helens we no longer make plate glass, and since the introduction of the process we have sold more than 100 million square feet. It took seven years to develop the process and there are still many improvements which we hope to make, but it is a process which is inherently simple in conception, though very close control has, of course, to be kept during all the stages of the process.

There are other flat glass processes, rolled plate and patterned glass, heat treated glass and so on, but they are not our main products and I do not propose to describe them here.

We are now making glass by the two processes—Float and Sheet.

Float is used mainly in the high quality markets—mirrors, motor car windscreens, and Sheet mainly for house windows.

The emphasis in the processes is rather different. In Float a very high degree of planimetry is required as well as a very high standard for inclusions such as bubble. In sheet the emphasis is on the highest possible production consistent with a quality acceptable in the ordinary window. There is one other difference—Float is mainly made in $\frac{1}{4}$ in. thickness and Sheet mainly about half that thickness.

In both processes the tank furnace which holds over 1000 tons of glass much be fed with a very consistent mixture of high quality raw materials. The sand which forms 70% of the batch is mainly obtained locally, and its production and treatment is a very carefully controlled process. Iron is the main obnoxious impurity and the iron content is closely controlled, mainly by the blending of different qualities of sand from the various faces in the sandfield.

Inhomogeneity in the glass causes either gross defects causing rejection or distortion which is more noticeable in sheet glass. Distortion is caused either by inhomogeneity in the furnace coming either from the raw materials or solution of the refractories in the tank furnace, or from the non-uniform treatment of the glass ribbon during the forming processes.

Progress in both processes consists in a series of developments all aimed at producing a standard quality at ever higher speeds. There is usually a bottleneck somewhere—as in most processes. It may be that the refractories in the furnace are not sufficiently good to allow higher melting rates. This is tackled by obtaining or developing better refractories and then this is followed by increasing the fuel input and drawing higher tonnages from the tank. Usually when this is done there are immediate problems in the drawing process itself, a lack of uniformity in kiln atmosphere conditions leading to worse distortion in Sheet glass, or annealing problems which in a vertical process like the Sheet process are not very easy to solve, but progress is made in this field until we are back to the melting capacity again and the cycle starts once more. This process of gradual improvement will continue in this way, but as speeds increase other problems arise.

One example is I think of general interest. On the Float process the ribbon emerges from the annealing lehr at a width of up to 130 in. and at a speed of up to 150 in/min. This ribbon must be examined before it is cut so that the cutting which is done by automatic machine can be set to cut close to a fault and thus save a considerable amount of wastage which would be thrown away if the fault was placed near the middle of a plate.

Investigation of the examination of glass by really experienced and very conscientious examiners has shown that it is probably impossible to examine consistently at these speeds, and, therefore, automatic examination systems must be and have been devised—not an easy problem because the electronic eye finds it far more difficult than the human eye to distinguish between some dust on the surface of the glass and an inclusion of the same size in the glass. However, the automatic scanner will find either all the faults above a given size which pass under it, or it will find none, and it is not difficult to check whether it is or is not functioning. Some experiments we did with a series of plates containing borderline faults passing a series of examiners showed the difficulty of the human examiner working at high speed. We found in fact no correlation between the faults and the rejections, nor was there any examiner who was consistent.

Similarly with our automatic cutting machines. A manual cutter will put a cut on the glass with a steel wheel or a diamond, will apply pressure with two fingers and a thumb and will remove a strip a few inches wide by 12 ft long. To do this automatically is very difficult and to get a perfectly square cut with no chips, flanges or flakes has so far defeated us, though we are improving.

In furnace control too we are making steady headway. Logging almost every conceivable variable temperature at many points, furnace pressure, speed, quality and in one case wind direction, we can find the important variables—one of the most important being variation in itself. I well remember seeing someone go up to a man who was having trouble in starting a motor mower. He made a few adjustments and started it easily. When asked what to do to make it start as easily in the future he said, " Leave the damn thing alone and don't fiddle ". An excellent maxim for glass makers but one which one can rarely follow because thickness changes demanded by sales means variations of furnace load and so forth.

These are some of the problems with the existing production processes but we must also be looking ahead for the better process or radical improvements in the existing process—more efficient melting processes—our existing processes are running at a thermal efficiency of about 25–35%—better properties of our products—for instance, stronger glass—and more and more we are becoming more highly mechanized.

All these steps involve research and development on a very large scale and the demand for really high quality science graduates and engineers increases every year, but I am sure that the emphasis must be on quality.

We take into research and development every year quite a few graduates who come from many disciplines. Some chemists, physicists or engineers straight from university, some with Ph.D.'s in their first degree subject or with a Ph.D. in glass technology, but it is the quality of the man that counts much more than his discipline and I must say that I rather wonder at times whether we really need the new postgraduate schools of glass technology with which we are threatened. The existing department at Sheffield turns out some excellent people but at times has difficulty in finding enough applicants of high quality.

However, time and the presence or absence of applicants will probably settle this for us. In the meantime my *crie de coeur* is " more and better scientists and engineers, please "!

RECENT DEVELOPMENTS IN PLASTICS FABRICATING PROCESSES

By D. GRANT*

SYNOPSIS

The rapid expansion of the plastics industry is closely related to the developments in the processes used for converting or fabricating the basic raw materials into finished products. Thermosetting resins which harden when subjected to heat and pressure and become subsequently infusible, are almost all fabricated using the compression moulding process. The main development in this process has been in the more efficient use of the equipment. This has been achieved by pre-heating the moulding powder, improved heating and control systems and automatically operated presses.

The two main processes for the thermo-plastic resins which make up the greater part of the plastic materials in current use are extrusion and injection moulding. Developments of these two processes in the past decade are discussed and the equipment used is described. In both processes the main developments are related to the use of heat generated by the shearing action of an extruder screw in the plastic melt. This method of operation makes it possible to overcome some of the properties of plastic materials which limit the methods by which they can be processed.

THE expansion of the Plastics Industry, which celebrated its centenary last year, has accelerated in the past fifteen years to an extent that has put it amongst the fastest growing industries. The reasons for this comparatively sudden expansion cannot be clearly and simply stated but undoubtedly they are related as much to changes in economic conditions as to technical advances. This, however, does not in any way belittle the technical advances that have occurred. Many entirely new materials have been discovered and economic methods of producing them developed. Of equal importance has been the development of the converting or fabricating processes, and it is perhaps this latter field which has contributed most.

Plastics are divided into two main types based on thermo-setting and thermoplastic resins. By definition all plastics materials can be caused to flow at some stage in their existence under the influence of heat and pressure. During the fabrication process some plastics materials harden and become subsequently infusible, and these are termed the thermosetting materials. Because of this thermosetting characteristic the fabrication processes for these materials are more difficult, but the articles produced have a wider useful temperature range. The thermoplastic materials soften when they are heated and cannot be cured as can the thermosetting resins. In terms of easy processing the thermoplastic materials are far superior and can be reworked since they will always soften on re-heating.

Thermosetting Resins

The thermosetting resins include phenolformaldehyde (the original Bakelite resin), urea and melamine formaldehyde, polyester and epoxy resins. The difficulties encountered in fabricating this type of plastic material are related to their curing and becoming permanently hard after only a limited heating time, and to the small temperature range during which their viscosity makes it possible to force them through dies and into moulds. The curing of thermosetting resins is both time and temperature dependent and by use of suitable accelerators these factors can be controlled.

* Bone Brothers Limited, Manor Farm Road, Wembley, Middlesex.

Compression Moulding

Compression moulding is the most important processing technique used for thermosetting resins. In this process a pre-determined quantity of moulding powder is placed in the mould cavity, which is heated. The mould is then closed and pressure applied so that as the material heats up and its viscosity drops it flows to fill the whole of the cavity. The pressure is maintained for a pre-set period to enable the moulding to cure before the pressure is released and the mould opened.

Compression moulding presses are normally down-stroking hydraulically-operated machines. They are usually self-contained with their own hydraulic pumps and accumulators, although where a shop contains a number of large presses these are sometimes run from a central hydraulic system. The main developments in the field of compression moulding have been concentrated on making the best possible use of the press time. Machines have been fitted with automatic material feed and ejection of the final moulding, and complete automatic operation of the press. In addition attention has been paid to reducing the time that the moulding material has to be in the mould by preheating, and both high-frequency and induction heaters are used for this preheating process. Induction heating has also come into considerable use for the heating of press platens, and whether this heating is by induction or resistance heaters, or by the use of steam, accurate methods of temperature control are normally employed. Better control of the movement of the press piston itself has been achieved by more sophisticated hydraulics.

For the moulding of thermosetting materials into parts incorporating delicate inserts, the compression moulding process has been modified to what is termed transfer moulding. In the transfer moulding process the thermosetting resin is heated and subjected to pressure in a separate chamber before it is forced through a nozzle into the mould. In some respects the transfer moulding process resembles the injection moulding process which is used for thermoplastic materials. As will be appreciated from the comments made earlier, the transfer moulding process accentuates the problem of melting and forcing the thermosetting material into the mould without premature curing. The feed nozzle between the melting vessel, or transfer pot, and the mould has to be sized so that the shear

S

heat generated by forcing the melt through the small orifice is not sufficient to cause curing before the mould is full.

The developments in recent years of both the compression and transfer moulding processes have been concentrated on refining the equipment and improving the process controls. Phenolic type moulding powders have a very wide application in the electrical engineering industry and the newer of these thermosetting resins, Melamine, is now in very wide use in the domestic field, particularly for the manufacture of crockery.

Fig. I.—*Bradley and Turton VA-10/2-1E three-station fully automatic compression moulding press unit*

This new material can be produced in attractive pastel shades and has an extremely hard surface. Fig. 1 is a photograph of a compression moulding press of recent design in which three press units are combined on a common bedplate with a common hydraulic system. These multiple press units are coming into greater use as they can give a considerable reduction in labour usage.

Reinforced Plastics

Before leaving the thermosetting resins and proceeding to discuss the fabricating processes for thermoplastic resins, mention should be made of reinforced plastics which use thermosetting materials. The most important of this type of plastic uses glass fibre as the reinforcement and polyester or epoxy resins to bind the fibres together. Polyester resins, which are the most used for this type of product, are thermosetting and may be cured quickly at low temperatures and pressures. Most of the glass fibre reinforced plastics are still made by manual operation. The moulds are coated with the resin and then filled alternately with glass fibre, in the form of fabrics or non-woven mats, and with the resin which is rolled into the reinforcement so as to ensure complete filling of the

spaces between the fibres, and the exclusion of air. The mould used can be of either the male or female type according to the shape and size of the article to be produced. The applications of resin and glass fibre are built up to the required thickness, after which they are allowed to cure. Resins are available which will cure at room temperature and with the application of only very light pressures, to give mouldings of satisfactory physical properties. The most promising development to improve the process of manufacturing reinforced plastic mouldings is that using a spraying technique. Spraying equipment is available which will feed simultaneously into the mould, chopped up glass yarn together with resin and catalyst. On completion of the spraying it is necessary to consolidate the laminate before curing. This spraying method is in use for the manufacture of parts such as washing-machine liners.

A further development in the manufacture of reinforced plastics mouldings is the technique known as matched metal moulding. This method mechanises the production of preforms in the reinforcing material by using preforming machines which chop the reinforcing fibre into preset lengths, and transfers this fibre into the moulding chamber, where it is deposited on the inside of the mould to form a continuous fibre mat. When a suitable thickness of mat has been deposited a light spray of resin is given so that the mat can then be transferred to the press mould. This process is likely to lend itself more readily to mechanization than any other used in the reinforced plastic moulding process. The equipment is far more elaborate and expensive than the simpler processes described earlier and thus this matched metal moulding process can only be used economically for large numbers of components.

Thermoplastics

The thermoplastic resins make up by far the greatest part of the plastics materials in current use. These include the olefine group with polythene, polypropylene and polytetraflourethylene, and the vinyl group with polystyrene, polyvinyl chloride and polyvinylidene chloride. The olefine and vinyl polymers are undoubtedly the basic materials of the plastics industry today, but there are many other interesting thermoplastics materials such as acrylic resins, polyamide or nylon resins, and the newer polycarbonate and polyformaldehyde resins. As their temperature is increased these materials soften and reach a viscosity which makes it possible to readily manipulate the melt and form it into continuous shapes or specific mouldings. They also have in common a latent instability, which differs from one to the other, but which will cause them to degrade or decompose if they are maintained at too high a temperature for too long a period of time. Thus in the processing of these thermoplastic materials it is necessary to bring them to an adequately low viscosity to make their processing easy, but in doing this they must not be overheated nor maintained at this processing temperature for an excessively long time. With some of these materials such as unplasticized PVC the easy processing temperature is so close to the decomposition temperature that there are severe limitations to the processing techniques that can be employed. Other materials such as polythene are extremely tolerant to processing conditions and can be reprocessed many times without serious degradation.

The viscosity characteristics of thermoplastics are extremely important in understanding their processing possibilities. Fig. 2 shows the apparent viscosity–temperature curves for a number of different materials indicating how different these can be. It must also be borne in mind that plastic materials as a group are very poor conductors of heat and this makes the process of melting more difficult.

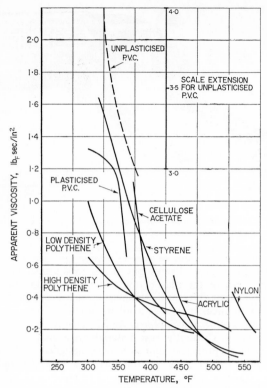

Fig. 2.—*Apparent viscosity–temperature relationship for various thermo-plastics*

Extrusion

The most important process in the fabrication of plastics is probably the extrusion process. This is first used on the polymerization plant when the plastic raw materials are being manufactured. In most processes the thermoplastic is produced in the reaction vessel as a melt or as a solid powder and in both cases they must be converted into regular shaped pellets. For this purpose they are fed to large extruders which convert them into strips or laces which are then cut into pellets.

The extruder consists basically of an archimedean screw rotating inside a hard cylinder which is heated from the outside. The screw conveys the granules which take in heat from the cylinder wall and which in time thus become molten. The screw is designed so that it has a diminishing flight volume as the granules feed along it, and this causes them to compact as well as to soften. A die is fitted to the end of the extruder barrel and the screw forces the molten material through this die into the shape or form required. Fig. 3 shows diagrammatically the essential features of an extruder.

Screw extruders were first used for thermoplastics extrusion in the early 1930's. The first machines were adaptations of rubber extruders which have screws of only 6–10 diameters length, and which are normally steam heated. Rubber is fed to the extruder as a hot molten strip and the purpose of the screw is merely to force the rubber through the die which shapes it into the required form. The viscosity of rubber compounds is very high and the shearing action of the screw generates considerable heat. To prevent the rubber from curing on the extruder screw it is necessary to minimize this shear heat and for this reason the screw design for rubber has a very deep flight and little if any compression from the feed to the discharge end.

Feeding cold granulated thermoplastics to rubber extruders soon exposed considerable limitations in these machines for processing the new materials. It became necessary to extend the length of the extruder screw and barrel, and to fit restricting devices at the discharge end of the barrel to give compression and to encourage mixing and the generation of shear heat.

The extrusion process is difficult to analyse because of the many variables involved, but in 1953 the DuPont Company in America published a series of papers which analysed the flow of a melt in an extruder screw and went further than had any previous work. Other analyses had certainly been made prior to this group of papers, and indeed a paper published in *Engineering* in 1928 by Rowell & Finlayson describing screw pumps has been a starting point for many investigators in the plastics extrusion field. The publication of the DuPont papers in 1953 at a time when the plastics industry was beginning to expand at a fast rate, initiated many more theoretical and practical investigations of the extrusion process and led to a far better understanding of the mechanism involved. In particular this theoretical analysis explained many of the empirical rules which had been established, and led to a still more rapid development of extrusion machinery.

Thermoplastic melts are non-Newtonian fluids and only approximate solutions have been determined describing their flow in a screw channel under both isothermal and adiabatic conditions. These analytical solutions are of considerable

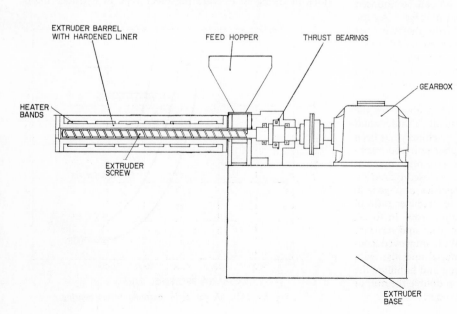

Fig. 3.—*Diagrammatic arrangement showing main features of a screw extruder*

practical value, and they show the relationship between output and power requirements relative to the geometry of the extruder and the apparent viscosity of the plastic melt. The simplified equation for the output of a melt extruder is :

$$Q = \alpha N - \frac{\beta}{\mu} \cdot \frac{\Delta P}{L}$$

where Q = volumetric output

N = screw speed

μ = apparent viscosity

L = length of screw over which pressure rise ΔP occurs

α and β are geometric constants.

The total power requirement is described by the equation:

$$dZ = AN^2 \mu\, dL + Q\, dP + BN^2 \mu\, dL$$

where Z = total power

A is a coefficient containing geometric terms but also including a flow relationship

B is a geometric constant.

The theoretical analyses so far referred to have been used on a screw extruder which is fed with a molten material. In practice the thermoplastic materials are more often fed as solid granules and are melted during the process. It is not difficult to analyse the conveying of these granules by the screw, but the analysis of the flow at the change in phase between solid granules and a melt is extremely complicated and so far this has not been satisfactorily completed.

In the melt extrusion process the relative motion between the screw and the barrel wall causes shearing of the material in the screw channel. The power consumed in shearing the polymer is converted into heat and contributes to the temperature rise of the resin. The amount of heat generated in the plastic material increases as the screw channel is made shallower or longer, and as the screw speed is increased. The rheological properties of the plastic also have an important influence on the amount of heat generated by the mechanical working of the polymer on the extruder screw. High melt viscosities and a low dependence of viscosity on temperature and shear rate contribute to increased power consumption and a greater generation of heat within the plastic during extrusion. The amount of heat generated in the plastic by mechanical working can also be increased by imposing a restriction at the discharge end of the extruder barrel. This restriction can be imposed by reducing the die opening or by using a valve. As the restriction to flow is increased the output from the screw per revolution is reduced, the head pressure increased, and consequently the plastic is subjected to a greater amount of shear. This increase in the amount of working to which the plastic is subjected improves the mixing of the material on the extruder screw and increases the temperature.

Taking into account the relationships shown above for the operation of a screw extruder it is not difficult to understand why the main development in this type of machinery has been towards longer and longer screws and higher-powered machines. These developments of the extruder have been aimed at achieving higher outputs of products made to closer tolerances, and greater consistency of physical properties and general quality. In the past ten years the length to diameter ratio of the extruder screw has increased on average from 16 to 24, and the extruder has been fitted with drive gear and bearings of approximately twice the capacity. With improved consistency of quality in the plastic raw material and also with improvements in the methods of quenching and handling the extrudate, it has been possible to more than double the output achieved from a given diameter screw extruder.

Fig. 4.—*Bone Brothers 8 in. heavy duty extruder of* 25 : 1 *screw length to diameter ratio and* 300 *h.p. drive gear*

This doubling of the output is also associated with the development of the plastic raw materials. In the original development of different thermoplastics such as polythene and PVC the number of grades available was extremely limited, and these were therefore of average flow characteristics to suit all processes. Currently these materials are available in a very wide range of properties and each one is designed to give flow characteristics and physical properties to suit specific applications. The developments that have taken place in the past ten years have thus been made jointly between the raw material supplier and the machine manufacturer. As advances are made by one the limitations of the other's product have become more obvious.

From the mechanical design point of view the increased demands put on this equipment have not created insuperable problems. The gearbox transmitting the motor power has had to be increased in capacity, and current designs allow for the transmission of 30 h.p. on a $2\frac{1}{2}$ in. diameter extruder and up to 300 h.p. for extruders of 8 in. screw diameter. For special purposes, and particularly for the compounding of the plastic raw materials, even higher powers are employed. The machine shown in Fig. 4 is an 8 in. extruder with a 300 h.p. drive gear. With the increased outputs and screw speeds now employed higher pressures are generated in the extruder barrel and a greater load transmitted to the thrust bearing. The thrust bearing has been found to be one of the greatest limitations in trying to operate the older type of extruder under

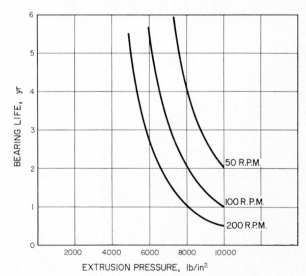

Fig. 5.—*B-10 life for* $2\frac{1}{2}$ *in. extruder thrust bearing*

P.V.C.

POLYTHENE

Fig. 6.—Screw designs for three different plastics

NYLON

higher loads. Provided, however, that these requirements are known, there is no difficulty in accommodating very high pressures at comparatively high screw speeds. Both parallel and spherical roller thrust bearings are employed, and on the larger machines such as that illustrated, tandem bearings are used so that even at a die pressure of 10,000 p.s.i. and with the screw running at 150 rev/min a bearing life of over five years can be expected. Fig. 5 shows the relationship between bearing life, pressure, and screw speed, and from this it can be seen how important it is to specify clearly the requirements for the machine.

Increasing the length of the extruder screw and the capacity of the extruder drive unit will not in itself give the increased output required from this type of machinery. The most important factor in being able to successfully use the increased power available is the design of the screw. Very considerable development work has been carried out to determine the optimum screw design for different thermoplastics and for the production of different products such as pipe, film, sheet, cable insulation and sheathing. If the screw thread is too deep and lacks adequate compression, then at high outputs the melt will not be homogeneous and a uniform output will not be achieved. It has been found essential for materials such as polythene, polypropylene and polystyrene to have screws with a compression ratio of approximately 4 : 1. In itself this compression ratio is not as important as is the actual depth of the screw at both the feed end and in particular at the discharge end. To improve the consistency of output from the screw it is usual to have a parallel discharge section which acts as a metering pump. The depth of this section is extremely important in ensuring homogeneity and a uniform output. In designing a screw the depth of the pumping or metering section must be determined first and is related to the viscosity characteristics of the plastic to be extruded. Having established the depth of the metering section, the depth of the screw flight at the feed end can be determined together with the profile of the screw root from the feed point to the metering section.

The compression ratio of the screw and the way in which the root diameter is reduced for different types of thermoplastic is usually based on practical experience. It is to some extent related to the melting characteristics of the plastic, for example, with nylon which has a sharp melting point the transition from the feed depth to the metering depth is often carried out in only one flight. Normally, however, the feed section is kept at a constant root diameter for a third of the screw length

and for a further third of the screw length a gradual compression is introduced to change from the feed depth to the metering section depth (Fig. 6).

To achieve high outputs of good quality product it is necessary to overcome the limitation imposed by the poor thermal conductivity of the plastic. As has already been mentioned the action of the screw rotating inside a stationary barrel causes shearing of the molten polymer and the generation of heat. This has led to the use of extrusion conditions which have been described as adiabatic, or more accurately as autogenous, where the majority of the heat put in to the plastic is generated by the shearing action of the screw and only a very small percentage is taken in by conduction from the barrel walls. The ability of an extruder to generate this working heat is related to the screw design and to the machine having adequate power. There have been suggestions that the extruder should be designed to operate autogenously and thus eliminate the cost of expensive temperature controls. In practice this has not been found to be feasible and most modern high-powered extruders are fitted with accurately controlled heating and cooling systems. Barrel cooling is a feature which is now common to most extruders but which only five years ago was the exception rather than the rule. Fluid, air, and vapour cooling systems are employed depending on the quantity of heat that it is expected to extract and on the particular operating conditions.

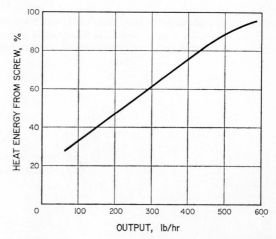

Fig. 7.—Percentage screw motor energy converted to useful heat in polythene on a 4½ in. extruder at 320°C melt temperature

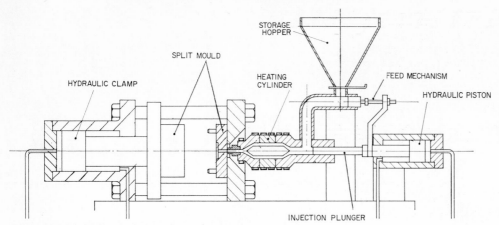

Fig. 8.—*Diagrammatic representation of plunger type injection
moulding machine*

In practice it is only the use of heat generated by shearing the plastic on the screw that makes it possible to obtain a homogeneous melt at high speeds and outputs, and full appreciation of this use of shear heat is probably the most important recent development in the extrusion of thermoplastics. Fig. 7 shows the percentage screw motor power put into the polymer as heat at different outputs using a $4\frac{1}{2}$ in. extruder.

Injection Moulding

Injection moulding is one of the major fabricating processes for thermoplastics, producing at high speed, and often automatically, precision parts. These parts range in size from articles such as washers weighing a few grams up to refrigerator linings or transparent roof domes weighing nearly 20 lb.

Basically injection moulding is a simple cyclic process. The thermoplastic granules are heated until they melt, and are then forced into a cold mould where the melt re-solidifies to produce an exact replica of the mould. Fig. 8 shows diagrammatically the arrangement of an injection moulding machine. A feed mechanism at the base of the storage hopper meters a constant volume of granules into the injection cylinder. This cylinder has around it electric heaters from which the granules take up heat by conduction from the cylinder walls. The piston or plunger activated by hydraulic pressure compacts the granules at the rear of the heating cylinder. The pressure thus generated is transmitted through the column of granules and forces the molten plastic at the other end of the cylinder through a nozzle into the mould.

The piston stroke, the injection pressure, and the injection cylinder temperatures are selected to suit the thermoplastic being moulded, and the particular shape and size of the mould. As with extrusion, the ease of operating this process is closely related to the thermal and flow characteristics of the plastic.

The ideal properties required by thermoplastic moulding compounds differ from those required for extrusion. In particular, the shear rates to which the melt is subjected as it is forced through the nozzle are higher, and to fill the mould which can have long, tortuous and narrow flow paths, requires a more fluid melt. Special moulding grades have been developed to give high outputs and efficiencies and also to ensure that the mouldings produced are of satisfactory physical properties.

The thermoplastic melt injected into the mould is at a high temperature, and since the moulding must be completely solid before it is ejected, greater production is obtained by applying cooling to the body of the mould. This cooling is achieved by water circulation and in some cases refrigerated water is employed. The colder the mould the higher the cooling rate of the moulding, but very high cooling rates can freeze in moulding strain. For this reason the mould temperature must be accurately controlled, and with technical mouldings from materials such as nylon and polyformaldehyde the mould temperature is often elevated. A compromise has to be reached between mould temperature and output so as to give a satisfactory strain-free product.

There has been a considerable and rapid development in this country of the use of unplasticized PVC for pipes and fittings required by the building industry. The injection moulding of rigid PVC pipe fittings is difficult and limited by the heating system used on the injection cylinder. Rigid PVC is highly viscous and therefore difficult to mould without using very high melt temperatures. This material is also prone to thermal decomposition and this limits the temperatures that can be employed. To achieve a melt temperature and viscosity to give satisfactory flow in pipe fitting moulds, the wall of the injection cylinder often reaches the threshold temperature above which the PVC will char, and the efficiency of moulding this type of product has been extremely low. This limitation in the injection moulding machine design has been overcome by incorporating an extruder. The rigid PVC is

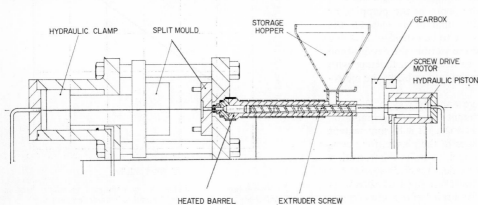

Fig. 9.—*Diagrammatic representation of screw type injection
moulding machine*

Fig. 10.—*Cravens H.P.M. 200-H-6/8 piston type injection moulding machine*

melted on the extruder screw and by using the shear heat and better melting efficiency, the correct melt temperature is achieved with lower cylinder wall temperatures. Fig. 9 shows the arrangement of a screw plasticizing injection moulding machine which also uses the screw as the injection plunger.

The use of screw plasticizing in injection moulding is undoubtedly the major plastic machinery development in the past decade. As well as making it possible to mould materials of poor thermal stability, screw plasticizing gives greatly increased plasticizing capacities without increasing the size of the machine. This development has brought with it a new concept of designing the injection moulding machine to suit the particular moulding job. Moulding machines have in the past been specified by the clamp tonnage and plasticizing capacity, and standard combinations were almost universal. With screw plasticizing a number of combinations of clamp and injection unit are available, and the screw unit can also be used as a pre-plasticizer feeding an injection unit. The basic piston type injection moulding machine is shown in Fig. 10. This machine has a plasticizing capacity of 80 lb/h of polystyrene, as compared with 200 lb/h for the screw plasticizing injection moulding machine of comparable size shown in Fig. 11.

Fig. 12 shows one of the largest injection moulding machines built. It has a 1500-ton mould clamp and a pre-plasticizing extruder, with a plasticizing capacity of over 650 lb/h, mounted vertically above the plunger injection cylinder.

The difference in the plasticizing capacity of the screw unit as compared with the plunger type injection cylinder is so great that it has opened new possibilities for the use of injection moulding machines. Materials which have been extremely

Fig. 11.—*Cravens H.P.M. 200-IX-15 screw plasticizing injection moulding machine*

difficult or almost impossible to mould can now be formed into intricate shapes, and the weight of moulding that can be produced has been greatly increased for a given size mould clamp.

Blow Moulding

In considering recent developments in fabricating plastics, the blow moulding process used to produce detergent bottles and a wide range of other products must also be mentioned. This is not a new process, but the development of different grades of polythene giving bottles having thinner and stiffer walls, and resistant to the cracking effect of detergents, has brought a tremendous increase in its use. The process has become more economic and this has led to refinements in machinery design. The greatest advance has been the use of cross-head dies in which the orifice can be adjusted whilst extruding and the thickness of the wall of the bottle varied according to its shape. This process has been fully automated with rotary tables and multiple moulds to overcome the main production limitation of the cooling time in the mould. Bottles made from PVC are of considerable interest for the packaging of food and oils, but the processing of this material

Fig. 12.—*Cravens H.P.M. 1500-PFX-200 screw pre-plasticizer plunger injection moulding machine*

because of its thermal instability is as difficult in this process as in injection moulding. A new process has been developed for unplasticized PVC bottles in which tube is extruded separately and cut into lengths, and the pieces of tube are then re-heated and formed into bottles and containers on a separate machine.

Conclusion

The plastic industry is still young and fast growing, and as would be expected the rate of development in the equipment used for fabricating these new materials is great. Only fifteen years ago the major processes were justifiably looked upon as a " black art ", whereas today they can be considered to have reached the fringe of applied science. There is nevertheless a long way to go before we have a full understanding of the mechanisms involved, for although the chemistry of plastics is most advanced and precise, the physics is only beginning to approach a similar state. Much more work needs to be done in the fields of melt flow and heat transfer, and this is perhaps indicative of the absence, so far, of a chemical engineering approach to the problems of plastics processing. The continued expansion of the plastics industry will be dependent on the development of equipment to make processing and fabricating easier and more economic, and this will only be achieved if there is greater co-operation between the material manufacturers, the machinery designers and centres of fundamental research.

It is most encouraging that Plastics and their fabrication processes should have been included in this Symposium on " Advances in Materials ". In the first 100 years of its existence the plastics industry has developed materials and products which have been fully tried and accepted by a wide range of other industries. Because of the difficulty in predicting long-term effects such as creep and oxidation it has sometimes taken many years of painstaking testing before these new products could be fully accepted, but the reserve of knowledge and experience necessary to minimize such delays is fast accumulating. The uniformity of plastics products has on occasion been suspect, but recent developments of the fabricating machinery now ensure that there is accurate control of pro-

cess conditions and consequently a consistent product. It is therefore with confidence that we can look forward to a greater understanding of both the new materials and the fabricating processes used by the plastics industry, and to the time when these products will be looked upon by other industries as conventional rather than new.

Acknowledgment

I would like to thank the Institution of Chemical Engineers for their kindness in inviting me to present this paper. I have tried to describe the more important basic developments in the plastics fabricating processes but in covering such a wide field many interesting and important aspects have had to be omitted.

DISCUSSION OF PAPERS PRESENTED AT THE SIXTH SESSION

The CHAIRMAN said that Lord Bowden, the Principal of the Manchester College of Science and Technology, had hoped to take the Chair for the final session. Unfortunately, he had had to go to London for an important debate in the House of Lords and was unable to be present, but sent his regrets.

The last session of the symposium was concerned with the forming and fabrication of the materials which had been considered, and three papers were to be given.

Mr. W. F. HARRIS said that there had been a report in *Rubber & Plastics Age* in January, 1964, of extruders running with screw speeds of 1500 and 1800 rev/min. He asked if Mr. Grant could give some idea of the way in which wear had been overcome in such machinery, particularly mechanical wear in the barrel and the sleeve.

Mr. GRANT said that wear had not become apparent as a problem but very few machines ran at the speeds mentioned. High-speed extrusion had been suggested 10 to 12 years ago in this country and considerable work had been done on it. but it was not, in fact, as attractive as it at first appeared.

Some people were certainly running with very small diameter extruders, obtaining comparatively high outputs, but the problem was the one which he had tried to highlight—that of getting the heat into the material by mechanical working. On the high-speed extruder, the whole of the screw acted as a conveyor and the melting occurred only on the cone at the end of the screw. There was difficulty in obtaining a melt which was really homogeneous and this was the limitation. There were extruders running at 300 to 400 rev/min being used for the compounding of plastics where homogeneity was not so important, and with these extruders there had not been any problem with wear. He thought that the reason was that the plastic itself acted as a very good lubricant between the screw and the barrel.

Mr. N. H. RAY said that, since the mechanical properties of glass were chiefly dependent upon its surface condition, and since one side of float glass was both physically and chemically different from the other, perhaps Dr. Pilkington would say whether there was a mechanical difference and whether float-glass windows ought to be fitted one way round rather than the other.

Dr. PILKINGTON said that this depended on what was required from the window. The difference was very small. The firm had done a lot of work which had been published, or was to be published shortly, on the strength tests, if this was what Mr. Ray was thinking about, of the two different faces, inwards or outwards, and the effect was really insignificant.

There could be many variations and more or less material could be incorporated in the bottom surface from the molten metal bath and with suitable treatment a semi-transparent one-way glass could be made if required; but with regard to strength, he did not think Mr. Ray needed to worry and he was sure that the motor manufacturers were using it now entirely as in the $\frac{1}{4}$-in. field in toughened glass windscreens.

Professor R. W. CAHN referred to high-speed forming methods and said that he would be intrigued to know what maximum practical pressures could be achieved by the pulse methods as compared with explosive methods. Experiments were to be undertaken in his department on recrystallization of explosively deformed materials and he was going to be interested to discover whether the behaviour of steel on annealing changed when the pressure level during the previous pulse had exceeded the critical level at which a phase transformation occurred. He wondered whether the critical value could be reached by non-explosive pulse-forming methods.

Mr. PUGH said that the question was a difficult one to answer. No reliable information on the magnitude of the pressures developed in electrohydraulic forming appeared to be available. This was because of the difficulty in trying to measure pressure in the presence of the large electrical and magnetic fields associated with the discharge which tended to swamp the signals obtained by any electrical method. Further whilst other methods of measuring pressure existed, the response time of the system had to be very short, which again tended to restrict the choice to an electrical method. Attempts to measure pressure had been made in the U.S.A., but these were generally measured at some distance from the spark and were significantly lower than those obtained in explosive forming.

Professor CAHN asked if purely metallographic experiments could not be done so that if the pressure was exceeded on the steel sample, there were phase changes and one could tell whether the limiting pulse pressure had exceeded 130 kilobars.

Mr. PUGH said that it was true that metallographic tests of the kind envisaged by Professor Cahn could be done and in fact had been done with explosives by C. Smith. As far as he knew, however, such tests had not been carried out on materials deformed by electrohydraulic methods. He was not aware of any experiments where the electrohydraulic discharge had been set off in contact with the specimen and thought it unlikely that pressures of the order mentioned could be achieved by other than contact explosives.

The CHAIRMAN said that very roughly, on the figures given, it seemed that twice as much power was put in to the screw extruder for twice as large a throughput. He wondered where the extra energy had come from to provide the extra heat to which reference had been made.

Mr. GRANT said that it was true that approximately twice as much power was required to double the throughput. That was because the major factor in power requirement was the total heat content of the plastic extruded. The pressure energy was a very small part of the total, and could be ignored. The extra energy came either from the extruder motor or the heaters on the extruder barrel, and Fig. 7 indicated, for a particular $4\frac{1}{2}$ in. diameter screw extruder, the percentage of the total heat content of the extrudate derived from the drive motor. As the screw speed and hence the output increased a greater portion of the heat was derived from the motor rather than from the barrel heaters, The motor power was converted into heat by the shearing action of the screw on the plastic as it passed along it, and the shear rate was related directly to the screw speed.

Mr. P. ANTONISSEN wished to ask a question on the liquids at levels over one-quarter million p.s.i. Most liquids solidified at lower pressures. Mr. Pugh had not referred to that. In the paper, Mr. Pugh mentioned SAE 30 which, he seemed to recall, was a particularly bad one to use, and had been known to solidify in the region of 30 000 p.s.i.

Mr. PUGH said that there had been insufficient time to touch on this problem. Mr. Antonissen was quite right in saying that if liquids were subjected to a high enough pressure they would solidify. At pressures of 200 to 300 ton/in² all known liquids would have frozen. In the case of oil SAE 30, this had been used successfully up to pressures of 60 to 70 ton/in². It was one of the few liquids which was known to take as a dispersion the molybdenum disulphide used as a lubricant for the billet. If it was necessary to go to higher pressures, as for very difficult materials, other liquids had to be used. Castor oil and methylated spirits could be used at pressures up to about 90 and 100 ton/in². At higher pressures still, say 150 to 200 ton/in², isopentane could be used, whilst the Russians used a mixture of 40 per cent glycol in glycerine. Clearly, the liquid used depended on the extrusion pressure required.

Mr. F. C. VAN GENTEVOORT said that Mr. Pugh had described the extrusion process: as soon as extrusion was taking place, there was a seal between the billet and the die; but how did one start building up pressure, because one had to avoid throwing the liquid out of the die?
On page 247, Pugh described the extrusion of a plastic rod with a length/diameter ratio of about 8000. It was not clear to him how it was put into the die.

Mr. PUGH, referring to the first question, said that this was something that he had omitted from the presentation of the paper, as time was short. In fact, it was not necessary to seal the billet before starting because a nose was produced on the billet, by machining or some other way, whose angle was roughly the same as the angle of the die into which it was inserted. One did not have to match the angles exactly and it was sufficient that there should be some area of contact between the nose of the billet and the die. When the pressure built up the total force acting downwards on the top of the billet would be the pressure multiplied by the area of the billet. For equilibrium, this must be equal to the force acting over the small area of contact so that the pressure in this region was sufficiently high to cause local deformation. This resulted in a closer match between the billet nose and the die entry, thus providing a most effective seal.
The second question referred to the extrusion of wire and this was the subject of the film which would be shown shortly. A model extrusion apparatus had been made up to demonstrate the process at an exhibition. In order to show what went on inside the high pressure container the apparatus was provided with a container made of perspex. This meant, however, that the pressure inside it had to be limited to a low value and it was possible to extrude a plastic rod only. A length of rod approximately 8000 times its diameter was taken and wound on a reel, similar to a reel of cotton. The reel was mounted on trunnions inside the container. One of the free ends of the plastic rod was necked in tension and cut at the minimum diameter in order that it could be passed through the die orifice. It was then pulled until the full diameter of the rod was in contact with the die, thereby ensuring a fluid seal was formed.

Mr. G. H. WEST said that his department had recently been investigating the temperature dependence of viscosity of various thermoplastics from both theoretical and practical aspects with a view to applying the results to polymer processing. He would be interested to know under what conditions of shear rate the viscosity–temperature relations shown in Fig. 2 of Grant's paper had been obtained and whether the curves were purely experimental or derived on the basis of a particular theory such as the WLF equation.

Mr. GRANT said that the shear rate/viscosity relationship was of tremendous importance, and the whole of the operation of the machine, and in particular attempts at theoretical analysis, depended on this.
It was very difficult to obtain data and that shown on the graph had been taken at very low rates of shear, approximately corresponding to the melt flow index measurement. This was very much lower than one would expect to obtain in an extruder, but the problem was to obtain data measured at practical shear rates.

Mr. S. W. HALLWOOD asked what beryllium material had been used for hydrostatic extrusion. How did the mechanical properties of extrusions produced by that means compare with properties from extrusions of similar material but produced by conventional means?

Mr. PUGH said that the material which had been vacuum cast and hot extruded was supplied by AWRE. He had no information regarding the properties of the material. Since the handling of beryllium is hazardous the extruded samples were passed back to AWRE, who were properly equipped to handle and examine them. The specimens were not large enough for any extensive examination, nor were they large enough for mechanical testing. He would, in general, not expect the properties to be significantly different from those of material subjected to this amount of cold work. On the other hand, it should be noted that recent work by Bullen and Wain had suggested that the pressure soaking of chromium had endowed it with considerable ductility on subsequent testing at atmospheric pressure.

Mr. L. S. EVANS said that, during the morning, those present were told about chemical methods of toughening sheet glass, Chemcor. Would Dr. Pilkington say whether glass treated in that way would be available in Britain?

Dr. PILKINGTON said that he could not say at present. He thought Dr. Shaver was present and that he might know of plans at the moment, but he himself knew of no plans at present to make this. It would depend very much on the demand for it in various fields. He thought it was correct to say that in the U.S.A. the main demand was for opaque types of glass which had exceptionally strong properties. This was used mainly in the field of restaurant ware. As far as he knew, there were no plans to manufacture it in this country yet, though, if there was a demand which was large enough, obviously this would occur.

Dr. W. W. SHAVER said that he thought that was correct. At present, restaurant ware was the product, and a sheet for windows of a certain size. It was, however, in its infancy.

Mr. EVANS said that that raised a general point regarding material for chemical engineering plant. The chemical engineer was in rather an unfortunate position because there were many materials he could use but he was never a very big user of them, so that he found it difficult to interest producers in his small off-take of such materials. He realised that it was a difficult problem, but if there was some way of overcoming it, he was sure it would ease the task of chemical engineers in handling obnoxious materials.

The CHAIRMAN said that the laws of economics still applied.

Dr. PILKINGTON said that this was the answer. Speaking for the glass industry, he felt it was largely a question of volume of demand. There were two sizes of operation: one was the very big operation which was turning out many hundreds of tons a week, and this was quite uneconomical when an attempt was made to reduce it to an individual demand of one ton. Many weeks of operation had to be built up before it could possibly be justified. On the other scale, it was possible to manufacture a number of things for rather specialist plant which some people in the industry did have for this specific purpose, but once this type of operation was used the cost went right up and people found that although it might have very good physical or chemical properties, the price did not justify the improvement of the properties.

Professor R. W. CAHN asked what the prospects were of experimental or small-quantity users getting ceramics of a chemically machinable type. That came into Dr. Pilkington's second category, for small quantities, but the Corning Company in America found it economic. Was there any prospect of there being a set-up in Britain, or accessible in Britain, where small quantities of chemically-machinable ceramics could be obtained.

Dr. W. W. SHAVER said that there was a problem of supplying, particularly the technical materials requiring special finishes. As time went on, the lines of communication were improving and the Electrosyl Company was actually making specialised resistors now and they would be the people who could advise on chemically-machined glass and other things in the electronics field. He could put Professor Cahn in touch with the proper source.

The CHAIRMAN took up Dr. Pilkington's point about the type of technical staff required. He said that he could generalize by saying, did the industry want men well trained in the primary technologies and basic sciences, or did it want more in the way of people trained in special technologies? Did people generally feel that Pilkington's view was correct and that the main requirement was for people trained on a broad basis? He would agree with that himself.

Mr. J. S. ROBINSON said that Mr. Pugh had shown at the beginning of his paper that he relied on a high-pressure ambient to increase the ductility and hence make extrusion possible. The tools were also subjected to the same ambient; what effect did it have on their mechanical properties? Would Mr. Pugh comment on likely changes in other properties under high pressures above 100 ton/in^2—say doubled, or up by one order?

Mr. PUGH said that he was not sure that he had understood the question correctly. The object of applying hydrostatic pressure was to produce conditions in the product such that cracking could not start. Thus, although in extrusion into atmospheric pressure the net load on the product was nothing, the distribution of stress across the product would vary. It would be tensile on the outside and compressive on the inside, and in most extrusions the tendency was to get tensile stresses on the outside of the product. If these were big enough, the product would crack. All one was doing by superimposing a hydrostatic compressive stress was to reduce the tensile stress everywhere and particularly that on the outside of the product, which could be reduced below the value at which the product would crack. This did not necessarily mean that anything magical was being done about properties.

As far as the die was concerned, the hydrostatic pressure merely gave it external support in the same way as a conventional extrusion die was supported by surrounding it with shrink rings to prevent it cracking.

If the questioner was asking about the effect of much higher pressure on materials this opened up a vast field. The world of Bullen and Wain was relatively new. They had found that if chromium, which was a very brittle material having a reduction of area of almost nothing in a normal tensile test, was put in a pressure chamber at 10,000 atm and then taken out and retested in the tensile machine, the new reduction of area could be as great as 45 per cent. This was quite a marked change. If the pressure was considerably increased it was known that there were quite radical changes in structure and properties. Professor Cahn had mentioned phase changes in iron at 130 kilobars and crystal structures were changed in other materials. The classical case was the conversion of carbon to diamond, in which case temperature was needed as well. This, however, opened up a huge field and he could not go into this in a short time. There were several conferences being held on this subject generally, to which he could refer the speaker.

Summing up

Dr. H. M. FINNISTON said that the organisers of the conference were to be complimented on the excellence of their arrangements for collecting and distributing the papers in advance of the meeting and for the hospitality enjoyed by the participants. He asked those present to join him in thanking the organisers for the work which had been done before and during the conference, and would have to be done afterwards.

His first difficulty had been to decide how to present in summary what had happened in the 20 hours of continuous talking. The most obvious way was to take session by session and attempt to summarise each of the papers within the sessions. He felt that this was a little like presenting the conference guests with a predigested second helping of the main course and that this would be neither appetising nor acceptable. He would, therefore, attempt to establish whether the intent of what was billed as an interdisciplinary symposium had been achieved. Had the conference furthered the interdisciplinary movement in materials science and technology?

The word "interdisciplinary" was now fashionable and glamorous, and every time something became fashionable and glamorous people tended to lose something of their critical faculties. The conference had certainly brought together experts from different disciplines; of that there was no question. It had also brought together 30 papers from different disciplines by people educated in different professions and with experience gained in different ways. He did not think, however, that it had been a truly interdisciplinary conference in the open sessions, although his interpretation of what an interdisciplinary symposium should be could differ from that intended by the organisers.

An interdisciplinary conference of the type in which they had engaged ought to try to achieve exchanges of ideas and concepts, of know-how and of practice from different disciplines, so that all parties could look at their previous ideas, concepts and practices and techniques and see whether or not these could be improved upon or added to from outside their discipline; it also involved exchanges on the marriage of different materials in which different disciplines were expert and the consequences and problems of such " interdisciplinary materials ". In these respects he thought the conference had failed to meet its target. He had tried to find the correct phrase for this and had reached the conclusion that the participants, both from the rostrum and from the floor, suffered from " mental homosexuality "; within any one discipline individuals had had mental intercourse with each other but had by design or accident avoided or evaded intercourse between professions. This was a considerable loss and removed part of the anticipated excitement and the potential advantages to be gained from an interdisciplinary as opposed to a professional instutional meeting.

The 30 papers before the conference divided broadly into three groups, not all equal. The first group was concerned with the structure of materials in general, and the effects of structure on properties; the second dealt with the behaviour of materials in special circumstances to meet the requirements of engineers or demands for some kind of machine or equipment; the third reviewed new and developing materials and processes. In the light of the previous remarks on interdisciplinary attitudes to these sets of papers, he wished to comment on some of the things he would have liked to have heard, said or debated at the conference.

Take as example the question of structure. The structure of solids concerned in the very broadest of senses—crystal structure, lattice imperfections, microstructure and macrostructure—the whole architecture of solid bodies whether metallic, ceramic or polymeric. The metallurgists present had heard something of the crystal chemistry of polymers and of order and disorder and (in the case of glass) partial order and partial disorder. Polymer chemists had been entertained to what for them must be a relatively new incursion into imperfections, dislocations, vacancies, interstitials and groups of these in the form of networks, stacking faults and grain boundaries. Ceramists had been lectured on multi-phase component systems both of metallurgical alloys and other heterophase systems involving the effects of the nature and size of the second phase, its distribution, its shape on the properties of materials. The papers had shown that properties were vitally related to structural features and that these features were not necessarily confined to one type of solid but obtained in all solids in greater or lesser degree. But the consequences and implications of these general structural features on all disciplines studying solids and not just on the experts knowledgable of particular types of solids had not been brought out in the lectures or in the debate which followed.

Professor Kennedy had pointed out how the electron microscope, which had been used many years to show dislocation networks in metals, had also more recently provided evidence of dislocation networks in nylon. Immediately Professor Kennedy said this, the nylon or any other polymer expert ought to have fired questions on dislocations in metals and whether what happened in metals through dislocation happened in polymers. But this had not occurred. As the Clarke and Murray paper showed, the ceramists had cottoned on to the idea quickly that dislocation theory as applied to metals could go far to help explain the mechanical behaviour of ceramics. Fracture of ceramics was technologically as important as fracture in metals and ceramists could gain much from looking at what metallurgists had gleaned about this phenomenon and applying it to ceramic materials as far as theory and fact would allow.

On this same question of applying general scientific concepts on different disciplines, Dr. Finniston was impressed by Professor Douglas's comment that the intention of modern glass technologists was to try and change glass from an amorphous material into a material with some crystalline structure and hence with different and enhanced properties. Professor Douglas was interested therefore in the nucleation

and growth of crystals in a liquid glass. Immediately this interest by a glass expert in crystal formation in a super-cooled liquid was expressed, the metallurgists should have sprung to the aid of Professor Douglas with their comparable experience in the metallic field. The phenomenon of nucleation and growth in a wide variety of circumstances was always being discussed by metallurgists, not only in the formation of crystals from the liquid state but also in the formation of second phases from solids. Nor did the application of nucleation and growth theory and knowledge stop here. The electrical breakdown of insulating liquids and solids was due to the formation of gas bubbles which excited an immediate interest in the nucleation of the gas bubbles and their growth. But the creation of gas bubbles was also a result of fission in uranium under certain conditions so the nuclear technologist also had an interest. Reference was made in one paper to foamed polyurethane. Were not polymer chemists therefore also interested in the formation of gas bubbles and how they nucleated and grew? It was on this general theme, this bringing together of general ideas and trying to disperse them among disciplines and determine their relevance and importance between different disciplines, that he had hoped the conference would make impact.

He thought that Mr. Holliday, one of the organisers, had seen it in the same light as he (Dr. Finniston) was suggesting when he had said " We ought to have a one-day conference on fracture ", because he, a chemist, was worried about Griffith cracks. What was missing was the exchange between glass, polymer, ceramic and metallurgical experts discussing one common feature of materials structure and behaviour—Griffith cracks. The matters that various professional interests had in common (even if they did not at first realise these common interests) had not been brought into the open. Through the heterogeneity of papers, each one confined to a specific class of material, the issue before the conference became too concerned with individual disciplines and not with the interdisciplinary exchanges which should have taken place.

Once one said " We will generalise concepts between the disciplines " one required a class of person whom he did not think was present in significant number and who should be represented more forcefully at future conferences; this was the theoretical physicist with experience of practical science or the applied mathematician who could think in models. He thought Mr. Holliday and Dr. Mann in their paper came close to this; they had taken a generalised concept and tried to show what was the effect of changing the second phase in a complex heterophase system without reference to specific materials. This kind of model-making and model-thinking which ignored specific materials and therefore related to all materials, was rightly in the province of the theoretician. Everybody in every discipline tried to be his own theoretician but an attempt should be made to bring about interdisciplinary attitudes through the use of the independent model-thinker. He himself had no great faith in these people to produce something of earth-shattering importance. They were rarely right—more often wrong—but such people were stimulating and they did have ideas which led to new thinking in specific disciplines along lines which would not otherwise be tried.

Since he was a metallurgist, he found himself on occasion not understanding the terms which other disciplines used. He had been very confused when there had been a discussion on crystalline polymers. What was said then was not quite what he, as a metallurgist, understood as a crystal. Reference was made to long chain molecules which had a certain structural pattern, very much more complex than that to which the metallurgist or ceramist was accustomed; crystallinity was thought to have been achieved by packing these regular molecules together. The greater the degree of packing, the more crystalline the material. He was not sure whether this was the idea intended or not, because it had never dawned on him that by sheer packing, crystallinity was achieved. This was the kind of thing he would like to have had cleared up and debated to see what structural tracks polymer chemists were following and whether metallurgists or ceramists could help or be helped. Now that there were crystalline polymers, if the word " crystalline " meant anything resembling what metallurgists meant by crystalline, polymer scientists and metallurgists ought to begin to get together to discuss crystalline behaviour to see whether metallurgists could help the polymer scientist or vice versa.

One point which came out very strikingly during the conference was the question of surfaces and their properties. It was not dealt with in any single paper, but people from the floor kept asking questions about bonding and about cracks starting from surfaces. This subject could merit a conference to itself with metallurgists, chemists, physicists, etc., participating. What was the atomic situation at a surface? How did surfaces react and how did this differ from the behaviour in the interior of a solid? The problem of surfaces applied not only to the surface free to the atmosphere but to the internal surface of pores in materials, thus involving all disciplinary interests.

He had spoken about structure in the atomic sense so far. But there were also exchanges which could be made in macro- or micro-structures. To give an example, fibre-reinforced metals had been discussed; was this not scientifically akin to fibreglass? Was it not also akin, if fibres were replaced by holes, to foam structures? Was there not a similarity between the foam structure and graphite which had been discussed also? Graphite was an alloy of 90% carbon and 10% holes! This kind of alloy was quite distinctly different from 100% carbon or a graphite with 1% holes. The geometric features vital to the development of new materials should have been discussed more freely and certainly free from disciplinary ties.

The emergence of materials made from components from different disciplines had been of interest. Metallurgists had for many years been trying to mix metals and ceramics. Their only success had been in the hard tool industry, where tungsten carbide bonded with either nickel or cobalt had been used. Nuclear technologists were considering using cermets of oxides or carbides in a metallic matrix as fuel for future reactors because this was the only way to get the high irradiation and corrosion resistance needed for future high performance duty. People were entering the fibre-reinforced metal field. It might be that other things should be mixed together. If nothing good (in the practical sense) turned up, at least one would know what not to do!

This marriage of materials would raise in its wake a considerable number of problems on how to fabricate them, and therefore the last series of papers on fabrication techniques showed what new techniques may have to be examined to get any advantage from these mixtures of materials. Again, it would have improved matters if the different disciplines had shown how the new processes might influence their present practices.

He had been very depressed as always by the class of paper concerned with providing data in respect of some specific engineering problems. It seemed that the data could only be done the hard way, as was quite clear from the paper by Messrs. Tyzack and Nichols. Perhaps it was not fortuitous that both came from the UKAEA. Their work was all very logical, thorough and painstaking—but very depressing. He would have liked to see a little more ingenuity shown on behalf of engineers, a little more science and a little more imagination brought into the attack—and a little more encouragement from engineers to apply science as well as scientific method.

Not enough attention was perhaps being paid to the quanti-

tative aspects of materials work. Data was accumulating in the materials field at a tremendous rate. What general conclusions were to be drawn from this mass of figures was not being examined in anything like enough detail. He would not like to examine it in the way Mr. Pugh examined it, by leaving out all the points which did not fit! By and large, he thought that the point would be taken by everyone present that they had a real need to try to quantify as much as possible, even if it only meant the production of empirical formulae which would not satisfy pure scientists. A good empirical formula was better than no formula at all.

The conference had ended with a description of new processes. He wished to generalise a little about these. Metallurgists had long reached the conclusion that the fabrication history of a material and indeed the history of a material from its very inception could influence the properties markedly. What had been demonstrated was that new processes were now possible but that these new processes were really based on one very general consideration; they were the use of old forms of energy in new surroundings. By using high pressure (at high rates), by using high magnetic fields, by using chemical processes, by using explosive forming, different forms of energy were being used to do a job in a specific way. This general feature would develop rapidly; for example, the electromagnetic manner of forming was based on using magnetic fields which were quite trivial but with future superconducting magnets of 50 to 100 kilogauss there might have to be a change of mind about the technique of applying this method. With bursts of energy from laser beams which were fantastic, though of short duration, there might be a change in attitude and practice about how to weld, join or cut materials. This was obvious, but a less obvious feature was the fact that this processing might give structures which were quite radically different from those obtained by conventional processes. It might well be that on explosive forming, the dislocation networks resulting would be radically different from the networks obtaining when other deformation methods were used. If this were to happen, it raised a host of questions. Professor Kennedy had shown how important dislocation networks were. Besides directly modifying the mechanical properties of materials to combine say strength with ductility with different kinds of networks, it might be possible to precipitate phases in a different fashion and further change the properties.

It was unfortunate that the economics of processes had entered into the discussion, since this was not an interdisciplinary technical matter. It was, in fact, a general feature better debated in a different gathering.

He had in the past been a little harsh on metallurgists by saying that they continued to meet the demands of the engineers by guess and by God, more generally by guess because he never thought that God was on the side of the materials expert. There were signs, however, that a little more science was being done towards future developments. It always surprised him that when engineers made demands the materials experts somehow met them more or less, though always late. But once the materials man had got near the original target, he was asked for something else. Success had perhaps engendered in many materials experts the feeling that there was nothing too difficult for them to achieve, but he was not sure whether, if they attempted this task only by guess and by God, they would continue to be successful. Professor Owen had shown, in the case of maraging steels, and to a lesser extent ausformed steels, that an attempt was being made to introduce science (albeit still empirical) into the development of high-strength steels. He would like to see this approach reinforced by inter-disciplinary exchange. Dr. Roberts' paper on the chemistry of ceramics, for example, had brought out the fascinating things that could be done by changing the valency of elements in a ceramic. Although this was easy to do with some ceramic compounds, more attention ought to be paid to this "mechanism" in chemical fields in general.

He hoped that the organisers would forgive him for thumping them on the head while patting them on the back. It had been well worth while having the conference and he thought that many people would have derived some benefit from it, though not perhaps as much as might have been anticipated. Since he did not want to be destructive, he would finish by commenting on the form the next interdisciplinary conference might take. The essential thing was that it should not consist of a heterogeneous mixture of papers covering such a wide field but should concentrate on specific aspects which were common to the widest variety of materials possible.

As an example of what he would like to see debated he quoted grain boundaries in materials. It was important to the ceramist to do something to control grain boundaries; grain boundaries were a problem faced by the metallurgist every time he operated his craft; the glass expert would be faced with grain boundaries in crystalline glass and the polymer scientist might have them in crystalline polymers.

Or again, fracture and plastic deformation processes in materials might be worth two days of anybody's time. Metallurgists had done much work in defining slip planes, slip directions, twinning mechanisms and this was spilling over into ceramics. One wanted to know what the differences were in the slip and twinning planes and mechanisms of various classes of materials. Why, for example, did it differ so radically between ceramics? Did materials like nylon show plastic deformation properties of a kind that had been seen in metals or ceramics; if so, did they occur on rational planes or irrational planes, and what at any rate did " plane " mean in polymers?

Professor Douglas had said that glass did not have to be made with silica but could be made with a variety of other oxides. Metallurgists made alloys from a variety of elements. He would like to see discussions on lines which attempted to show how future " alloys " were chosen by glass, ceramics and metallurgical experts.

The things he had been talking about did not apply throughout to all the materials, so that the people invited to give papers ought to be selected to provide what was likely to be useful to the people participating in the conference.

Finally, the interdisciplinary movement which had been started was unlikely to gain anything like the momentum it deserved unless there was far greater movement and closer association between laboratories than had been the case to date. Being at a conference for three days was pleasant, but it was not a very effective way of achieving the interdisciplinary exchange which he thought everyone wanted.

The CHAIRMAN said that he felt, as one outside the materials field, that one thing which had been achieved on this first occasion was to bring to the notice of people in one field work which was going on in others which was relevant, and of which they might well have been quite unaware. The experts might have known all the things of interest to them in other fields but he ventured to doubt it.

On behalf of the North Western Branch, he said that they were pleased to be associated with the venture and expressed thanks to the many people who had been concerned with it.

Professor FRANK MORTON said that, after Mr. Finniston's excellent summing up, the spicy sweet, he would provide the final coffee. He thanked delegates very much for attending.

On behalf of the Institution of Chemical Engineers he thanked the many people who had made the conference successful and who had made it possible. Even if it had not met all the points and all the things one hoped for from such a conference, it had established a first dictionary by which interdisciplinary discussion might be established.

First of all, on behalf of the Institution, he thanked Mr. Holliday, the Vice-Chairman of the North-Western Branch and Chairman of the Working Party on Materials of the Institution, for bringing the conference into being. The Institution had started with the objective of trying to obtain information from experts in materials which would be of value to chemical engineers, and finding ways and means of bringing before chemical engineers information on new materials, their properties and uses. It was obvious from discussions that there was need for education. Whether, in the future, materials science would become an educational discipline in its own right, whether it would best be dealt with at postgraduate level or a welding of various disciplines, he did not know; but from the discussions it appeared that there was a need to talk about education in this field, and quite a lot of progress had been made at this conference.

Professor Morton thanked the Organising Committee, particularly Mr. Michael Shaw, Mr. Brian Street, the Programmes Organisers, and Dr. Sutherland, who arranged some of the social events.

Without the authors there could be no symposium. It was realised that the Institution was a hard task-master, insisting, as it did, that whenever possible papers should be preprinted. This sometimes made authors work harder than they wished to, but it enabled the Institution to obtain sufficient papers for people to read beforehand, thus making a lively discussion more certain. By experience of many symposia, the Institution had established that the preprinting of papers was very valuable to those attending, and he asked authors to bear with the Institution when they asked for papers a little earlier than usual. He thanked all the authors for the papers which had made the conference so successful and also for fitting them into so tight a schedule in presentation.

He also thanked the Session Chairmen for carrying out their very difficult task and encouraging such excellent discussion.

Professor Morton indicated that he had also to thank the College authorities for the use of the building and equipment, but, since the Renold Building was designed specifically to attract such symposia, it would be realised that the College authorities did not really need thanks; all they needed to know was that it had been used and delegates had enjoyed themselves.

The College staff, and the stewards, had helped. Mr. Shepherd and Mr. Mason had worked indefatigably. Behind all this organisation were three people, Mr. Shepherd, Mr. Mason and Dr. Brennan, and Professor Morton extended thanks to them. He also thanked in advance all the organisations which were accepting visitors.

Professor ZWIKKER said that it was only fair to add a few words on behalf of the foreign visitors to the symposium —a vote of thanks and a few words of praise. They thanked the North-Western Branch of the Institution for their hospitality, and they thanked their British friends for the kind reception they had encountered during the three days.

He added a word of praise to the Organising Committee for its thorough work and the smoooth running of the symposium. He and his colleagues had enjoyed their stay very much and went home with the happiest remembrances of their three days in Manchester.